McGRAW-HILL PUBLICATIONS IN THE
ZOÖLOGICAL SCIENCES

A. FRANKLIN SHULL, Consulting Editor

ANIMAL ECOLOGY

ANIMAL ECOLOGY

With Especial Reference to Insects

BY

ROYAL N. CHAPMAN

Dean of the Graduate School of Tropical Agriculture and Director
of the Pineapple Experiment Station, University of Hawaii;
Formerly Professor of Zoology and Entomology,
University of Minnesota

McGRAW-HILL BOOK COMPANY, Inc.

NEW YORK AND LONDON

1931

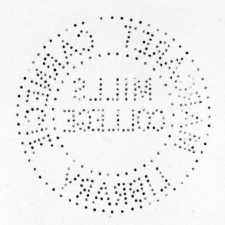

THE MAPLE PRESS COMPANY, YORK, PA.

To
MY FORMER GRADUATE STUDENTS
WHOSE INSPIRATION AND AID MADE
THIS VOLUME POSSIBLE

PREFACE

The subject matter of this volume had its origin in a course in Insect Ecology which was given at the University of Minnesota beginning in the year 1917. The course underwent a gradual evolution and was never given twice the same. In 1925 the lecture notes appeared in mimeographed form for the students. Since that time, the present manuscript has been in the process of preparation and continual revision. In some phases of the subject matter results of new researches have been appearing so rapidly that it has been difficult for the work of revision to keep up with the current literature. In 1930 it became evident that the manuscript must be closed even though it would necessitate the neglect of certain new publications.

The volume is now presented for publication in the hope that it may prove useful to students and research workers in the field of animal ecology. There is no feeling that the method of outlining the subject matter is necessarily superior to any other method or that the examples which have been chosen to illustrate the various principles are the most important ones to be found in literature. If the volume fulfills its purpose in aiding those engaged in ecological research it will soon become out of date.

In so far as possible the material presented has been quantitative. This is not so much because the descriptive observations of naturalists are less valuable, but rather because the quantitative results of experimental research lend themselves more readily to critical consideration.

During the course of the preparation of the manuscript, the author has been aided so much by colleagues at the University of Minnesota and in the various entomological laboratories in different parts of the United States and Europe that it is difficult to do justice in thanking them for their many kindnesses. All of the authors who are cited throughout the volume in connection with the materials furnished for tables and illustrations are due special thanks for their kind cooperation. Dr. Volterra gave permission to reprint his paper on the fluctuations of the numbers of animals as an appendix to this work, thus making it readily available to those interested in insect ecology.

Special thanks are due to Dr. W. A. Riley, Professor A. G. Ruggles, Drs. S. A. Graham, V. E. Shelford, E. Booker Klugh, and Chancey Juday.

vii

The author also wishes to thank Mrs. Marie Spriestersbach, Misses Frieda Hinnenkamp and Lilian Baird, and Messrs. Ralph King and John Stanley for aid in the preparation of the manuscript and bibliography. The author, however, assumes full responsibility for the accuracy of the manuscript.

ROYAL N. CHAPMAN.

THE UNIVERSITY OF HAWAII, HONOLULU,
August, 1931.

CONTENTS

ANIMAL ECOLOGY

CHAPTER I

INTRODUCTION

Animal ecology, as conceived at present, is of relatively recent origin although there is much truth in the statement that ecology is nothing more than scientific natural history. Certain foundations for our present conceptions of ecology were laid in earlier years by naturalists, physiologists, zoogeographers, and biometricians.

Buffon (1707 to 1788) is pointed out by Lankester as the only prominent writer on natural history who could be accorded historic rank in the field of natural history during this early period. Buffon himself opposed the then orthodox study of the structure and classification of animals, and called attention to the "bionomics" or inter-relations of organisms. He popularized descriptions of his observations to a certain extent in 44 volumes published during six years while he was keeper of the royal garden.

Alexander von Humboldt (1764 to 1859), a botanist and explorer, laid certain foundations in the field of distribution of organisms in connection with descriptions of species and the factors of climate and geography affecting them.

Malthus (1772 to 1844) in his "Essay on the Principles of Population" (1806) laid foundations in biometrical work which have had a great influence in biology. This work served as an inspiration for Wallace, Darwin, and other biologists as well as investigators in the field of statistics.

Isidore Geoffroy Saint-Hilaire in his "Histoire générale des règnes organiques" (1859) stated in the introduction that the last volume of his work would be devoted to the subject of "ethology." Unfortunately, this volume of his work was never published and we have, therefore, only his statement in the introduction to the earlier volume as to what this subject matter would be. He defined ethology as follows: "The study of the relations of the organism within the family and the society, in the aggregate and in the community." The laws of ethology were said to relate to the instinct, habits, and in general to the "external manifestations of organisms." This announcement, by Saint-Hilaire, of his intention to publish a volume on ethology defined as above is taken by some authors to constitute priority over the term "ecology" which has

1

come into current use. It seems quite evident that Saint-Hilaire was defining the subject matter which we now consider that of ecology.

Haeckel (1869) used the term "Oekologie" and defined it as comprising the "relation of the animal to its organic as well as its inorganic environment, particularly its friendly or hostile relations to those animals or plants with which it comes in contact." He considered oekologie to include the general economy of the household of nature.

The present branch of biology which we designate as ecology has been synthesized from these various beginnings and has been augmented by numerous investigations such as those of Hensen (1887), Möbius (1877), and others, which demonstrated the possibility of quantitative methods and emphasized the conception of an ecological unit or biocoenose. It is this conception of a unit of association bound together by the interdependence of the organisms which formed the association which has lent a great impetus to the development of ecology.

The advance of plant ecology has been more rapid than that of animal ecology. This has been due largely to the fact that plants are sessile and lend themselves to study of local distribution more readily than do animals. Thus the distribution of plants and plant association over geographic areas, and the distribution of plant associations in a series of ecological succession has made much more rapid progress than has the study of animal associations. Warming's textbook on plant ecology did much to bring together and organize the material of plant ecology and stimulate further work.

The subject matter of animal ecology has been brought together to a certain extent by several authors. Adams' (1913) "Guide to the Study of Animal Ecology" has served as a source book of literature. Shelford's (1913) "Animal Communities" is essentially a description of the animal communities in the region of Chicago, Ill.; but it contains generalizations with regard to the subject matter of ecology in general, and pays particular reference to the organisms of various communities. Borradaile's (1923) "The Animal and Its Environment," gives an elementary treatment of animal ecology including general descriptive matter from natural history, and relatively little quantitative analysis of the environment. Other publications on the subject of animal ecology are widely scattered through the literature. Pearse (1926) published his volume on "Animal Ecology" which brings together a great deal of the material on the subject that is largely descriptive.

Elton's (1927) "Animal Ecology" has a dynamic viewpoint which is stimulating. It has aimed to present principles and has well-organized material. Some authors seem to wish to emphasize the complexity of nature without any attempt to show order. Elton has attempted to show that there may be order even in the most complex systems. He emphasizes the importance of the food chains in nature and the relative numbers of animals without setting up complicated systems of concepts and classification.

Shelford (1929) published his volume "Laboratory and Field Ecology." In the introduction of this volume he calls attention to the field of biocoenology, or the study of the associations of organisms, and emphasizes its importance. However, the volume in general is devoted very largely to the subject of autecology, and to the methods of analysis of environmental factors. In the second volume of Schröder's "Handbuch der Entomologie," dated 1929, the first chapter by Anton Handlirsch is entitled "Biologie (Ökologie-Ethologie)." This is devoted very largely to the life history of insects in relation to their physical and biotic environment.

The British Ecological Society of London began the publication of *Journal of Ecology* in 1913. This was originally and is still largely dominated by plant ecologists. The Ecological Society of America was founded in 1916 and began the publication of *Ecology* in 1920 as a quarterly journal in which original papers and reviews of significant literature are published. In the pages of this journal, animal ecology has been very well represented. The various abstract journals, and the various indexes to biological literature, are now classifying material under the heading of ecology and thereby aiding the ecologists in finding the significant literature which is so widely scattered throughout the publications on biology.

Publications on aquatic organisms furnish some of the best examples of the quantitative work. The purely descriptive work on the natural history of various animals is voluminous, and often contains observations which are interesting merely because they are curious. The popularization of such phases of ecology has attracted the attention of the public but has undoubtedly been a hindrance to the progress of ecology as a serious branch of science. Such work has not only tended to congest literature, but it has added descriptive detail to a subject which needs more than anything else to be cleared of details until it has been organized on the basis of verified facts supporting fundamental principles. After such organization has been brought about, many of the details which are now cited as being curious may be evaluated and tabulated in the scheme of things as being significant supporting evidence for the fundamental principles, or as mere coincidence of little scientific importance.

THE SUBJECT MATTER OF ANIMAL ECOLOGY

The subject matter of biology or the study of organisms may be divided on the basis of the biological phenomena which are studied into certain fundamental branches. We have thus: morphology, or the study of the structure of organisms; taxonomy, or the study of the phylogenetic groups of organisms and their relationship to each other; and physiology, or the study of functions of organisms. The inter-relations of organisms in nature may be considered under the subject matter of ecology which is closely related to physiology, and in the minds of some biologists should be a subdivision of it. It has been said that ecology, when reduced to its lowest terms by a process of analysis, becomes physiology; that physiology, when reduced to its lowest terms by a process of analysis, becomes physiological chemistry; that physiological chemistry may in a similar way be resolved into biochemistry; biochemistry resolved into chemistry itself; and chemistry itself resolved into physical chemistry; and physical chemistry resolved into physics. However this may be, it is clear that an organism consisting of cells and organs is a physical structure combined in such a way as to produce a very complicated organism of cells and organs, and that these systems of cells and organs have certain characteristics as an organism. A thorough understanding of the physical structures which go to make up this system is of fundamental importance to physiology. Similarly the associations of organisms dealt with in ecology consist of organisms which, in turn, are these same physical systems. It is therefore essential that the ecologist have a thorough understanding of the principles of physics, chemistry, and physiology, in order that he may be familiar with the fundamental properties of the organisms which make up the associations with which he is to deal. For this reason it is necessary to incorporate into the subject matter of ecology much that is essentially physics, chemistry, and physiology. However, as will be pointed out in the course of the present volume, the behavior of systems of population is often dependent upon the characteristics of the organisms themselves as units. Their rates of reproduction, food requirements, etc., are characteristics of the organisms as such. Within the limits of the physical conditions of the environment which permit the normal functioning of the organisms, the reactions of the populations are dependent upon the characteristics of the organisms themselves and are relatively independent of the physical conditions, so long as they remain within the limits of the toleration of the organism.

The word "ecology" comes from the Greek root "oikos" meaning home. Literally ecology may be defined as a treatise of the home relations of organisms. This is essentially Haeckel's definition, which has already been given. Shelford (1913) gave the following definition: "Ecology is that branch of general physiology which deals with the organism as a whole, with its general life processes as distinguished from the more special physiology of the organs, and which also considers the organism with particular reference to its usual environment." In his more recent volume Shelford (1929) says that the third division of biological sciences is bioecology, which is the sociology of organisms. Further, he says,

At the present time there is no need and little justification for the term "autecology" as it has been interpreted relative to animals or for that matter for the use of the term ecology referring to particular species as very commonly construed. Ecology is a science of communities. A study of the relations of a single species to the environment conceived without reference to communities and, in the end, unrelated to the natural phenomena of its habitat and community associates is not properly included in the field of ecology.

The subject matter of ecology was subdivided by Schröter into autecology (1896) and synecology (1902). Autecology is derived from the Greek root, "autos," meaning self; and synecology from the Greek prefix "syn," meaning together. A committee of which Schröter was a member made a report to the Third International Botanical Congress in 1910 (Article 8b) as follows: "The term 'ecology' comprises the whole of the relations existing between the individual plants or plant associations of one part of the station to the other part. Ecology, the study of conditions of environment and of adaptation of plant species is if taken isolately 'autecology,' if taken in association 'synecology.'" On the basis of this definition we may therefore analyze the environment considering each of the physical and biotic factors which go to make it up separately as autecology. In so doing we may be applying the methods of physics, chemistry, and physiology, and it is difficult to see how we may properly appreciate the various factors unless we have so considered them. We may also study the species of organisms which go to make up the associations separately, and all this would be considered under the subject matter of autecology. When these physical factors are put together and considered as weather or climate making up the environment of organisms, and when we consider the various species of organisms in the natural associations in which they occur and study their interrelationships with each other and with the environment, we are then considering the subject matter of synecology. In the study of autecology it is quite evident that the work is bordering very closely on the field of physiology and might quite properly be considered as just an aspect of physiology. It is this aspect of autecology which has given rise to such statements as those of Shepardson (1929), that ecology is a viewpoint rather than a branch of science.

In turning to the subject matter of synecology and the treatment of the interactions of species on each other as a fluctuation of population, as is done in the Appendix by Dr. Volterra, we realize that we have come to a field which is no longer that of general physiology, but stands out more distinctly as that of ecology. Adams (1913) proposed the term "individual ecology" to represent the conception apparently identical with that of Schröter for autecology. Adams expressed this conception as the study of an individual or species either in a restricted environment or throughout its entire geographic range and including all its relationships to the complete environment. Since Schröter's term has priority and is more generally accepted, it seems best to adopt it. Adams also

proposed the term "associational ecology" for the study of the relationships of animals, groups, or those associated in the same habitats and
environments. Again this term seems to be the same concept that is
expressed in Schröter's synecology. Du Rietz (1921) presented a diagrammatic representation of various theories of the division of the subject
matter of biology and in this included the term "idiobiology" for the
same concept of the study of the individual organism.

Autecology will be interpreted as including the study of the various
physical factors of the environment in relation to insects and other
animals. It is true that this will be essentially physiology, but the
viewpoint will be that of the factor as a part of the animal environment.
This will be followed by a study of the individual characteristic of the
organism and the two main headings will be "Physical Autecology" and
"Biotic Autecology." In the consideration of biotic autecology it is
very difficult to draw a distinct line between the so-called "autecology"
and "synecology," for as soon as the biotic factors begin to operate upon
an organism, we have the interaction of organisms which might be
interpreted as being synecology.

Synecology will be considered as population systems on the basis of
biotic potential and environmental resistance, and as distributional and
descriptive ecology. The discussion of population systems is supple-
mented by the Appendix by Dr. Volterra. Distributional synecology
will include the consideration of the distribution of the associations of
animals in space as chorology or zoogeography, and their distribution
in time as chronology or succession. Distributional synecology is thus
dynamic. Under the chapters on descriptive synecology various types
of environments will be considered. It is necessarily impossible to give
an exhaustive study of any environment, or to list all the species that
belong to the various associations.

BIBLIOGRAPHY

ADAMS, C. C.: "Guide to the Study of Animal Ecology," The Macmillan Co.,
New York, 1913. 149 pp.

BORRADAILE, L. A.: "The Animal and Its Environment," p. 399, Frowde and
Hodder & Stoughton, London, 1923.

BUFFON, DE, GEORGES LOUIS LECLERC: "Histoire naturelle et particulière,"
1749-1804. 44 vol.

DU RIETZ, EINAR: "Zur methodologischen Grundlage der modernen Pflanzen-
sociologie," A. Holzhausen, Wien, 1921. 267 pp.

ELTON, CHARLES: "Animal Ecology," p. 207, Sidgwick & Jackson, Ltd., London,
1927.

HAECKEL, ERNST: Entwicklungsgang und Aufgaben der Zoologie, *Jenaische
Ztschr.*, **V**: 353, 1869.

HENSEN, VICTOR: Ueber die Bestimmung des Plankton, *Ber. 5, Kommiss. d.
wissenschaftl. Untersuch. d. deutsch. Meere*, Berlin, 1887.

HUMBOLDT, ALEXANDER VON: "Ideen zu einer Geographie der Pflanzen," Tübin-
gen, 1806.

MALTHUS, THOMAS ROBERT: "Essay on the Principles of Population," 1806.

MÖBIUS, K.: "Die Auster und die Austernwirtschaft," Berlin, 1877. 126 pp.

PEARSE, A. S.: "Animal Ecology," p. 417, McGraw-Hill Book Company, Inc., New York, 1926.

ST. HILAIRE, ISIDORE GEOFFROY: "Histoire générale des règnes organiques," 1859,

SCHRÖTER, C., and O. KIRCHNER: "Vegetation des Bodensees," Lindau, Teil I; 1896; Teil II, 1902.

SCHRÖTER, C., and C. FLAHAULT: Rapports et propositions. Nomenclature phytogéographique, *Actes du IIIᵉ Congrès International de Botanique*, Brussels, 1910.

SHELFORD, V. E.: "Animal Communities in Temperate America," p. 362, The University of Chicago Press, 1913.

————: "Laboratory and Field Ecology," p. 608, Williams & Wilkins Co., Baltimore, 1929.

SHEPARDSON, WHITNEY H.: "Agricultural Education in the United States," p. 132, The Macmillan Company, New York, 1926.

CHAPTER II

LIGHT AS AN ECOLOGICAL FACTOR

Life, as we know it on the earth, would be quite impossible if it were not for the receipt of radiant energy from the sun. It will not be necessary to dwell at length upon the general importance of solar radiation, a part of the energy of which is made available in heat for the earth and a part for chemical reactions. For the present, attention will be confined to the radiant energy which falls within the limits of human vision, and to the region of the solar spectrum lying on either side of this, which we ordinarily think of as light. The radiant energy which is characterized by the longer wave lengths will be considered under the topic of Temperature. From the standpoint of logic, we might well treat radiant energy as one subject, for it is often difficult to differentiate between heat and light. From the standpoint of practical pedagogical procedure, there are certain advantages in differentiating between these subjects.

Light may be defined as radiant energy within the limits of human vision. For our present purposes, we shall include all the shorter wave lengths of radiant energy up to and including the visible spectrum. We have thus included all the energy which is made use of by plants through photosynthesis and which is stored as coal, oil, and other natural resources of the earth directly or indirectly used by animals.

Before proceeding with the consideration of light as a factor in animal ecology, it is well to pause for a moment to consider light as such. There is possibly no conception more fundamental to physics than that of the nature of light; yet probably the most important current question in physics is the formulation of a conception of light which will be in full accord with all the facts which are now before us in regard to this form of energy. The student is referred to the most recent textbook in the field of physics and to the current literature in physics for a further consideration of this question, which involves almost our entire understanding of energy and matter as they exist in our universe. It is through light that we gain much of our information with regard to our physical environment. For our present consideration we shall look upon radiant energy as an endless procession of waves, each wave consisting of a mass of units or corpuscles, and the troughs between the waves as intervals in which these corpuscles are present in very small numbers. The frequency of the waves, or the distance from one wave to another, may be taken as a measure of the different characteristics of radiant energy.

A figure is presented (Fig. 1) which may aid in orienting the portion of radiant energy which we are considering as light, with respect to radiant energy in general. The first line at the top represents radiant energy up to a frequency of 20,000 meters. Most of this energy is that which is made use of in radio communication. On a scale as large as this, we can hardly perceive the area covered by what we are now considering as light. This is also true of the second line, which goes out for 40 meters; while the third line has been greatly magnified so that its

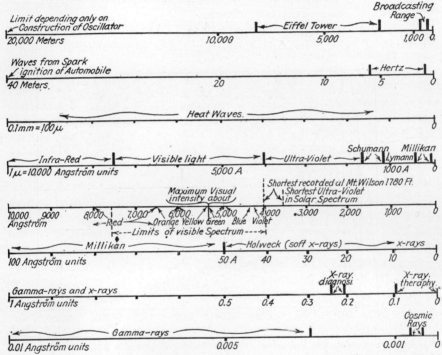

FIG. 1.—Diagram of wave lengths of radiant energy. Each line represents a scale of wave lengths ranging from meters on the top line to hundreths of an Angström unit on the bottom line. If the entire wave length included in the top line had been drawn on the scale of the bottom line it would extend from the earth to the nearest fixed star. (*Taken from various sources; chiefly from Dr. John Tate.*)

entire length goes out to a frequency of one-tenth of one millimeter. But even yet this line is occupied very largely by waves which we know as heat. The fourth line represents only one one-hundredth of the third line; and it is here for the first time that we are aware of the visible spectrum, which is shown more in detail in the fifth line. It is only that region which lies roughly between about 4,000 and 8,000 Angström units which is visible to us as light. There are shorter invisible rays which come to us from the sun, but the shortest of these are filtered out by the atmosphere of the earth as the rays approach us. Our maximum visual intensity does not lie in the middle of the visible spectrum, but slightly to the short side.   The greatest chemical or actinic effect is found in the shorter waves of the visible spectrum; while the longer waves are characterized by heat.   The sixth, seventh, and eighth lines drawn in this diagram locate some of the various types of shorter rays.   New investigations of these shorter wave lengths are coming forth every day with the perfection of the technique which will make observations possible. Investigation emphasizes the importance of these short rays, and the so-called "cosmic rays" seem to be very important in our conception of the balance of energies in our universe.

There are two important conceptions to be gained from this consideration of light.   The first is that light as a physical factor is not a

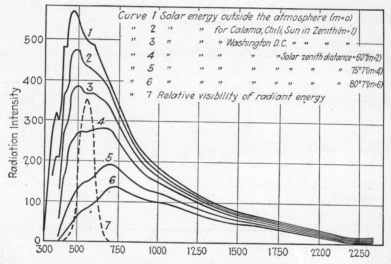

Fig. 2.—Normal solar radiant-energy curves, showing the distribution in the normal solar spectrum outside the atmosphere.   Wave lengths are given in millimicrons; 1 millimicron = 10 Angström units.   (*Kimball*, 1919.)

simple entity, but a group of radiations which we shall consider under one head for the purpose of convenience.   The biologist who considers that his field is complex and that the field of physics is simple, will do well to consider what is involved in light including both the evidence as to the constitution of a single light wave and the great array of waves with all the characteristics belonging to their different lengths.   If the diagram presented had all been drawn on the scale of the last line at the bottom, it would have extended from the earth to the nearest fixed star.

The second important consideration for the biologist is the fact that the field of physics, only a short time ago, considered its conception of light as almost a dogma.   But it is at the present time engaged in the process of reconstructing its conception of such a fundamental factor as light; and in this reconstruction, it has been necessary to cast aside many old and classical conceptions in order to bring theories into harmony with facts. Since this has been found necessary in the field of physics, biologists may expect finality on relatively few subjects during our present generation.

Methods of Measuring Light.—It is quite obvious from the consideration of the composition of light that it would be very difficult to make a measure, as to the quantity and quality of light, which would be equally applicable throughout the entire range. In the shorter wave lengths in our visible spectrum and the region immediately adjacent to it, we have a great chemical energy. In the longer wave lengths, we have heat involved. Any device which depends upon heat in making a measurement will measure the longer rays with relative accuracy, but the shorter rays with greater inaccuracy. Any device which depends upon chemical activity will measure the shorter rays with a greater accuracy, and the longer rays with less accuracy. Any device which depends upon brightness of light will measure, with any degree of accuracy, only that portion which lies near the center of the visible spectrum.

In an ecological investigation, it is necessary to measure not only the quality but the quantity of light present. This makes the problem doubly difficult. The types of instruments commonly in use for the measurement of light may be classed as: (1) pyrheliometers, (2) spectrographs and spectrometers, (3) photometers or actinometers, and (4) illuminometers. The first two, pyrheliometers and spectrometers, are the most satisfactory to the physicist, but are probably less practical for the ecologist.

A general consideration of the methods of measurement has been given by Klugh (1927).[1] Shelford (1929) gives a description of various methods of measuring light. The pyrheliometer is a standard instrument, the readings of which can be reduced to gram calories per square centimeter of surface. The principle depends upon the absorption of heat from the solar radiation. Various types have been made: the Smithsonian silver disc (Smithsonian Miscellaneous Collection, 1913), and other types made by Marvin, Kimball (1919), Angström (1919), and the more recent one by Gorczýnski (1924). In this instrument a thermopyle is mounted in a clock movement to follow the path of the sun. A Richard recording millivoltmeter is connected to record the thermo-electric current on a strip of paper. Since it is considered that

[1] This paper gives the results of comparative readings taken by the Moll-Richard-Gorczýnski pyrheliometer, the MacBeth illuminometer, the Nutting polarization spectrometer, the Heyde aktinophotometer, the Drew justophot, the Wynne exposure meter and the neutral wedge with rhodamine "B" paper. The Canadian Research Council sponsored the experiments to obtain direct comparisons of these instruments for ecological investigations.

the thermo-electric current generated by the thermopyle, when exposed to the sun's rays, is proportional to the radiation intensity, it is possible to convert the reading directly into gram calories per square centimeter per minute of time. By the use of various color filters intercepted between the sun and the thermopyle, it is possible to study the intensity of the various qualities of light. In so doing, however, one is, in the last analysis, measuring the heat of the various light rays, and not the actinic properties of these rays.

Buxton (1926) devised a radiation integrator, which consists of a glass bulb welded within a vacuum sphere through which the light shines on the bulb. The latter is blackened in order that it may absorb the heat from the sun's rays. A tube extends from the bulb out through the sphere and down into a shelter, which protects it from the sun's rays. A certain quantity of alcohol is contained in the black bulb. The sun's rays evaporate the alcohol, which is then condensed in the tube, since it is shielded from the sun's rays and therefore cooler. The tube into which the alcohol is condensed, is calibrated to read in cubic centimeters. The readings are taken at intervals not longer than one day, and the readings of the quantity of alcohol which has been condensed are used as a measure of the amount of radiation during the period. The instrument has been standardized against Gorczýnski's pyrheliometer, and the readings converted into calories. Buxton believes this method to be preferable to that of a black and white bulb thermometer, similar to that used by Graham (1920). In the latter case two thermometers, standardized against each other, are mounted side by side in a box which protects them from the wind. One bulb is blackened; the other one, painted white; and the difference between the two thermometers is read off in degrees. The maximum difference for any given period is taken as 100 per cent of light.

Carter (1930) compared the readings which he obtained from a black and white bulb atmometer with the readings from a Kimball pyrheliometer, and concluded that the readings as given by the black and white atmometer cups were essentially like those of the Kimball recorder. All of the pyrheliometer methods are alike, in that they depend upon the heat of the sun's radiation. And it is possible in many cases that the ecologist will be interested not in the heat but in the actinic effect of the sun's radiation.

Spectrographs and Spectrometers.—From the standpoint of a study of the quality of light, nothing can be more satisfactory than a spectrograph. However, this instrument is cumbersome and difficult to use in the field. Furthermore, if quantity of light is to be measured, it is necessary to make a long series of exposures comparing the long exposures with the short ones in order to arrive at even a rough quantitative measure. It would seem that a field spectrograph which could make a series of comparative readings for quantitative measurement would be of great advantage to the ecologist.

Photometers or actinometers depend upon the chemical reaction caused by the sun's radiation on an emulsion on a paper, film or glass plate. The range of sensitivity depends very largely upon the emulsion which is on the plate. The quantitative measurements made by the earlier photometers (Clements, 1905) were limited almost entirely to comparative measures.

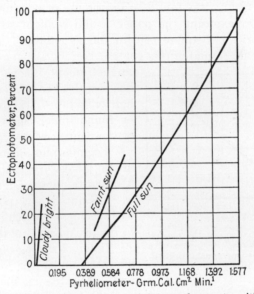

Fig. 3.—Comparison in total light energy, of the ectophotometer with a Moll-Richards-Gorczynski pyrheliometer. The graphs represent comparisons at different light intensities; from left to right, cloudy bright, faint sun, and full sunlight. (*Klugh*, 1927.)

The ectophotometer of Klugh (1925 and 1927) employs a set of standard color filters and the use of rhodamine "B" paper.[1] Klugh has calibrated this instrument so that it may also be read in terms of total light energy in gram calories per square centimeter per minute of time. This instrument, therefore, is able to read both quality and quantity of light and is sensitive enough to be read even at night in starlight and moonlight. When the total light energy in full sunlight, as read by the ectophotometer, is compared with the readings of the Moll-Richard-Gorczýnski pyrheliometer, there is practically a straight-line relationship; but in faint sun or in cloudy bright light, the relationship is not a straight-line one, on account of the greater sensitivity of the ectophotometer as

[1] Rhodamine is one of the triphenylmethane papers and Klugh (1927) gives instructions for making and standardizing it.

compared with the pyrheliometer. This instrument, the ectophotometer, may be used for various purposes on land; or the aquatic model, in water.

A simpler type of photometer, which consists of the use of neutral wedges with rhodamine "B" paper, is described by Klugh (1927). He used various wedges obtained from the Eastman Company, with gradations from one to one-half, one to one-tenth, one to one-hundredth, and one to one-thousandth. The one to one-hundredth wedge proved the most satisfactory. It was mounted in a frame, which made it possible to make exposures 30 seconds or longer. The most satisfactory method of reading the results was found to be the use of a standard tint, which was prepared by exposing the paper to full sunlight with the value of 1.61 gram calories per square centimeter per minute. A standard tint was then made up to match this color. For the satisfactory use of such

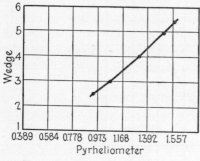

Fig. 4.—Comparison of the neutral wedge and rhodamine "B" paper with the Moll-Richards-Gorczynski pryheliometer. (*Klugh*, 1927.)

an instrument, it is necessary to establish a scale of equivalence between the lighter and the darker tints which may be found under the various portions of the neutral wedge.

A similar photometer has been used in the laboratory at the University of Minnesota, in which a Goldberg wedge was mounted in a pocketkodak box with a shutter, which made it possible to make exposures of different lengths of time. Printing-out paper was mounted under the Goldberg wedge, and exposures made for different periods of time. Readings were then made by comparing the times of exposure with the tint on the printing-out paper. Since the wedge is calibrated for a per cent of light transmitted, it is possible to find a point on the wedge at which the change in tint of the paper is fairly discernible. This serves for a comparison of light intensities between the two environments. By taking a series of exposures on a strip of paper, it is possible to draw a line connecting the various portions which show the slightest change in tint. By comparing the percentage of light required to make a change in tint in the paper, a comparison of the light in the environment is made.

Shelford and Kunz (1929) and Shelford (1929) describe the use of various types of photo-electric cells for the measurement of light. These may be used either for direct reading or for recording through the use of a potentiometer recorder. Shelford believes that the photo-electric cell offers the best possibility for measuring intensity (quantity) and quality of light. The present limitation to this method seems to be in getting cells which are standardized. The principle depends upon the emitting of electrons by a metal when exposed to light. The variations in the cells are nearly as great as the variations in the light. The day will probably come when cells will be dependable enough for accurate work such as is required in ecology. The photo-electric cell has the limitation of not reading the red end of the spectrum.

Illuminometers have the advantage of giving a reading in foot-candle power. There are several types of field instruments which are made and which can be used to good advantage. They, in the end, depend upon the ability of the reader to compare a standard light with the light reflected from a disc exposed to the sun, or the light of the environment.

For a further consideration of the measurements of light from the standpoint of an ecologist, the student is referred to the papers by Klugh (1927) and Shelford (1929).

Methods of Controlling Light.—Light is the subject of a great deal of investigation at the present time from the standpoint of both physics and biology. One of the difficulties which has been confronted is that of controlling light for experimental purposes. Biologists, including entomologists, have usually considered it necessary to carry on all experiments in hothouses in order that the organisms might be exposed to what is called "normal sunlight." We now know that the glass of these houses intercepts what little ultraviolet light has been able to filter through the atmosphere of the earth. Consequently, the light in these houses is not normal. At the present time, we have glass on the market which is supposedly transparent to ultraviolet light, although there is some question as to how rapidly this glass will age and become opaque to ultraviolet light. Artificial light has been used as a substitute for daylight for many years. It has been used chiefly to lengthen the day during the period of the year when natural daylight is limited in time. The flaming carbon arc is one of the most satisfactory from the standpoint of spectrum, but it requires a great deal of care, needing almost continual attention.

Harvey (1922) and others have grown plants from seed to fruit entirely by the use of artificial light, no sunlight being involved at all. The nitrogen-filled tungsten filament (Mazda) lamp, mounted in reflectors, is used in most cases. The spectrum is quite similar to that of natural sunlight with the exception of some of the blues and violets. These bulbs require little attention, and the quantity of light can be varied either by distance or by the size of the bulb used. Automatic switches can easily be arranged for turning the lights on and off at any desired time. In experimental work with insects, the primary consideration seems to be to maintain the host plant under normal conditions. The primary requirement seems, therefore, to be that of plant physiology, and the literature on this subject is constantly growing and needs continual attention. Shelford (1929) discusses the general subject of the control of light for experimental purposes.

LIGHT AS A FACTOR IN ANIMAL ECOLOGY

Attention has already been called to the broad, general significance of light in all life. There are few living things which we can conceive of as existing on our earth without the presence of sunlight; even those that are at present adapted for living in darkness depend for their food and ultimate source of energy upon some forms which are directly dependent upon sunlight. It is the greatest single source of energy for biotic systems. It will not be necessary to dwell at length upon this general biological consideration. An appreciation of the importance of chlorophyll as a mechanism of photosynthesis and thereby the basic source of energy used by biotic systems will be taken for granted. Attention will be turned to the animal organism, especially the insect, as a mechanism which is affected in various ways in its energy transformation by the presence of light. In addition to that, insects in general have special organs for the perception of light, so that they may be guided in their activities in searching for food and avoiding enemies.

Effects of Light on Physical and Chemical Processes.—Every organism consists of a physical structure which accommodates the biotic system. It is, therefore, of fundamental importance to examine the effect of light upon the mechanism of this physical structure, before proceeding to other phenomena which may be classed as affecting the biotic system of the organism. In the consideration of the characteristics of the various parts of the spectrum of light, it has been pointed out that the shorter wave lengths are characterized by their chemical activity. We may, therefore, expect these short waves to have a great effect upon the physical mechanism of the organism. It is probably a generally recognized fact that light must be absorbed in order to have an effect.

A study of the effect of light and the physical processes which underlie the animal mechanism is attracting very wide attention at the present time. A detailed consideration of these new discoveries lies in the field of general physiology and will not be gone into in detail at this time. We may cite as an example Tröndle's demonstration (1910) that a weak light reduces the permeability of the cell membrane, a moderate light increases it, and a strong light diminishes it. Here, then, is a process of fundamental physiological importance which has an optimum light intensity. Either increasing or decreasing the light changes its functioning. Similar conditions are repeated over and over in the physical systems of nature, and therefore may be looked upon as of fundamental importance to all biotic systems.

Effects of Light on Biological Processes.—Biological journals are crowded with new contributions on the effect of light upon animals and plants. The tendency of modern research is to study certain wave lengths of the spectrum. Consequently, most of the current papers are on the effect of various rays of light, but as yet the entire subject has not been summarized and the work evaluated in a comprehensive publication.

Much of the earlier work was done mainly to compare sunlight with darkness. Thus, Yung (1878) performed some crude experiments, in which he placed one lot of frogs' eggs in a dish in front of a window, where they never received the direct rays of the sun. Another he kept constantly in the dark. Under these conditions, which presumably were identical except for the presence or absence of light, the tadpoles in the light grew faster than those in the darkness. Davenport (1908) summarized the earlier work which had been done on organisms in general, and Bachmetjew (1907) gave a summary of work on insects. Some of the work up to this time was at least roughly quantitative. Belcard (1858) is classically quoted for his study of the effect of light on the flesh fly, *Musca*, under various colors of light, in which he found that the size varied; giving the largest under violet; the next under blue, red, white; and under green the smallest. It is stated that the larvae which developed under the violet light were three times the length and thickness of those under the green light. Gal (1898) reared the silkworm, *Bombyx mori*, under different lights, and noticed that the growth was different. The adult females laid more eggs and the cocoons were of larger size under green light. Next in order, so far as size of cocoons was concerned, came yellow, red, blue, white, and violet. The number of eggs from the female, however, did not follow this same order. It will be noticed that neither the order of size given by Gal nor that given by Belcard follows any particular system so far as the length of rays of the various lights is concerned. There may be some question, therefore, as to the significance of these earlier experiments. The nature of the evidence probably does not warrant general conclusions at the present time.

With all respect to the earlier literature, it may be of more advantage to turn attention to the later and more critical papers on the effect of light on biological processes. Davey (1919) studied the effect of x-ray upon mass cultures of *Tribolium*, and found that it was possible to prolong the life of a mass culture with a small daily dosage of x-ray. When the dosage was increased, the death rate approached that of the normal culture; but when it was increased still more, the culture died very quickly. Figure 5 shows graphically the general results of Davey's experiment. It is interesting to note that the time required for 50 per cent of the culture to die was 40 days in the control, and was prolonged to as much as 75 days in the experiments with about the optimum dose of x-ray. In these experiments, precautions were taken to see that x-ray was the only factor varying. It is not contended that x-rays are always present as a normal part of light in nature. It is quite likely, however, that by a study of the effect of some of these special rays, we may gain some fundamental information with regard to the action of light rays in general. If the time comes when all of the rays have been studied in detail, we may be able to correlate the information on all of these rays

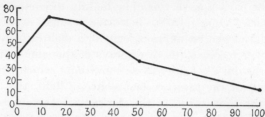

FIG. 5.—Graph showing the time required for 50 per cent of a *Tribolium* culture to die, plotted against the daily dosage of x-ray to which they were exposed. (*Constructed from data taken from Davey*, 1919.)

and form a general idea as to the physiological effect of light as such on organisms.

Packard (1926) made a study of the effect of x-rays upon *Drosophila* eggs for the purpose of determining whether or not they would be suitable material for measuring the quantitative biological effect of x-rays. This author did not find a stimulating effect of the low dosage of x-ray, but concluded that the Bunsen-Roscoe law of light intensity and time applied

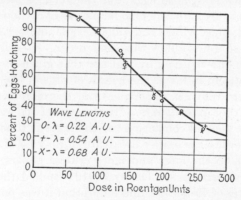

FIG. 6.—The relation between the dosage in Roentgen units and the death rate of *Drosophila* eggs. (*Packard*, 1927.)

here. This would mean that a shorter time at high intensity and a longer time at low intensity would give equal effects. In summarizing some of his experiments, he concludes that the mortality curves for *Drosophila* eggs have the same characteristics regardless of the dosage, but that the steepness of the curves varied with the intensity of the x-rays. Packard (1927) concluded that homogeneous x-rays of equal intensity but different wave lengths, varying from 0.22 to 0.68 Angström units, produced the same quantitative biological effect on *Drosophila* eggs, and he found this to be true also for heterogeneous beams of equal intensity. Figure 6 is of interest because it seems to indicate that within the region of 0.22 to 0.68 Angström units, which covers in general the field of soft *x*-rays, there is not a great deal of difference in the quality of the rays themselves.

In further experiments, Packard found that by varying the distance in such a way that two beams of different wave lengths would give the same intensity, the effects for any given intensity were the same, even though one of the rays was in the region of soft *x*-rays and the other in the region classified as hard *x*-rays. The particular point of interest here is that these experiments seem to indicate that the nature of the

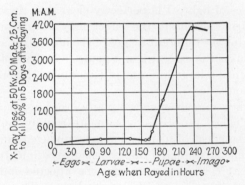

Fɪɢ. 7.—Graph showing the variation in susceptibility to *x*-rays with age in *Drosophila melanogaster*. (*Mavor*, 1927.)

effect is the same over a considerable range of wave lengths, when intensity as measured in Roentgen units[1] remains the same.

Mavor (1927) made a study of the susceptibility of *Drosophila* to *x*-rays in various parts of its life cycle. The graph in Fig. 7 shows the general results which were obtained. The eggs and larvae seem to have about the same amount of resistance, but during the pupal stage a very surprising change takes place. About 20 hours after pupation the resistance of the flies begins to increase, and at the end of pupation the resistance of the animals is about 35 times that at the beginning of the period. Mavor suggests that resistance begins to develop when the imaginal organs have been developed, and that this increases during the growth and differentiation of these organs. With regard to the effect of *x*-ray upon the rate of development, Mavor states that there is no evidence of any pronounced retardation, because of the exposure to *x*-ray.

[1] A Roentgen unit (German system) is that amount of *x*-rays which will produce, in 1 c.c. air at 760 mm. pressure and 20°C., an ionization current of one electrostatic unit.

Packard (1915) investigated the effect of some of the shorter rays upon *Drosophila*. The gamma and beta rays of radium were used, and the author concluded that the eggs and larvae of *Drosophila* are not appreciably affected by gamma rays. The rates of growth are apparently not changed at all, and the adults which emerge from larvae reared under conditions in which they were exposed to gamma rays are fertile. With regard to the beta rays, it is stated that larvae and pupae show no external changes even after an hour's exposure to a high intensity of beta rays. When the adults emerge, they are at first sterile, but soon become fertile. This seems to suggest that the oocytes may have been affected by the beta rays, and that the eggs which are later produced have been developed since exposure to the beta rays.

As a result of the work which has already been done on the effect of the short waves of light, it is perfectly clear that these rays may have a very great effect, also that the effect may vary from one insect to another, and during the different stages of the life history of any individual insect. Since this is the case, it is not going to be possible to make broad generalizations until a large amount of experimental work has been done and reported upon.

Work on higher animals suggests many other important effects upon the rates of biological processes. Data are rapidly being accumulated with regard to the effect of ultraviolet light upon vitamin D in the food of animals. Some preliminary unpublished experiments in this laboratory indicate that certain insects may be affected indirectly by food which has been eradiated with ultraviolet light. These will be referred to later in the chapter on Nutrition.

The effects of the longer rays of light upon the rates of the biological processes of insects have received less critical attention than those of the shorter rays. It has been the usual assumption that the ultraviolet portion of the rays of sunlight are necessary for the metabolism of insects. A search of the results of careful experimental work seems, at the present time, to lead to the conclusion that if the light conditions are sufficient for the host plant to grow normally, the insects will grow normally, and that those which do not require living host plants do not require light. Parker (1930) grew grasshoppers under artificial light and supplied the food daily. Under these conditions no alteration of rate of biological processes was noticed as compared with those which were reared in daylight. Wadley (unpublished thesis) reared aphids upon plants under artificial light conditions, and concluded that their growth was normal so long as the plants were normal. Northrop (1926) published the results of some experiments in which he ran mass cultures of *Drosophila* at a constant temperature of 25°C., one series being exposed to light and another being kept in darkness for 230 generations. Food was very carefully controlled in this case, both series receiving sterile yeast as food. Since the lengths of the larval, pupal, and adult life were practically the same in both series, the author concluded that there was no evidence to show that inbreeding, absence of light, or growth in the absence of bacteria had any effect either on the duration of life or on the ability of the organisms to resist unfavorable bacteria. In the laboratory at the University of Minnesota, the author has reared *Tribolium confusum* during a period of 12 years in the absence of sunlight. Many of the cultures have been reared in continual darkness, and others at most have been exposed to the ordinary electric light used for laboratory observation. There is no evidence that the absence of light has made any difference whatever in the periods of the various stages of the life history, or in any other perceptible way.

It is known that certain insects, particularly those feeding upon green host plants, are affected by the length of day and, therefore, by light.

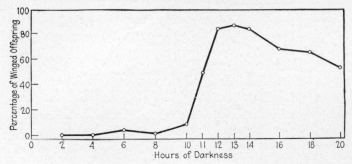

FIG. 8.—Curve showing the effect upon wing production of alternating the aphids between six hours of light and various periods of darkness. (*Shull*, 1929.)

Kellerman (1926) has given a summary of work on photoperiodism in plants and has summarized the important literature, showing that plants are definitely affected by the length of day. This is an interesting ecological factor because, leaving aside cloudiness, the length of daylight is definitely fixed by the angle of incidence of the sun's rays at various times of the year. Marcovitch (1923), Shull (1927, 1929a and 1929b), and others have given attention to the effect of photoperiodism on the production of winged individuals among the aphids. However, aphids are such highly complex organisms that it is not easy to experiment with them and make certain as to the quantitative effect of various factors affecting their lives with their varying sex ratio, their winged and wingless forms, and their peculiar method of reproduction. Shull (1927) found that *Macrosiphum* produces more winged individuals if reared under alternating light and darkness, than if reared in continual light. Continual darkness gives about as few winged individuals as continual light. Further investigation (Shull, 1929a) has shown a sharp increase of wing production to be correlated with an increase of darkness from

10 to 12 hours; a maximum effect with 12 to 14 hours of darkness; and a gradual decline in wing production for longer periods of darkness. The effect of the alternating light and darkness is apparently upon the parent, or upon the young before they are born. Starvation in darkness did not increase the number of winged individuals, but starvation in eight hours of light alternating with 16 hours of darkness gave the maximum number. It seems evident in this case, therefore, that it is a case of photoperiodism rather than the effect of light as such, for the rearing in continual light gives about the same results as rearing in continual darkness. Temperature is important as affecting the production of wings in alternating light and darkness. At temperatures higher than 20°C. few winged individuals are produced under any conditions of light and darkness, while the maximum effect is secured at lower tem-

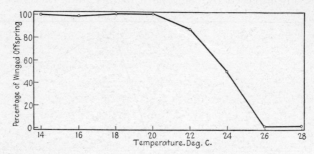

Fig. 9.—Curve showing the inhibiting effect of high temperature on wing production by alternating light and darkness, alternation of 8 hours light with 16 hours of darkness produces wings in almost all the offspring at all feasible temperatures up to 20°C., but rapidly loses this effect at higher temperatures. (*Shull*, 1929.)

peratures (Shull, 1929a). In nature these aphids develop winged individuals in the fall, when food becomes scarce, and days become short. This is important in their ecology, for they must migrate to another host at this time and, in the absence of wings, they would be powerless to do so.

The conclusions which may be drawn at the present time on the general subject of the effect of light upon the rate of metabolism of insects cannot be put in the form of broad generalizations, because of the lack of information. It is, however, encouraging to note that at least in certain cases light is not an important direct factor. Such insects as *Drosophila* and *Tribolium* apparently may continue to be reared under artificial-light conditions for experimental work, and it does not need to be considered that the experiments are at fault because natural sunlight is not being used. This is a great advantage, because there is hardly another ecological factor so difficult to control and experiment with as light; and if we may leave it out during the investigation of other factors, it will be an enormous advantage.

Effects of Light on Color, Form, and Structure.—In considering the effect of light upon the color of insects and attempting to evaluate the voluminous literature upon the subject, it is necessary to keep in mind the fact that there are several possible ways in which light may act upon color. For the present, attention is to be called to the effect of light, during the development of an individual organism, upon its color. This may come about either through the effect of light upon the development of the pigment in a fixed pattern, or, as is the case in other groups of animals, by stimulating the organism to rearrange its pigment to produce a pattern which the individual may change from time to time.

Poulton (1890) gave a summary of color of animals up to that date. Bachmetjew (1907) gave a summary of literature upon color of insects affected by light. Poulton cites experiments in which the larvae of certain butterflies, probably *Vanessa*, were reared on light and dark backgrounds and the chrysalis colored accordingly; those from light backgrounds became light colored, and those from dark backgrounds, dark colored.

Katheriner (1900) reports experiments on *Vanessa* in which the larvae were reared under various light conditions. Those exposed to daylight on a white background gave very light pupae; those exposed to daylight on a black background or to blue light gave dark pupae. In red light or yellow light the pupae were orange or yellow. Poulton considered that these effects were those of light upon the development of pigment; and this, in a way, formed the basis for his work upon protective coloration and mimicry. Standfuss (1894–1895) and others have carried on a series of experiments in which they have noted the effect of light upon the larvae as expressed in the adult which emerged. Hase (1929) reported the action of ultraviolet rays in inhibiting the formation of pigment in certain parasite wasps.

In much of this experimental work, due care was not taken to distinguish between the effects of low temperature and darkness. It is, therefore, difficult to evaluate these results. It seems, however, quite definite that light has a very important rôle in influencing pigmentation, and that certain organisms under certain conditions are light colored on light backgrounds, and dark colored on dark backgrounds. Folsom (1922) states that certain authors have considered this ability of insects to develop a light pigment on a light background and a dark pigment on a dark background as permanent protective coloration which may be regarded as stereotyped and the highly specialized end-stage of a more ancient ability to change color in response to color changes in the environment. The ability of certain crustaceans, fish, amphibians and reptiles to change their color in response to changing environment is well known. Some of the lizards are particularly adept in making quick changes from one color to another in response to the changed color of the environment

Folsom quotes Wheeler as stating that this ability still exists in the case of some grasshoppers and mantids.

Perkins (1928) investigated the case of the shrimp (*Palamonetes*), in which the chromatophors expand or contract when the shrimps are placed upon backgrounds of different color, the chromatophors being expanded on black backgrounds and contracted on light backgrounds. In this case the photoreceptors are apparently in the eyes; for when the eyes are removed, the chromatophors are continually expanded.

Biedermann (1892) investigated the case of tree frogs and found that the migration of the pigment in the chromatophors was governed by receptors located in the toes, and that when these were anesthetized the frogs were no longer able to change their chromatophors to match the surroundings.

All of these reactions may be interpreted as methods used by the organisms to conceal themselves. In the cases just cited the individual organism can change its color from time to time to match its immediate surroundings. In the case of insects cited previously, where the pigment develops to a light color on a light background and a dark color on a dark background, there can be no change after the pigment is once developed. In the case of the chrysalis of lepidoptera, which are permanently attached, there is no occasion to change the color unless the background should change.

Modern experimental work seems to be becoming increasingly critical of such interpretations. It is admitted that there may be a process of selection in which the conspicuous animals are destroyed and the less conspicuous remain, but the usefulness of the adaptation seems to be in question. It would seem that the general proposition, when considered by and large, would have to be accepted, that the development of protective colors is of value to the organism. Physiological experiments are hardly to the point in determining whether or not these protective colors are valuable. When experiments have been performed to show whether or not members of a population which do or do not have protective coloration survive or are eliminated, we will have information which is to the point.

The effect of light upon the structure of organisms in general is a subject hardly well enough developed to be discussed to advantage. We know in general that animals which live in the absence of light have certain characteristics. Cave animals are classically quoted as being light colored and blind. Biologists of today find themselves in an embarrassing situation when considering such cases. We have, on the one hand, the seemingly overwhelming evidence of general evolution, into which the cases of blind animals in caves seem to fit very nicely. We have, on the other hand, the skeptical attitude of genetical research, which denies the possibility of the inheritance of acquired characters, which seems to be implied in all interpretation of the structure of organisms which have lived in the darkness for generations. Consideration of this question leads us rather naturally to the next minor subheading.

The Effects of Light on the Mechanism of Heredity.—The development of our modern field of genetics with the allocation of various factors in genes that can quite definitely be assigned to places on different chromosomes, seemed at first to shut out all possibility of environmental influence in determining the hereditary characteristics of organisms. It seemed for a time that an organism was predestined to have certain definite characteristics entirely regardless of what its environment might be like. The only possibility of any effect by the environment seemed to be in selecting whatever heredity might present to it. Just now we seem to be entering upon a new era; for it has been found that while these genes may be definitely allocated upon the chromosomes, the fact is that environment may affect the behavior of these chromosomes and thereby affect the destiny of the genes. Therefore, environmental factors may affect the hereditary characteristics of organisms through the mechanism which determines the position which genes are to have on chromosomes and thereby, in their positions, the new cells. The mechanism of heredity, which first looked as if it would rule the effect of environment out, now becomes the agent through which environment is seen to act.

Weinstein very aptly stated that it is no more correct to say that the characteristics of an organism are determined entirely by heredity than it is to state that the area of a rectangle is controlled entirely by its altitude. The environment is the second dimension in determining the characteristics of the organism, just as length is the second dimension of a rectangle, which with altitude determines the area.

As was the case in connection with the effect of light upon the metabolism of organisms, so in this case, we have more evidence accumulated as to the effect of the short rays upon the mechanism of heredity than we have of the effects of the visible spectrum of light.

The work of Muller (1925 to date) has been stimulating in showing how x-ray may affect the phenomena of crossing over and the production of mutations in *Drosophila*. The publication of new results is occurring almost daily at the present time, for it is possible now by the use of x-ray to produce in a few minutes more mutations than have been known throughout the entire previous history of the work on the genetics of *Drosophila*. It is not possible as yet to make generalizations as to these results further than to state that it has been unquestionably demonstrated that a physical factor of the environment may affect the mechanism of heredity in such a way as to determine the hereditary constitution of the organisms which have been exposed to this factor.

Reference will again be made to the effect of physical factors of the environment upon heredity in connection with the chapter on temperature.

The Effects of Light on the Behavior of Animals.—The behavior of animals has become a highly technical branch of physiology and psychology, and will be referred to here only as it relates to the field of ecology, no attempt being made to give a critical consideration of animal behavior. Mast (1911) gives a summary of the general work of the effect of light on the behavior of organisms. Other citations in the bibliography will aid the student in determining the various types of work which have been done in this field.

In considering the behavior of animals with respect to light, it is necessary to distinguish between those organisms which see in the sense of perceiving images, and those which are able to perceive only the difference between light and darkness. Practically all adult insects have eyes which form images, and are therefore able to see. Many of them in immature stages, however, perceive only the difference between light and darkness. In the early history of the development of the theories with regard to the reaction of organisms to light, it was assumed that the organism acted as a machine, being either positive or negative, and that no other reaction was possible. However, our more recent interpretations seem to indicate that these reactions are extremely complicated and cannot be conceived of as simple machines which go toward or away from light, depending only upon the intensity of the light. It seems evident that there are many factors of the environment which control the condition of the organism at the time of the reaction and that may modify the action of light as such.

Light may affect animals by producing a response which may be in the nature of an increase or a decrease or may be, in fact, any change in the activity of the organism. The familiar Bunsen-Roscoe law states that the time of exposure is inversely proportional to the light. This is familiarly expressed in the formula which states, that intensity times time equals a constant (IT = constant). In this case, light is considered as visual intensity. Light of the different wave lengths, however, may have different values in stimulating organisms. It is interesting to compare the results of Laurens and Hooker (1920) in studying *Volvox*, with the results obtained by Mast (1917) in studying the reaction of blow-fly larvae to light (Fig. 10). Laurens and Hooker used the intensity of different wave lengths which were necessary to get a response. The minimum intensity of any light became a measure of its effect upon the *Volvox*. The lower the intensity required for a minimum effect, the greater the effect of that wave length. Mast developed an interesting technique of comparing two converging rays with each other and using the relative intensities of one as compared with the relative intensities of the other in measuring the effect. It is significant to note that with both of these methods of investigation and with *Volvox* in one case and larvae of the blow fly in another, almost the same point of the spectrum gives the maximum effect (Fig. 10). This is at about 5,000 Angström units. It is to be noted that this is not at the point of maximum intensity to the human eye, but at a point with considerably shorter wave lengths. This is in accordance with the results of Lutz (1924), which seem to indicate that insects are sensitive to shorter wave lengths than is man, therefore seeing more of the violet and possibly farther into the ultraviolet than we can.

Light is an important factor as a medium through which organisms react in seeking food and avoiding enemies. The reactions of insects to light have been studied considerably, and the earlier literature tended to produce dogmatic conclusions with regard to their reactions. Dolley (1916) made a rather careful study of the reactions of *Vanessa* to light, and concluded that many of the former conclusions were not justified. He found that if one of the eyes of the butterfly was blackened, it could still orient itself with the other eye. This does not support the theory that if one eye is illuminated and the other is not, an automatic mechanistic reaction takes place over which the insect has no control. He further showed that with experience they bettered their reactions.

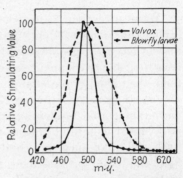

Fig. 10.—The relative stimulating value of spectral lights of equal energy content as ascertained from the determination of the minimal duration of exposure necessary to produce a reaction. (*Adapted from Mast, 1917, and Hooker, 1920.*)

It is also well recognized at the present time that other environmental factors may modify the reaction to light. Minnich (1919) found that while the honey bee is strongly positive in its response to light at ordinary temperatures, this reaction may be reversed at low temperatures.

There is ample evidence to demonstrate that certain insects, at least, react to sight as well as simply to the presence or absence of light. It is possible that some of the literature of natural history has overemphasized the value of sight as such. It is natural to attempt to interpret insects' reactions in terms of human vision, and probably the naturalist of the past erred in this direction. It is also perfectly evident that physiologists have tended to interpret reactions entirely in terms of phototropisms and have neglected all other possibilities in so doing. It is necessary to base judgment on fact, and at the same time not let a few facts influence judgment.

Abbott (1919) in investigating the reactions of certain isopods to directive rays of light concluded that they were usually negative and that this reaction resulted in keeping them in their normal environment, which is under logs and stones. Their prompt reaction to an increase of light was also interpreted as protective, as in a case when logs or stones were removed exposing them to light suddenly.

Allee and Stein (1918) concluded that the reactions of certain aquatic insects were determined by the rate of metabolism of the individual insect. In such a case any environmental factor which might influence the rate of metabolism would also influence the reaction to light. Perhaps we are eventually to come to look upon reactions to light in some such way as this. We may thus see how difficult it would be to draw any valid conclusions from a few observations under set laboratory conditions.

When attention is turned to many of the ecological problems which involve the factor of light upon the seasonal and diurnal activities of insects having a geographic distribution which may be correlated with length of day, with their escape from enemies, and their discernment of food, the difficulty of getting any true evaluations of the situation seems almost staggering. However, the situation is to be interpreted rather as encouraging than discouraging. Even the very field of physics, which is involved in formulating a conception of the constitution of light, is itself still in an uncertain condition. An attempt to write an account of light and its importance in ecology at the present time may be compared to the writing of a single chapter in a continued story, and leaving off when only that first chapter is finished. New publications from results in this field are coming out daily, and some of the results are so startling that when we have finished reading one, we wait almost in suspense for the next.

An attempt has been made to cite the papers of importance which have bibliographies connected with them. It is not contended, however, that these are the most important papers or that all of the important papers are there. However, it will serve as a guide to the student who wishes to go further into the subject of light as an ecological factor.

BIBLIOGRAPHY

LIGHT

ABBOTT, C. G.: The Sun's Energy Spectrum and Temperature, *Astrophys. Jour.*, **34**: 197–208, see p. 203, 1911.

ABBOTT, C. H.: Reactions of Land Isopods to Light, *Jour. Exptl. Zool.*, **27**: 193–246, 1919.

ADAMS, J.: Duration of Light and Growth, *Ann. Bot.*, vol. 38, **151**: 509–523, 1924.

ALLEE, W. C., and E. R. STEIN: Light Reactions and Metabolism in May-fly Nymphs, *Jour. Exptl. Zool.*, **26**: 423–458, 1918.

ANGSTRÖM, ANDERS: Note on Comparisons between Pyrheliometers and on the Difference between the Angström Standard and the Smithsonian Standard, *U. S. Monthly Weather Rev.*, **47**: 798–799, 1919.

ANGSTRÖM, ANDERS: A New Instrument for Measuring Sky Radiation, *U. S. Monthly Weather Rev.*, **47**: 795–797, 1919.

BACHMETJEW, P.: "Experimentelle entomologische Studien," 10, 944, 31 figs. W. Engelmann, Leipzig, 1907.

BAGG, H. J., and C. C. LITTLE: Hereditary Structural Defects in the Descendants of Mice Exposed to Roentgen-ray Irradiation, *Amer. Jour. Anat.*, **33**: 119–145, 1924.

BAILEY, L. H.: Some Preliminary Studies of the Influence of the Electric Arc Lamp upon Greenhouse Plants, *Cornell Agr. Expt. Sta. Bull.* 30, 1891, and 1893.

BANNIER, G.: Influence de la lumière électrique continue sur la forme et la structure des plantes, *Rev. gén. bot.*, vol. VII, pp. 241–244, 289–306, 332–342, 409–469, 1895.

BAYLISS, W. M.: "Principles of General Physiology," 2d ed., chap. XIX, pp. 548–579, Longmans, Green and Co., London, 1918. 858 pp.

BEHR, ELLINOR H.: Color Changes in Fishes Induced by Light Rays of Varying Wave Lengths, *Anat. Rec.*, **37**: 142, 1927.

BELCARD, J.: Note rélative à l'influence de la lumière sur les animaux, *Compt. rend. acad. sci.*, **46**: 441–443, 1858.

BIEDERMANN, WILHELM: Ueber den Farbenwechsel der Frösche, *Pflüger's Arch. Physiol.*, **51**: 455–508, 1892.

BRAID, K. W.: The Measurement of Light for Ecological Purposes, *Jour. Ecology*, **11**: 49–63, 1923.

BUENO, J. R. DE LA TORRE: Phototropism in Heteroptera, *Bull. Brooklyn Ent. Soc.*, **9**: 90–96, 1914.

BUXTON, P. A.: The Radiation Integrator in Racus, an Instrument for the Study of Radiant Heat Received from the Sun, *Jour. Hyg.*, **25**: 285–294, 1926.

CARPENTER, F. W.: The Reactions of the Pomace Fly (*Drosophila ampelophila* Loew) to Light, Gravity, and Mechanical Stimulation, *Amer. Naturalist*, **39**: 157–171, 1905.

CARTER, WALTER: Ecological Studies of *Eutetix tennellus* Baker, *U. S. D. A. Tech. Bull.* No. 206, 1930. 115 pp.

CLEMENTS, F. E.: "Research Methods in Ecology," Lincoln, 1905. 334 pp.

COBLENTZ, W. W.: "Instruments and Methods Used in Radiometry," Pt. III. The Photoelectric Cell and Other Selective Radiometers, 1919.

———: "Report on Instruments and Methods of Radiometry," 1921.

COBLENTZ, W. W. and H. KAHLER: A New Spectropyrheliometer and Measurements of the Component Radiations from the Sun and from a Quartz-mercury Vapor Lamp, *U. S. Bur. Stand. Sci. Pap.* 378, pp. 233–247, 1920.

CONDON, E. U., and H. M. TERRILL: Quantum Phenomena in the Biological Action of X-rays, *Jour. Cancer Research*, **11**: 324–333, 1927.

CRAIGHEAD, F. C.: Direct Sunlight as a Factor in Forest Insect Control, *Proc. Ent. Soc.*, Wash., **22**: 106–108, 1920.

CROWTHER, J. A.: The Action of X-rays on *Colpidium Colpoda*, *Proc. Roy. Soc.*, London, ser. B, **100**: 390–404, 1926.

CROZIER, W. J.: Wave Length of Light and Photic Inhibition of Stereotropism in Tenebrio Larvae, *Jour. Gen. Physiol.*, **6**: 647–652, 1924.

DAVENPORT, C. B.: "Experimental Morphology," The Macmillan Company, New York, 1908. 488 pp.; 7 index; extensive bibliography.

DAVEY, WHEELER P.: The Effect of X-rays on the Length of Life of *Tribolium confusum*, *Jour. Exptl. Zool.*, **22**: 573–592, 1917.

———: Prolongation of the Life of *Tribolium confusum* Apparently Due to Small Doses of X-rays, *Jour. Exptl. Zool.*, **28**: 447–458, 1919.

DIETRICH, E. O.: The Effect of Temperature on the Light Sensibility Curves of Different Types of Selenium Cells, *Phys. Rev.*, **8**: 191–194, 1916.

DOLLEY, W. L.: Reactions to Light in *Vanessa antiopa*, with Special Reference to Circus Movements, *Jour. Exptl. Zool.*, **20**: 357–419, 1916.

DÜRKEN, B.: Ueber die Wirkung farbigen Lichtes auf die Puppen des Kohlweisslings (*Pieris brassicae*) und das Verhalten der Nachkommen, *Arch. mikros. Anat. u. Entwickl.-mech.*, **99**: 222–389, 1923.

FOLSOM, JUSTUS WATSON: "Entomology with Special Reference to Its Ecological Aspects," P. Blakiston's Son & Co., Inc., Phil., 1922. 477 pp.

GAL, JULES: "L'influence des lumières colorées sur le développement des vers à soie," 1898.

GARNER, W. W., and H. A. ALLARD: Effect of the Relative Length of Day and Night and Other Factors of the Environment on Growth and Reproduction in Plants, *Jour. Agr. Research*, **18**: 553–606, 1920.

GORCZYŃSKI, LADISLAUS: On a Simple Method of Recording the Total and Partial Intensities of Solar Radiation, *U. S. Monthly Weather Rev.*, **52**: 299–301, 1924.

GRAHAM, S. A.: Factors Influencing the Subcortical Temperature of Logs, 18th Report, State Entomologist of Minnesota, 1920, pp. 26–42.

GUARINONI, DR.: Ueber den Einfluss des violetten Lichtes auf die Seidenraupen, *Zentral. Agr. Chem.*, **1**: 207–208, 1872.

HANSON, FRANK BLAIR: The Effects of X-rays on Productivity and Sex Ratio in *Drosophila melanogaster*, *Amer. Naturalist*, **62**: 352–362, 1928.

HARTLINE, H. KEFFER: Influence of Light of Very Low Intensity on Phototropic Reactions of Animals, *Jour. Gen. Physiol.*, **6**: 137–152, 1923.

HARVEY, NEWTON E.: The Production of Light by the Fishes Photoblepharon and Anomalops, *Carnegie Inst. Wash. Papers* from the Dept. of Marine Biol., **18**: 45–60, 1922.

HARVEY, R. B.: Growth of Plants in Artificial Light from Seed to Seed, *Science*, vol. LVI, pp. 366–367, 1922.

———: Growth of Plants in Artificial Light, *Bot. Gaz.*, vol. 74, pp. 447–451, 1922.

HASE, ALBRECHT: Durch Quarzlichtbestrahlung erzwungene Pigment veränderungen bei Insekten (Schlupfwespen), *Arch. f. Dermatol. u. Syphil.*, 1929.

HERMS, W. B.: The Photic Reactions of Sarcophagid Flies, especially *Lucilia caesar* L. and *Calliphora vomitoria* L., *Jour. Exptl. Zool.*, **10**: 167–226, 1911.

HESS, WALTER, N.: Reactions to Light in the Earthworm, *Lumbricus terrestris* L., *Jour. Morph.*, **39**: 515–542, 1924.

HILL L., and A. EIDENOW: The Biological Action of Light, *Proc. Roy. Soc.*, ser. B, **95**: 163–180, 1923.

HOLMES, S. J.: The Selection of Random Movements as a Factor in Phototaxis. *Jour. Compar. Neurol. & Psychol.*, **15**: 98–112, 1905.

———: The Reactions of Ranatra to Light, *Jour. Compar. Neurol. & Psychol.*, **15**: 305–349, 1905.

KATHERINER, L.: Versuche über den Einfluss des Lichtes auf die Farbe der Puppe vom Tagpfauenauge (*V. io* L.), *Biol. Zentralbl.*, vol. XIX, **21**: 712–718, 1899.

———: Versuche über den Einfluss der verschiedenen Strahlen des Spektrums auf Puppe und Falter von *V. urticae* L. und *V. io* L., *Illus. Ztschr. Ent.*, **VI**: 7–9, 1900 and 1901.

KELLERMAN, K. F.: A Review of the Discovery of Photoperiodism: the Influence of the Length of Daily Light Periods upon the Growth of Plants, *Quart. Rev. Biol.*, **1**: 87–94, 1926.

KIMBALL, H. H.: Variations in the Total and Luminous Solar Radiation with Geographical Position in the United States, *U. S. Monthly Weather Rev.*, **47**: 769–793, 1919.

———: The Distribution of Energy in the Visible Spectrum of Sunlight, Skylight, and Total Daylight, *Proc. Int. Congress on Illumination*, pp. 501–515, 1928.

KLUGH, A. BROOKER: Ecological Photometry and a New Instrument for Measuring Light, *Ecology*, **VI**: 203–237, 1925.

————: A Land Model of the Ecological Photometer, *Ecology*, **8**: 174–176, 1927a.

————: A Comparison of Certain Methods of Measuring Light for Ecological purposes, *Ecology*, **8**: 415–427, 1927b.

KUSNEZOV, N. J.: Zur Frage über die Lichtexperimente mit Lepidopteren, *Ztschr. wiss. Insektenbiol.*, **2**: 43–44, 1906.

LAURENS, H., and H. D. HOOKER: Studies on the Relative Physiological Value of Spectral Lights, *Jour. Exptl. Zool.*, **30**: 345–368, 1920.

LEE, S. C.: Factors Controlling Forest Successions at Lake Itasca, Minn., *Bot. Gaz.*, **78**: 129–174, 1924.

LIPPMANN, ARTHUR, and HANS VÖLKER: Beiträge zur Frage der Stoffwechsel-beeinflussing durch Ultraviolettbestrahlung, *Klin. Wchnchr.*, **7**: 213–214, 1928.

LIST, THEOD.: Ueber den Einfluss des Lichtes auf die Ablagerung von Pigment, *Arch. Entwickl. Mech. Organ.*, **8**: 618–632, 1899.

LOEB, J.: Einfluss des Lichtes auf die Oxydationsvorgänge im thierischen Organismus, *Pflüger's Arch. Physiol.*, **42**: 393–407, 1888.

LOEB, J., and H. WASTENEYS: The Relative Efficiency of Various Parts of the Spectrum for the Heliotropic Reactions of Animals and Plants, *Jour. Exptl. Zool.*, **20**: 217–236, 6 figs, 1916.

————: "Forced Movements, Tropisms and Animal Conduct," J. B. Lippincott Company, 1918. 209 pp., 42 figs.

LUNDEGÄRDH, HENRIK: Pflanzenökologische Lichtmessungen, *Biol. Zentralbl.*, **43**: 405–431, 1923.

LUTZ, F. E.: A Study of Ultraviolet in Relation to the Flower-visiting Habits of Insects, *Ann. N. Y. Acad. Sci.*, **29**: 471–528, 1924.

MACDOUGAL, D. T., and H. A. SPOEHR: The Measurement of Light in Some of Its More Important Physiological Aspects, *Science* **45**: 616–618, 1917.

MARCOVITCH, S.: Plant Lice and Light Exposure, *Science*, n. s., **58**: 537–538, 1923.

MAST, S. O.: "Light and the Behavior of Organisms," John Wiley & Sons, Inc., New York, 1911. 410 pp.

————: The Relation between Spectral Color and Stimulation in the Lower Organisms, *Jour. Exptl. Zool.*, **22**: 471–528, 1917.

————: Reversal in Photic Orientation in Volvox and the Nature of Photic Stimulation, *Ztschr. f. vergleichende Physiol.*, **5**: 730–738, 1927.

MAST, S. O., and W. L. DOLLEY: The Relation Between the Stimulating Efficiency of Intermittent and Continuous Light, *Amer. Jour. Physiol.*, **72**: 84–88, 1925.

MAVOR, J. W.: An Effect of X-rays on Inheritance, *Albany Med. Jour.*, pp. 209–220, 1922.

————: Studies on the Biological Effect of X-rays, *Amer. Jour. Roentgenol.*, **10**: 968–974, 1923.

————: A Comparison of the Susceptibility to X-rays of Drosophila melanogaster at Various Stages of Its Life-cycle, *Jour. Exptl. Zool.*, **47**: 63–83, 1927.

MINNICH, DWIGHT ELMER: The Photic Reactions of the Honey-bee, *Apis mellifera*, *Jour. Exptl. Zool.*, **29**: 343–425, 1919.

MULLER, H. J.: The Regionally Differential Effect of X-rays on Crossing over in Autosomes of Drosophila, *Genetics*, **10**: 470–507, 1925.

————: Induced Crossing-over Variation in the X-chromosome of Drosophila, *Amer. Naturalist*, **60**: 192–195, 1926.

MULLER, H. J., and A. L. DIPPEL: Chromosome Breakage by X-rays and the Production of Eggs from Genetically Male Tissue in Drosophila, *Brit. Jour. Exptl. Biol.*, **3**: 85–122, 1926.

NECHELES, HEINRICH: Observations on the Causes of Night Activity in Some Insects, *Chinese Jour. Physiol.*, **1**: 143–155, 1927.

NORTHROP, JOHN H.: Duration of Life of an Aseptic *Drosophila* Culture Inbred in the Dark for 230 Generations, *Jour. Gen. Physiol.*, **9**: 763–765, 1926.

PACKARD, CHARLES: The Effects of the Beta and Gamma Rays of Radium on Protoplasm, *Jour. Exptl. Zool.*, **19**: 323–353, 1915.

————: The Measurement of Quantitative Biological Effects of X-rays, *Jour. Cancer Research*, **10**: 319–339, 1926.

————: The Quantitative Biological Effects of X-rays of Different Wavelengths, *Jour. Cancer Research*, **11**: 1–15, 1927.

PARKER, G. H.: The Phototropism of the Mourning-cloak Butterfly, *Vanessa antiopa* Linn., "Mark Anniversary Volume," pp. 453–469, Henry Holt & Company, New York, 1903.

PARKER, G. H., and B. M. PATTEN: The Physiological Effect of Intermittent and Continuous Lights of Equal Intensities, *Amer. Jour. Physiol.*, **31**: 22–29, 1912.

PARKER, J. R.: Some Effects of Temperature and Moisture upon *Melanoplus mexicanus*, *Mexicanus* Saussure and *Camnula pellucida* Scudder (Orthoptera), *U. of Mont. Ag. Expt. Sta. Bull.* 223, p. 132, 1930.

PATTEN, B. M.: The Changes of the Blowfly Larva's Photosensitivity with Age, *Jour. Exptl. Zool.*, **20**: 585–598, 1916.

PEARSE, A. S.: The Reactions of Amphibians to Light, *Proc. Amer. Acad. Arts & Sci.*, **XLV**: 161–208, 1910.

PECKHAM, G. W. and E. G.: Sense of Sight in Spiders with Some Observations on Color Sense, *Trans. Wis. Acad. Sci., Arts and Letters*, **10**: 231–261, 1895.

PERKINS, E. B.: Color Changes in Crustaceans, Especially in Palaemonetes, *Jour. Exptl. Zool.*, **50**: 71–105, 1928.

POULTON, EDW.: An Inquiry into the Cause and Extent of a Specific Color Relation between Certain Exposed Lepidopterous Pupae and the Surfaces Which Immediately Surround Them, *Proc. Roy. Soc.*, London, 1887. **XIII**: 94–108; *Philos. Trans.*, vol. 178, pp. 311–441, 1887.

POULTON, EDWARD BAGNALL: "The Colours of Animals," Kegan Paul, Trench, Trübner & Co., Ltd., London, 1890. 360 pp.

POWERS, G. E., E. A. PARK, and N. SIMMONDS: The Influence of Radiant Energy upon the Development of Xerophthalmia in Rats: a Remarkable Demonstration of the Beneficial Influence of Sunlight and Out-of-Door Air upon the Organism, *Jour. Biol. Chem.*, **55**: 575–597, 1923.

PULLING, H. E.: Sunlight and Its Measurement, *Plant World*, vol. **22**: 151–171, 187–209, 1919.

RÁDL, E.: Ueber den Phototropismus einiger Arthropoden, *Biol. Zentralbl.*, **21**: 75–86, 1901.

————: Untersuchungen über die Lichtreactionen der Arthropoden, *Pflüger's Arch. Physiol.*, vol. **87**: 418–466, 1901.

————: "Untersuchungen über den Phototropismus der Thiere," W. Engelmann, Leipzig, 1903. 186 pp.

RAMAN, C. V.: On the Molecular Scattering of Light in Water and the Color of the Sea, *Proc. Roy. Soc.*, ser. A, vol. **101**: 64–80, 1922.

ROWAN, WILLIAM: On Photoperiodism, Reproductive Periodicity, and Annual Migrations of Birds and Certain Fishes, *Proc. Boston Soc. Nat. Hist.*, **38**: 147–189, 1926.

RÜHL, FRITZ: "Ueber die Einwirkung verschiedenfarbigen Lichtes auf die Raupen," 1886.

RUMER, G. A.: Effect of Röntgen Rays on the Tobacco, or Cigarette, Beetle and the Results of Experiments with a New Form of Röntgen Tube, *Jour. Agr. Research*, **6**: 383–388, 1916.

Rump, Walther,: Die Streustrahlung der Luft, *Fortschr. Geb. Röntgenstrahlen*, 38: 58–67, 1928.

Schlieper, Carl: Ueber die Helligkeitsverteilung im Spektrum bei verschiedenen Insekten, *Ztschr. vergleich. Physiol.*, 8: 281–288, 1928.

Schmujdinowitsch, W. J.: Der Einfluss des Sonnenlichtes und verschiedener Sonnenstrahlen auf die Entwicklung des Maulbeeren-seidenfalters, "Arb. kaukas. Seidenz. Stat.," vol. II, pp. 111–114, 1889; Tiflis, 1891.

Segelken, J. G.: The Determination of Light, *Ecology* 10: 294–297, 1929.

Shelford, V. E., and F. W. Gail: A Study of Light Penetration into Sea Water Made with the Kunz Photo-electric Cell with Particular Reference to the Distribution of Plants, *Pubs. Puget Sound Biol. Sta.*, No. 3, pp. 141–176, 1922.

Shelford, V. E.: "Laboratory and Field Ecology," Williams & Wilkins Co., Baltimore, 1929.

Shelford, V. E., and J. Kunz: Use of Photoelectric Cells for Light Measurement in Ecological Work, *Ecology*, pp. 298–311, 1929.

Shull, A. Franklin: Duration of Light and the Wings of Aphids, *Anat. Rec.*, 37: 136, 1927.

―――: The Effect of Intensity and Duration of Light and of Duration of Darkness, Partly Modified by Temperature, upon Wing-production in Aphids, *W. Roux' Arch. f. Entwicklungsmech. d. Organismen*, 115: 825–851, 1929a.

―――: Determination of Types of Individuals in Aphids, Rotifers, and Cladocera, *Biol. Rev.*, vol. IV, pp. 218–248, 1929b.

Standfuss, M.: Ueber die Gründe der Variation und Aberation des Falterstadiums bei den Schmetterlingen; *Insektenbörse*, XI: 199–201, 209–210, 217–218, 225–226, 1894; XII: 4–5, 13, 22–23, 29–30, 36–37, 1895.

Terao, Arata, and Nooki Wakamari: The Effect of Uranium Radiation on the Silkworm, *Bombyx mori L.*, *Proc. Imp. Acad. Japan*, pp. 188–191, 1926.

Toy, F. C., and F. C. Ghosh: "Absorption of Light by the Goldberg Wedge," 1920.

Tröndle, A.: Der Einfluss des Lichtes auf die Permeabilität der Plasmahaut. *Jahrb. wiss. Bot.*, 48: 171–282, 1910.

Wadley, Francis Marion: Ecology of Toxoptera graminum with Special Reference to Northern Outbreaks, Ph. D. thesis (unpublished), University of Minnesota, 1928.

Wager, H.: The Action of Light on Chlorophyll, *Proc. Roy. Soc.*, ser. B, 87: 386–407, 1914.

Walter, H. E.: The Reactions of Planarians to Light, *Jour. Exptl. Zool.*, V: 35–162, 1907.

Weber, L.: Ueber das Verhalten der Insekten dem Röntgenschen Lichte gegenüber, *Abhandl. u. Ber.* XXXXII *des Ver. f. Naturk. zu Cassel über das* 61. *Vereinsjahr*, vols. XXXI and XXXII, 1896–97.

Weinstein, Alexander: "Heredity and Development in Chemistry and Medicine," pp. 25–72, ed. by Julius Stieglitz, The Chemical Foundation, New York, 1928.

Weismann, A.: "The Germ-plasm, a Theory of Heredity," transl. by W. N. Parker and H. Rönnfeldt; pp. 399–409 are on climatic variations in butterflies; Charles Scribner's Sons, New York, 1898.

Yung, E.: Contributions à l'histoire de l'influence des milieux physiques sur les êtres vivants, *Arch. Zool.*, vol. VII, pp. 251–282, 1878.

Zeleny, John: The Influence of Temperature on Photo-electric Effect, *Phys. Rev.*, vol. XII, pp. 321–339, 1901.

Zon and Graves: Light in Relation to Tree Growth, *U. S. Forest Service Bull.*, p. 92, 1911.

CHAPTER III

TEMPERATURE AS AN ECOLOGICAL FACTOR

Attention will now be turned to that portion of radiant energy which lies just beyond the longest wave lengths of the visible spectrum, which we have considered under light; and this is temperature. There is probably no other physical factor in the ecology of animals which has received more attention than has temperature. This is partly because its effects are so very evident, and partly because of the great variation of temperature in time, in both the diurnal and the annual cycles, and in space over the surface of the earth. It probably affects animals more evidently and in more ways than any other factor. The factor itself is measured more easily than any other, and in general the correlation between the changes in temperature and the effect upon the animals is usually very apparent.

It might have been more logical to have headed this chapter "Heat" rather than "Temperature," inasmuch as it follows immediately the consideration of light which is another form of radiant energy. In dealing with heat we would be confined in our measurements to gram calories per square centimeter, as an expression of the quantity of radiant energy. In dealing with temperature we may use the degrees of a thermometer scale. Temperature may be defined as the condition of the body which determines the transfer of heat to or from other bodies. The thermodynamic measurements which we shall deal with in this chapter are on the temperature scale, rather than measurements of the quantity of radiant energy. Consequently, it has seemed wise to deal with it under the heading, Temperature. Indeed, it is this ever-present transfer of energy which becomes one of the most important physical factors of the environment.

General References to Literature on Temperature.—From the point of view of general physiology, we find the effect of temperature well summarized by Bayliss in the last edition of his book. Scattered citations on the effect of temperature upon insects were well summarized by Bachmetjew in 1901 and 1907. It is regrettable that we have no summary of the scattered literature since this monumental work. Such a summary would bring our knowledge down to date. Davenport (1908) summarized literature on animals in general, and tabulated certain critical temperatures for various species. Kanitz (1915) gives a general discussion of the effects of temperature on biological processes mainly from a purely physiological standpoint. Shelford (1929) reviews methods of measuring and controlling temperature.

Experimental Methods of Measuring Temperature.—Temperature is measured by the change in a physical condition which has been shown to bear a linear relationship to changes of temperature. The thermodynamic scale is independent of the properties of any material substance. It is based solely upon the laws of thermodynamics and is accepted as a standard scale of temperature. On this scale, temperatures are proportional to the pressure or volume of an ideal gas at a constant pressure or volume. When volume is maintained as constant, temperature is proportional to the pressure. When pressure is maintained constant, temperature is proportional to the volume. Absolute zero on the thermodynamic scale is that temperature at which the pressure of a fixed mass of an ideal gas maintained at a constant volume becomes zero.

The usual scales of measurement of temperature are all related to the effect of temperature on water. Fahrenheit obtained a low temperature by the use of ice and salt, and assumed this to be the lowest obtainable temperature and therefore called it 0°. He made an approximation of the temperature of the human body for 100°, though he was not quite correct in this. The freezing point of water was accidentally 32°, and the boiling point 212°. On the Fahrenheit scale, 1° = $\frac{1}{180}$ of the difference between the freezing and the boiling point of water. On the Réaumur scale, which starts with the freezing point of water as 0°, 1° equals $\frac{1}{80}$ of the difference between the freezing and boiling points of water.

The centigrade scale, which is based on the freezing point of water as 0° and the boiling point of water as 100°, is the simplest and most logical to use for ordinary purposes. However, even this may be misleading for certain phenomena in connection with which a so-called "absolute scale" is used. The absolute zero of the thermodynamic scale is −273°C., or −459.4°F. It is interesting to note that this "absolute scale" is based upon a theoretical "0" arrived at by calculation.

The general consideration of thermometry, together with literature, will be found in "International Critical Tables," volume I, page 52, 1926, and in Wood and Cork (1927).

The expansion and contraction of gases, liquids, and solids and the constants of certain thermo-electric phenomena are the common ones used in thermometry. By far the most common thermometer is the mercury glass thermometer, in terms of which nearly everyone visualizes temperature change. The application of the mercury glass thermometer is limited by the freezing point of mercury at −38.85°C., and also by its size, which renders it difficult to use in certain inaccessible or very small places. Other liquids, such as pentane, alcohol, and toluene, are often used in the place of mercury. Their properties may be determined in "International Critical Tables." It is sometimes convenient to make metal thermometers, in which case two strips of metal are fastened side by side, one of them having a higher expansion coefficient than the other. When the temperature rises, the metal with the high expansion coefficient expands more rapidly than the other, which causes the laminated bar of metal to bend, with the metal of the high-expansion coefficient on the convex side and the one of the low coefficient on the concave side. A lever attached to one end of this laminated bar will indicate changes in temperature when a scale has been properly calibrated. This form of thermometer is taken advantage of in many recording instruments.

Thermo-electric methods of measuring temperature are very convenient where precision is wanted, or where temperature is to be taken in an inaccessible place. These, in general, consist of two types: resistance thermometers and thermocouples. The theory of the resistance thermometer is based upon the fact that the resistance which a metal, usually platinum, offers to the passage of an electric current, is proportional to the temperature. Such thermometers may be made with extreme accuracy. The use of such thermometers, however, has the limitation which goes with such laboratory equipment as is required for the extreme accuracy of measurement of resistance to an electric current. It is difficult to make an accurate resistance thermometer for use in a small space. Consequently, they are restricted to certain types of laboratory work requiring accuracy but not demanding measurement in a small space.

The thermocouple method is the most usual and most convenient thermo-electric method employed in ecological work. Robinson (1927) gives a brief description of this principle. Thermocouples depend upon the fact that when two dissimilar metals are joined, an electromotive force is set up at the point of contact, and that the amount of electromotive force is directly proportional to the temperature at that point of contact. This energy apparently represents the excess of electrons emanating from one of the metals as compared with those from the one with which it is in contact. Tables of the thermo-electric properties of metals have been prepared ("International Critical Tables," Vol. I, p. 57). Copper and constantan, an alloy, are very suitable for temperatures within the range of ecological importance and they both have the advantage of being relatively non-corrosive. When two junctions are made and one is held at 0°C. and the other at a higher temperature, the electromotive force from the warmer junction will pass the weaker current from the colder junction, making the measurable current in the system equal to the difference in temperature between the two junctions. Since the temperature of one junction is known to be 0°C. (this couple being surrounded by ice and water), it is necessary to know only the factor for converting the electromotive force, as read in millivolts, into degrees centigrade. If an ordinary voltmeter is used, the resistance of the wires leading from the couple to the voltmeter will be an unknown factor in reducing the current which reaches the voltmeter or galvanometer.

A number of types of potentiometers and pyrovolters have been designed and manufactured which eliminate the factor of resistance in the circuit and thus make direct readings possible. Thermocouples make it possible to read temperatures in inaccessible places, such as in insect bodies, under the bark of trees, and at various depths in the soil. A series of junctions may be connected with the constantan wire from a cold junction in such a way that any one of the copper wires may be put in connection with the pyrovolter or potentiometer by means of a switch, as shown in Fig. 11. In this way a series of temperatures may be read in succession by simply closing one switch at a time to connect the junction at the point where the temperature is desired to be read.

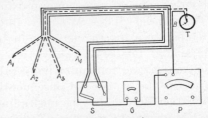

Fig. 11.—Arrangement for multiple thermocouple assembly with warm junctions scattered. (*Robinson*, 1927.) $A_1 - A_4 =$ warm junctions. $T =$ thermos bottle. $B =$ cold junction. $S =$ switch. $G =$ galvanometer. $P =$ potentiometer.

Methods of Recording Temperature.—Various types of thermographs are constructed for meeting almost any requirement of laboratory or field conditions. In general, they are metal- or liquid-expansion thermometers connected with levers and pens for writing the thermographs on a record. The form of the record may be either a disc of paper which revolves, or a strip of paper which is wound about a revolving drum. Some of these instruments are so constructed that the sensitive element may be several meters from the recording instrument itself. The thermo-electric method is coming more and more into use in connection with recording instruments. Commercial firms are now making recording potentiometers and wheatstone bridges which make it possible to have continuous records made at long distances from the sensitive point. The specifications of these machines may be obtained from the catalogs of standard-instrument makers (Shelford, 1929). The apparatus is fairly expensive; but when it is considered that it may record as many as 16 or 18 points, it will be found less expensive than as many separate thermographs.

The computation of the mean temperature from the record is important. Hartzell (1919) has shown that the so-called "mean temperature" computed by averaging the maximum and minimum temperatures for the day is much more apt to give a discrepancy which is positive than one which is negative. The true daily mean temperature is equal to the altitude of a rectangle, the area of which is equal to the area of the thermograph record from the base 0°. If the record extended below 0°, the negative area would, of course, have to be included in computing the area of the thermograph record. Hartzell concluded that a good approximation for the daily mean temperature may be arrived at by dividing the sum of the hourly temperature by 24. This gives the mean hourly temperature as an approximation of the daily mean temperature. The United States Weather Bureau commonly computes the mean temperature for the day by dividing the sum of the maximum and minimum temperatures by two. This is far from accurate, as the maximum and minimum temperatures are usually attained for only a short period of time. Consequently, the resulting mean as given by the Weather Bureau may be misleading.

Methods of Controlling Temperature.—It is probably true that there has been more equipment installed in biological laboratories for the control of temperature than for the control of any other factor. Various devices have been employed for the production of heat and cold, for the recording of temperature, and for the turning on and off, of the sources of heat or refrigeration. The source of energy for either heat or refrigeration is commonly electricity. Consequently, the thermostat must consist essentially of a switch to turn on and off an electric current, regardless of the sensitive mechanism that may be used in responding to the temperature changes. It is usually not practical to have the thermostat act directly upon the current used for the heat or refrigeration, for the reason that the high voltage will produce an arc when the thermostat is barely in a position of opening or closing. There are several methods of obviating this difficulty. There are several cheap thermostats on the market with rugged points which are able to stand whatever arcking occurs when the current is made and broken.

Another method is the use of a rocking mercury valve. This consists of a glass tube sealed at both ends and pivoted in the middle. One of the contact points is at the center of the tube, and the other at one end. Enough mercury is introduced into the tube to extend from the lower end to the middle when the tube is tilted. The sensitive element of the thermostat is so arranged that it will throw the tube from the position of a tilt in one direction to a tilt in the other direction. This takes place suddenly, and the mercury is poured from one end of the tube to the other. When it is at one end of the tube, the mercury makes the contact between the two electrical points, and the circuit is closed. When the mercury is toward the other end of the tube, the two points are left separate, and the circuit is open.

A third and more usual method of avoiding the arcking of the heavy current is by having a secondary current created by batteries or furnished through a transformer. This secondary current is made and broken by the sensitive element of the thermostat, and this weak current acts upon an electromagnet which makes and breaks the current on the heating

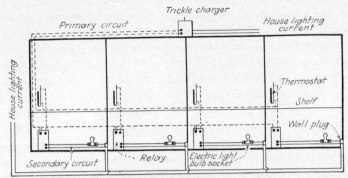

Fig. 12.—Diagram showing electric connections for one or several temperature cabinets (toluol-mercury thermostat). (*Robinson*, 1928.)

circuit. Robinson (1928) has shown a connection for such a circuit. He also describes a mercury-toluene thermostat which is very successful. This can be made to operate within a small fraction of 1°C., and is very cheap. Figures 12 and 13 show the circuit for a series of cabinets and also the connection for one of the mercury-toluene thermostats.

Harvey's modification of the Beckman thermometer principle is a very delicate thermostat which has wires projecting into the space occupied by the mercury column. By adjusting the amount of mercury in the bulb, the point at which the secondary current is to be made or broken can be controlled to an accuracy of several hundredths of one degree.

In addition to a sensitive thermostat, it is necessary to have a proper source of heat and refrigeration. Any ideal temperature control must be so arranged that the temperature can be raised or lowered whenever necessary. Heat can be supplied conveniently by either a series of resistance coils or ordinary electric lamps. These

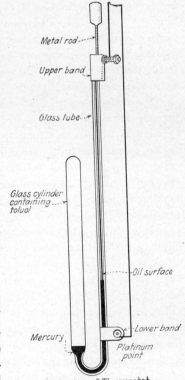

Side View of Thermostat

Fig. 13.—Side view of thermostat. (*Robinson*, 1928.)

may be baffled to prevent the light from interfering with the experiment, if necessary. To get a very careful temperature control, it is necessary to have a small heating element controlled by the thermostat, and the rest of the heat supplied by manual control. If the thermostat operates a large heating unit, there is apt to be a fluctuation in the temperature curve as the elements go on and off. The air in the cabinet should be circulated to prevent any pocketing or stratification.

There are various methods of producing refrigeration which are described by Kanolt (1924). Where only a slight cooling is required, ice may be used, but with a continual source of inconvenience. Where only very small chambers are to be cooled, it is possible to produce a temperature as low as $-54.9°$ by using proper mixtures of calcium chloride and snow. For freezing point determinations, a Dewar flask may be used. This is surrounded by a vacuum chamber similar to the filler of an ordinary thermos bottle. Material to be frozen may be put in a tube which is projected down into the flask through a cork stopper. The tube may then be surrounded by ether through which air is aspirated. With a little experience, it is possible to produce a very even gradient of temperature reduction. This same apparatus may be used with a copper coil connected to a tube of compressed carbon dioxide with a reduction valve leading to the copper coil. This method is very satisfactory in a room where the relative humidity is low. If the humidity is high, there will be the difficulty of the formation of dew and freezing with the copper tubes.

The most common and convenient method of producing refrigeration for experimental work is by means of the compression and expansion of various liquids in which the heat of expansion and evaporization are taken advantage of. Ammonia, carbon dioxide, sulphur dioxide, and other compounds may be used. The degree of cooling will depend upon the difference in pressure between the high and the low sides of the expansion valve. It must be remembered, however, that the capacity for heat will be governed by the quantity of gas which is circulating through the refrigeration coils. Consequently, if the valve is only slightly open, there may be a great difference of pressure on the two sides of the valve, but the quantity of gas in circulation may be so small that its capacity for removing heat will be greatly curtailed. There are many commercial machines on the market which operate very efficiently and dependably as refrigeration units.

Many devices are described in literature for controlling temperature for ecological research. One of the simplest devices is a long chamber which may be from two or three feet to 10 to 15 feet long, constructed of some good heat conductor. Some of those which are on the market in Europe are made of copper. In one end there is an ice chamber, and at the other end there is a heating unit. These are usually so arranged that small containers may be placed in the chamber various distances between the refrigeration unit and the heating unit. The distance between the heating and refrigeration units, at which the small container is placed, controls the temperature to which it is exposed.

Figure 14 shows one of the units which is used in the temperature research laboratory of the Division of Entomology at the University of Minnesota. There are a series of six cabinets surrounded by insulation with double glass doors on the top and at the side. Each cabinet has its own mercury-toluene thermostat with the corresponding relays mounted at the end. Each unit operates at a temperature 5°C. above or below the adjacent units. All cabinets operating below 27°C. are supplied with a coil, through which brine is circulated by a pump con-

Fig. 14.—Temperature cabinets at the University of Minnesota.

trolled by another thermostat system. The temperatures are recorded by a Leads-Northrop multiple recorder, which is shown at the extreme right of the figure. Each cabinet below 27°C. has a double system of temperature control, one for refrigeration and the other for heat. Daylight lamps are mounted above the cabinet for use when necessary. Each unit of the system has its own set of manual valves on the brine circulation, and it is possible to set the valves in such a way that the cabinets receive about the right amount of circulation of brine, the pump which circulates the brine being controlled by a thermostat. Refrigeration is, therefore, automatic after the valves have once been set by hand for the desired intervals for each cabinet.

TEMPERATURE AS A FACTOR IN ANIMAL ECOLOGY

Animals are profoundly affected by temperature in many ways. Probably no other single factor has a greater effect upon their geographic distribution on the earth, or upon the periods of their activities during the annual cycle. Within the limits of temperature in which they are active, the rate of their metabolism and consequently their rate of growth and reproduction and the resultant population are controlled. Their behavior, their form and structure, and even the mechanism of heredity, all come within the influence of this general and far-reaching environmental factor. The influence of temperature extends even farther than this, in that it affects nearly all of the other physical factors of the environment. The moisture in the air, the pressure of gases, and the movement of the air must all be interpreted in terms of the temperature which is operating at the time. In evaluating physical factors it is probably a correct generalization to state that light affects temperature, and temperature affects everything else.

General Effects of Temperature upon Animals.—Animals with regard to their relationship to temperature fall into two natural groups. One, the poikilothermic or cold-blooded animals, has no precise mechanism for regulating the temperature of their bodies. Consequently, their body temperatures follow more or less closely that of the surrounding medium. The other group, the homoiothermic or warm-blooded animals, has a mechanism which maintains the temperature of their bodies more or less constant and independent of the surrounding medium. The group of homoiothermic animals includes the mammals and the birds which are set apart from all other animals in that they essentially carry their environmental temperature with them.

The ability to regulate temperature is developed very early in the ontogeny; and as Kendeigh and Baldwin (1928) have shown, nestling wrens at first are poikilothermic, but very soon become homoiothermic. Certain of the mammals which hibernate to conserve energy during the cold weather become essentially poikilothermic during that period, as will be described under the heading of Dormancy.

Insects are all poikilothermic. There are, however, certain interesting exceptions in connection with some of the social insects. The honey bees are able to maintain their temperature as a colony, though individually they are not. A colony of bees, then, looked upon as an ecological unit, might be considered homoiothermic. They rear their brood at a more or less constant temperature and also control the temperature of the colony within certain limits during the winter. Many social insects control the temperature of their immediate environment by conserving the heat from their metabolism. Hase (1926) found that the larvae of the wax moth were able to maintain the temperature of their immediate surroundings at 11 to 17° above that of the laboratory.

It is not strictly true that the body temperature of poikilothermic animals varies with the temperature and is always the same as the temperature of the surrounding medium. During the time of activity a certain amount of energy is continually being transformed into heat in the body; and as long as the rate of radiation from the body is less than the rate of production of heat within the body, it follows that the body temperature will necessarily be somewhat above that of the surrounding medium.

Rogers and Lewis (1916) found that the temperature of most poikilothermic vertebrates was very close to the temperature of the surrounding medium, with a slight lag in the larger forms. Pirsch (1923) measured the temperature of the honey bee and found that they tended to be slightly warmer than air at low temperature as long as they were active. At high temperatures they maintained themselves slightly below the temperature of the environment, presumably by increased evaporation. Their ability to maintain their body temperature below that of the surrounding air, however, was very much limited. When they could no longer resist the high temperature, death followed, and the temperature of the bees then assumed the temperature of the surrounding air. Poikilothermic animals are active only within certain limits of temperature above and below which they are inactive. Various terms have been proposed to designate these limits of activity. Possibly the most accepted and expressive terms are the minimum effective temperatures for the lower point of activity, and the maximum effective temperatures for the upper limits of activity.

Shelford (1927) uses the term, "temperature threshold"; and other authors have proposed the term, "developmental zero." The latter term is not very acceptable because it implies that there is no metabolism going on, which is obviously incorrect. Below the minimum effective temperature, life continues in a temperature zone of dormancy. At a still lower temperature, dormancy is terminated by death, at a point which may be called the absolute minimum temperature. In a similar way, life continues above the maximum effective temperature in the state of dormancy, where there are no outer manifestations of activity. Again, a greater extreme of temperature produces death at the point representing the absolute maximum temperature.

A further consideration of the conditions of dormancy due to extremes of temperature will be taken up under the heading of Dormancy.

Between the limits of minimum and maximum effective temperatures, there is a zone in which poikilothermic organisms are active. Somewhere within this zone, there is a point which may be termed the optimum temperature, where life is at an optimum, not necessarily with respect to rates of processes but at which conditions are generally most favorable for the organism. It is difficult to formulate a precise definition of optimum temperature. Probably the most significant definition would be this: that the temperature at which there is the least environmental resistance to the biotic potential of the organism is the optimum temperature (see page 183).

Effects of Temperature on Physical and Chemical Processes.—Before entering upon a discussion of the effect of temperature on biological processes, it will be well to pause and consider briefly the nature of the effects of temperature on the physical and chemical processes of the structure of an organism.

It is hardly necessary to state that temperature has a profound effect upon all physical processes for, as a matter of fact, our knowledge of temperature is based upon the changes of physical processes, as for example, the volume of mercury under different temperature conditions. One has only to scan the pages of the "International Critical Tables" to see how widespread this effect is. There have been many attempts to formulate a precise equation to express the nature of the effect of temperature upon these processes.

Van't Hoff (1884) made a statement of the general principle of the effect of temperature on chemical reactions, which has since then often been cited in literature as "Van't Hoff's law," although it was nothing new at the time that he stated the principle, nor did he intend at the time to state anything which would be formulated as a law. This seems to be a good example of how the statement of an eminent man may be made into a dogma by subsequent students. In his lectures in Berlin, Van't Hoff referred to this relationship of temperature to chemical reaction with the simple statement that by far the larger portion of reactions seemed to fall between a doubling and trebling as the result of a rise of 10°C. It is true that he gave it formal expression as:

$$\frac{K_t + 10}{K_t} = 2.$$

He then expressed this logarithmically in such a way as to take care of any other difference than 10°C., and reduced it all to a 10° basis. He gave the example of the saponification of ethyl acetate by soda, which solved for a value of 1.89, and followed this by the statement that, while the great majority of reactions took place with a quotient of 2 or 3, the table which followed would show the general range. In this table he gave examples which varied all the way from 1.2 to 7.14. It seems perfectly evident, therefore, that he had no intention of interpreting this as a law, but simply as a general principle which varied within wide limits.

However, the amount of increase of a chemical reaction for 10° is now designated as Q_{10}, and supposed to have a value of 2. This Q_{10} is almost a sacred number in the literature of physiology.

Arrhenius (1889) proposed a formal expression of this same relationship based upon the absolute temperature scale by introducing a constant, the function of which is to bring Q_{10} more closely to a value of 2. He wrote the expression $K_1 = K_0 e^{\frac{\mu}{2}\left(\frac{T_1 - T_0}{T_1 T_0}\right)}$. In this expression T_0 and T_1 are the two temperatures reckoned from the absolute temperature scale. K_0 is the velocity of the reaction at the lower temperature T_0, and K_1 is the velocity at the higher temperature T_1. The Greek letter μ is the constant, which is introduced to make the ratio 2, which is the numerator of this fraction, a constant. The value of μ for most biological processes ordinarily lies between 12,000 and 16,000. He also said that there was no essential difference existing between the processes studied in general chemistry and those produced by living organisms or enzymes as measured by the values for μ.

This method of comparing the rates of biological reactions with those of chemical reactions has been seized upon by various physiologists, and the value of μ, or the letter q, as it is sometimes written, has been used for examining the nature of various physiological reactions. Snyder (1911) in commenting upon this type of work states:

Remembering at the same time that Prof. William Ostwald has referred to the influence of temperature upon chemical reactions as "one of the darkest chapters in chemical mechanics," what shall we say of temperature and its influence upon physiological action . . . The present author believes that the matter is more complex than that of chemical reaction, as dark as that may be.

Proponents of the theory contend that chemical reactions may be compound reactions, and that during a portion of the reaction one of the component parts may constitute a master reaction. During another portion another component reaction may be the master, the result being that the curve of the velocities would not be a simple curve, but a compound curve. Different portions of it would have to be considered differently, and consequently there is no reason why the simple Q_{10} should apply throughout the entire length. Therefore, the value in Arrhenius' equation for μ would have to be changed depending upon the master reaction controlling the compound reaction at any particular time. It seems, therefore, that many physical or chemical reactions are so complex that it is difficult to make a simple formula approximating the nature of the effect of temperature applied to them very generally. Q_{10} values, as ordinarily quoted in literature, have no statistical value at all. This can best be appreciated by referring to Van't Hoff's table, where the values run from 1.2 to 7.14. This must be borne in mind in turning attention to the effects of temperature upon biological processes.

Effects of Temperature on Biological Processes.—Turning attention now to biological processes, which, as has already been stated, rest upon a physical structure which should obey the physical laws, we have a case which is even more complicated than that which has just been considered under physical and chemical processes.

In comparing the activities of an organism with the rate of physical and chemical processes, we might make a distinction between the basal metabolism of an organism, which may be compared quite directly with a physical and chemical process, and the general activity of an organism including the search for food, reproduction, and so on. In measuring the oxygen consumption or carbon-dioxide output of a quiet organism, we have a process which is quite comparable to that of the more complicated physical and chemical reactions. But when we have an organism which spends part of its energy in the search of food and in reproduction, we have added to our simple process the activity which insures that the process will go on. Energy, therefore, is being used for the getting of food to make sure that there will be material for oxidation and for reproduction, insuring that there will be a mechanism for carrying on the oxidation in another generation. The basal metabolism of the quiet organism is very likely a matter of purely physiological consideration, though of importance to ecology. The total activity of the organism is of importance to ecology directly, and is a matter primarily for ecological consideration.

The fact that there is a general quantitative relationship between the activities of organisms and the temperature has been recognized for centuries. Réaumur (1736) recognized that there was a quantitative relationship and suggested that the total heat as expressed in temperature summations required to produce complete growth was a constant. In making these summations, Réaumur used all of the temperature above zero on his thermometer, which means all temperatures above the freezing point of water. Von Oettingen (1879) recognized the straight-line relationship and introduced a definite point on a temperature scale to represent zero not as the freezing point of water, but as a threshold of development for the organism. Since this time there have been a series of investigators attempting to formulate a principle which would state definitely the linear relationship of the rates of biological processes to the temperature scale. These have been recently well summarized by Peairs (1927) and Ludwig (1928).

In 1913 Sanderson and Peairs published rather extensive data on the effect of constant temperature on rates of insect development, showing that the reciprocal of the time-and-temperature curve was a straight line and that above the threshold of development time multiplied by time temperature gave a constant. The next year Krogh (1914) published his generalizations based on the rates of processes in various types of animals and formulated a principle which has since often been spoken of as Krogh's law. He concluded that Vant Hoff's and Arrhenius' principles did not give a good approximation to the rates of biological processes, and he advanced the formula:

where $V_t + 10° = V_t + K10$,
     V represents the velocity at any one temperature, and
     K is the increase in velocity,
     $K10$ being the increase in velocity 10°C.

This statement differs from that of Van't Hoff in that the constant is added, instead of being multiplied, to the rate at one temperature in order to obtain the rate at a higher temperature. This means that an increase of 1°C., within certain limits, always produces the same acceleration in rate of development. The limits within which this straight-line relationship applies are usually spoken of as the limits of normal development. The time temperature curve is, within these limits, a hyperbola, and the rate temperature curve is a straight line. It was not contended by Krogh, and possibly by no one else, that this rate temperature line was straight throughout the entire temperature scale, or even down to the minimum effective temperature or threshold of development. Krogh showed that as the threshold of development was approached the line of actual development deviated above the theoretical line, and that at higher temperatures it deviated by dropping below the theoretical straight line.

Jacobs (1928) reviewed the possibilities of applying a definite rule to processes which are involved in the physiology of organisms, and showed how impossible it is to expect such expressions as those of Van't Hoff and Arrhenius to apply to many processes which are involved in the physiology of animals.

Peairs (1927) and Ludwig (1928) have shown that of all the generalizations with regard to the relationship between velocity of biological processes and temperature, the principle as expressed by Sanderson and Peairs (1913) and Krogh (1914) is probably as good a generalization as any. Ludwig showed that the adaptation of Arrhenius' formula by Crozier (1924) cannot well be applied at least to the Japanese beetle (*Popillia japonica* N.). The following table from Ludwig shows the values for μ obtained for the various stages in the life history of this beetle. These values according to the formula of Arrhenius as used by Crozier should be constant, but it will be noticed that they vary from a $-27,000$ to a $+66,000$ and that in one stage, that of the second instar, they vary from a $-6,175$ to a $+65,298$. These variations in the value of μ are often interpreted as indicating that different master reactions are obtained during the different stages of the life cycle.

Bayliss (1924) points out that there are many processes, such as diffusion and adsorption which take place simultaneously with the chemical processes, and states that the velocity of the process as a whole

TABLE I.—VALUES OF μ OBTAINED FOR THE JAPANESE BEETLE[1]

Temperature, °C.	Egg	First instar	Second instar	Third instar	Pupa
13 −15	......	......	....	....	44,914
15 −17.5	43,225	32,707	....	....	33,215
17.5–20	29,734	66,565	....	....	26,065
15 −20	......	......	65,298		
20 −22.5	24,117	35,946	24,462	−27,105	19,934
22.5–25	20,352	11,255	33,912	−18,092	19,207
25 −27.5	11,688	9,175	− 439	....	14,523
27.5–30	12,211	124	−6,175	....	7,321
27.5–31	8,676				
30 −32.5	......	......	....	....	6,175
30 −33	−259				
32.5–35	......	......	....	....	−8,909

[1] LUDWIG, *Physiol. Zoology*, vol. I, no. 3, p. 379, 1928.

may be conditioned by the factor which takes place at the slowest rate. In many cases this might be diffusion. It is known, of course, that during the pupal stage, for instance, the processes going on are quite different during histolysis and histogenesis. It is difficult, however, to understand why a second instar larva might have a μ value at temperatures from 15 to 20° of 65,000 and a μ value of −6,000 at 27°.

Janisch (1925) and others have attempted to construct exponential curves which would aid in interpreting the data in terms of straight-line relationships with deviations above and below the so-called "normal limit."

All of these attempts to get an empirical relationship expressed mathematically may be looked upon as of purely physiological interest and merely as attempts to approximate the effects of temperature on very complicated processes. Attention will now be called to the use of the principle of Krogh (1914) or of Sanderson and Peairs (1913) in ecological work, the assumption being that the principle was at least usable.

The following graph of Krogh's (1914b) experiment with developing frog's eggs will serve to illustrate a number of facts with regard to this principle. This curve is based upon the time required for certain changes in segmentation to take place. It will be noted that all of the points between 7° and 20° lie on the straight line. If the straight line is extended downward, it will intersect the axis of the abscissa at 2.7°C., which will mean that, theoretically, no segmentation could take place at this temperature. By using this point and letting x = temperature in degrees centigrade and letting y = the time factor, we may express the value of the points on the time temperature curve as $(x − 2.7)y = K$.

Krogh's curve shows that the rate of segmentation deviated from the straight line at about 7° and that the rates at lower temperatures were greater than might be anticipated. This is generally true of biological processes and means that the value 2.7° for the minimum effective temperature, which may be arrived at by projecting the straight line, is not a true value for the point at which the process will stop. Shelford calls this theoretical point the "*a*" point. It is important to note, however, that this theoretical point can be used in calculating a constant for points on the hyperbolic curve, while the true minimum effective temperature (threshold temperature) could not be used in this way because it lies outside the hyperbolic curve.

At the upper end of the curve there is likewise a deviation from the straight line. This is to be expected if we recognize an optimum tempera-

ture and a maximum effective temperature as separated on the temperature scale. The point at which the curve deviates from the straight line will approximate the optimum temperature, beyond which the process is slower than would be anticipated on the basis of the rates of development at the lower temperatures. The temperature at which the development stops would obviously represent the maximum effective temperature. Krogh's curve further illustrates the inadequacy of Van't Hoff's principle in even approximating the rates of development. The values of Q_{10} for the process of segmentation

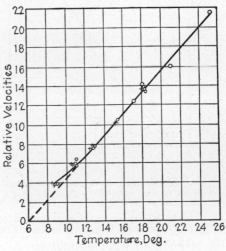

FIG. 15.—Graph of the temperature-velocity relationship for the development of frog eggs (*Krogh*, 1914.)

in the frog's eggs are compared with the values for the constant as computed from the time and effective temperature in the following table:

Q_{10} Values of Van't Hoff	K Values of Krogh
3– 5°Q_{10} = 5.3	7.7°$(x - 2.7)y = 2,410$
5–10°Q_{10} = 4.1	10.2°$(x - 2.7)y = 2,490$
10–15°Q_{10} = 3.0	12.55°$(x - 2.7)y = 2,303$
15–20°Q_{10} = 2.0	16.9°$(x - 2.7)y = 2,325$

It will be noticed that the Q_{10} values decrease from 5.3 at the lower temperature to 2 at the higher temperature, while K constant of Krogh remains relatively constant throughout the entire range. Illustrations of the application of this principle may be found in Sanderson and Peairs (1913) and Peairs (1927).

Attention must be called to the fact that each stage of the life cycle of an organism may have separate temperature characteristics. This is well illustrated in the study which Ludwig (1928) made of the Japanese beetle. Table II gives the value for the constant times' temperature minus the threshold value for the various stages of the life cycle for the temperature range in which it normally lives. It is important to note that the third instar is dependent for its length not only upon temperature, but upon the length of the other instars. When the other

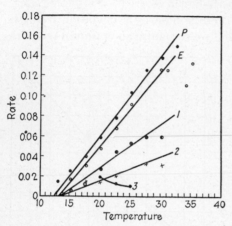

instars are long, it is relatively short, and when they are relatively short, it is relatively long. This is probably due to a nutritional and maturity factor which will be referred to later in the chapter on nutrition. In no two stages are the values for the day degrees the same. And when the day degrees for the entire life cycle are totaled, the values are slightly different for each temperature. The following figure, which is taken from the complete data of Ludwig, shows how the values for rates of development at each temperature conform to the straight line. Each stadium

FIG. 16.—Comparison of the rates of development of each stage of the Japanese beetle. (*Ludwig*, 1928.)

of the life history has a different temperature coefficient, as is shown by the inclination of the straight line.

TABLE II.—DAY-DEGREES REQUIRED FOR THE COMPLETE LIFE-CYCLE OF THE JAPANESE BEETLE[1]

Stage	20°C.	22.5°C.	25°C.
Egg	146.3	141.5	133.2
First instar	245.1	201.0	221.9
Second instar	456.9	448.2	351.9
Third instar	340.6	676.8	1,141.9
Pupa	128.2	129.0	122.0
Total	1,317.1	1,596.5	1,970.9

[1] LUDWIG, *Physiol. Zool.*, vol. I, no. 3, p. 384.

The difference in the temperature characteristics of the different stages of the same organism is a general one. In fact, it is probably true that the same stage of different insects may be more alike than the different stages of the same species.

Another example is illustrated in the study of grasshoppers. In the following graphs (Figs. 17, 18, 19, 20), the curves of time and temperature, as well as the reciprocals, are shown for the different stages

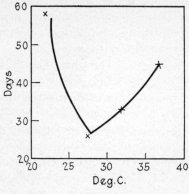

FIG. 17.—Time-temperature curve for the development of eggs of *Melanoplus mexicanus mexicanus* (Grasshopper). (*Parker*, 1930.)

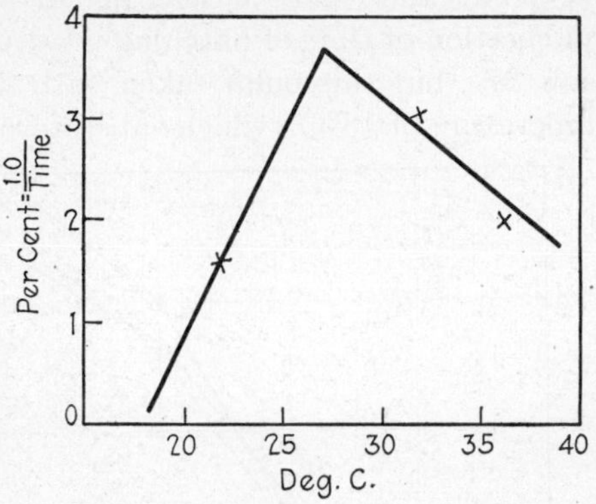

FIG. 18.—Velocity-temperature curve for the development of eggs of *Melanoplus mexicanus mexicanus*. (*Parker*, 1930.)

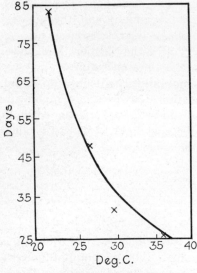

FIG. 19.—Time-temperature curve of development of nymphs of *Melanoplus mexicanus mexicanus*. (*Parker*, 1930.)

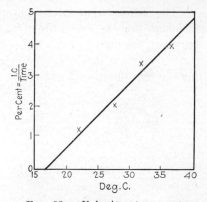

FIG. 20.—Velocity-temperature curve of development of nymphs of *Melanoplus mexicanus mexicanus*. (*Parker*, 1930.)

in the life cycle of a grasshopper, *Melanoplus mexicanus*. It is evident from these that the rates of development for the different stages of the same species may be so different that it will be necessary to make separate calculations for each stage. The time- and temperature-development curves for the eggs and nymphs of *Melanoplus mexicanus* are taken from Parker (1930). The data on the hatching of the eggs are interesting, as the optimum temperature is at about 27°, and above this point the time is lengthened and the curve representing this prolongation of time of hatching is a hyperbola. There is only one point below 27°, but this point taken with 27° indicates a minimum effective temperature of 18°C., which substantiates laboratory experience.

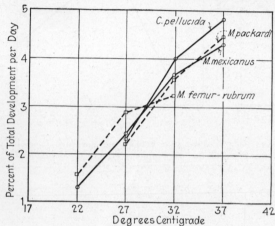

Fig. 21.—Rates of nymphal development of four species of grasshoppers at constant temperatures of 22°, 32° and 37°.

The time of hatching at the various temperatures is the average time in each case. At 22° the time varied from 42 to 100 days (probable error +3.879), at 27° from 23 to 28 days, at 32° from 21 to 38 days, and at 37° from 23 to 68 days. The rate was most uniform at 27° where conditions were optimum, and the greatest variation came at the higher and lower temperatures.

The data on nymphal development do not indicate a definite optimum, although there is a deviation from the reciprocal of the time-temperature curve at the higher temperatures. The values for Q_{10} and the constant $[(x - 17)y]$ are given to show the relative constancy of the two values for the nymphal development of *Melanoplus mexicanus*.

22° constant = 425	22–27°Q_{10} = 3.46
27° constant = 490	27–32°Q_{10} = 3.26
32° constant = 450	32–37°Q_{10} = 2.40
37° constant = 500	

In this case the maximum difference in the values for the constant is 75, which is 11.9 per cent of its mean value. The maximum difference in the values of Q_{10} is 1.06, which is 34 per cent of its mean value. Therefore, Krogh's approximation is better than the Q_{10} of Van't Hoff.

Shelford (1927) proposes a developmental unit based upon the differences between the amount of development in one hour at one temperature and the amount of development in one hour at one degree higher temperature. He terms this the developmental unit of one hour of one degree of mean medial temperature, defining medial temperature as that temperature within which the temperature-rate curve is a straight line. This is a convenient unit for use in making calculations of the effect of out-of-door temperature. It is possible to obtain a mean hourly temperature throughout the period and then apply the unit for one degree of mean medial temperature to the temperatures out of doors. This will be returned to under the consideration of the effects of climate upon insects.

Bodenheimer (1924) calls attention to the formula of Blunck as being a new expression for the relationship of time and development. It is, however, an expression of the same fundamental nature as that involved in Sanderson, and Peairs, and Krogh and the expressions of many others.

The validity of work done with constant temperatures is often called into question from the point of view of ecology, for the reason that temperatures in environments usually are not constant. Probably the time has not yet arrived for making generalizations with regard to the effects of alternating temperatures on animals in general. It is certain that the evidence before us at the present time is not all in agreement. Shelford (1929) states that

the crucial variable-temperature experiments must be done with minimal medial temperatures occurring at night and with temperatures rising to maximal medial during the day. These experiments will usually show an acceleration of development as compared with constant temperatures of the same numerical value as the mean of hourly readings of the variable temperatures.

In the codling-moth pupa the acceleration amounted to 7 per cent, as shown by a decrease in the developmental total.

Ludwig (1928), as a result of his study on the Japanese beetle, drew certain conclusions with regard to the effect of alternating temperatures upon this insect. He says that the effect produced by alternating temperatures depends upon the temperatures involved.

1. If one of the temperatures is above the optimum of development and the other is between the threshold and the optimum, the rate is retarded.

He believes this can be explained by the assumption that in general the rate of development is retarded at temperatures above the optimum. Therefore, when all the rates are taken into consideration, there is a general slowing due to a sort of algebraic sum of a series of rates, all of those which are lying above the optimum showing a retardation.

2. If both the temperatures alternating are between the threshold and the optimum of development, neither an acceleration nor a retardation of rate is produced.

3. If one of the temperatures involved is below the threshold of development and the other is between the threshold and the optimum, the rate is accelerated . . . However, if the threshold temperature is used as a minimum in the calculation of the mean-constant temperature, the rate falls on a straight line.

It is, of course, true that wherever the threshold or minimum effective temperature is involved, the question may be raised as to whether or not the true threshold value is known and whether there may not have been some development at temperatures below that at which it is assumed that development stopped.   Ludwig believes that his generalizations may help to explain some of the apparent contradictions in the results of various investigators, since most of these people work under field conditions where the temperatures involved usually go below the minimum effective or threshold values.   There is, however, certain evidence which seems very dependable and which cannot be harmonized with the conclusions of Ludwig.

There seems to be no better example than the data of J. R. Parker.

TABLE III.—COMPARISON OF THE RATE OF DEVELOPMENT OF *M. mexicanus* NYMPHS AT CONSTANT AND ALTERNATING TEMPERATURES

Some nymphs held at constant temperatures from time of hatching until they became adult; others held at a low temperature for 16 hours daily, and at higher temperatures for eight hours daily.   Twenty nymphs used for each set of temperatures.

CONSTANT TEMPERATURES

Temp., °C.	Days in nymphal stage	Percentage of total nymphal development per day
22	85	1.176
27	49	2.040
32	30	3.333
37	25	4.000

ALTERNATING TEMPERATURES

| 16 hr. daily at low temp. 8 hr. daily at high temp. | Low temp. | | High temp. | | Total per cent development at const. temp. rate | Theoretical days in nymphal stage at const. temp. | Actual days in nymphal stage at altern. temp. | Per cent development per day at const. temp. | Per cent development per day at altern. temp. | Per cent increase in rate of development at altern. temp. |
	Days	Development per cent	Days	Development per cent						
22 and 27	40.00	46.80	20.00	40.80	87.60	68.5	60	1.46	1.66	13.7
22 and 32	32.66	38.21	16.33	54.37	92.50	52.9	49	1.89	2.04	7.9
22 and 37	27.33	31.97	13.66	54.64	86.60	47.3	41	2.11	2.44	15.6
									Average...	12.4
12 and 27	71.33	0	35.66	72.74	72.74	147.0	107	0.68	0.93	36.7
12 and 32	40.66	0	20.33	67.69	67.69	90.0	61	1.11	1.64	47.7
12 and 37	32.66	0	16.33	65.32	65.32	75.0	49	1.33	2.04	53.3
									Average...	45.8

In this case nymphs of the grasshopper, *Melanoplus mexicanus*, were used in the experiment.   All conditions other than temperature were maintained as nearly constant and equal as possible.   A condition of alternating temperature was simulated by keeping the grasshoppers for eight hours at a higher temperature and for 16 hours at a lower temperature during each 24-hour period. The nymphs were hatched from eggs collected in the fields in the same locality, and were divided into lots of 20 each, and exposed to the conditions of the experiment. Four lots were held respectively at constant temperatures of 22, 27, 32, and 37°C. for 24 hours each day. The other lots were so divided that three were kept for 16 hours at 22°; and then one of the lots for eight hours at 27°; another for eight hours at 32°; and another for eight hours at 37°. This was to simulate a night at 22°C. with days at the three temperatures described. Three other lots were held at 12°C. for 16-hour periods; and then given eight-hour periods at 27, 32, and 37°, respectively. Table III gives Parker's results for these experiments. In this table the author has summed up the total time spent at the low temperature and the total time spent at the high temperature, and then has evaluated this time in per cent of development on the basis of the constant-temperature experiments. When the per cents of development for the sum of all the nights and the sum of all the artificial days are added together, he obtains not 100 per cent of development but considerably less.

The per cent of increase in rate of development, as given in the table, is arrived at by taking the difference between the per cent of development per day at constant and at alternating temperatures on a percentage basis. In the case of *Melanoplus mexicanus* nymphs, the threshold temperature is 17°. Consequently, the second series was exposed to temperatures lower than the threshold temperature; and the acceleration was much greater than that of the first series, which was exposed to a temperature of 22° and presumably never ceased development. The case of Parker's data on the hatching of eggs is perhaps an even better example of the effect of alternating temperatures than the one just cited for the nymphs.

The grasshopper eggs used in these experiments were collected from the field in the spring, and then exposed to the experimental conditions described. The general principle involved in these experiments is exactly like that used with the alternating temperatures on grasshopper nymphs. Two species of grasshoppers were involved, and it will be noticed that the general nature of the effect was the same in the case of both species. The per cent of acceleration when 22° was used in a 16-hour artificial night was less than that when 12° was used for the artificial night. The per cent of acceleration, however, is so great that it seems to leave little doubt as to what happened in this series of experiments. (See Table IV taken from Parker, 1930.)

The acceleration found in the experiments with the eggs is very much greater than that found in the experiments with the nymphs of the grasshoppers. This may be explained on the basis of the past history of the eggs. They were laid during the previous summer, were in the soil over winter exposed to various low temperatures, and then collected in the spring. It was found that if the eggs of *Melanoplus mexicanus* were placed at 0°C. immediately after they were laid, and then later exposed to higher temperatures of 27, 32, and 37°, they developed much

TABLE IV.—COMPARISON OF THE RATE OF DEVELOPMENT OF *M. mexicanus* AND *C. pellucida* EGGS AT CONSTANT AND ALTERNATING TEMPERATURES

Over-wintered field-collected eggs kept at constant high temperatures until hatched. Some also held at low temperatures for 16 hours daily and at higher temperatures for 8 hours daily. Two hundred eggs used for each set of temperatures.

CONSTANT TEMPERATURES

Temp., °C.	*M. mexicanus* Days to hatch	*M. mexicanus* Per cent development per day	*C. pellucida* Days to hatch	*C. pellucida* Per cent development per day
22	13	7.69	13	7.69
27	7	14.20	8	12.50
32	5	20.00	6	16.66
37	4	25.00	5	20.00

ALTERNATING TEMPERATURES, *M. mexicanus*

16 hr. daily at low temp. 8 hr. daily at high temp.	Low temp. Days	Per cent dev. at const. temp. rate	High temp. Days	Per cent dev. at const. temp. rate	Total per cent dev. at const. rate	Theoretical days to hatch at const. temp.[1]	Actual days to hatch at altern. temp.	Per cent dev. per day at const. temp.	Per cent dev. per day at altern. temp.	Per cent increase in rate of dev. at altern. temp.
22 and 27	5.33	40.9	2.67	37.9	78.8	10.1	8	9.9	12.5	26.2
22 and 32	4.00	30.7	2.00	40.0	70.7	8.4	6	11.9	16.6	39.4
22 and 37	3.33	25.6	1.67	41.75	66.3	7.5	5	13.3	20.0	50.3
										Average...38.6
12 and 27	9.33	0	4.67	66.3	66.3	21.1	14	4.7	7.1	51.0
12 and 32	6.00	0	3.00	60.0	60.0	15.0	9	6.6	11.1	68.1
12 and 37	5.33	0	2.67	66.7	66.7	12.0	8	8.3	12.5	50.6
										Average...56.5
C. pellucida										
22 and 27	6.00	46.1	3.00	37.5	83.6	10.7	9	9.3	11.1	19.3
22 and 32	4.67	35.9	2.33	38.8	64.7	9.3	7	10.7	14.2	32.7
22 and 37	4.00	30.7	2.00	40.0	70.7	8.4	6	11.9	16.6	39.5
										Average...30.5
12 and 27	9.33	0	4.67	58.3	58.3	24.0	14	4.1	7.1	73.1
12 and 32	6.77	0	3.33	55.4	55.4	18.0	10	5.5	10.0	81.8
12 and 37	6.00	0	3.00	60.0	60.0	15.0	9	6.6	11.1	68.1
										Average...74.3

[1] Theoretical days to hatch at constant temperature rate =

$$\frac{\text{actual days to hatch at alternating t.} \times 100}{\text{total per cent of dev. at constant t. rate}}$$

more rapidly than they did when placed directly at these constant temperatures. The acceleration found varies directly with the constant high temperature to which the eggs were returned, and amounted to over 136 per cent at 27°, 357.5 per cent at 32°, and 558 per cent at 37°. The acceleration increased at all three temperatures with the length of time exposed to the low temperature until a period of 242 days was reached. Exposing the eggs to 0° for from 240 to 500 days resulted in only a very slight increase in the rate of development. When the eggs were partially developed before they were exposed to low temperature, there was also an acceleration; but in this case the maximum acceleration was reached at about 60 days instead of 240 days, as in the case when undeveloped eggs were placed at low temperature.

A comparison was made by Parker between the effect of exposing partially developed eggs to 0°C. for a period of time before returning them to a high temperature, and exposing another lot to 8°C. before returning it to a high temperature. It was found that the acceleration was greater when exposed to 0° than when exposed to 8°. It would be difficult to explain these results on the assumption that some development went on below the minimum effective temperature, for those which were exposed to the lowest temperature had the greatest acceleration.

Parker's results on the effect of temperature on the eggs of grasshoppers are of great ecological significance. These grasshoppers lay their eggs during the latter part of the summer and early fall. Some of the eggs go through considerable embryonic development before cold weather arrives, but in the spring they all hatch at approximately the same time. In the experiment it was found that exposure to low temperature for about 60 to 240 days gave the maximum acceleration. Beyond that period of time it made little difference. This is approximately the length of time that these eggs are exposed to low temperature in nature. Since the hatching of eggs is retarded by temperatures above 27°C., those eggs which are laid relatively late in the summer or early in the autumn and are exposed to high temperatures are retarded, and later are accelerated by the low temperature of the winter. Furthermore, the eggs which develop during late summer are accelerated the least by low temperature, and *vice versa*. The result is that nearly all eggs are brought out at about the proper time in the spring.

It is possible to look upon the question of the effect of varying temperatures as the normal effect, and that of constant temperatures as abnormal. From this point of view, it would seem more logical to speak of the retarding effect of constant temperature, rather than of the stimulating effect of alternating temperatures. There are, however, a large group of organisms which live in environments which are very constant in temperature as, for example, organisms living in the bottom of deep lakes. It is very possible, therefore, that it will not be wise to make generalizations which supposedly apply to all animals until we know more about the effects of temperature on these forms.

Dawson (unpublished thesis) found that alternating temperatures apparently had little effect upon the cocoons of certain moths, which are ordinarily exposed to great variations of temperature. It seems most likely that some ecological grouping will be made of organisms, and it will be found that temperature behavior will vary with ecological conditions. This is a promising field of research for the future. The varying temperatures of nature are the most important from an ecological point of view, but it has probably to pass through the laborious stage of physiological investigation of constant temperature in order to lay a foundation for the understanding of the varying conditions of nature.

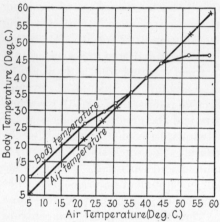

FIG. 22.—Graph showing the relation of body temperature of Italian bees with the surrounding air. (*Pirsch*, 1923.)

The Extremes of Temperature. Attention has already been called to the fact that the rates of biological processes are slowed down as temperatures approach the extreme. This slowing down is much more noticeable and much more gradual as the low temperature is approached, and is so rapid at the higher temperature that it is hardly noticeable, the organism passing from a rapid rate to a secession of development very quickly. Lists of extremes of temperature which various insects have been known to endure have been published by Bachmetjew (1907), Davenport (1908), Folsom (1922), and others. The absolute maximum temperature is in general in the region of 48°C. There is seemingly less variation in the absolute maximum temperature among the various species than in the absolute minimum temperature. Presumably the coagulation of protein is involved in death at the high temperatures. Pirsch (1923) found that honey bees seemed to be able to depress their temperatures slightly at very high temperatures (Fig. 22). This depression is due presumably to evaporation and can be maintained for only a very short period of time and only through the range of a few degrees centigrade.

Chapman, Parker, Mickel, and others (1926) found that there was not necessarily a correlation between the absolute maximum temperature which an insect might endure, and the environment in which it lives. The Bembix wasps, some of the predominant species of the sand dune, are not able to endure high temperatures. They escape them through their behavior by alternately digging for a few seconds on the surface of the hot sand and flying about rapidly a few inches above, where the air temperature is considerably lower. It was found that species from the forest had neither the ability to endure the high temperature nor the protective reaction to avoid it. Reaction to avoid high temperature is much more certain than reaction to avoid low temperature, for activity is usually rapid and the organism can act to escape the extremes. But at low temperatures, where activities are already greatly slowed, reaction may be very sluggish and very indefinite.

Johnson (1895) cites the example of a Stratiomyid larva found in a hot spring by Bruner supposedly at 69°C. It seems uncertain as to whether the larva was actually at this temperature, which is 20° higher than would be expected. Brues (1928) made a study of the fauna of the hot springs of the Western United States, and found that the flies (*Diptera*) and the beetles (*Coleoptera*) were very abundant. Among the *Diptera* he found one species of *Stratiomyidae* (*Odontomyia*) at a temperature between 49 and 50°C. Table V shows the general results of the stratiomyid family in general, and it will be seen that they range from 28 to 50°C. In the case of these thermophilous insects, there can be no doubt that they endure the temperature of the water which surrounds them, for there is no known mechanism for their depressing their temperature below that of the surrounding medium. The temperatures endured by the beetles go through almost the same range. Figure 23 shows the distribution of species as Brues found them in hot springs. It will be noticed that relatively few of them are able to endure temperatures as high as 45 and 46°. Only five species were taken in water above

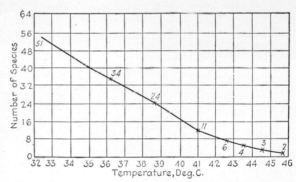

FIG. 23.—Graph illustrating the number of species of water beetles collected in hot springs at temperatures from 32° to 46°C.

40°C. Brues states that probably no beetles are reported to have been found in water the temperature of which is higher than 46°, except some reported in records which are possibly slightly in error.

Graham (1922) found certain buprestid larvae living under bark at a temperature of 52°C., and found also that a large percentage of larvae at the higher temperatures under bark were killed. It would be possible to continue to cite records of high temperatures which have been endured by insects; but it seems sufficient to call attention

TABLE V.—TEMPERATURE, SPECIFIC GRAVITY AND pH OF WATER WHEN CERTAIN DIPTEROUS LARVAE WERE FOUND[1]

Hot spring, No.	Temperature, °C.	S. G.	pH	Name
1	38.7	1.0039	8.1	Odontomyia sp. No. 1
4	39–46.7	1.0212	8.3	Odontomyia sp. No. 2
5	35	1.0012	8.5	Stratiomyia No. 1
8	33	1.0030	8.0	Odontomyia No. 4
10	43–47	1.0014	7.3	Odontomyia No. 5
10	43–47	1.0014	7.3	Stratiomyia No. 2
10	43–47	1.0014	7.3	Oxycera sp.
10	43–47	1.0014	7.3	Nemotelus sp.
11	30–40	1.0016	5.7–6.5	Stratiomyia No. 1
13	28	1.0021	6.7	Stratiomyia No. 1
18	49–50	1.0008	8.1	Odontomyia No. 3
20	38	1.0014	8.6	Odontomyia No. 4
22	38	1.0014	7.8	Odontomyia No. 2
22	38	1.0014	7.8	Odontomyia No. 4

[1] BRUES, 1928.

to the fact that the general range of high temperature which may be endured by insects is rather constant, 48 to 52°C. being the absolute limit of authentic record. The organisms which live in environments of unusually high temperature may have a slightly higher maximum

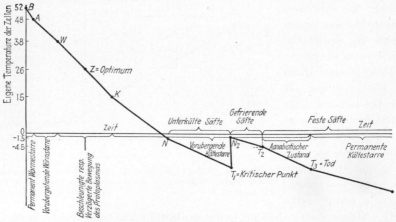

FIG. 24.—Bachmetjew's illustration of the effect of temperature upon protoplasm. (*Bachmetjew, 1901.*)

effective temperature, and they must have a very precise reaction to high temperature in order to avoid the conditions which would bring about death.

The effects of low extremes of temperature have received more consideration from investigators than have the effects of high extremes.

Bachmetjew (1901) made rather extensive investigations and summarized the early literature on the subject. His classical diagram (Fig. 24) illustrates his conception of the action of low temperature. Temperature is indicated on the vertical axis; and time, as involved in the lowering of temperature, is indicated on the horizontal axis. The insect may be cooled below the freezing point without being injured. The freezing point may be past, and the insect may exist in an undercooled condition. When it does freeze, the heat of crystallization will be equal to the undercooling temperature, and the body temperature will rebound to the freezing point. Cooling will again proceed; and when the insect reaches the undercooling point the second time, death follows, according to Bachmetjew's conception.

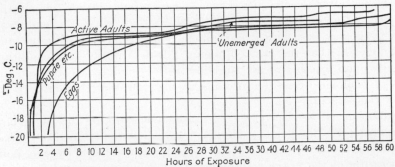

Fig. 25.—Fatal time-temperature for all stages of the life cycle of *Bruchus obtectus* Say (*Carter*, 1925.)

The more recent contributions to our knowledge of the ability of insects to endure low temperatures tend to indicate that not only temperature but moisture is involved. The subject becomes highly technical, and for the most part is of purely physiological interest. It will be referred to here briefly, and taken up more fully under the heading of Dormancy.

It may aid somewhat in understanding the effects of low temperature, if we distinguish between the intensity factor and the capacity factor. Some organisms are able to endure a temperature at which they become dormant, but are not able to endure it for a long period of time. Others are able to endure a low temperature for a short period of time, but do not have the capacity to endure such low temperatures over a long period. Some organisms die if they become dormant for a long period; others are able to endure low temperatures so long as they do not freeze. Freezing, however, is fatal to them. Still others are able to endure freezing, and may continue in this state for a long period of time. It would seem, in general, that the tropical insects, including those of tropical origin, do not have the capacity for enduring dormancy. This is true of *Tribolium confusum*, which will die in a few weeks at 7°C.

Carter (1925) made a study of the effects of low temperature upon the bean weevil in all the various stages of its development. The general results are indicated in Fig. 25. This graph shows the correlation between the temperature and the time involved in killing. Carter concluded that none of the stages could endure temperature of more than −19° for longer than a few hours' time.

Payne (1926) got evidence that certain insects which are normally exposed to extremes of temperature undergo a hardening during the fall of the year, during which time their freezing points are depressed and their ability to endure cold is increased. In the spring the reverse of this process occurs. She also found that the highest per cent of larvae killed in nature occurred in the spring, when cold spells were experienced after the freezing point, and endurance of low temperature had been altered. This seems to indicate that, while the endurance of freezing may be a purely physiological question, it is of importance in ecology, in that the per cent being killed in out-of-door conditions depends upon whether or not they are able to endure freezing and just what physiological condition obtains at the time that they are exposed to low temperature.

Robinson (1928) has given a detailed account of the method of determining freezing points. He has shown that the temperature taken by piercing an insect with a thermocouple is not the true freezing-point temperature of the insect. He devised a method whereby the external temperature is taken, and the internal temperature is calculated from a correlation chart. Figure 26 shows Robinson's thermojunction and insect holder for taking the contact temperatures by the use of the thermocouple and pyrovolter, or potentiometer. In Fig. 27 the correlation is shown between the actual contact temperature as read and the internal temperature of the insect. The correlation chart is made by connecting the insect with an internal and external thermocouple junction. The insect is then placed in the constant-temperature cabinet, and the internal and external temperatures read at a series of constant low temperatures. After this chart has once been made up, it is possible, in the study of the same species, to read the external temperature and calculate the internal temperature from the chart.

Robinson (1927) found that the pupae of the promethea moth, which are exposed to low temperature in nature, may be frozen and endure dormancy in this frozen condition for months, since they are able to endure a temperature of −35°C. and survive.

A provisional generalization may therefore be made, that tropical insects which are not normally exposed to extremely low temperatures are unable to endure dormancy. In general, insects of temperate regions, which hibernate in exposed conditions, are able to endure freezing and survive; and such other insects as migrate into the soil, or

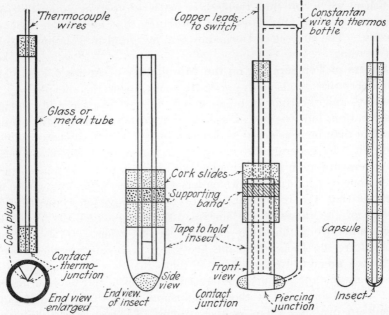

Fig. 26.—A thermojunction with insect holder for use in making contact temperature determinations. (*Robinson*, 1928.)

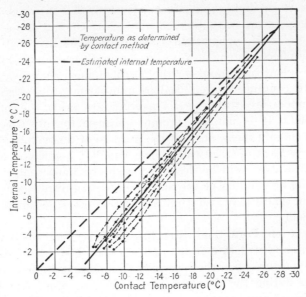

Fig. 27.—A correlation chart to be used in determining the actual internal temperature of an insect from its surface temperature as recorded by contact. (*Robinson*, 1928.)

in other ways provide themselves with protection against freezing temperatures, are able to endure dormancy, but are unable to endure freezing. The subject of Dormancy will be found in a discussion under that heading.

Effects of Temperature on the Morphology of Animals.—The effect of temperature as an environmental factor upon the morphology, the structure, and the color of organisms is, in part, a purely physiological consideration; but it is also of ecological importance, in that the resulting organism may be considered as characteristic of a definite environmental condition. In general, the information which we have of the effects of temperature upon the morphology of organisms may be placed in two classes: one, the information which has come from systematists, who have observed that the representatives of a species which come from one extreme of the range of the species differ morphologically from those which come from the other extreme of the range. If the extremes involved are the Tropics and the Arctics, it is usually assumed that the differences are due to the effect of temperature. Bachmetjew (1907) cites many instances which undoubtedly belong to this class of information. No doubt many of these conclusions are well founded, but it is difficult to evaluate them in the absence of direct observations. In the second class of information we have that which comes to us from direct observations made under more or less controlled conditions. It is possible to subdivide this information into that in which the correlation of temperature with the morphological change seems apparent although there is no explanation of the mechanism involved, and that in which the effect of temperature has been studied and a mechanism found which seems to account for the morphological changes.

Literature contains a great deal of information with regard to the effects of temperature; these records may fall into any of the three classes just described. It is not the present purpose to tabulate all these cases and to classify them, nor is it the purpose of this volume to discuss in detail the subject of "Entwicklungsmechanik." A few of the apparently authentic cases will be described with the hope that it will lead to a better understanding of the action of temperature upon form and structure, and that it may also stimulate further investigation in this very interesting field.

The Effect on Form and Structure.—The effect of temperature upon the form and structure of an organism may arise from a differential effect of temperature upon the several contemporaneous processes which are going on during the development of the organism, resulting in a greater acceleration of some processes and an inhibition of certain other processes.

Hegner (1919) reports that the spines of the protozoan *Arcella* are longer when developed at high temperature than at low temperature.

There may even be some ecological significance in this condition, for the viscosity of water and consequently its buoying effect in supporting such a protozoan is reduced at high temperature, but the increase in the surface of the organism from a longer spine will result in a greater ability of the organism to float. However, the particular point of interest here is Hegner's statement that the spines are longer when the organisms are developed at high temperature than when they are developed at low temperature.

Another case is reported by Roberts (1918), who states that a difference of 4 or 5°C. gave longer wings in the mutant form of *Drosophila*, which is called vestigial, than did 29 generations of selective mating. This mutant race of *Drosophila* has small wings. The length of the wings varies, but they are always small. The variation of these short wings is effected by temperature, and the difference of temperature of 4 or 5°, as just stated, gives longer wings than 29 generations of selective mating.

Gerould (1924) reports that he was able to reduce the size of the wing of *Colias* by rearing it at low temperature. This seems to be consistent with the other literature which has just been cited.

If we are to turn our attention to some of the older experiments, we shall find a long series of papers by Standfuss, Merrifield, and others on the effect of temperature upon various lepidoptera. Bachmetjew (1907) summarized these results in which various stages of *Vanessa uritica* were subjected to various temperatures. The adults resulting from exposures to low temperature were like the small variety *polaris* of Lapland; while those which developed at high temperatures gave rise to large adults similar to the variety *ichmuse* of Sardinia. This is not cited as an example of the inheritance of an acquired character; it is simply cited as an example of an organism which is so affected by low temperature that it appears like the individuals which live in the northern regions, or when subjected to a high temperature the resulting adults appear like those of the southern range of the species. The northern ones are small, which is consistent with the results of Gerould (1924), and they are darker in color than the southern ones.

Kühn (1926) found that there were four fundamental pattern systems which behaved more or less independently in *Vanessa*, and were effected by subjecting the pupae to low temperature. The period of maximum sensitivity for the hind wing was 12 to 36 hours after pupation; and for the fore wing, 24 to 36 hours after pupation.

There are many other cases which may logically belong under the effect of temperature on the mechanism of heredity though it seems probable that it is difficult to make a distinction between the effect of temperature upon the mechanism of heredity and the effect of temperature upon the processes of development, as we normally think of them in ontogeny. Possibly the fundamental nature of the effect is much the same regardless of whether it takes place during the process of chromosome arrangement, or later when cells are proliferating. For the sake of convenience, the cases which seem to be concerned with the mechanism of heredity as such will be considered under that heading.

Effect on Color.—What has been said with regard to the effect of temperature upon morphology in general might be repeated with regard to the effect of temperature upon color, in that the literature on this subject is very voluminous and much of it consists of superficial correlations of temperature and color. There are, however, certain pieces of careful experimental work which seem to indicate very definitely not only that color is affected by temperature, but that there is a mechanism which is affected by temperature and which determines the color. It will be quite impossible to attempt to evaluate all the various evidence which has been published as to the effect of temperature upon color. A few examples will be selected in the hope that they may show rather definitely how temperature may act in this way.

Knight (1924) investigated the color pattern of *Perillus bioculatus*, which had been observed under field conditions to be black and white during hot dry periods, and red and black during cooler periods of the year. In this case the white tended to be replaced by yellow and red; and the black portions of the pattern, to be more extensive at the low temperature. Under experimental conditions, nymphs were reared through to the adult stage at high temperatures, and gave the white-marked adults. When nymphs were reared through at low temperatures, the patterns were dark. When adults of a light color pattern were placed at a low temperature, they began to show the yellow and red coloration. An investigation of this pigment has shown that in this case it is carotin, and that the blood of the potato beetle larva, on which *Perillus* feeds, is saturated with this pigment. The potato beetle gets the pigment from the potato plant, which probably synthesizes it. *Perillus* then obtains this pigment in its food. When metabolism is going on rapidly at high temperatures, the pigment is oxidized. At low temperatures the oxidation is less rapid; and some, at least, of the pigment is deposited in the hypodermis of the insect and thus appears in its patterns, giving a light-yellow to a dark-red color, depending upon how much has been deposited. When this pigment is deposited in the hypodermis of the body wall of adult bugs, it is permanently placed and is not oxidized later even at high temperatures. Knight concludes:

In the case of *Perillus* then, it appears that the physiological activity of the insect which is modified by the temperature is oxidation, influenced by the physical activity of the insect, and that this is the fundamental explanation of the pigment variations.

The black color of *Perillus* is also influenced by temperature, being more abundant at the lower temperature. Knight concluded that this was melanin, as was found by Gortner in 1911, and that it was deposited in the cuticula.

Toumanoff (1926) studied the effect of temperature and darkness on the melanism of *Dixippus morosus*, and found melanism developed at high temperature and inhibited at low temperature. Toumanoff concluded that the lack of melanism at low temperature might be due to several things: a diminution of the absorption of oxygen necessary for the reaction at the low temperature; or perhaps a general effect upon metabolism which failed to produce the necessary polypeptid and tyrosin, which constitute the chromogen; or the fact that the low temperature affects the action of oxidase and tyrosinase, which are involved in the development of the melanin.

Gerould (1924) states that he has found that the amount of melanin in the markings of the butterfly, *Colias*, varies inversely with the temperature. He does not seem to distinguish between the formation of the pigment and its deposition. He states that any factor which will interfere with the reaction of tyrosin, tyrosinase, and oxygen will interfere with the formation of the pigment melanin. From this statement it seems difficult to understand how low temperature would increase the amount of melanin formed and thereby give darker color at lower temperature, as Gerould states that it does.

Schlottke (1926) found that the pigment which develops at the points of attachment of the muscles in the parasitic wasp, *Habrobracon*, bears a linear relationship to temperature. There is less pigment at high temperature than at low temperature. When they are reared at first at low temperature and then raised to high temperature, they become lighter than those which are reared constantly at high temperature.

The Effect of Temperature on the Mechanism of Heredity.—Environment and heredity have been looked upon as two opposing forces in nature, ever since the stability of the species was demonstrated. When some of the first laws of heredity were definitely outlined and the evidence in their support was being amassed, it was the opinion of many biologists that the characteristics of organisms were determined by heredity and that environment was in no way able to influence them. We now have a much better conception of these two factors in determining the structure of an organism. Weinstein's statement has already been quoted; to the effect that it is no more possible to state that the characteristics of an organism are more dependent upon heredity than environment, than it is to state that the area of a rectangle is more dependent upon its altitude than its base.

We are now in a position to consider the effect of temperature upon the mechanism of heredity in much the same way that we would consider its effect upon any other physical or biotic phenomenon. It may be possible to differentiate between (*a*) the effects of temperature upon the position of genes and the behavior of the chromosomes, and (*b*) the effect upon the processes of development which go on after the cells have been fertilized and have started their development, in differentiating the various organs of the animal. We may again turn to the monumental work of Bachmetjew in summing up the early literature on temperature and heredity. It is to be noticed that the "object" of much of the early work was to produce new species through the effect of temperature. The interest here will be in trying to find a correct interpretation of the effect of temperature upon the mechanism of heredity and thereby upon the organisms which live under various environmental conditions.

Seiler (1920) reported that extreme heat caused the sex chromosomes of *Taleoporia tubulosa* to remain in the egg at the time of reduction division, thus increasing the number of potential females.

Mann (1924) made a study of the stability of genes, and used high temperature in a series of experiments. It was found that the percentage of males was increased at high temperature, such as 31.5°C.; but that the percentage was decreased when the progeny were again returned to a temperature of 25°C. There is no implication in this case that the effect produced would be operative beyond the individuals which were developed from the germ cells which had been exposed to this high temperature.

Plough (1917) studied the effect of temperature on the phenomenon of crossing over in *Drosophila*. It does not seem difficult to conceive of a possible effect of temperature upon such a phenomenon as crossing over, for the chromosomes must obey the physical laws which have to do with their movement during the various processes involved in maturation division. It seems logical that certain environmental factors might affect the rate and extent of the movement of the chromosomes during mitosis; and temperature is certainly a factor which might do this through viscosity, surface tension, and various other physical phenomena. Plough found that the extent of crossing over was increased at high and at low temperature, and that a minimum amount of crossing over took place during a range of temperature between about 20 and 27°. The general results of his investigation are shown in Fig. 28. This is a case in which hereditary characters might appear to be greatly affected by the environmental conditions having to do with different temperatures.

It has recently been found that mutations, which presumably occur in nature as rare but normal accidents, may occur more frequently under certain temperature conditions. Geneticists seem inclined to look upon mutation as the most important phenomenon in nature concerned with the change in the genetic constitution of an organism. If this proposition is accepted and the work which has been referred to is substantiated, we then have an example of temperature affecting the hereditary constitution of an organism in a most profound way.

Hersh (1924b) observed the effect of temperature upon the dominance of one character over another.

In some cases dominance seemed to be influenced by temperature, while in other cases it was not influenced at all. In a heterozygous stock of *Drosophila* with various eye characteristics, 27°C. seemed to be a critical temperature for change in dominance. Zeleny and his

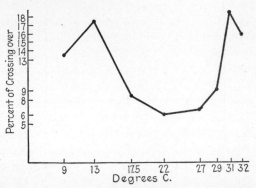

FIG. 28.—The effect of temperature on crossing over in *Drosophila*. (*Plough*, 1917.)

students have made a thorough study of the eye of *Drosophila* as affected by heredity and certain environmental conditions.

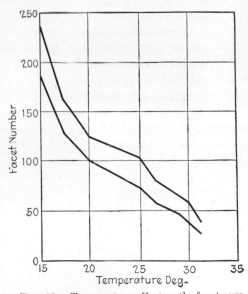

FIG. 29.—Temperature effect on the facet number in low selected bar stock of *Drosophila*. (*Krafka*, 1920.)

Krafka (1920) investigated the effect of temperature on certain "mutants" of *Drosophila* which have a small number of facets in the eye and are termed "bar-eye." He also had another strain known as ultra bar-eye. He found a linear relationship between the number of eye facets and the temperature under which the flies were reared, the mean facet numbers varying from about 28 at 31°C. to 189 at 15°C. In the ultra bar stock the same linear relationship obtained; but the numbers were lower, being about 14.57 for the mean facet number at 31°C., and 51.51 at 15°C. (See Figs. 29 and 30 for the distribution of facet numbers.) When these results are compared with those of Hersh (1924), an interesting comparison may be made between the normal full-eyed *Drosophila*, the mutant bar-eye, and ultra bar-eye. In the normal full-eyed *Drosophila*, Hersh found that there was nearly a straight-line relationship between temperature and number of facets. Above

27°C. the change in facet number was much less, and the result deviated from the straight line (see Fig. 31.) The normal full-eyed *Drosophila* varies from between 900 and 1,000 facets at 15°C. to about 700 at 27°C. The largest number of facets which may be produced in the so-called "mutant" bar-eye at low temperature is much less than the lowest number produced in the full-eyed *Drosophila* at high temperature. In comparing the bar-eye and the ultra bar-eye, however, it is found that there is an overlapping in the mean facet numbers, for as many as 51.51 may be produced at 15° in the ultra bar-eye, and as few as 28.85 at 31° in the bar-eye. The result is that we have two genetically distinct strains which can be made alike, as to the mean facet number, by rearing one at a low temperature and the other at a high temperature. Under the conditions of nature, these two strains might well be confused on the basis of mean facet number.

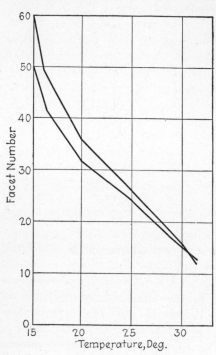

Fig. 30.—Temperature effect on the mean facet number in the ultra-bar stock of *Drosophila*. (*Krafka*, 1920.)

There would, however, be no possibility of confusing the mutant with the

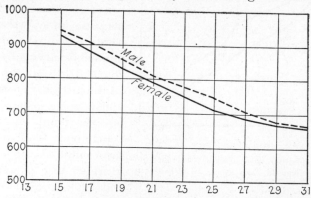

Fig. 31.—Mean facet values in full-eyed *Drosophila* plotted in terms of temperature. (*Hersh*, 1924.)

normal full-eyed *Drosophila;* for the fewest facets that can be produced by high temperature in the normal full-eyed *Drosophila* is far greater than the highest number in the bar-eyed *Drosophila*.

Krafka believes that the linear nature of the relationship between the eye-facet number and the temperature indicates that it is a result of a differential effect of temperature on the processes concerned with the development of the eye facets as compared with the rest of the individual. He also found that the effect of temperature in determining the number of eye facets is operative during a rather restricted period. At 27°C. this period is said to occur between the end of the third and the end of the fourth day, and to have a duration of about 18 hours. At 15°C. this period is at the end of the eighth day following a first day at 27°C. In this case the period is 72 hours long. Krafka examined a number of hypotheses, in the light of the data at hand, without being able to demonstrate definitely what the nature of the process which causes the change in facet number might be. It seems certain that this is of the nature of the effect of temperature on development rather than of the mechanism of heredity.

Zeleny (1928) reports that this culture of *Drosophila* has been continued over a long period of time without any definite effects upon the inheritance of the character.

There are other examples of the effect of temperature upon the size and length of the wings of *Drosophila* (Nadler, 1927), and of other factors on other species, which show that temperature may affect the mechanism of development in such a way as to give rise to individuals having a definite correlation between the temperature and the characters developed.

Effect of Temperature on the Behavior of Animals.—Changes in temperature constitute stimuli to which animals react, as in the case of other physical factors of the environment, to choose an optimum condition. This reaction is well known in the case of temperature, and will not be considered further except as an illustration of the effect of temperature upon reactions of poikilothermic animals.

The mechanisms by which poikilothermic animals react to unfavorable temperatures are themselves affected by the temperatures. Consequently, when such an animal encounters an unfavorably low temperature, its movements will be slowed and its reaction in avoiding this low temperature will be retarded. If the temperature is very low, the animal may become torpid before the reaction is complete. In the case of an unfavorably high temperature, the movements will be very rapid and the avoiding reaction accelerated, unless the temperature is so extreme that it produces a depressing effect.

The universal effect of temperature upon biotic processes extends to the effect of temperature upon the reactions of animals to all sorts of stimuli. It is necessary to interpret the reaction of animals to any stimulus in terms of the temperature under which the reaction is brought about. Consequently, certain animals may be positive to one stimulus at one temperature and negative to the same stimulus at a different temperature. The change of certain animals in their reactions to light is a classical example of this temperature effect. Many animals are negative to light at low temperature, and positive at high temperature. This effect of temperature is undoubtedly an important factor in controlling the complex system of stimuli and reactions which govern the diurnal activity of animals.

An interesting example of the reaction of an insect to the diurnal changes of temperature is furnished by a leaf-mining beetle, *Taphrocerus gracilis*, belonging to the family *Buprestidae* (Chapman, 1923). In the field it was observed that at high temperatures the adult beetles were positive to light and reacted by flying when stimulated mechanically. At low temperatures they were negative to light and contracted their appendages and permitted themselves to fall when stimulated mechanically. Inasmuch as the beetles retired to the axils of the leaves at low temperatures, their falling at this time merely resulted in their coming to rest in crevices in the axils of the leaves. Such a reaction at high temperature while they were feeding near the ends of the leaves would result in their falling into the water in which their host plant grows. At high temperature they are positive to light and react to mechanical stimuli by flying. Consequently, when feeding on the tips of the leaves they fly when mechanically stimulated, and do not fall into the water.

Observations on these beetles during the diurnal cycle of their activity indicated that the change of temperature had a profound influence upon all of their activities. Under controlled laboratory conditions they could be brought out of their retirement into the light by raising the temperature, and returned to their hiding places by lowering the temperature. It is known that the time of flight, feeding reaction, oviposition, and many other functions are controlled by the temperature in the diurnal cycle.

Effects of Temperature on the Geographic Range of Animals.—This subject is referred to in this place merely for the purpose of completeness of the discussion on temperature. It will later be referred to under the subject of the distribution of animals as correlated with climatic influences. The obviousness of the effect of temperature upon the geographic range of animals called early attention to this subject. Many investigators attempted to mark out zones of animal distribution on the basis of temperature alone, neglecting all other factors.

Merriam (1894) based his "life zones" on his so-called "laws of temperature control." He stated: "Animals are restricted in their northern distribution by the total quantity of heat during the season of their growth and reproduction," and "Animals are restricted in their southern range by the mean temperature of a brief period during the hottest part of the year."

These statements imply that animals may live as far north as the season will permit sufficient units of time and temperature for the completion of the cycle. It neglects the fact that animals are often limited in their northern distribution by the extremes of temperature during the winter. Most of this work has been based upon a summation of time and time temperature above some assumed minimum effective degree of temperature. The zones of Merriam were thus based upon a summation of temperature. Merriam states that the temperature sums which he gives as characteristic of the various zones were obtained by summing the temperatures above 43°F. from spring to fall and that the conversion from centigrade to Fahrenheit was made. Such procedure does not give his results. He summed the total number of degrees Fahrenheit for each day from spring to fall, starting with the first day above 43°F. The conversion was made from Fahrenheit to centigrade, but no account was taken of the fact that "0" in the Fahrenheit scale is 32°F. lower than on the centigrade scale. Consequently, all of his values given in degrees centigrade are incorrect.

Bodenheimer (1927) made a study of two weevils, *Sitophilus oryza* and *Sitophilus granaria*. He calculated the constant for time and temperature for *S. oryza* as 358.8, and for *S. granaria* as 523. It does not follow, however, that *oryza* is to be found in the North, and *granaria* in the South. It is just the opposite, even though *oryza* requires the lower number and *granaria* the higher number of day degrees. The curves of development when plotted as time and degrees cross near the middle, so that *oryza* develops relatively more rapidly at high temperatures, and *granaria* more rapidly at low temperatures. Consequently, *Sitophilus granaria* is the northern species; and *Sitophilus oryza*, the southern species. This is in conformity with the actual conditions; but it could not be deduced on the basis of the sum of time and time temperature required for the completion of the life cycle.

BIBLIOGRAPHY

TEMPERATURE

ABBE, CLEVELAND: First Report on the Relations between Climate and Crops, *Bull. U. S. Weather Bur.*, p. 36, 1905.

ADAMS, C. C.: "Guide to the Study of Animal Ecology," The Macmillan Company, New York, 1913. 183 pp.

ALLEE, W. C.: Note on Animal Distribution Following a Hard Winter, *Biol. Bull.* **36**: 96–104, 1919.

————: Studies in Marine Ecology: IV. The Effect of Temperature in Limiting the Geographical Range of Invertebrates of the Woods Hole Littoral, *Ecology*, **IV**: 341–354, 1923.

ARRHENIUS, SVANTE: Ueber die Dissociationswärme und den Einfluss der Temperatur auf den Dissociationsgrad der Elektrolyte, *Ztschr. Phys. Chem.*, **4**: 96–116, 1889.

BACHMETJEW, P.: Über die Temperatur der Insekten nach den Beobachtungen in Bulgaria, *Ztschr. wiss. Zool.*, **66**: 521–604, 1899.

――――: "Experimentelle entomologische Studien. I. Temperaturverhältnisse bei Insekten," Leipzig, 1901. 160 pp.

――――: Die Lage des anabiotischen Zustandes auf der Temperaturkurve der wechselwärmen Thiere, *Biol. Zentralbl.*, **XXI**: 672–675, 1901.

――――: "Experimentelle entomologische Studien. II. Einfluss der äusseren Faktoren auf Insekten," Sofia, 1907. 944 pp.

BALL, F. R.: Notes sur l'effet de la température sur les chrysalides, *Ann. soc. ent. belg.*, vol. **45**: 385–388, 1901.

BAYETT, H. C.: Physiological Responses to Heat, *Physiol. Rev.*, **7**: 531–599, 1927.

BAYLISS, W. M.: "Principles of General Physiology," 2d ed., pp. 1–736, esp. pp. 43, 45, and 458, Longmans, Green and Co., New York, 1918.

――――: "Principles of General Physiology," 4th ed., Longmans, Green and Company, New York, 1924.

BEHRE, E. H.: An Experimental Study of Acclimation to Temperature in Planaria dorotocephala, *Biol. Bull. Mar. Lab.*, Woods Hole, **35**: 277–317, 1918.

BERGER, ROBERT: Beiträge zum Melanismus der Schmetterlinge, *Soc. Ent.;* vol. VI, p. 180; vol. VII, Nos. 20–21; **4**: 27–28; **5**: 35–36; **6**: 44–45; **7**: 52–53; **8**: 59–60; 1892.

BLACKMAN, F. F.: Optima and Limiting Factors, *Ann. Bot.*, **19**: 281–295, 1905.

BLISS, CHESTER I.: Temperature Characteristics for Prepupal Development in *Drosophila melanogaster, Jour. Gen. Physiol.*, **9**: 467–495, 1926.

BLUNCK, H.: Die Entwicklung des *Dytiscus marginalis* L. vom Ei bis zur Imago, *Ztschr. wiss. Zool.*, **121**: 279–321, 1923.

BODENHEIMER, F. S.: On Predicting the Development Cycles of Insects. 1. *Ceratitis capitata* Wied, *Bull. Soc. Roy. Ent. Égypte*, pp. 149–157, 1924.

BOUNHIOL, J. P., and L. PRON: Sur la température optima du développement ovarien et de la ponte chez la daurade ordinaire (*Chrysophrys aurata*). *Compt. rend. soc. biol.*, **79**: 29–31, 1916.

BRITTON, S. W.: Effect of Lowering Temperature on Homoiothermic Animals, *Quart. Jour. Exptl. Physiol.*, **13**: 56–68, 1922.

――――: The Effects of Extreme Temperatures on Fishes, *Amer. Jour. Physiol.*, **67**: 411–421, 1924.

BROWN, L. A.: Temperature Characteristics for Duration of an Instar in Cladocerans, *Jour. Gen. Physiol.*, **10**: 111–119, 1926.

BRUES, CHARLES T.: Studies on the Fauna of Hot Springs in the Western United States and the Biology of Thermophilous Animals, *Proc. Amer. Acad. Arts & Sci.*, vol. 63, **4**, 139–228, 1928.

CALVERST, PHILIP B.: Relations of a Late Autumnal Dragonfly (*Odonata*) to Temperature, *Ecology*, **7**: 185–190, 1926.

CARTER, WALTER: The Effect of Low Temperatures on *Bruchus obtectus* Say, an Insect Affecting Seed, *Jour. Agr. Research*, **31**: 165–182, 1925.

CASTLE, W. A.: The Life History of *Planaria velata*, *Biol. Bull. Mar. Biol. Lab.*, **53**: 139–144, 1927.

CHAPMAN, ROYAL N.: Observations on the Life History of *Taphrocerus gracilis* Say (Beetle, Family Buprestidae), *Cornell Univ. Agr. Expt. Sta. Memoir* **67**: –13, 1923.

CHAPMAN, ROYAL N., C. E. MICKEL, J. R. PARKER, and others: Studies in the Ecology of Sand Dune Insects, *Ecology*, **7**: 416–426, 1926.

CHAPMAN, ROYAL N.: Temperature as an Ecological Factor in Animals, *Amer. Naturalist*, vol. LXII, pp. 298–310, 1928.

COMIGNAN, J.: Contribution à l'étude du determinisme du fouissement chez quelques arthropodes, *Compt. rend. soc. biol.*, **95**: 293–294, 1926.

CONNELL, A. B.: Measuring Soil Temperature by Standard Thermometer Suspended in Iron Pipe, *Ecology*, **4**: 313–316, 1923.

COOK, WILLIAM C.: Studies on the Flight of Nocturnal Lepidoptera, *Minn. State Ent. 18th Rept.*, pp. 43–56, 1920.

————: The Distribution of the Pale Western Cutworm, *Porosagrotis orthogonia* Morr.: A Study in Physical Ecology, *Ecology*, **5**: 60–69, 1924.

————: Some Weather Relations of the Pale Western Cutworm, *Porosagrotis orthogonia* Morr.: A Preliminary Study, *Ecology*, **7**: 37–47, 1926.

————: Some Effects of Alternating Temperatures on the Growth and Metabolism of Cutworm Larvae, *Jour. Econ. Ent.*, **20**: 769–782, 1927.

CRAIGHEAD, F. C., and W. K. LOUGHBOROUGH: Temperatures Fatal to Larvae of the Red-headed Ash Borer as Applicable to Commercial Kiln Drying, *Jour. Forestry*, **19**: 250–254, 1921.

CROZIER, W. J.: On Biological Oxidations as Function of Temperature, *Jour. Gen. Physiol.*, **7**: 189–216, 1924.

CROZIER, W. J., and T. B. STIER: Temperature Characteristic for Locomotor Activity in Tent Caterpillars, *Jour. Gen. Physiol.*, **9**: 49–54, 1925.

CROZIER, W. J.: On Curves of Growth, Especially in Relation to Temperature, *Jour. Gen. Physiol.*, **10**: 53–73, 1926.

DAVENPORT, C. B., and W. E. CASTLE: Studies in Morphogenesis, III. On the Acclimatization of Organisms to High Temperatures, *Arch. Entwickl. Mech. Organ.*, II: 227–249, 1895.

DAVENPORT, C. B.: "Experimental Morphology," chap. VIII, Action of Heat upon Protoplasm, pp. 219–267 and bibliog., The Macmillan Company, New York, 1908.

DAWSON, RALPH WARD: Studies on the Causes of Dormancy among Insects, with Special Reference to the Polyphemus Moth, Univ. of Minn., unpublished, Ph.D. thesis, 1929.

DELCOURT, A.: Temperature on the Development of Notonecta, *Assoc. franç. avanc. sci.*, **36**: 244–245, 1908.

DELF, E. M.: Studies of Protoplasmic Permeability by Measurement of Rate of Shrinkage of Turgid Tissues. I. The Influence of Temperature on the Permeability of Protoplasm to Water, *Ann. Bot.*, **30**: 283–310, 1916.

DEWITZ, J.: Physiologische Untersuchungen auf dem Gebiet der Schädlingsforschung, *Naturw. Ztschr. d. Forst- u. Landwirtschaft*, **X**: 539–549.

DIXEY, FREDERICK A.: Mr. Merrifield's Experiments in Temperature-variation as Bearing on Theories of Heredity, *Trans. Ent. Soc.*, London, pt. III, pp. 439–446, 1894.

DÖNHOFF,: Beiträge zur Physiologie I. Ueber das Verhalten kaltblütiger Thiere gegen Frost Temperatur, *Arch. Anat. u. Physiol. u. wiss. Med. von Reichert u. Du Bois-Raymond*, p. 724, 1872.

DORFMEISTER, GEORG: Ueber die Einwirkung verschiedener, während der Entwickelungsperioden angewendeter Wärmegrade auf die Färbung und Zeichnung der Schmetterlinge, *Mitt. d. naturw. Ver. Steyrmark*, pamphlet, pp. 99–108, Graz, 1864.

DORFMEISTER, G.: Ueber den Einfluss der Temperatur bei der Erzeugung der Schmetterlingsvarietäten, *Mitt. naturw. Ver. Steyrmark*, Jahrg. 1879; Graz, 1880. As pamphlet 8 pp.

DUCLAUX, E.: De l'influence du froid de l'hiver sur le développement de l'embryon du ver à soie, et sur l'éclosion de la graine. *Compt. rend. acad. sci.*, Paris, **69**: 1021–1022, 1869.

Duclaux, E.: De l'action physiologique qu'exercent, sur les graines des vers à soie, des températures inférieures à zero, *Compt. rend. acad. sci.*, Paris, **83** : 1049–1051, 1876.

Edwards, W. H.: Experiments Upon the Effect of Cold Applied to Chrysalids of Butterflies, *Psyche*, **3** : 1–6, 15–19, 75–76, 1880.

Federley, Harry: Lepidopterologische Temperatur-Experimente mit besonderer Berücksichtigung der Flügelschuppe, Separatus aus "Festschrift für Palmen," no. 16, Helsingfors, 1905. 117 pp.

Ferguson, Allan: On the Variation of Surface Tension with Temperature, *Phil. Mag.*, **31** : 37–47, 1916.

Fischer, E.: Neue Experimentelle Untersuchungen und Beobachtungen über das Wesen und die Ursache der Aberrationen in der Faltergruppe Vanessa, Berlin, 1896.

————: Zwei sonderbare Aberrationen von *Vanessa antiopa* und eine neue Methode zur Erzeugung der Kälteaberrationen, Sonderdruck aus der *Illustr. Wchnschr. Ent.*, Neudamm, 1897.

————: Weitere Untersuchung über das procentuale Auftreten der Vanessen Aberrationen, *Soc. Ent.*, vol. XVI, **7** : 49–51, **8** : 58–59, 1901.

Folsom, Justus W.: "Entomology with Special Reference to Its Ecological Aspects," 3d rev. ed., pp. 350–362, P. Blakiston's Son & Co., Inc., Phil. 1922. 502 pp.

Fries, E. F. B.: Temperature and Frequency of Heart Beat in the Cockroach, *Jour. Gen. Physiol.*, **10** : 227–237, 1926.

Frings, Carl: Bericht ueber Temperatur-Experimente in den Jahren 1908–11. *Soc. Ent.*, Stuttgart, **27** : 21–24, 29–30, 35–36, 37–38, 42–43, 1912.

Gauckler, H.: Untersuchungen über beschleunigte Entwicklung überwinternder Schmetterlingspuppen (Treiben der Puppen), *Illus. Ztschr. Ent.*, vol. IV, **7** : 12, 15. 1899. As pamphlet 8 pp.

Gerould, S. H.: Seasonal Changes in the Melanic Pigmentation in Butterflies of the Genus Colias, *Anat. Rec.*, **29** : 93–94, 1924.

Glaser, O.: Temperature and Forward Movement of Paramecium, *Jour. Gen. Physiol.*, **7** : 177–188, 1924.

Glenn, P. A.: The Influence of Climate upon the Green Bug and Its Parasite, *Kans. Univ. Bull.*, vol. 9, **2** : 165–200, 1909.

Graham, S. A.: Factors Influencing the Subcortical Temperatures of Logs, *Minn. State Ent. 18th Rept.*, pp. 26–42, 1920.

————: Effect of Physical Factors in the Ecology of Certain Insects in Logs, *Minn. State Ent. 19th Rept.*, pp. 22–40, 1922.

Griffiths, A. B.: Recherches sur les couleurs de quelques insectes, *Compt. rend. acad. sci.*, **115** : 958–959, 1892.

Groves, J. F.: Temperature and Life Duration of Seeds, *Bot. Gaz.*, **63** : 169–189, 1917

Hartzell, F. Z.: Comparison of Methods for Computing Daily Mean Temperatures: Effect of Discrepancies upon Investigations of Climatologists and Biologists-*N. Y. Expt. Sta. Bull.*, **68** : 3–35, 1919; also *U. S. Monthly Weather Rev.*, **47** : 799–801,

Harvey, R. B.: Relation of the Color of Bark to the Temperature of the Cambium. in Winter, *Ecology*, IV : 391–394, 1923.

Hase, Albrecht: Über Wärmentwicklung in Kolonien von Wachsmottenraupen, *Naturwissenschaften*, **14** : 995–997, 1926.

————: Ueber Temperaturversuche mit den Eiern der Mehlmotte (*Ephestia kuehniella* Zell), *Arch. Biol. Reichsanst. d. Land u. Forstw.*, **5** : 109–133, 1927.

————: Aufgaben und Einrichtung des Laboratoriums für physiologische Zoologie and der biologischen Reichsanstalt für Land- und Forstwirtschaft zu Berlin-Dahlem nebst Beschreibung einiger neuer daselbst gebauter Apparate, *Zool. Anz.*, LXXIII: 151–183, 1927.

Hawkes, O. A.: On the Massing of the Ladybird, *Hippodamia convergens* (Coleoptera) in the Yosemite Valley, *Proc. Zool. Soc.*, London, vol. II, pp. 693–705, 1926.

HEGNER, R. W.: The Effects of Environmental Factors upon the Heritable Characters of *Arcella dentata* and *Polypora*, *Jour. Exptl. Zool.*, **29**: 427–441, 1919.

HEIMBURGER, H. V.: Reactions of Earthworms to Temperature and Atmospheric Humidity, *Ecology*, **5**: 276–282, 1924.

HERNANDEZ, JESUS: The Temperature of Mexico, *U. S. Monthly Weather Rev.*, *supp.* 23, 1923. 24 pp.

HERSH, A. H.: The Effect of Temperature upon the Heterozygotes in the Bar Series of *Drosophila*, *Jour. Exptl. Zool.*, **39**: 55–71, 1924.

HERSH, ROSELLE KARRER: The Effect of Temperature upon the Full-eyed Race of *Drosophila*, *Jour. Exptl. Zool.*, **39**: 43–53, 1924b.

HEYDER, H. C. VAN DER: On the Influence of Temperature on the Excretion of the Hibernating Frog *Rana voresceus* Kalm, *Biol. Bull.*, **XLI**: 249–255, 1921.

HOOKER, H. D.: Liebig's Law of the Minimum in Relation to General Biological Problems, *Science*, n. s., **46**: 197–204, 1917.

HOPKINS, ANDREW D.: Modifying Factors in Effective Temperature; or, a Principle of Modified Thermal Influence on Organisms, *U. S. Monthly Weather Rev.* 4, **48**: 214–215, 1920.

————: Bioclimatic Zones Determined by Meteorological Data, *U. S. Monthly Weather Rev.*, **49**: 299–300, 1921.

HOWARD, L. O.: Some Temperature Effects on Household Insects, *U. S. Dept. Agr. Bur. Ent. Bull.* **6**, n. s., pp. 13–17, 1896.

————: A Note on Insects Found on Snow at High Elevations, *Ent. News*, **29**: 375–377, 1918.

HUBBARD, H. G.: Insect Life in the Hot Springs of the Yellowstone National Park, *Canad. Ent.*, **23**: 226–230, 1891.

HUBBS, CARL L.: Variations in the Number of Vertebrae and Other Meristic Characters of Fishes Correlated with the Temperatures of Water During Development, *Amer. Naturalist*, **56**: 360–372, 1922.

HUSAIN, M. A. and H. D. BHASIN: Preliminary Observations on Lethal Temperatures for the Larvae of *Trogoderma khapra*, a Pest of Stored Wheat, *Rept. Proc.*, *4th Ent. meeting*, held at Pusa, February 1921; Calcutta, 1921. pp. 240–248.

IRMSCHER, EMIL: Zum Entstehen der Aberrationen in der Natur, *Illustr. Ztschr. Ent.*, vol. 5, **11**: 166, 1900.

JACKSON, HARTLEY H. T.: An Apparent Effect of Winter Inactivity upon Distribution of Mammals, *Jour. Mammal.*, **1**: no. 2, 58–64, 1920.

JACOBS, MERKEL H.: Acclimatization as a Factor Affecting the Upper Thermal Death Points of Organisms, *Jour. Exptl. Zool.*, **27**: no. 3, 427–442, 1919.

————: The Complex Nature of the Effects of Temperature on the Rates of Certain Biological Processes, *Amer. Naturalist*, vol. LXII, no. 681, pp. 289–297, 1928.

JANISCH, ERNST: Ueber die Temperaturabhängigkeit biologischer Vorgänge und ihre kurvenmässige Analyse, *Pflüger's Arch. Physiol.*, **209**: 414–436, 1925.

JENNINGS, H. S.: "Behavior of the Lower Organisms," New York, 1906.

JOHNSON, CHARLES W.: A Review of the Stratiomyia and Odontomyia of North America, *Trans. Amer. Ent. Soc.*, **22**: 227–278, 1895.

KANITZ, ARISTIDES: "Temperatur und Lebensvorgänge," 1915.

KANOLT, C. W.: The Production of Cold, *Jour. Opt. Soc. of Amer.*, **9**: 411–453, 1924.

KENNEDY, CLARENCE H.: Some Non-nervous Factors that Condition the Sensitivity of Insects to Moisture, Temperature, Light and Odors, *Ann. Ent. Soc. Amer.*, **20**: 87–106, 1927.

KENDEIGH, C., and S. P. BALDWIN: Development of Temperature Control in Nestling House Wrens, *Amer. Naturalist*, **62**: 249–278, 1928.

Kleist, Frank von: Nährungsaufnahme und Kälte beim Bienenvolk, *Arch. Bienenk.*, **1**: 4, 1919.

Knight, Harry H.: Studies on the Life History and Biology of *Perillus bioculatus* Fabricius, Including Observations on the Nature of the Color Pattern, *Minn. State Ent. 19th Rept.*, pp. 50–96, 1922.

Knight, Harry H.: On the Nature of the Color Patterns in Heteroptera with Data on the Effects Produced by Temperature and Humidity, *Ann. Ent. Soc. Amer.*, **17**: 258–272, 1924.

Krafka, Joseph, Jr.: The Effect of Temperature upon Facet Number in the Bar-eyed Mutant of *Drosophila*, Pts. I, II, and III, *Jour. Gen. Physiol.*, **2**: 409–464, 1920.

Kramer, P.: Reflexionen über die Theorie durch welche der Saison-Dimorphismus bei den Schmetterlingen erklärt wird, *Arch. Naturgesell.*, **44**: 411–419, 1878.

Kredel, F. E.: Notes on the Temperature of the Sloth, *Jour. Mammal.*, **9**: 48–51, 1928.

Krodel, Ernst: Durch Einwirkung niederer Temperaturen auf das Puppen-stadium erzielte Aberrationen der Lycana-Arten: corydon Poda und damon Schiff (Lep.), *Allg. Ztschr. Ent.*, **9**: 49–55, 103–110, 134–137, 1904.

Krogh, August: Ein Mikrorespirationsapparat und einige damit ausgeführte Versuche über die Temperatur-Stoffwechselkurve von Insektenpuppen, *Biochem. Ztschr.*, **62**: 266–279, 1914a.

———: On the Influence of Temperature on the Rate of Embryonic Development, *Ztschr. Allg. Physiol.*, **16**: 163–177, 1914.

———: On the Rate of Development and CO_2 Production of Chrysalides of *Tenebrio molitor* at Different Temperatures, *Ztschr. Allg. Physiol.*, **16**: 178–190, 1914.

Kühn, Alfred: Über die Änderung des Zeichnungsmusters von Schmetterlingen durch Temperaturreize und das Grundschema der Nymphalidenzeichnung, *Nachrichten Ges. Wiss. Göttingen*, Math.-Phys. Kl. 1926 (2), pp. 120–141.

Lambert, F.: Influence d'une faible diminution de la chaleur pendant les derniers jours de l'elévage sur les cocons des vers à soie du mûrier, *Ann. école natl. agr.*, Montpellier, vol. I, no. 6, 1899.

Lee, M. O.: Studies on the Oestrus Cycle in the Rat. III. Effect of Low Environ-mental Temperatures, *Amer. Jour. Physiol.*, **78**: 246–253, 1926.

Lewith, S.: Ueber die Ursache der Widerstandsfähigkeit der Sporen gegen hohe Temperaturen. Ein Beitrag zur Theorie der Desinfektion, *Arch. Exptl. Path.*, **26**: 341–354, 1900.

Lichtenstein, J.: "Monographie des aphidiens. Les pucerons," Partie I. Genera; Montpellier, 1885. 188 pp.

Lillie, R. S.: Temperature Coefficients in the Activation of Starfish Eggs by Butyric Acid, *Biol. Bull.*, **32**: 131–158, 1917.

Linden, Marie Gräfin v.: Untersuchungen über die Entwicklung der Zeichnung des Schmetterlingsflügels in der Puppe, *Ztschr. wiss. Zool.*, vol. LXV: pp. 1–49, 1898.

Loeb, J., and J. H. Northrop: Is There a Temperature Coefficient for the Dura-tion of Life? *Proc. Nat. Acad. Sci.*, **2**: 456–457, 1916.

———: On the Influence of Food and Temperature upon the Duration of Life, *Jour. Biol. Chem.*, **32**: 103–121, 1917.

Ludwig, Daniel: The Effects of Temperature on the Development of an Insect (*Popillia japonica* Newman), *Physiol. Zool.*, vol. I, no. 3. pp. 358–389, 1928.

Malpighius, Marcellus S. P.: "Dissertatio Epistolica de Bombyse," 1669; E. Maillot, translator; Montpellier, 1878.

Mann, Margaret C.: A Demonstration of the Stability of the Genes of an Inbred Stock of *Drosophila melanogaster* under Experimental Conditions, *Jour. Exptl. Zool.*, **38**: 213–244, 1924.

Marchand, Werner: Thermotropism in Insects, *Ent. News*, **31**: 159–165, 1920.

MARINESCO, G. and J. MINEA,: L'action de la température sur le phénomène de la réaction à distance des cellules nerveuses de la Grenouille, *Compt. rend. soc. biol.*, **79**: 456–458, 1916.

MARTINI, E.: Ueber die Wärmesummenregel, *Ztschr. angew. Ent.*, vol. xi, **2**: 301–305, 1925.

MAUCHA, R.: Upon the Influence of Temperature and Intensity of Light on the Photosynthetic Production of Nannoplankton, *Verhandl. Internat. Ver. theoret. und angew. Limnologie*, Zweite Versamml., pp. 381–401, 1924.

MERRIAM, C. HART: The Temperature During the Season of Reproductive Activity Determines the Distribution of Life, *North Amer. Fauna*, no. 10, 1890.

————: The Geographic Distribution of Animals and Plants in North America. "U. S. Dept. Agr. Yearbook," pp. 203–214, 1894.

————: Laws of Temperature Control of the Geographic Distribution of Terrestrial Animals and Plants, *Nat. Geogr. Mag.*, **6**: 229–238, 1894.

————: Life Zones and Crop Zones of the United States, *U. S. Dept. Agr. Bur. Biol. Survey Bull.* 10, pp. 9–73, 1898.

MERRIFIELD, F.: The effects of artificial temperature on the colouring of several species of Lepidoptera, with an account of some experiments on the effects of light, *Trans. Ent. Soc.*, London, pt. I, pp. 33–44, 1892.

————: Temperature Experiments in 1893 on Several Species of Vanessa and Other Lepidoptera, *Trans. Ent. Soc.*, London, pt. III, pp. 425–438, 1894.

————: President's address. General Operation of Temperature. *Trans. Ent. Soc.*, London, pp. LXXVIII–CXI, 1905.

MOBINS, K.: Einige allgemeine Bemerkungen über die Körperwärme der Bienen, *Eichstädt. Bienentg.*, **19**: 37–38, 1863.

MORGLUS, SERGIUS: The Effect of Environmental Temperature on Metabolism, *Amer. Jour. Physiol.*, **71**: 49–59, 1924.

MÜLLER-ERZBACH, W.: Die Widerstandsfähigkeit des Frosches gegen das Einfrieren, *Zool. Anz.*, **14**: 383–384, 1891.

MUSSEHL, F. E.: Ueber das Winterleben der Stockbienen, *Oken's Isis*, p. 572, 1836.

NADLER, J. ERNEST: Effects of temperature on Length of Vestigial Wing in *Drosophila virilis*, *Genetics*, **11**: 584–589, 1927.

NECHELES, HEINRICH: Über Wärmeregulation bei wechselwarmen Tieren. Ein Beitrag zur vergleichenden Physiologie der Wärmeregulation, *Pflüger's Arch. Physiol.*, **204**: 72–86, 1924.

NEWPORT, GEORGE: On the Temperature of Insects, and Its Connection with the Function of Respiration and Circulation in this Class of Invertebrate Animals, Roy. Soc., London, *Phil. Trans.*, CXXVII, Part II, pp. 259–339, 1837.

O'CONNOR, J. M.: On the Mechanism of Chemical Temperature Regulation. *Proc. Roy. Soc.*, London, ser. B, **89**: 201–212, 1916.

OETTINGEN, AUGUST VON: Archiv für Naturo, Doplater Lignoscn, 1879. Phenologie von der Liv. Esth. und Kurlands, **8**: 1–112.

PANTIN, C. F. A.: Temperature and the Viscosity of Protoplasm, *Jour. Mar. Biol. Assoc. United Kingdom*, **13**: 331, 1924.

PARKER, G. H.: The Effects of the Winter of 1917–1918 on the Occurrence of *Sagartia luciæ* Verrill, *Amer. Naturalist*, **53**: 280–281, 1919.

PARKER, J. R.: Some Effects of Temperature and Moisture upon *Melanoplus mexicanus mexicanus* Saussure, and *Camnula pellucida* Scudder (Orthoptera), *U. of Mont. Ag. Expt. Sta. Bull.* 223, p. 132, 1930.

PAYNE, NELLIE M.: Freezing and Survival of Insects at Low Temperatures, Univ. of Minn., unpublished Ph.D. thesis, 1925. 88 pp.

————: The Effect of Environmental Temperatures upon Insect Freezing Points, *Ecology*, **7**: 99–106, 1926.

Peairs, L. M.: The Relation of Temperature to Insect Development, *Jour. Econ. Ent.*, **7**: 174–179, 1914.

———: Some Phases of the Relation of Temperature to the Development of Insects, *West Va. Univ. Agr. Expt. Sta. Bull.* 208, 1927. 62 pp.

Pirsch, G. B.: Studies on the Temperature of Individual Insects, with Special Reference to the Honey Bee, *Jour. Agr. Research*, **24**: 275–288, 1923.

Plateau, F.: Résistance à l'asphyxie par submersion; action du froid; action de la chaleur; temp. maximum, *Bull. acad. roy. sci. belg.*, vol. 34, nos. 9 and 10, 1872.

Plough, H. H.: The Effect of Temperature on Crossing-over in *Drosophila*, *Jour. Exptl. Zool.*, **24**: 147–209, 1917.

Plough, Harold H., and Maurice B. Strauss: Experiments on Toleration of Temperature by *Drosophila*, *Jour. Gen. Physiol.*, **6**: 167–176, 1923.

Pospelov, V. P.: The Influence of Temperature on the Maturation and General Health of *Locusta migratoria*, L., *Bull. Ent. Research* **16**: 363–367, 1926.

Powers, Edwin B.: Influence of Temperature and Concentration on the Toxicity of Salts to Fish, *Ecology*, **1**: 95–112, 1920.

Prochnow, Oskar: Die analytische Methode bei der Gewinnung der Temperatur-aberrationen der Schmetterlinge, *Biol. Zentralbl.*, **34**: 302–308, 1914.

Przibram, H.: Temperaturquotienten für Lebenserscheinungen der *Sphodromantis bioculata* Burm. (Zugleich: Aufzucht der Gottesanbeterinnen; VIII. Mitteilung). *Arch. Entwickl. Mech.*, **43**: 28–38, 1917.

Quajat, E.: Effetti di una prolungata svernatura sul e uova del filugello a seconda della varie razze, *Ann. staz. bacol.*, **XXX**: 85–96, 1903.

———: Svernatura autunnale interrotta da temporanei ritorni a elevato calore, *Ann. staz. bacol.*, **XXXII**: 33–42, 1904.

Rahm, P. G.: Ist der Lebensvorgang bei den Tieren der Mossfauna im erstarrten Zustand zur herabgesetzt oder ganz unterbrochen? *Verhandl. Naturhist. Ver. Preuss. Rheinlande*, **82**: 377–383, 1925 (1926).

Ransom, B. H.: Effects of Refrigeration upon the Larvae of Trichinella Spiralis, *Jour. Agr. Research*, **V**: 819–854, 1916.

Réaumur, de M.: "Mémoires pour servir à l'histoire des insectes," Paris, 1736. 2 vols.

Roberts, Elmer: Fluctuations in a Recessive Mendelian Character and Selection, *Jour. Exptl. Zool.*, **27**: 157–192, 1918.

Robinson, Wm.: The Thermocouple Method of Determining Temperatures, *Ann. Ent. Soc. Amer.*, vol. XX, **4**: 513–521, 1927.

———: Construction and Installation of a Toluol-Mercury Thermostat, *Ann. Ent. Soc. Amer.*, **XXI**: 607–613, 1928.

———: A Study of the Effect of Surgical Shock on Insects. Determination of the Natural Undercooling and Freezing Points in Insects, *Jour. Agr. Research*, vol. 37, no. 2, pp. 743–755, 1928.

Rogers, Charles G., and Elsie M. Lewis: The Relation of the Body Temperature of Certain Cold-blooded Animals to That of Their Environment, *Oberlin Coll. Lab. Bull.* 16, 1916. 15 pp.

Rühl, F. B. Ueber die Beschleunigung der Entwicklung überwinternder Puppen durch erhöhte Temperatur, *Soc. Ent.*, vol. II, **18**: 138–139, 1887, **18**: 145–146, 1888.

Ruhmer, G. W.: Die Uebergänge von *Araschina levana* L. zu *Var. prorsa* L. und die bei der Zucht anzuwendende Kältemenge, *Ent. Nachr.*, vol. XXIV, pp. 37–52, 1898.

Sanderson, E. D.: The Relation of Temperature to the Hibernation of Insects, *Jour. Econ. Ent.*, **1**: 56–65, 1908.

———: The Relation of Temperature to the Growth of Insects, *Jour. Econ. Ent.*, **3**: 113–140, 1910.

SANDERSON, E. D., and L. M. PEAIRS: The Relation of Temperature to Insect Life. *N. H. Coll. Agr. Expt. Sta. Tech. Bull.* 7, 1913. 125 pp.

SCHLOTTKE, EGON: Über die Variabilität der schwarzen Pigmentierung und ihre Beeinflussbarkeit durch Temperaturen bei *Habrobracon juglandis* Ashmead. *Ztschr. wiss. Biol. Abt. C.; Ztschr. vergleich. Physiol.*, **3**: 692–736, 1926.

SCHONFELDT, J.: Die Muskelthätigkeit der Biene in Bezug auf Wärmeentwicklung. *Eichstädt. Bienenzeitung*, **22**: 221–223, 1866.

SEILER, J.: Geschlechtchromosomen-Untersuchungen an Psychiden, *Arch. Zellforsch.*, **15**: 249–268, 1920.

SENIOR-WHITE, RONALD: Physical Factors in Mosquito Ecology, *Bull. Ent. Research*, **16**: 187–248, 1926.

SHAPLEY, HARLOW: Notes on the Thermokinetics of Dolichoderina Ants, *Proc. Acad. Nat. Sci.*, **10**: 436, 1924.

SHELFORD, V. E.: An Experimental Investigation of the Relations of the Codling-moth to Weather and Climate, *Ill. Nat. Hist. Survey Bull.*, 16, pp. 307–440, 1927.

————: "Laboratory and Field Ecology," Williams & Wilkins Co., Baltimore, 1929. 608 pp.

SHREVE, FORREST: Soil Temperature as Influenced by Altitude and Slope Exposure, *Ecology*, **5**: 128–136, 1924.

SIMPSON, C. B.: The Codling Moth, *U. S. Dept. Agr. Bur. Ent. Bull.*, pp. 9–105, 1903.

SINCLAIR, J. G.: Temperatures of the Soil and Air in a Desert, *U. S. Monthly Weather Rev.* 50, 142–144, 1922.

SNYDER, C. D.: On the Meaning of Variation in the Magnitude of Temperature Coefficients of Physiological Processes, *Amer. Jour. Physiol.*, **28**: 167–175, 1911.

SNYDER, CHARLES D. and ALEIDA: The Flashing Interval of Fireflies—Its Temperature Coefficient—an Explanation of Synchronous Flashing, *Amer. Jour. Physiol.*, **51**: 536–542, 1920.

SNYDER, T. E. and R. A. ST. GEORGE: Determination of Temperatures Fatal to the Powder-post Beetle, *Lyctus planicollis* LeConte, by Steaming infested Ash and Oak Lumber in a Kiln, *Jour. Agr. Research*, **28**: 1033–1038, 1924.

SQUIRES, ROY W.: Tree Temperatures, *Minn. Bot. Studies*, vol. I, ser. 2, **26**: 425–459, 1894.

STANDFUSS, M.: Ueber die Gründe der Variation und Aberration des Falterstadiums bei den Schmetterlingen. *Insektenbörse*, vol. XI, **21**: 199–201, **22**: 209–210, **23**: 217–218, **25**: 225–226, 1894; vol. XII, **1**: 4–5; **2**: 13; **3**: 22–23; **4**: 29–30, **5**: 36–37, 1895.

STICKNEY, FENNER: The Relation of the Nymphs of a Dragonfly (*Libellula pulchella* Drury) to Acid and Temperature, *Ecology*, **3**: 250–254, 1922.

SUMMERS, JOHN N.: Effect of Low Temperature on the Hatching of Gipsy-moth Eggs, *U. S. Dept. Agr. Bull.* 1080, 1922, 14 pp.

TAYLOR, GRIFFITH: Control of Settlement by Humidity and Temperature, *Commonwealth Bur. Met.*, **14**: 1–32, 1916.

TAYLOR, G. F.: Some Improvements on the Needle Type Thermocouple for Low Temperature Work, *Jour. Indus. and Engin. Chem.*, **12**: 797–798, 1920.

TOUMANOFF, K.: L'action combinée de l'obscurité et de la température sur la mélanogénèse chez *Dixippus morosus*, *Compt. rend. soc. biol.*, vol. XCIV, pp. 565–566, 1926.

TOUMEY, J. W., and P. W. STICKEL: A New Device for Taking Maximum and Minimum Soil Temperatures in Forest Investigations, *Ecology*, **6**, 171–178, 1925.

TOWER, W. L.: On the Origin and Distribution of *Leptinotarsa decem-lineata* Say, and the Part that Some of the Climatic Factors Have Played in Its Dissemination, *Proc. Amer. Assoc. Adv. Sci.*, **49**: 225–227, 1900.

URECH, FRIEDERICH: Beobachtungen von Kompensationsvorgängen in der Farbenzeichnung bezw. unter den Schuppenfarben an durch thermische Einwirkungen entstandenen Aberrationen und Subspecies einiger Vanessa-Arten. Erwägungen darüber und über die phyletische Rekapitulation der Farbenfelderung in der Ontogenese, *Zool. Anz.*, **500**: 163–174; **501**: 177–185; **502**: 201–206, 1896.

———: Ergebnisse von Temperatur-Experimenten an *Vanessa io* L. *Illus. Ztschr. Ent.*, **3**: 177–179, 198–200, 211–213, 1898.

———: Kennzeichnung und kritische Bemerkungen über Terminologisches, Wärmeenergisches und Farbenevolution meiner erzielten Aberrationen von *Vanessa io* und *urticæ*, *Zool. Anz.*, vol. XXII, no. 582, pp. 121–133, 1899.

VAN LEEUWEN, W. STORM, and M. VAN DER MADE: Über den Einfluss der Temperatur auf die Reflexfunktionen des Rückenmarkes von Warmblütern und Kaltblütern, *Pflüger's Arch. Physiol.*, **165**: 37–83, 1916.

VAN'T HOFF: "Études de dynamique chimique," Müller, Amsterdam, 1884. 215 pp.

———: Lois de l'équilibre chimique dans l'état dilue gazeux ou dissous, *Kong. Svenska Vetensk. Akad. Handl.* **21**: no. 17, 1885.   41 pp.

VERLOREN, M. C.: On the Comparative Influence of Periodicity and Temperature upon the Development of Insects, *Trans. Ent. Soc.*, London, vol. I, 3d ser., pp. 63–69, 1862–1864.

VERNON, H. M.: The Relation of the Respiratory Exchange of Cold-blooded Animals to Temperature, *Jour. Physiol.*, **17**: 277–292, 1894.

VISHER, S. S.: "Climatic Laws," John Wiley & Sons., Inc., New York, 1924. 96 pp.

VOGEL, FRIEDRICH WILHELM: "Die Honigbiene," Quedlinburg, 1800.

WARD, HENRY B.: Some of the Factors Controlling the Migration and Spawning of the Alaska Red Salmon, *Ecology*, **2**: 235–254, 1921.

WASMANN, E.: Parthenogenesis bei Ameisen durch künstliche Temperaturverhältnisse, *Biol. Zentralbl.*, **11**: 21–23, 1891.

WEBSTER, F. M., and W. J. PHILLIPS: The Spring Grain-Aphis or "Green Bug," *U. S. Dept. Agr. Bur. Ent. Bull.* 110, 1912.   153 pp.

WEBSTER, G. S.: The Laws of Heat Transfer, *Engineering*, **16**: 1–3, 69–70, 131–132, 228–230, 1923.

WEISMANN, AUG.: Neue Versuche zum Saison-Dimorphismus der Schmetterlinge, *Zool. Jahrb.*, *Abt. System., Geogr. u. Biol. Tiere*, **8**: 611–684, 1895.

WILLIAMS, C. B.: A Short Bioclimatic Study in the Egyptian Desert, *Egypt. Min., Agr., Tech. and Sci. Serv. Bull.*, 1923.   29 pp.

WOLFER, A.: Revision of Wolf's Sun Spot Relative Numbers, *U. S. Monthly Weather Rev.*, **30**: 171, 1902.

———: Tables of Sunspot Frequency for the Years 1902–1919, *U. S. Monthly Weather Rev.*, **48**: 459, 1920.

WOLTERECK, R.: Über Veränderung der Sexualität bei Daphniden, *Internat. Rev. Gesamm. Hydrobiol. u. Hydrog.*, **4**: 90–128, 1911.

WOOD, W. P., and J. M. CORK: Methods of Measuring, Recording and Controlling Temperature, *Pyrometry*, p. 207, 1927.

YAGLOW, C. P.: Temperature, Humidity, and Air Movement in Industries: the Effective Temperature Index, *Jour. Indus. Hyg.*, **9**: 297–309, 1927.

YOUNG, WM. C., and H. H. PLOUGH: On the Sterilization of *Drosophila* by High Temperature, *Biol. Bull. Mar. Biol. Lab.*, **51**: 189–198, 1926.

ZELENY, CHARLES: The Effect of Long Subjection to Constant Temperature upon Bar-eye of *Drosophila melanogaster*, *Anat. Rec.*, **41**: 114, 1928.

ZELENY, JOHN: The Influence of Temperature upon the Photo-electric Effect, *Phys. Rev.*, 1901.

ZESELSKI, T.: Bienenzucht, gegründet auf der Wissenschaft und der langjährigen Praxis oder die rentabel Bienenwirtschaft. I. Theil. Die Natur der Biene; Kasan, 1893.

ZOETHOUT, W. D.: On Some Analogies between the Physiological Effects of High Temperature, Lack of Oxygen, and Certain Poisons, *Amer. Jour. Physiol.*, vol. II, pp. 220–242, 1899.

CHAPTER IV

MOISTURE AS AN ECOLOGICAL FACTOR

Introduction.—There is no other substance which contributes so largely to the structure of organisms as water does. It is the general presumption that life was originally aquatic, and it is true that organisms have never entirely freed themselves from an environment which must contain a certain amount of water. One of the fundamental necessities for all organisms is to maintain a certain balance between the moisture in their bodies and the moisture in the surrounding environment. The amount of moisture contained in the bodies of various species of organisms varies greatly. Some of the aquatic organisms have only a fraction of 1 per cent of substances in addition to the water of their bodies. Amphibious organisms are able to endure the greatest fluctuations in the moisture content of their bodies. Xerophytic animals may be adjusted to very low moisture content, but in general in such cases the variation in the moisture content cannot be great. In terrestrial environments the variation of moisture in geographic range is very marked and is one of the outstanding factors in controlling animal distribution. The distribution of moisture in the annual cycle is usually very marked, and serves as an easy method of distinguishing between the various types of environment.

Characteristics of Moisture as an Ecological Factor.—Moisture as an ecological factor differs from the two which we have just considered, in that light and heat were forms of energy which are made use of by animals, but moisture is a medium in which all organisms live. It may be so concentrated as to constitute an aquatic environment, or be so dilute as to be characterized as an arid desert; but it must, nevertheless, be present as an essential part of the environmental medium. All food which the organisms take into their bodies must contain at least a minimum amount of water present as such, or potentially present in the compounds which are to be broken down by the animal's metabolism.

Moisture may be present as a solid, liquid, or vapor. But organisms are concerned with it chiefly as liquid and vapor. The ever-recurring cycle from liquid to vapor and from vapor to liquid is of fundamental importance, whether considered in its largest sense as a balance between the water and water vapor of the entire earth; as precipitation and evaporation over given areas; as the great series of cycles within cycles which involve the metabolism of organisms and the maintenance of a balance between the intake and loss of water; or even down to the individual cells of the organisms. In all of these exchanges, an equilibrium

84

between the two phases of liquid and vapor must be maintained. For the environment, the ratio between precipitation and evaporation is important. For the individual organism, the ratio between moisture intake and moisture loss is of great importance. The problems involved in these cycles extend from those of purely physiological interest, involving the water films on colloidal particles within the cells, to the action of water as an agent in erosion as concerned with problems of geology and physiography. In this great range there is much of direct concern to the ecologist.

Methods of Measuring Moisture.—When attention is turned to the measurement of moisture as an ecological factor, it must first of all be realized that there are several phases of this factor which may be measured. We may distinguish first of all between the measurement of the state of moisture which may include the moisture content of the medium, whether it is air in which it is expressed as humidity, or whether it is a solid medium, such as soil; or a nutrient medium, in which it may be measured and expressed as per cent of weight or volume. The alternative is to measure the rate of change from one phase to another, in which case we may measure precipitation and evaporation. All of these measurements are important, and the ones which are to be taken depend very largely upon the type of problem in which the ecologist happens to be interested. For convenience we shall take up first the measurement of the state of moisture, and later the measurement of the change in phase of moisture.

The state of moisture in the air is usually expressed in relative humidity, in whatever way the reading may be made. The relative humidity is the amount of moisture present in a space as compared with the amount required to produce a condition of saturation at the same temperature and atmospheric pressure. It is expressed as per cent of saturation, and is an important expression because it represents the state of equilibrium of the atmosphere in the moisture cycle. The absolute humidity is the amount of moisture by weight in a given volume of space. In the English system this is expressed as the number of grains of moisture per cubic foot. Or it may also be expressed as grams per cubic meter. The expression of absolute moisture is very definite; but its determination is difficult, and it does not take into consideration conditions under which the moisture is present in the space. Consequently, relative humidity is much more significant than absolute humidity.

Marvin (1915) gives a good description of the method of determining the relative humidity of the air. Bongards (1926) gives a thorough discussion of the theory of gases and vapors as well as the methods and instruments involved in measuring and recording humidity. Carrier (1911) and Shelford (1929) may also be consulted.

The relative humidity of a space may be determined: (1) by ascertaining the dew point, (2) by the wet-bulb depression on a wet-and-dry bulb thermometer, (3) by some type of hygrometer which may involve chemical solutions or the hygroscopic coefficient of some material which is commonly hair. The psychrometer, which involves the principle of the wet-and-dry bulb thermometer, is the most common instrument used. The United States Weather Bureau uses a sling psychrometer, which consists of two standardized thermometers mounted side by side, one with the bulb projecting below that of the other. This bulb is covered by a wick, which may consist of silk or muslin. The wick is moistened with distilled water, and the psychrometer is then whirled through the air to give a uniform rate of air movement over the wet bulb. This is essential to produce evaporation at a given rate. The psychrometer is whirled through the air and read at intervals to determine the lowest point of the wet bulb. When this is past, the temperature of the wet bulb begins to rise, and the operator knows that he has obtained the lowest depression. The difference between the wet and the dry bulbs is then read and referred to a table which has been prepared by the Weather Bureau on the basis of a series of experiments under various conditions of humidity and pressure. Several types of tables and graphs are now available. They usually involve the readings of the dry bulbs and the depression of the wet bulbs, and from these the relative humidity may be taken.

Such a psychrometer is not convenient to use in a small space. Therefore, various types of cog psychrometers have been made. These consist essentially of mounting two thermometers in either an egg-beater or a cream-whip mechanism, so that they are whirled through a small circle by a mechanical means. Gray (1929) has described a convenient form of cog psychrometer (Fig. 32).

The dew-point determination is probably the most dependable for use in small spaces. Marvin (1915) and Shelford (1929) described mechanisms for making this determination. A small silver tube can be mounted in a test-tube clamp and filled with ether. A thermometer is then mounted in the ether, and air is aspirated through to lower the temperature by evaporation. It is necessary to observe very carefully and to lower the temperature on a very slow gradient in order to note the first appearance of moisture deposited on the surface of the silver tube. The temperature then must be read accurately. The relative humidity may be determined from tables which may be found in Marvin (1915), "International Critical Tables," Vol. I, and various other books of physical and chemical constants. It is necessary to read the dry-bulb temperature at the same time that the dew-point temperature is read.

Holtzmann (1924) devised a simple mechanism for determining the dew point in small spaces. It consists essentially of a silvered rod of metal of low heat conduction which is so maintained that one end can be warmed by a resistance coil, and the other end may be cooled by an evaporation mechanism. The instrument is mounted in such a way that it is possible to observe the metal rod, which has a line drawn around it near the middle; and in this line a thermocouple is mounted. The one end of the rod is cooled, and the point at the edge of the moisture which is being deposited moves slowly along toward the warmer end. Precisely as this mist reaches the line, the temperature is read by means

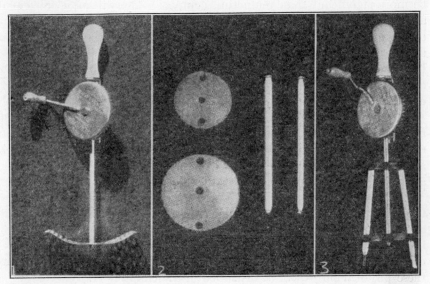

Fig. 32.—Cog psychrometer. The steps in making a readily available cream whipper into a psychrometer. 1. The cream whipper. 2. Thermometers and rubber disks ready to assemble. 3. Model completed and ready for operation. (*Gray*, 1929.)

of the thermocouple. The opposite end of the rod is then warmed and the area of mist is driven back toward the cool end. As this reaches the line the second time, the thermocouple is read again. The mean of the two readings gives a very accurate dew point. A mechanism of this type is useful in small breeding cages.

The hygrometer principle may also be made use of in small spaces. Commercial hygrometers usually consist of human hairs, the expansion and contraction of which is governed by their hygroscopic coefficient. By consulting the "International Critical Tables" Vol. I, one will receive many suggestions as to materials which might possibly be used in hygrometers. The expansion and contraction of many of these materials show an almost straight-line relationship as compared with the temperature and the relative humidity of the air. In the chemical hygrometers, sulphuric acid is the solution most commonly used. Shelford (1929) gives certain details of this method.

The moisture content of a medium other than air, such as food, soil, or wood, is usually stated in per cent of the total weight or per cent of dry weight, and is generally determined by evaporating a material to dryness. This may be done at a temperature of 105°C., and evaporation is usually continued until the curve of loss of weight flattens out.

The per cent of moisture present does not necessarily give a significant indication of the state of moisture in a solid or semi-solid medium. In the case of soil, a measure of the availability of moisture for plants may be more significant than the actual content. The wilting coefficient of a plant is a biotic measure of the available water. The wilting coefficient of a soil is the moisture content of the soil, expressed in percentage of dry weight at the time when the leaves of a plant growing in that soil first undergo a permanent reduction in moisture content as a result of a deficiency in the soil-moisture supply. This wilting coefficient is nearly constant for any species.

A physical measure of the available moisture is expressed as the moisture equivalent, which is the per cent of moisture that a soil can retain in opposition to a centrifugal force equal to 1,000 times that of gravity. This is a convenient measure, since it has been shown to bear a straight-line relationship to the wilting coefficient.

Another physical measure is the hygroscopic coefficient. This is the moisture content of a soil when in equilibrium with a saturated air at 20°C. These measures all reflect the fact that water may be present in a medium as free water, capillary water, adsorbed on the surface of colloids, or combined in the various compounds. The significance of these physical states will be discussed in the chapters on Synecology.

Wilson (1921) also describes a method for determining the moisture equilibrium of a material by exposing it to a known vapor tension over a solution of sulphuric acid.

Zeleny (1909) devised a method of measuring the content of a material by the resistance offered by the material to the passage of an electric current. Robinson (1926) has modified this method to make it applicable to the determination of the free water in an insect and in certain other materials. The method is a delicate one and requires a considerable amount of apparatus for accurately determining the resistance to an electric current of about one volt with 1,000,000 ohms resistance. The more accurate determination of the amount of moisture present in a medium, which may be solid or liquid, is based upon the freezing-point depression. The literature of Robinson (1926), Bouyoucos (1921), and others is referred to for the technique for this method of determining moisture content.

The change in state of the moisture is ordinarily measured in precipitation and evaporation. Precipitation is measured very simply by the use of cylinders, as described by Marvin (1903). These normally stand vertically, and either may be straight cylinders, or at some point below the top may be narrowed down in diameter by a funnel in order to increase the depth of water. The ratio of increase of depth to the narrowing of the cylinder being known, it is possible to make a more accurate measurement of a small amount of precipitation. These normally are measured for 24-hour periods.

The evaporation which represents the change of water from liquid to vapor is one of the most important measurements of the moisture cycle, for all organisms are exposed to a certain amount of evaporation. The rate of evaporation may be a measure of the temperature, vapor tension of the surrounding medium, the rate of air movement, and the barometric pressure. The following table from Shelford (1914) illustrates the influence of various factors on rate of evaporation.

TABLE VI.—A COMPARISON OF THE RATE OF FLOW AND EVAPORATING POWER OF THE AIR WHEN TEMPERATURE AND HUMIDITY ARE APPROXIMATELY CONSTANT[1]

Approximate velocity, meters per second	Approximate evaporation, c.c. per hour	T.°C.	R. H. per cent	Increase in flow	Increase in evaporation
0.012	0.25	22.4	50	1	1.0
0.026	0.40	22.2	53	2	1.6
0.052	0.75	22.2	53	4	3.0
0.104	1.50	22.2	53	8	6.0
0.208	2.00	22.2	54	16	8.0
0.416	2.60	22.2	53	32	10.4

[1] SHELFORD, 1914.

Evaporation may be read as the evaporation from a free surface of water of known area, or from a mechanism known as an evaporimeter. Evaporation from a free surface has a number of limitations, as accidents may happen to it in the field to affect the water level, and it is also difficult to measure accurately a water level and to maintain it in such a way that the rate of evaporation is not affected by the change in level. The most commonly accepted type of evaporimeter is the Livingston porous-cup atmometer (Livingston, 1908 and 1915). They are made as cones and as spheres. The spheres are the later type, which have uniform exposure to the sun's radiation; but unfortunately readings from spheres cannot be transformed into readings from cones. These atmometers are furnished standardized or unstandardized. The standardized ones are very desirable. They may be returned to the manufacturers and re-standardized at various periods. These are ordinarily mounted, so that it is possible to read the amount of water which has been evaporated directly from the jar containing the water.

Figure 33 shows the type which has been used in this laboratory at the University of Minnesota for reading evaporations over short periods of time. There is simply a double connection to the atmometer, one connection leading only to a U-tube, which is graduated in one-hundredths of a cubic centimeter. The other connection, which leads directly to the water reservoir, is provided with a cock, which makes it possible to shut off the source of water. To make a reading, the water is drawn up into the U-tube by suction, and the direct connection to the reservoir then closed off. The evaporation from the atmometer then proceeds directly from the calibrated U tube. When moved to a new atmosphere, such an atmometer must be permitted time to come into equilibrium. Thereafter accurate readings over a few minutes may be made with the aid of a stop watch.

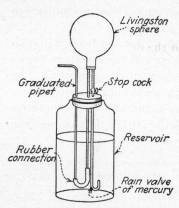

FIG. 33.—Graham's atmometer mounting for short-time readings of evaporation.

There are certain restrictions in the use of the Livingston atmometer. It can not be used below freezing temperature; and, if exposed to rain, some valve must be introduced to prevent water from backing up into the reservoir.

Various mechanisms are described in the literature for checking the effect of rain. Nearly all of them have a slight coefficient, in that all mercury valves permit a slight displacement of the mercury when the suction on the atmometer is relieved by the rain. Graham devised a very simple method which has a small correction coefficient. It consists of a small bulb blown in one side of the J-shaped tube, which provides the water to the atmometer from the reservoir. A small drop of mercury is introduced into the tube; and, when the atmometer is drawing water, this mercury is lodged in the small bulb. When there is a back pressure due to rain, the mercury runs out into the J-tube and prevents water from returning to the reservoir.

Reinhard has devised an ingenious mounting, the description of which has not been published. It is shown in Fig. 34. In this case, the atmometer is mounted on a level with the water reservoir. The suction of the atmometer and the pressure of the water reservoir may be balanced by raising or lowering the air-supply tube. This atmometer has been operated under a water tap without any back pressure into the water reservoir. It must necessarily have a very rigid construction in order to prevent leakage at the joints.

Bates (1919) devised an evaporimeter constructed on much the same principle as that of a plant leaf. This was done because he felt that air movement was too much of a factor in the rate of evaporation from a Livingston atmometer. Bates' evaporimeter consists of a horizontal disc mounted on a tube, through which a round wick leads up to a flat wick in the space between the upper and lower surfaces of the disc. The water is led up the round wick from the reservoir to the flat wick, from which it evaporates into the space in the disc. The aqueous vapor is diffused through holes in the lower surface of the disc much as it diffuses through the stomata of leaves. The upper surface of the disc is polished to reflect the sun's rays and thus prevent insolation from becoming too strong an influence. The Bates evaporimeter is said to be capable of withstanding freezing, which is not the case with other evaporimeters. However, it has one disadvantage. It is a difficult matter to standardize it, and to compare its readings with those of other instruments.

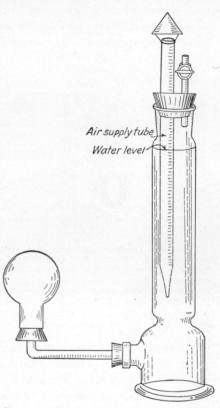

Air supply tube
Water level

Methods of Recording Moisture Conditions.—Methods of recording moisture conditions are, in general, methods of recording the measurements of the state of moisture or the change of phase of moisture.

The most usual method of recording the state of moisture is by use of a recording hygrometer. This usually consists of a human-hair hygrometer with a lever which writes a record on a revolving drum. These instruments are used in the U. S. Weather Bureau, and

Fig. 34.—Reinhard's rainproof atmometer mounting.

are supplied by Julian Friez. They are, in general, fairly satisfactory, but must be standardized against a sling psychrometer. It is important in making the standardization to make sure that the instruments are equally well standardized at the two extremes of relative humidity. There are also several forms of wet-and-dry bulb recording thermometers on the market. These are very satisfactory, but it is very necessary to see that the wick covering the wet bulb is always clean and properly moistened. The principle of the recording resistance thermometer may also be used in connection with recording humidity by supplying one of two resistance thermometer bulbs with a wick, and exposing them to the movement of air, as must be done in all psychrometric methods.

Recording the change of state of moisture may also be done by various devices. It is possible to connect a float with the rain gage and write the record on a recording drum by means of a pen and lever, which must of course be protected from the rain.

For recording evaporation, several ingenious devices have recently been described. Chalkley and Livingston (1929) have devised a method of recording the rate of evaporation through a float on mercury in a U tube, which represents the capillary pull of the atmometer against a restricted water supply. Figure 35 shows this instrument. It has the difficulty of being complicated and requiring a number of tight joints. In the field work of the University of Minnesota, it has been found practical to use the special mounting of atmometer already described in Fig. 33 by making readings with a stop watch over 15-minute periods at various times during the day. These seem to represent very well the rates of evaporation under different conditions of the day.

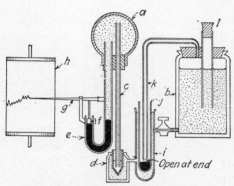

Fig. 35.—Diagram of the rate-recording atmometer: *a*, porous, porcelain sphere; *b*, main reservoir; *c*, water-supply tube; *d*, resistance member; *e*, mercury manometer; *f*, cork float; *g*, penlever; *h*, clock-driven drum for record sheet; *i*, auxiliary reservoir; *j*, float for water-level control, *k*, air supply tube to main reservoir; *l*, filling tube. (*Chalkley and Livingston*, 1929.)

Methods of Maintaining Constant Moisture Conditions.—The control of humidity for experimental purposes involves humidification and dehumidification. Various simple devices may be used for humidifying the air. It is possible to maintain a small experimental chamber relatively constant by having a constant water surface exposed to the air where the temperature conditions are relatively constant. Dehumidifying, however, is much more difficult, and it is very necessary in experimental work. Experience has shown that, in general, it is better to employ standard apparatus for this important type of experimental work.

There are, in general, two methods of maintaining constant humidity. One is by the use of the dew point of the air, in which case the point of saturation of the air is controlled, and the ratio between this dew point and the ultimate temperature of the air controls the relative humidity. The second method is the use of solutions of various vapor tensions which are calculated to maintain air in equilibrium with them at the proper relative humidity.

The principle which is used in the Carrier air-conditioning cabinet is very satisfactory in experimental work. The air is circulated continually through the cabinet, and at each circulation passes into a dew-point chamber and then to a heating chamber, on its way to the experimental chamber. Figure 36 shows the Carrier cabinets in operation in the

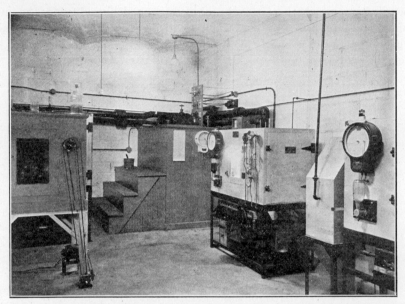

FIG. 36.—Carrier cabinets for the control of temperature and relative humidity in the temperature laboratory at the University of Minnesota.

temperature laboratory at the University of Minnesota. To the end of one of these cabinets is attached the dehumidifying chamber in which the air is cooled by coming in contact with water coils. The saturation of the air at the dew point is insured by an atomizer which blows a fine spray of water into the air when required. The humidity of the air is controlled through a silk-thread hygrostat. This hygrostat turns on the water in the atomizer when the relative humidity of the air is too low. Temperature is controlled by a metallic expansion thermostat. The dew point of the air will be limited by the ability of the machine to cool the air and to produce the spray at the temperature desired. It is possible to use a salt solution for the spray at dew points below freezing and to use refrigeration coils to produce low dew points.

Vapor tension humidifiers are satisfactory for certain experiments in small chambers. Sulphuric acid is also often used for this purpose. It is necessary to make sure that the air comes into equilibrium with the sulphuric acid. "International Critical Tables," Vol. I, may be consulted for data on the solutions which can be used; also Wilson (1921) (Fig. 37). The air may be drawn through the solutions or forced through by pressure and should pass through a glass air-trap chamber before passing into the chamber where the experimental animals are kept. It is difficult to check the action of these solutions and to keep the sulphuric acid standardized as to specific gravity, as it obviously will gain or lose water depending upon whether it is humidifying or dehumidifying the air. It has been found practical to mount a small wet-and-dry bulb thermometer in a tube and to connect this with the air stream at times, in order to check the relative humidity.

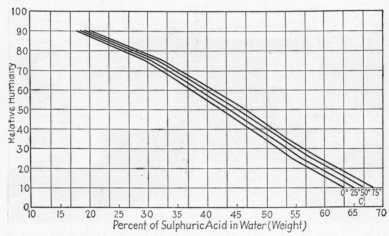

Fig. 37.—Graph showing the percentage by weight of chemically pure sulphuric acid in water required to produce various percentages of relative humidity when in equilibrium with air at different temperatures. (*Data from Wilson*, 1921.)

Headlee (1917) used supersaturated salt solutions in place of the sulphuric-acid solutions for obtaining certain constant-humidity conditions. The following table gives a list of convenient salt solutions which may be used in this way. It is necessary to use chemically pure salts and to make sure that the air comes into equilibrium with the saturated solution. This method has the advantage in that, if there is some precipitated salt in the bottom of the container and some water on top, it is supersaturated and, therefore, a standard solution is being maintained. It has been found that these solutions work better in humidifying than in dehumidifying. Consequently, it has been the practice to pass the air first through chemically pure sulphuric acid of a specific gravity of 1.84 and then through the salt solution desired. Difficulty is always experienced because of the fact that salt precipitates on the tubes where the air passes through the solution. These need to be cleaned almost daily. Difficulty has also always been experienced in obtaining the theoretical values for relative humidity. It is always necessary to check the relative humidity which is being obtained by the use of the wet-and-dry bulb thermometer in a tube. This wet-and-dry bulb thermometer must also be standardized against air of known relative humidity, which is being moved through the tube at the same rate as the air in the experimental chamber.

TABLE VII.—TABLE OF THEORETICAL VALUES OF RELATIVE HUMIDITY OBTAINED WHEN AIR IS IN EQUILIBRIUM WITH SUPER-SATURATED SOLUTIONS OF CERTAIN SALTS[1]

Salts	Percentage of relative humidity at 27°C.
Lithium chloride (LCl$_2$)	7.164
Calcium chloride (CaCl$_2$)	25.97
Sodium hydroxide (NaOH)	30.72
Aluminum chloride (AlCl$_3$)	37.01
Copper nitrate [Cu(NO$_3$)$_2$]	45.71
Sodium bromide (NaBr)	56.18
Sodium chloride (NaCl)	73.414
Sodium nitrate (NaNO$_3$)	80.035
Potassium sulphate (K$_2$SO$_4$)	89.78

[1] Headlee.

Shelford (1929) gives a good discussion of the maintenance of constant relative humidity conditions. In experiments where it is necessary to maintain the evaporating power of the air at a constant rate, this may be done by controlling the relative humidity, the temperature of the air, and the rate of flow. Evaporation may be measured by introducing an atmometer into the stream of air to read the rate of evaporation.

For maintaining the moisture content of soil at a constant, it is most practical to weigh the soil and add moisture at regular periods to make up for the loss of evaporation.

For all experimental work under controlled moisture conditions, it is necessary to study the problem to be investigated and decide on the basis of each problem what type of control will be best adapted to the problem at hand.

MOISTURE AS A FACTOR IN ANIMAL ECOLOGY

Animals participate in the general moisture cycle of nature, in that they are continually taking in a certain quantity of moisture and losing a certain quantity. They, therefore, may be affected by the moisture cycle of their own metabolism and by the general moisture cycle of the environment in which they live. The atmosphere involved in their respiratory exchanges, the medium involved in their nutrition, and the general cycle of precipitation and evaporation in their surrounding medium, all affect them. It is oftentimes difficult to analyze the situation and determine which of these various effects is the more direct and the more important.

Bachmetjew (1907) summarized the early literature on the effect of moisture on insects; and since that time there have been various papers, some of which are listed in the bibliography. We have, however, no comprehensive summary of our knowledge on this subject at the present time.

Effects of Moisture on Physical Processes.—As in the case of other physical factors, before proceeding to study the effects of moisture upon organisms, we shall now pause to examine the effects of moisture on physical processes. Since all organisms are essentially aqueous solutions, we shall study the effect of various concentrations of materials in aqueous solutions. If we change the density of a salt solution, we change the various properties of it. The Table VIII shows the effect of the change of density of various salt solutions upon the surface tension as expressed in dynes per square centimeter. Inasmuch as surface tension is a very important factor in the mechanism of tissues and cells, we can see that they may very well be affected by the moisture content in this physical way. If we were considering the rate of contraction of the cells or the rate of division of cells, it is easy to see that they would be greatly influenced by such changes in surface tension as are expressed in the table. Inasmuch as this is largely a physiological question, we shall not take more time to present further examples of the effect of moisture content upon the mechanism.

TABLE VIII.—THE RELATION OF THE DENSITY OF AQUEOUS SOLUTIONS TO SURFACE TENSION

Solution	Density	T.°C.	Surface tension dynes per cm.
NaCl in H_2O	1.107	20	80.5
NaCl in H_2O	1.193	20	85.8
CaCl in H_2O	1.277	19	90.2
CaCl in H_2O	1.351	19	95.0

Effects of Moisture on the Rates of Biological Processes—Growth, Metabolism, Etc.—The evidence of the effects of moisture upon the rates of metabolism in general is very incomplete. We have, however, data for certain particular organisms which show that they have an optimum moisture condition and that above and below this there may be a depression. This is in accordance with the information which we already have on other physical factors. In examining the lists of examples which we have from research, it is evident that it is not always possible to measure the effect of humidity upon the rate of metabolism alone.

Mortality may sometimes be a better measure of the effect of humidity than rate of metabolism. It is also found that different stages in the life cycle of a single species differ more in their humidity relationships than do the same stages of different species.

Dendy and Elkington (1920) found that the rice weevil, *Sitophilus oryza*, required about 10 per cent of moisture in wheat in order to develop. In this case the larvae are entirely surrounded by their medium, as they burrow into the center of the wheat berry, and are therefore affected very largely by the moisture content of their nutritive medium.

Newstead and Morris (1920) found that the mite, *Aleurobius farinae*, developed rapidly when 13 per cent of moisture was present in the flour, but that development was slow at 12.4 per cent of moisture, and that the mites died in about two weeks when the moisture was reduced to 12.2 per cent. This seems to indicate that certain forms at least are extremely sensitive to moisture content.

Elwyn (1917) found that 100 per cent of relative humidity was the optimum condition for the development of *Drosophila*, and that a lower humidity greatly increased the mortality. However, the rate of development was found to be the same for 100 per cent, for 60 to 66 per cent, and for 0 per cent so long as the food medium was maintained properly. Dewitz (1902) reported a similar condition for *Lucilia*.

Parker (1915) studied the development of the sugar-beet root louse, and found that they might be killed by the addition of excess moisture to the soil. Moisture in this case has an important effect upon the hatching of eggs and the molting of the skin in the immature stages and the general development of the insects. In an experiment, Parker introduced a lot of 200 sugar-beet root lice under each of three conditions: (1) in dry soil; (2) in soil which was subirrigated; and (3) in soil which was wet from above through a method simulating a rain. When these conditions were maintained for two months, he found that in the dry soil the population had increased to 11,581. In the experiments which were subirrigated, the population had increased to only 750; and in that which had been wet, through frequent showers from above, to only 405. Two series of experiments gave essentially the same results.

Headlee (1917) chose *Mylabris (Bruchus) obtectus*, the bean weevil, for his experiments. These larvae burrow into the bean and live entirely within the bean, using the moisture content of the bean and their own metabolic moisture to maintain themselves. The beans, in turn, tend to come into equilibrium with the surrounding air. For this reason, Headlee considered that this species was well adapted for experiments to determine the effect of relative humidity upon the rates of development. The accompanying graph is taken from Headlee's data, and it shows that in general the development of larvae is most rapid at high relative humidity (Fig. 38). In studying the pupal stage, however, it was found that the development was more rapid at low humidities, being 22 days at 100 per cent and 14 days at 44.6 per cent. The eggs also hatched in six days at 100 per cent, and in four days at 23 per cent. In the case of this insect, one can get an algebraic sum of all the various effects of the different stages, which gives a shortening of the total life cycle at higher relative humidity as compared with the lower relative humidity.

In the study of other insects, Headlee (1917) found that the pupal period of the moth, *Sitotroga cerealella*, was lengthened by high humidity, being 17 days at 100 per cent and only 12 days at 21.8 per cent.

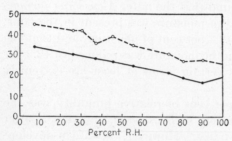

FIG. 38.—The development of the bean weevil (*Mylabris obtectus*) at constant temperature and various percentages of constant relative humidity. Broken line, one experiment; solid line, average of three experiments.

In earlier studies, Headlee (1913) found that *Toxoptera*, the green bug which feeds upon various small grains, developed at the same rate at 80°F. when the relative humidity was maintained at 37, 50, 70, 80, and 100 per cent. This seems to indicate that certain organisms which feed upon the sap of plants may be relatively independent of the direct effect of the humidity of the surrounding air. It is even possible that in some such organisms their problem is to dispose of excess water, rather than to be sure of maintaining a certain minimum of water.

Hennings (1907) obtained results from a study of *Typographichus*, a beetle which lives under the bark of trees, and found that the comparison of moist and dry conditions showed that the development was retarded by moist conditions. His experiments were run at temperatures of 14, 17, 20, and 24°; and he found that where the experiment under moist conditions was compared with that under

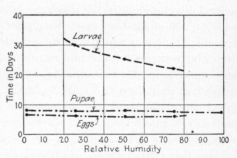

FIG. 39.—Duration of the stages of *Tribolium confusum* Duval at different relative humidities and 27°C. (*Holdaway's Thesis*, 1928.)

dry, development was retarded 13 days at 14°, 7 days at 17°, 7 days at 20°, and 6 days at 24°C. It is possible that in this case there may have been a complication due to the development of fungi giving some biotic resistance.

Holdaway (1928, unpublished thesis) studied the development of *Tribolium confusum* at various relative humidities under constant temperature conditions. He found that the egg and pupal stages were of almost exactly the same duration throughout the entire scale of relative humidity. The length of larval life, however, was shortened by increasing the humidity, as shown in Fig. 39. From the standpoint of per cent of mortality, however, he found that there was a greater survival of the larvae at high humidity, but a reduced survival of eggs and pupae, as is shown in Fig. 40. The larvae, therefore, have their per cent of survival increased and the length of time for development decreased by an increase of humidity; while the pupae and eggs do not have the time change but have the per cent greatly reduced by high humidity. It was true, however, that the greatest difficulty at high humidities was biotic resistance from fungi.

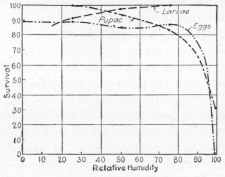

Fig. 40.—Viability of the stages at different relative humidities. Constant temperature of 27°C. (*Holdaway's Thesis,* 1928.)

Davies (1928) studied the effect of various constant-humidity conditions upon a series of species of *Collembola.* He measured the length

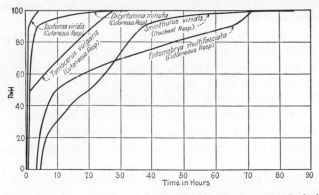

Fig. 41.—Fifty per cent mortality plotted against time and percentage of relative humidity. (*Data adapted from Davies,* 1928.)

of time which populations of *Collembola* could survive under starvation conditions, and took this time as a measure of the effect of humidity. It is quite possible, as he recognizes, that at some of the longer times the factor of starvation may have been important. The general results of his experiments are graphed in Fig. 41. This gives a series of species with various susceptibilities to low relative humidity. It is interesting to note that *Sminthurus viridis* has tracheal respiration, while the rest of them have cutaneous respiration. It is Davies' view that, in general, organisms with tracheal respiration are less susceptible to low humidity than those with cutaneous respiration. He believes that in the case of *Entomobrya multifasciata* there is some physiological adjustment in connection with the surface respiration. It is quite possible that the systems of evaporation from insects with and without trachea are quite different. Where trachea are not present, we have the simple matter of diffusion over the surface of the body. Where trachea are present, there is diffusion through the tracheal walls into the lumen of the tracheoles and then the process of diffusion from the openings of the spiracles.

Hazelhoff (unpublished) has said that he found no effects upon the opening and closing of the stomata of cockroaches due to different relative humidities, which seems to indicate that this organism was not reacting to humidity in so far as controlling diffusion by the opening and closing of the spiracles was concerned.

Heavy precipitation may act directly by mechanically removing certain insects from their host plants. This is common knowledge with regard to many plant lice, and it has been observed as an important factor in reducing the number of larvae of the larch sawfly, *Lygeonematus ericsonii*, by washing them to the ground where they are unable to regain a place on a host plant. Hail may also reduce the population of foliage-feeding insects as well as damage their host plant.

Carter (1927) suggested that the concentration of sap in plants in desert regions may have an important effect on the insects which feed upon them. As the soil moisture becomes reduced, the concentration of cell saps not only increases, but the sap is less abundant. Consequently, in the semi-arid regions, as the summer advances, organisms are forced to leave the plant, partly because of a reduced amount of sap and, partly, because of the concentration of the sap that is present.

Burger (1907) fed the meal worm, *Tenebrio molitor*, on dry bran, and found that the larvae lost weight but maintained their moisture content as almost constant until they died. After death the moisture was lost.

Babcock (1912) found that the larvae and adults of *Tribolium confusum* maintained a moisture content of around 50 or 60 per cent, while the moisture content of their food was in the neighborhood of 10 per cent. This seems to indicate that many of the insects are capable of maintaining the moisture content of their tissues as relatively constant.

Robinson (1928) graphed the relationship between the total water of food and the total water content of insects, as shown in Fig. 42. The heavy line drawn across the graph indicates a perfect correlation between the water content of the food and the water content of the insect. All of those forms which have a higher water content in the body than the food are adding to the water content of the food the water of metabolism. Some of the species which live upon food of very low moisture content must depend very largely upon the water which they get as a by-product of their metabolism.   It will be noticed that in most of the cases the water

content of the insect bears some relation to that of the environment. The upper, or broken, line presents a hypothetical condition in which the moisture content of the insect would be exactly the same as that of the environment.   None of the cases falls on this line, and only two or three occur in its vicinity.   This indicates factors other than those which come into effect in the total water content of the insect. The degree of the deviation of the broken line indicates the extent of the influence of these other factors.

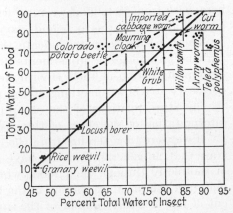

FIG. 42.—Relationship between water content of insects and their food. (*Robinson*, 1928.)

The water binding capacity of the different species is shown in Fig. 43, where a correlation has been made between the total water of the individual and the amount which is held in a bound condition on the

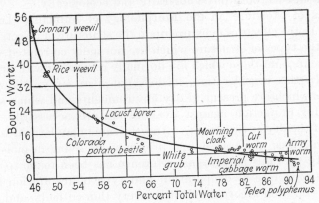

FIG. 43.—Relationship between water content and percentage of it which is bound by colloids. (*Robinson*, 1928.)

colloids.   Those species which live on comparatively dry food and have a small percentage of water in their own tissues hold a large per cent of it in the bound form, which is secure against the forces of desiccation. For instance, the granary weevil, which has only 46 per cent total water, has 50 per cent of this in the bound condition. The rice weevil, with slightly more total water, namely 48 per cent, has a smaller portion, or 35 per cent of it, as bound water. The locust borer, with 50 per cent total water, binds 20 per cent. At the other end of the chart are the species which live on food high in water and which consequently have a high content of water themselves. A reverse order of conditions exists here; with from 58 to 92 per cent of water in their tissues, they have only a small amount of this as bound, varying from 9 to as low as 3 per cent.

These results seem to indicate that various species of insects have various physiological adjustments to protect themselves against the desiccating action of their environment. It is quite evident that it is necessary to know something of the physiology of the insect as well as the moisture relations of the environment in order to make a correct interpretation of the effect of the environment upon the insect.

If we were to generalize from the evidence before us, it seems safe to state that, in general, if insects have a moisture supply secured directly or indirectly through their food, which makes it possible for them to maintain the moisture content of the body, they are relatively independent of the moisture content of the surrounding medium. However, the moisture content of their food is affected by the surrounding medium. Consequently, there is always an indirect effect of the surrounding medium upon the insect. There may be also a direct effect in the event that the evaporation rate may be so great that they are unable to maintain a moisture content from their food source. Ecological literature, however, seems to be in need of a general summary on the effects of moisture upon insects, both physiologically and ecologically.

Effects of Moisture on the Morphology of Animals.—Turning our attention to the effects of moisture upon the structure of insects, we might consider the types of structure which are normally correlated with moist environments, and those which are normally correlated with dry environments. In this consideration, it does not necessarily follow that the structures which are present in dry environments and which seem to be adapted for protection against evaporation are necessarily developed because of the dry environment. And the same may be said with regard to the structures which are found in organisms living in moist environments. In previous paragraphs, reference has been made to the correlation between rate of evaporation and type of respiration in insects. Surface respiration is correlated with a very thin cuticula, and the heavy chitinous covering is associated with tracheal respiration. In the case of an insect covered with heavy chitinous covering, evaporation must take place mainly between the tissues and the tracheoles; and diffusion, then, takes place through the spiracles from the tracheal system to the surrounding atmosphere. Insects which fly rapidly through the air and are therefore exposed to conditions which will produce a very high rate of evaporation have well-developed tracheal systems and also tracheal air sacs. It is an interesting suggestion that these tracheal air sacs may act in conserving the moisture of the insect. The per cent of reduction of moisture content of the air in the large sac because of diffusion through a small opening is much less than that through an opening into a small lumen.

Literature seems to furnish us with very few cases of unquestioned evidence of the effect of humidity upon the structure of animals. The following table is given by Bachmetjew taken from data from Quajat.

Race of silkworms	Number of cocoons per "1 ko"		
	Dry air	Moist air	Normal
Round Chinese white.............	771	705	754
Yellow Indian....................	442	409	403
White Japanese...................	653	593	623

In all cases the silkworm seems to have produced larger cocoons when the larvae were reared in moist air. This seems to be fairly representative of the effects of humidity upon insects, but there is little in the way of definite data to support the generalization.

Andrews (1916) showed that the color of the rhinoceros beetle, *Dynastes tityrus*, is influenced by the moisture content of the atmosphere. Under moist conditions the chitin appears dark; under dry conditions, it appears light.

The effects of moisture on color seem to lack proof. Knight (1924) at first considered that moisture was an important factor in conjunction with temperature, in producing the color changes which he observed in *Perillus*. Later, when it became possible to control conditions with greater accuracy, he concluded that moisture was of minor importance. Thus, it is possible that much of the work summarized by Bachmetjew (1907) and scattered through the literature since that date, may be in error with regard to the effect of moisture.

Effects of Moisture on the Behavior of Animals.—Animals in many habitats have the opportunity to select the conditions of moisture in the same way that they may select light or temperature under other conditions. Literature of economic entomology cites certain cases in which moisture has been used in connection with insect traps (Dendy and Elkington, 1920).

Shelford (1914a and 1914b) and certain of his students and Hamilton (1917) studied the reaction of insects to air of different evaporating powers. An experimental gradient cage was so arranged that three

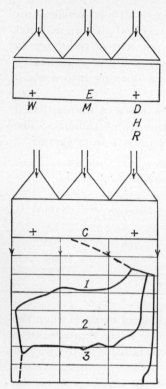

FIG. 44.—Showing the ground plan of the experimental cages in their relative positions. The hood which covered and separated them is not indicated. *E* is the experimental cage; *W*, the section used for wet air; *M*, for the air supplied directly from the pump; *D* (dry), *H* (warm), and *R* (rapid flow) indicate the section where the highest rate of evaporation was maintained. The crosses indicate the positions of the 1 candle-power lights; the arrows, the direction of the flow of air. The screen portions of the cage are represented by broken lines. *C* is the control cage similar to the experimental in every way except the kind of air supplied. Below this is shown the control record of an experiment during the first three minutes. The ruling of the paper used corresponds to half minutes and the figures are written in at the center. (*Shelford*, 1914.)

conditions of evaporating power of air could be moved across the cage (Fig. 44). The evaporating power of the air might be due to the rate of movement of the air, to the temperature of the air, or to the relative humidity of the air. The organisms were introduced in the center compartment of the cage and permitted to move back and forth. If they were sensitive to a difference in the evaporating rate of air, they would usually choose one side of the cage or the other. A record was kept on graduated paper in such a way that the path of the beetle back and forth across the cage could be shown by one dimension, and the time by the second dimension. The diagram (Fig. 45) represents results which

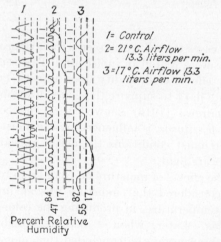

FIG. 45.—Reactions of *Evarthus sodalis* to moisture. (*Hamilton*, 1917.)

were obtained by Hamilton (1917) studying the reactions of larvae of one of the carabid beetles, *Evarthrus sodalis*. The three vertical columns in each experiment represent the air in the gradient, and the passage of time is indicated on the vertical scale. Certain individuals reacted more definitely than others. In general, it seemed that those insects which are normally exposed to gradients of evaporating power of air have the most precise reaction. Others are relatively indifferent to it.

Robinson (1926b) experimented with the reaction of certain grain weevils. These were introduced into a glass tube in which there was present wheat of various moisture contents. The experiments could be run for only a short period of time because of the fact that the wheat in the various parts of the tube tended to come into equilibrium with wheat in other parts. In this case it was not a simple reaction to moisture content, but a feeding reaction which was involved. Some of the wheat was too dry for the weevils to feed upon. The amount of frass which accumulated in the various sections of the tube was an index of the amount of feeding which was done in these places.

Certain wood-boring beetles seem to be very much influenced by the moisture content of the wood in which they are able to work. Soil insects undoubtedly react to soil moisture content in a rather definite way. The flight of many nocturnal moths seems to be influenced by relative humidity; as darkness comes on, at the end of the day, temperature falls and relative humidity rises. Our present discussion of the subject cannot be taken as final, but as an introduction to a subject which needs further investigation.

Effects of Moisture on the Geographic Range of Animals.—Temperature and moisture are so interrelated in controlling the geographic range of organisms that the two are often confused, and it is difficult to separate out either moisture or temperature as a definite controlling factor in the geographic distribution of animals. The subject is to be treated later in connection with climatology and with the geographic distribution of animals.

CHAPTER V

EFFECTS OF TEMPERATURE AND MOISTURE ACTING TOGETHER IN THE ECOLOGY OF ANIMALS

In measuring the effects of temperature and moisture upon animals, it has always been necessary to maintain all other factors as equal and constant when the effect of one was being measured. This is true of the analytical work of all ecology; and it is also true that in the conditions of the environment in general, when one factor changes, other factors are involved in the change also. It seems wise to stop at this time to consider what effect there may be from several factors varying together. We have just considered temperature and moisture, two of the most important and most fluctuating of the factors of environment, and it seems well at this time to consider the action of the two together as an illustration of the action of two environmental factors.

In this consideration let us make the distinction between the effect upon the organism of the two factors varying together and the effect upon the environment when two factors vary together. For convenience we shall consider first the effect upon the organism. It is true not only that temperature and moisture are associated in their natural fluctuations in nature, but that the effect of one is modified by the changes in the other. The information which we have with regard to the combined action of these two factors has come to us as a result of the two general methods which we possess for obtaining information with regard to natural phenomena. One is by the use of controlled laboratory experiments in which all conditions are made constant except those which are to be changed for the purpose of observing what effects may be produced by the changes. This method has certain obvious limitations of space and time in the conditions of the experiment and of the perception of the human senses in observing the effects. The other method is to take the facts from the conditions which exist in nature, and experiment with them by the use of refined biometrical methods which are capable of detecting certain effects which are not noticeable by general observation. This method has limitations due to the lack of available facts, and both methods are subject to faults of reasoning.

When we express the effects of two factors, we can do it most conveniently on a two-dimension surface, as will be shown presently. If we were to use more than two factors, we would require a three-dimension surface. We might even visualize a theoretical sphere, each diameter of which represents the dimension of some factor of the environment. The optimum condition of the organism would then be at the center of the sphere. We could make this figure a sphere by arbitrarily adjusting the length of each diameter so that the limits of toleration of the organism would always fall at the surface of the sphere. The outer surface of this sphere, then, would represent the limits of toleration of the organism with regard to all the factors of its environment; and the center of the sphere would represent the optimum condition with respect to all the factors of the environment.

Liebig recognized the fact that, when a multiplicity of factors was present and only one was near the limits of toleration, this one factor would be the controlling one. This generalization has been called "Liebig's law" and is useful in the analysis of complicated factoral influences.

Effects of Temperature and Moisture on Physical Processes.—Before proceeding with the effects of two factors upon a complicated organism, it will be well to look again to simple physical systems to determine what effects may be produced by changes of both moisture and temperature together. This is obviously a repetition of facts which are of common knowledge. Any constant on a physical scale is a constant only when all factors are involved as stated. The boiling and freezing points of all solutions may be changed by changing the concentration of the solvent in the solute. The freezing and boiling points of water are depressed when a material is put into the solution. One gram-molecular weight of dissolved substance in 100 c.c. water depresses the freezing point 18.7°C. The freezing point of ethyl dibromide is depressed 118° in this way, nitrobenzene 70°, and benzene 49°. In a similar way the boiling points of solutions may be elevated, and the elevation bears a constant ratio to the gram-molecular weight of dissolved substance. The boiling point of water is elevated 5.4°C. for one gram molecule of dissolved substance in 100 c.c. Since the water content of an aqueous solution varies the boiling and freezing points so much, it may be expected that the water content of a complicated organism will greatly affect the behavior of the organism in respect to temperature.

Effects of the Combined Factors of Heat and Moisture on Animals.— The facts with respect to the effects of temperature and moisture on physical systems, which we have just recited, will give a background for the understanding of physiology of cells, which are after all aqueous solutions. We now must turn our attention to an organism in which these cells are combined into tissues, and the tissues into the entire organs which constitute the organism. And the organism is presided over by certain governing processes and in general by physiology. Some of these governing processes have to do with the regulation of the temperature of the entire organism. Much attention has been turned to this, but it will be well to consider some of the generalizations of Hill (1908, pages 268–270).

For organisms in general, a moist cold atmosphere causes the organism to cool rapidly because of the rapid conduction of heat from its body in the moist atmosphere. Poikilothermic organisms have their metabolism decreased rapidly under these conditions, while homoiothermic animals are stimulated to increased metabolism in order to maintain their body temperatures.

In a cold but dry atmosphere, the heat loss will be less rapid because of less rapid conduction; and consequently, poikilothermic animals will have their temperatures reduced less rapidly, and homoiothermic animals will receive a less marked stimulus to increase their metabolism.

In a dry, warm atmosphere, evaporation on the surface of the body will be rapid. Consequently, there will be a cooling effect due to the heat of evaporation which will be lost by the animal. This makes the regulation of body temperature possible under high temperature in both poikilothermic and homoiothermic animals, for they are both alike in their lack of ability to reduce their temperatures in any other way than by evaporation from the surface, except as they may slow their general metabolism.

A moist, warm atmosphere does not permit evaporation on the surface of the body; and with rapid conduction there is no method for lowering the temperature of the body, and the animal very shortly comes into equilibrium, with the temperature of its body similar to that of the surrounding air.

There is no implication that this interpretation of the interdependence of temperature and humidity is especially new. It has been known for a long time, and in many cases recognized, that the effect of humidity is so slight that the temperature scale might be used alone, almost ignoring humidity. Inasmuch as we are especially interested in the effects of temperature and moisture upon insects, we will turn our attention to the graph of Pierce (1916), in which the effects of temperature and humidity are shown on a two-dimension surface.

The data used by Pierce were those from field notes, and the zones that he has drawn are hypothetical to a certain extent. But he illustrates the possibilities of this method of treatment from data. In Fig. 46 the dotted lines across the chart represent the cross-sections through the optimum temperature and the optimum humidity respectively. It may be seen that the weevils will be dormant at the optimum temperature, provided the humidity is extreme, or may be dormant at the optimum humidity, providing the temperature is extreme. The various combinations of temperature and humidity which produce equal effects upon the boll weevil are shown. There is a small zone about the optimum-temperature humidity in which development is most rapid. In any direction from this zone, development is slowed; and we get the next zone of equal development. These concentric zones of equal development may be thought of as contours, indicating the level of development. If this conception were represented by a pyramid instead of a flat surface, the height of the pyramid would represent the rate of development,

the fastest rate coming where the complete development takes place in the shortest period of time, at the intersection of the optimum temperature and the optimum humidity.

A somewhat similar figure was made by Huntington (1915) to represent the death rate of populations under different conditions of temperature and humidity on the days of the deaths.

It is interesting to note that the general nature of the figure obtained by Huntington was quite suggestive of that obtained by Pierce. However, the use of Huntington's data is open to a certain objection, as has been pointed out by the medical profession, because of the fact that it is not known definitely that temperature and humidity were a factor in producing death.

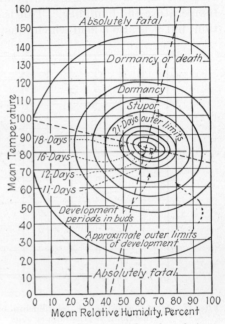

Fig. 46.—Graph showing the relations of humidity and temperature to cotton boll-weevil activity. (*Adapted from Pierce, 1916.*)

Another two-dimension surface to represent the effects of temperature and moisture has been plotted from the data of Parker (1930). In this case, however, the time for hatching was almost uninfluenced by relative humidity, and the surface presented is graphed for the per cent of hatching of the eggs. These eggs were maintained at different temperatures and humidities, as shown upon the graph in Fig. 47. The dots, and the figures by them, represent the per cent of hatch at the different conditions. The zones which are outlined in dotted lines have been interpolated. It will be seen that we have here an optimum relative humidity of about 90 per cent, and an optimum temperature of 27°. The per cent of hatching at 27° varies from 6 to 72, depending upon the relative humidity; and likewise the per cent of hatching at 90 per cent of relative humidity varies from 48 to 72, depending upon the temperature.

We can well be cautious in drawing broad generalizations from the examples which have been presented. The general nature of the effect of the two factors acting together seems to be well established for either one of the factors as a two-dimension surface rather than as a straight line.

Shelford (1926 and 1929) had attempted to evaluate the factors of temperature and humidity in phenological units. He has plotted the cross-sections of such figures which represent the lines of equal effect of temperature and humidity. This is a promising field of future investigation; but it is also a field which must be gone into with caution, if we are

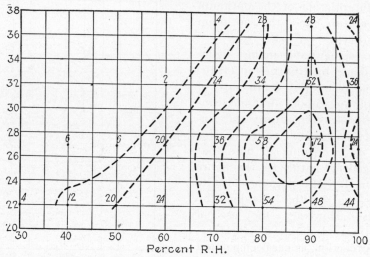

Fig. 47.—Graph showing the relationship between temperature and humidity and the hatching of grasshopper eggs. (*Adapted from Parker*, 1930.)

to draw generalizations which may be applied to species. The figures represented by the data of Parker and Pierce are alike, in that they show optimum zones and marginal zones in which, in the one case, mortality is extremely high, amounting to 100 per cent; and, in the other case, development is stopped, ending in dormancy, and beyond this going to death. But the optimum in one figure represents a high per cent of hatch, and the optimum in the other figure represents the highest rate of development. If we were to evaluate these in terms of a common denominator, that common denominator would have to be the change of population. This would also be true of many examples of insects which have been cited under the heading of the effects of heat and moisture; for their life cycle may be the same length under a whole series of humidities, provided temperature is constant.

However, death rates, and thereby population, may be affected by humidity. These concentric zones of temperature and humidity have been determined for relatively few organisms at the present time. Doubtless, future research will show that additional factors may be added to extend these zones in another dimension. But it seems rather evident from the literature which we have available at the present time that our understanding of them is not sufficiently clear to warrant generalizations which may be applied to all.

The effect of moisture and temperature acting together on human comfort has been investigated by the American Society of Heating and Ventilating Engineers in rather an elaborate series of experiments.

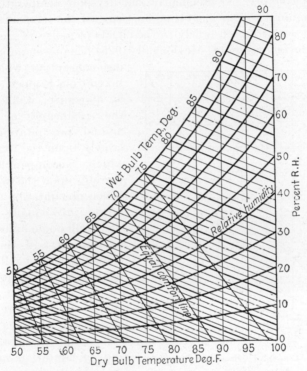

Fig. 48.—Chart of equal comfort or effective temperature. (All reference to temperature in degrees Fahrenheit.) (*Houghten and Yagloglou*, 1923.)

They have recorded the effects on internal and external body temperatures, pulse rate, blood pressure, rate of respiration, loss of weight, and various other measurable conditions under variations of temperature and humidity. A large number of subjects were permitted to enter chambers with different temperature and humidity conditions, and to record their sensations of comfort as agreeable, cool, warm, etc. When all of the data were assembled, they were found to be consistent in denoting that there are certain conditions of equal comfort. A chart was constructed (Houghton and Yagloglou, 1923) from which it is possible to determine the combinations of temperature and humidity which will give equal comfort. The two authors have referred to these conditions as a scale of "effective temperature." This term is quite different from that which has been used previously, and is intended to denote a scale of equal effects rather than the usual thermometer scale. From the chart of equal comfort (Fig. 48), it is shown that an equal condition of comfort may be found at 68°F. and 80 per cent of relative humidity, or 79° and 10 per cent of relative humidity. Within these limits, the subjects considered that the temperature was at the optimum of comfort. Consequently, our dry-bulb temperature scale is shown to be unreliable as measuring our sense of the temperature.

Turning our attention briefly to the effects of moisture and temperature upon the environment, McDougall (1925) has presented an interesting conception which he has taken from Köppen (1920). It is, of course, well known that the significance of a certain annual precipitation depends largely upon the temperatures which accompany it, and thereby upon the evaporation. When precipitation and evaporation are equally balanced, there will be no excess of water to run off. In the diagram (Fig. 49) McDougall has taken Köppen's conception of this critical point where evaporation and precipitation are equal, and has drawn the line B, which represents the evaporation rates and precipitation rates which are equally balanced. Environments in which the conditions lie above this line are classified as humid; and those which lie below it, as arid. All environments with less than half of the critical amount of precipitation are classified as arid; the others, as semi-arid. The consideration of environments will be referred to later under the subject matter of Synecology.

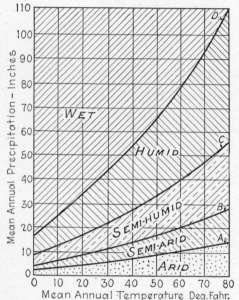

Fig. 49.—Chart of moisture, based on precipitation as influenced by temperature. (*McDougall*, 1925.)

The ability of organisms to endure the extreme conditions of their environment is affected by both temperature and moisture, as may easily be seen by consulting the diagrams based upon the data of Parker and of Pierce. This is now generally recognized, as literature contains many examples substantiating this generalization.

Bachmetjew (1907) quoted data from various authors to show that albumen with 25 per cent water coagulated at 47 to 80°C.; with 18 per cent water, at 80 to 90°C.; with 6 per cent water, at 145°C.; and water-free albumen, at from 160 to 170°C. This indicates again that the mechanism of an organism is profoundly influenced by its water content, and that the temperature scale of an animal is affected by this.

With respect to the ability of organisms to endure extremely low temperatures, we have some critical information which has recently been accumulated. Payne (1926) showed that if the larvae of *Synchroa*, which normally burrow under the bark of trees and are exposed to low

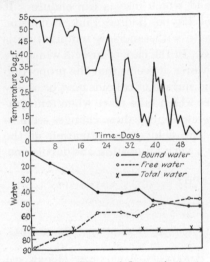

FIG. 50.—Effect of fluctuating outdoor temperatures upon percentage of bound and free water for the hardy *Telea polyphemus*. (*Robinson*, 1927.)

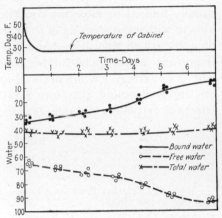

FIG. 51.—Showing reverse effect of a moderately low temperature upon the bound and free-water content of the nonhardy *Sitophilus granarius*. (*Robinson*, 1927.)

temperatures in the winter, are dehydrated under laboratory conditions, their freezing points will be lowered.

Robinson (1927) compared the effect of moisture conditions at low temperature upon insects which were hardy at low temperatures with those which were not. He found, in general, that there was a change not only in the moisture content, but in the state of the water present in the insect. In *Telea polyphemus*, a hardy moth which hibernates in the pupal stage, the moisture content changes very little during the fall, as is shown in Fig. 50; but the per cent of water in the free state, and of that bound upon the surface of the colloids undergoes a marked change when the outdoor temperature drops. The pupae of this insect are capable of withstanding freezing for months. Figure 51 shows the moisture condition of *Sitophilus granarius*, a weevil supposedly from the tropics, when temperature is being lowered. In this case there is a slight drop in total water, a decided drop in bound water, and an increase in free water; and the insects are unable to endure low temperatures. It seems, therefore, that the effects of extreme temperatures cannot be studied without being associated with moisture conditions, and that possibly death under extremes of the temperature is largely influenced by the moisture content and the state of the moisture in insects.

Payne 1929 has emphasized the importance of absolute humidity as expressed in millimeters of vapor pressure as an important factor in determining the intensity factor of cold which insects can endure. It seems quite definite from the work of Payne, Bodine, Fink, Robinson, and others that the ability of insects to withstand low temperature is usually limited by moisture conditions. In the case of insects which are able to withstand freezing of their free water, it seems that the proportion of water which they have bound on the surface of colloids may be a very important factor. The further changes which take place when temperature is extremely low are not well understood; but these changes seem to be irreversible and therefore fatal. The field of investigation of the effects of extremely low temperature is a very interesting and fertile one.

BIBLIOGRAPHY

MOISTURE

ABBE, C.: Relation Between Climate and Crops, *U. S. Dept. Agr. Weather Bur. Bull.* 36, p. 386, 1905.

ADAMS, C. C., GEORGE P. BURNS, T. L. HANKINSON, BARRINGTON MOORE, and NORMAN TAYLOR: Plants and Animals of Mount Marcy, New York, *Ecology*, pt. I: pp. 71–95; pt. II: pp. 204–234; pt. III: pp. 274–289, 1920.

ALLEE, W. C.: Measurement of Environmental Factors in the Tropical Rain-forest of Panama, *Ecology*, **7**: 273–302, 1926a.

———: Distribution of Animals in a Tropical Rain-forest with Relation to Environmental Factors, *Ecology*, **7**: 445–468, 1926b.

ANDREWS, E. A.: Color Changes in the Rhinoceros Beetle *Dynastes tityrus*, *Jour. Exptl. Zool.*, **20**: 435–456, 1916.

ARRHENIUS, O.: Vattnet some vegetations-faktor. I. Forberedande försök. *Kungl. Landtbr. Akad. Handl. och Tidskr.* **65**: 37–51, 1926.

BABCOCK, S. M.: Metabolic Water, Its Production and Rôle in Vital Phenomena, *Wis. Univ. Agr. Expt. Sta. Res. Bull.* 22, pp. 87–181, 1912.

BACHMETJEW, P.: Experimentelle entomologische Studien vom physikalisch-chemischen Standpunkt aus; vol. II. Einfluss der äusseren Factoren auf Insekten, 1907. 914 pp.

BACK, E. A., and C. E. PEMBERTON: The Mediterranean Fruit-fly in Hawaii, *U. S. Dept. Agr. Ent. Bull.* 536, 1918. 118 pp.

BAETIE, MARY V. F.: Observations on the Thermal Death Points of the Blow-fly at Different Relative Humidities, *Bull. Ent. Research*, **18**: 397–403, 1928.

BAILEY, VERNON: Sources of Water Supply for Desert Animals, *Sci. Monthly*, **17**: 66–86, 1923.

BALL, JOHN: Climatological Diagrams, *Cairo Sci. Jour.*, vol. 4, no. 50, 1910.

BARKER, C. W.: Notes on Seasonal Dimorphism of *Rhopalocera* in Natal, *Trans. Ent. Soc.*, London, pp. 413–428, 1895.

BATAILLON, E.: La métamorphose du ver à soie et le déterminisme évolutif, *Bull. sci. France et Belg.*, **XXV**: 18–55, 1893.

BATES, C. G.: A New Evaporimeter for Use in Forest Studies, *U. S. Monthly Weather Rev.*, **47**: 283–294, 1919.

BATES, CARLOS G. and RAPHAEL ZON: Research Methods in the Study of Forest Environment, *U. S. Dept. Agr. Bull.* 1059; 1922.   208 pp.

BAYLISS, W. M.: "Principles of General Physiology," chap. VIII, pp. 226–246, Longmans, Green and Co., New York, 1920.

BLACKMAN, F. F.: Optima and Limiting Factors, *Ann. Bot.*, **19**: 281–295, 1905.

BODINE, JOSEPH HALL: Physiological Changes during Hibernation in Certain *Orthoptera*, *Jour. Exptl. Zool.*, **37**: 457–476, 1923.

BONGARDS, HERMANN: "Feuchtigkeitsmessung," chap. VII, p. 322, R. Oldenbourg, München and Berlin, 1926.

BOUYOUCOS, GEORGE: A New Classification of the Soil Moisture, *Soil Sci.*, **II**: 33–47, 1921.

BRIGGS, L. J. and H. L. SHANTZ: The Wilting Coefficient for Different Plants and Its Indirect Determination, *U. S. Dept. Agr., Bur. Plant Indus. Bull.* 230, 1912.

BURGER, BRUNO: Über die Widerstandsfähigkeit der Tenebriolarven gegen Austrocknung, *Pflüger's Arch. Physiol.* **118**: 607–612 1907.

BURKHOLDER, WALTER H.: The Effect of Two Soil Temperatures on the Yield and Water Relation of Healthy and Diseased Bean Plants, *Ecology*, **I**: 113–124, 1920.

BUXTON, P. A.: "Animal Life in Deserts: A Study of the Fauna in Relation to the Environment," Edward Arnold and Co., London, 1923.   176 pp.

CALDWELL, J. S.: The Relation of Environmental Conditions to the Phenomenon of Permanent Wilting in Plants, *Physiol. Researches*, **I**: 1–56, 1913.

CAMERON, A. C.: The Relation of Soil Insects to Climatic Conditions, *Agr. Gaz. Canada*, **4**: 663–669, 1917.

CARRIER, W. H.: Rational Psychrometric Formulae. Their Relation to Problems of Meteorology and of Air Conditioning, *Jour. Amer. Soc. Mech. Engin,*. **33**: 1309–1350, 1911.

CARTER, WALTER: The Effect of Low Temperatures on *Bruchus obtectus* Say, an Insect Affecting Seed, *Jour. Agr. Research*, **31**: 165–182, 1925.

———: Population of *Euteltix tenella* Baker and the Osmotic Concentrations of Its Host Plants, *Ecology*, **8**: 350–352, 1927.

CHALKLEY, H. W., and B. E. LIVINGSTON: Atmometric Rates Read Instantaneously and an Automatic Continuous Recorder for Rate Fluctuation, *Ecology*, **10**: 37–46, 1929.

CLEMENTS, F. E.: "Research Methods in Ecology," pp. 17 and 334, Neb. State Univ. Publ. Co., Lincoln, 1905.

———: Drouth Periods and Climatic Cycles, *Ecology*, **2**: 181–187, 1921.

COLE, F. J. (1906): The Bionomics of Grain Weevils, *Jour. Econ. Biol.*, **1**: 63–71, 1905–1906.

COOK, WILLIAM C.: Studies on the Flight of Nocturnal Lepidoptera, Minn. State Ent., 18*th Rept.*, pp. 43–56, 1920.

———: The Distribution of the Pale Western Cutworm, *Porosagrotis orthogonia* Morr: a Study in Physical Ecology, *Ecology*, **5**: 60–70, 1924.

———: Some Weather Relations of the Pale Western Cutworm (*Porosagrotis orthogonia* Morr.); Preliminary Study, *Ecology*, **7**: 37–48, 1926.

DAVENPORT, C. B.: "Experimental Morphology," chap. II, pp. 58–70, The Macmillan Company, New York, 1908.

DAVIES, MALDWIN W.: The Effect of Variation in Relative ˙Humidity on Certain Species of *Collembola*, *Brit. Jour. Exptl. Biol.*, **6**: 79–86, 1928.

DEFOREST, H.: Rainfall Interception by Plants: An Experimental Note, *Ecology*, **4**: 417–420, 1923.

DENDY, A., and H. D. ELKINGTON: Report on the Vitality and Rate of Multiplication of Certain Grain Insects under Various Conditions of Temperature and Moisture, *Roy. Soc. (London), Grain Pests' (War) Comm. Rept.*, 7, 1920.

DEWITZ, J.: La suppression de la métamorphose chez des larves d'insectes, *Compt. rend. soc. biol.*, **54**: 747–748, 1902.

DICE, LEE R.: Some Factors Affecting the Distribution of the Prairie Vole, Forest Deer Mouse and Prairie Deer Mouse, *Ecology*, **3**: 29–48, 1922.

DIECK, GEORG: Beiträge zurs ubterranen Käferfauna Südeuropas und Maroccos, *Berl. Ent. Ztg.*, **13**: 337–360, 1869.

DORMO, C.: Papers on the Relation of the Atmosphere to Human Comfort, *U. S. Monthly Weather Rev.*, **54**: 39–43, 1926.

DOUGLASS, A. E.: Climatic Cycles and Tree Growth, *Carnegie Inst. Wash. Pub.* 289, 1919. 127 pp.

———: Evidence of Climatic Effects in the Annual Rings of Trees, *Ecology*, **I**: 24–33, 1920.

ELWYN, A.: Effect of Humidity on Pupal Duration and on Pupal Mortality of *Drosophila ampilophila* Loew, *Amer. Mus. Nat. Hist. Bull.* 37, pp. 347–353, 1917.

EMDEN, FRITZ VON: Über die Rolļe der Feuchtigkeit im Leben der Speicherschädlinge, *Anz. f. Schädlingskunde*, **5**: 58–60, 1929.

ENOCK, FREDERICK: The Life-history of the Hessian Fly, *Cecidomyia destructor* Say, *Trans. Ent. Soc.*, London, pp. 329–367, 1891.

FIELDE, ADELE M.: Observations on Ants in Their Relation to Temperature and to Submergence, *Biol. Bull.* **VII**: 170–174, 1904.

FINK, D. E.: Physiological Studies on Hibernation in the potato beetle, *Leptinotarsa decemlineata*, *Biol. Bull.*, **49**: 381–404, 1925.

FOLSOM, JUSTUS WATSON: "Entomology with Special Reference to Its Ecological Aspects," 3d rev. ed., pp. 364–373, P. Blakiston's Son & Co., Inc., Philadelphia, 1922.

FULLER, GEORGE D.: Evaporation and the Stratification of Vegetation, *Bot. Gaz.*, **54**: 424–426, 1912.

GAUCKLER, H.: Der Einfluss des Wassers auf das Leben der Raupen, *Illus. Wchnschr. Ent.* **II**: 295–296, 1897.

GIARD, A.: La méthode expérimentale dans l'entomologie, *Bull. soc. ent. France*, **4**: 57–63, 1896.

———: Sur l'éthologie des larves de *Sciara medullaris* Gd., *Compt. rend. acad. sci.*, Paris, vol. CXXXIV, pp. 1179–1185, 1902.

GILTAY, E.: Anatomische Eigenthümlichkeiten in Beziehung auf klimatische Umstände, *Nederl. Kruidk. Arch.*, **II**: 413, 1886.

GLENN, P. A.: Influence of Climate on Green Bugs and Parasites, *Kans. Univ. Bull.*, vol. 9, no. 2, 1909.

GORTNER, R. A. and W. F. HOFFMAN: Determination of Moisture Content of Expressed Plant Tissue Fluids, *Bot. Gaz.*, **74**: 308–313, 1922.

GRAY, H. E.: Construction of a Psychrometer for Small Spaces, *Ecology*, **10**: 355–358, 1929.

GREELEY, A. W.: On the Analogy between the Effects of Loss of Water and Lowering of Temperature, *Amer. Jour. Physiol.*, **6**: 122–128, 1901.

HABICH, OTTO: *Coenonympha pamphilus* L. ab. *Eburnea mihi*, *Jahresber. Ent. Ver.*, 1896. **VIII**: 29, Vienna. (Separatum.)

HALBFASS, W.: Die Bedeutung der Pflanze in Wasserhaushalt der Erde, *Internat. Rev. Gesamm. Hydrobiol. u. Hydrog.*, **15**: 264–267, 1926.

HAMILTON, CLYDE C.: The Behavior of Some Soil Insects in Gradients of Evaporating Power of Air, Carbon Dioxide, and Ammonia, *Biol. Bull.*, **32**: 159–182, 1917.

HANS, J.: "Handbook of Climatology," transl. by Ward, 1903.

HEADLEE, THOMAS J.: The Chinch Bug, *Kans. Agr. Col. Bull.*, p. 191, 1913.

———: Some Facts Relative to the Influence of Atmospheric Humidity on Insect Metabolism, *Jour. Econ. Ent.*, **10**: 31–38, 1917.

HEDERSTRAND, GUNNAR: The Influence of Thin Surface Films on the Evaporation of Water, *Jour. Physiol. Chem.*, **28**: 1245–1252, 1924.

HEIMBURGER, J. W.: Reactions of Earthworms to Temperature and Atmospheric Humidity, *Ecology*, **5**: 276–283, 1924.

HELLMAN, GUSTAV: Classification of the Hydrometers. With Notes and Comments by Prof. Charles F. Marvin, *U. S. Monthly Weather Rev.*, **44**: 385–392, 1916.

HENDERSON, L. J.: "The Fitness of the Environment," pp. 72–132 give general properties of water, 1913.

HENNINGS, C.: Beiträge zur Kenntniss der die Insektentwicklung beeinflussenden Faktoren, *Biol. Centralbl.*, **27**: 324–336, 1907.

HENRY, ALFRED JUDSON: Climatology of the United States, *U. S. Weather Bur. Bull.*, Q, 1906.

HERMAN, R. S. and W. HALL: Variation in Moisture Content of Flour During Storage, *Jour. Amer. Assoc. Cereal Chem.*, vol. 6, no. 3, p. 10, 1921.

HILL, LEONARD, ERSKINE: "Recent Advances in Physiology and Biochemistry," Longmans, Green and Co., London, 1908. xii and 740 pp.

HOLDAWAY, F. G.: An Experimental Study of the Growth of Insect Populations as Affected by Moisture, Together with a Study of Factors Which May Influence Sex Ratio in *Tribolium confusum*, Univ. of Minn., Ph.D. thesis, 1928.

HOLTZMANN, MACK: Determination of the Dew Point, *Physik. Ztschr.*, **25**: 443–445, 1924.

HOOKER, H. D.: Liebig's Law of the Minimum in Relation to General Biological Problems, *Science*, n.s. **46**: 197–204, 1917.

HOPKINS, ANDREW D.: The Bioclimatic Law, *Jour. Wash. Acad. Sci.*, **10**: 34–40, 1920.

———: Bioclimatic Zones Determined by Meteorological Data, *U. S. Monthly Weather Rev.*, **49**: 299–300, 1921.

———: Bioclimatic Zones of the Continents; with Proposed Designations and Classification, *Jour. Wash. Acad. Sci.*, **11**: 227–229, 1921.

HOUGHTEN, F. C., and C. P. YAGLOGLOU: Determining Equal Comfort Lines, *Jour. Amer. Soc. Heat. and Ventil. Engin.*, vol. 29, no. 2, pp. 165–193, 1923.

HUNTINGTON, ELLSWORTH: The Climatic Factor as Illustrated in Arid America, *Carnegie Inst. Wash. Pub.*, 1914. 341 pp.

———: "Civilization and Climate," Yale University Press, 1915. 333 pp.; 2d ed., 1922; 3d ed., 1924, 453 pp.

JEANNEL, R.: "Faune cavernicole de la France avec une étude des conditions d'existence dans le domaine souterrain," P. Lechevalier, Paris, 1927. 334 pp.

JOHNSON, JAMES: Constant Temperature and Humidity Chambers, *Phytopathology*, **18**: 227–238, 1928.

KAPF, E. W., K. ALLEN and J. S. FULTON: Progress in Public Health Climatology, *Amer. Jour. Pub. Health*, **15**: 195–198, 1925.

KINCER, J. B.: The Relation of Climate to the Geographic Distribution of Crops in the United States, *Ecology*, III: 127–134, 1922.

(*T*) KNIGHT, H. H.: On the Nature of the Color Patterns in *Heteroptera* with Data on the Effects Produced by Temperature and Humidity, *Ann. Ent. Soc. Amer.*, **17**: 258–272, 1924.

Köppen, W.: "Die Klimate der Erde," Walter de Gruyter Co., Berlin, 1923. 369 pp.

Kusdas, Wilh.: Einige Fälle vorzeitiger Entwicklung von Lepidopteren, *Insektenbörse*, vol. XIV, no. 5, pp. 26–27, 1897.

Lauritzen, J. I.: The Relation of Temperature and Humidity to Infection by Certain Fungi, *Phytopathology*, **9**: 7–42, 1919.

Lee, Frederic S., and Ernest L. Scott: The Action of Temperature and Humidity on the Working Power of Muscles and on the Sugar of the Blood, *Amer. Jour. Physiol.*, **40**: 486–550, 1916.

Livingston, B. E.: The Relation of Desert Plants to Soil Moisture and to Evaporation, *Carnegie Inst. Wash. Pub.*, 50, 1906. 78 pp.

————: Atmometry, *Science*, n.s., **28**: 319, 1908.

————: Atmometry and the Porous Cup Atmometer, *Plant World*, **18**: 21–30, 51–74, 95–111, 143–149, 1915.

————: Plant Water Relations, *Quart. Rev. Biol.*, **2**: 494–515, 1927.

Lyon, E. P.: Physiological Heat Regulation and the Problem of Humidity, *Trans. Amer. Soc. Heat. and Ventil. Engin.*, **27**: 113–121, 1921.

McConnell, W. J., and F. C. Houghten: Some Physiological Reactions to High Temperatures and Humidities, *Jour. Amer. Soc. Heat. and Ventil. Engin.*, **29**: 131–165, 1923.

McConnell, W. J., F. C. Houghten, and C. P. Yagloglou: Air Motion—High Temperature and Various Humidities—Reactions on Human Beings, *Jour. Amer. Soc. Heat. and Ventil. Engin.*, **30**: 199–230, 1924.

McDougall, Eric: The Moisture Belts of North America, *Ecology*, vol. **VI, 4**: 325–332, 1925.

MacDougall, D. T., and E. B. Working: Another High Temperature Record for Growth and Endurance, *Science*, n.s., **54**: 152–153, 1921.

Marchal, P.: Les gecidomyies des céréales et leurs parasites, *Ann. soc. ent. France*, vol. LXVI, pp. 1–105, 1897.

Martini, E.: Kritische Bemerkungen zur Theorie der "misanthropen" oder "zoophilen" Anophelen, *Arch. Schiffs- u. Tropen-Hyg.*, **26**: 257–263, 1922.

Marvin, C. F.: Psychometric Methods, *U. S. Dept. Agr. Weather Bur. Bull.* 235, 1900. 84 pp.

————: The Measurement of Precipitation, *U. S. Dept. Agr. Weather Bur. Bull.*, 1903; Instrument Div., *cir. E.*

————: Psychometric Tables, *U. S. Dept. Agr. Weather Bur. Bull.* 235, 1915. 87 pp.

Meisinger, C. LeRoy: Notes on Meteorology and Climatology. Physiological Meteorology, *Science*, n.s., **53**: 337–339, 1921.

Merriam, C. Hart: Life Zones and Crop Zones of the United States, *U. S. Dept. Agr. Bur. Biol. Survey Bull.*, 10, pp. 9–17, 1898.

Necheles, Heinrich: Observations on the Causes of Night Activity in Some Insects, *Chinese Jour. Physiol.*, **1**: 143–155, 1927.

Newstead, R. and H. M. Morris: Bionomic, Morphological and Economic Report on the Acarids of Stored Grain and Flour, *Roy. Soc. (London), Grain Pests' (War) Comm. Rept.*, 8, 1920. 15 pp.

Novakovsky, Stanislaus: The Probable Effect of the Climate of the Russian Far East on Human Life and Activity, *Ecology*, **III**: 181–202, 1922.

————: The Effect of Climate on the Efficiency of the People of the Russian Far East, *Ecology*, **III**: 275–283, 1922.

Parker, J. R.: Influence of Soil Moisture upon the Rate of Increase on Sugar-Beet Root-louse Colonies, *Jour. Agr. Research*, **IV**: 241–250, 1915.

PARKER, J. R.: Observations on the Clear-winged Grasshopper, *Minn. Univ. Agr. Expt. Sta. Bull.* 214, 1924. 44 pp.

————: Some Effects of Temperature and Moisture upon *Melanoplus mexicanus mexicanus* Saussure and *Camnula pellucida* Scudder (Orthoptera), Univ. of Minn., Ph.D. thesis, June, 1928.

PAYNE, NELLIE M.: The Effect of Environmental Temperatures upon Insect Freezing Points, *Ecology*, **7**: 99–107, 1926.

————: Absolute Humidity as a Factor in Insect Cold Hardiness, with Note on the Effect of Nutrition on Cold Hardiness, *Annals Ent. Soc. America*, vol. 22: 601–620.

PEARSE, S. A.: "Animal Ecology," McGraw-Hill Book Co., Inc., New York, 1926. 417 pp.

(*T*) PIERCE, W. DWIGHT: A New Interpretation of the Relationships of Temperature and Humidity to Insect Development, *Jour. Agr. Research*, **5**: 1183–1191, 1916.

PURSSELL, U. G.: Climatic Conditions of Minnesota, *Minn. Univ. Geol. Survey Bull.*, **12**: 10–30, **13**: 23–45, 1917.

REDWAY, JACQUES W.: Oscillations of Lake Levels and Changes of Climate, *Ecology*, **5**: 149–153, 1924.

REGEN, JOHANN: Untersuchungen über den Winterschlaf der Larven von *Gryllus campestris* L., *Zool. Anz.*, vol. XXX, **5**: 131–135, 1906.

REINHARD, CARL: Beobachtung über die Abgabe von Kohlensäure und Wasserdunst durch die Perspiratio cutanea, *Ztschr. Biol.*, **5**: 28–60, 1869.

RIGG, GEORGE B.: Some Factors in Evergreenness in the Puget Sound Region, *Ecology*, **2**: 37–47, 1921.

ROBINSON, WM.: An Electric Method of Determining the Moisture Content of Living Tissue, *Ecology*, **7**: 365–370, 1926.

————: Low Temperature and Moisture as Factors in the Ecology of the Rice Weevil, *Sitophilus oryza* L., and the Granary Weevil, *Sitophilus granarius* L., *Minn. Univ. Agr. Expt. Sta. Tech. Bull.* 41, 1926. 43 pp.

————: Water Binding Capacity of Colloids a Definite Factor in Winter Hardiness of Insects, *Jour. Econ. Ent.*, **20**: 80–88, 1927.

————: Water Conservation in Insects, *Jour. Econ. Ent.*, vol. 21, **6**: 898–902, 1928.

RÖSSLER, ADOLF: Die Schuppenflügler (Lepidopteren) des kgl. Regierungsbezirks Wiesbaden und ihre Entwickelungsgeschichte, Wiesbaden, 1881. 392 pp. (Aus den Jahrb. des Nassauischen Ver. für Naturk., Jahrg. XXXIII und XXXIV.)

RÜHL, FRITZ: "Die paläarktischen Gross-schmetterlinge und ihre Naturgeschichte," Leipzig, 1892.

————: Ueber *Bombyx lanestris* L. und *Bombyx arbusculæ*, *Soc. ent.*, vol. VII, **18**: 140–142; **19**: 151–152; **20**: 158; **22**: 173; **23**: 182–183; **24**: 187–188; 1892–1893.

————: Die Macrolepidopteren-Fauna von Zürich und Umgebung, *Soc. ent.*, vol. IV, **6**: 50–51, 1889; vol. V, **20**: 153–154, 1891; vol. VIII, **11**: 82–83; **13**: 97–98, 1893.

RUSSELL, T.: The Piche evaporimeter, *U. S. Monthly Weather Rev.*, **33**: 253–255, 1905.

SANDERS, N. J., and V. E. SHELFORD: A Quantitative and Seasonal Study of a Pine Dune Animal Community, *Ecology*, **3**: 306–321, 1922.

SCHICKENDANTZ, GEORG: Temperaturen und Sauerstoff im Sakrower See bei Potsdam, *Internat. Rev. Gesamm. Hydrobiol. u. Hydrog.*, **3**: 84–92, 1910.

SHAW, WILLIAM T.: Moisture and Altitude as Factors in Determining the Seasonal Activities of the Townsend Squirrel in Washington, *Ecology*, **2**: 189–193, 1921.

SHELFORD, V. E.: The Reactions of Certain Animals to Gradients of Evaporating Power of Air, *Biol. Bull.*, **25**: 79–120, 1913.

Shelford, V. E.: Modification of Behavior of Land Animals by Contact with High Evaporating Power, *Jour. Anim. Behavior*, **4**: 31–49, 1914.

————: The Importance of the Measure of Evaporation in Economic Studies of Insects, *Jour. Econ. Ent.*, **7**: 229–233, 1914.

————: Physiological Problems in the Life Histories of Animals with Particular Reference to Their Seasonal Appearance, *Amer. Naturalist*, **52**: 129–154, 1918.

————: Methods of Experimental Study of the Relations of Insects to Weather, *Jour. Econ. Ent.*, **19**: 251–261, 1926.

————: An Experimental Investigation of the Relations of the Coddling Moth to Weather and Climate, *Ill. Nat. Hist. Survey Bull.*, vol. XVI, pp. 307–440, 1927.

————: "Laboratory and Field Ecology," Williams & Wilkins Co., Baltimore, 1929. 608 pp.

Shive, J. W., and B. E. Livingston: The Relation of Atmospheric Evaporating Power to Soil Moisture Content at Permanent Wilting in Plants, *Plant World*, **17**: 81–121, 1914.

Shreve, Edith B.: Seasonal Changes in the Water Relations of Desert Plants, *Ecology*, **4**: 266–292, 1923.

Shreve, Forrest: The Vegetation of a Desert Mountain Range as Conditioned by Climatic Factors, *Carnegie Inst. Wash. Pub. 217*, 1915.

Shull, Charles A. (1916): Measurement of Surface Forces in Soils, *Bot. Gaz.*, **62**: 1–31, 1916; *Rev. Jour. Forestry*, **15**: 110–117, 1917.

————: Imbibition in Relation to Absorption and Transportation of Water in Plants, *Ecology*, vol V, pp. 230–241, 1924.

Sierp, H., and A. Seybold: Untersuchungen zur Physik der Transpiration, *Ztschr. wiss. Biol.*, Abt. E, **3**: 115–168, 1927.

Skorikow, A. S.: Neue Formen russischer *Collembola*, *Arb. Naturf.-Gesell., Universität Charkow*, vol. XXXIII, pp. 383–402, 1899.

Standfuss, M.: "Handbuch für Sammler der europäischen Gross-Schmetterlinge," 1891.

————: Ueber die Gründe der Variation des Falterstadiums bei den Schmetterlingen, *Insektenbörse*, vol. XI, **21**: 199–201; **22**: 209–210; **23**: 217–218; **24**: 225–226, 1894; vol. XII, **1**: 4–5; **2**: 13; **3**: 22–23; **4**: 29–30; **5**: 36–37, 1895.

————: "Handbuch der paläarktischen Gross-schmetterlinge für Forscher und Sammler," 2d ed., Jena, 1896, 392 pp.

Tarnani, I. K.: Ueber die Parasiten der Larven vom Maikäfer. (Vorläufige Mittheilung.) *Horæ Soc. Ent. Ross*, vol. XXXIX, nos. 1–2, 1899; vols. XLIV–L, 1900.

Taylor, Griffith: Control of Settlement by Humidity and Temperature, *Commonwealth Bur. Met. Bull.*, **14**: 1–32, 1916.

Taylor, W. P.: A Distributional and Ecological Study of Mount Rainier, Wash., *Ecology*, **3**: 214–237, 1922.

Thone, Frank: Rainproofing Valves for Atmometers: A Résumé, *Ecology*, **5**: 408–414, bibliog., 1924.

Tower, W. L.: On the Origin and Distribution of *Leptinotarsa decemlineata* Say, and the Part that Some of the Climatic Factors Have Played in Its Dissemination, *Proc. Amer. Assoc. Adv. Sci.*, **49**: 225–227, 1900.

Townsend, Charles H. T.: An Analysis of Insect Environments and Response, *Ecology*, vol. V, pp. 14–25, 1924.

Tyndall, J.: "The Forms of Water," 1880.

Vanha, J., and J. Stoklasa: "Die Rübennematoden (Heterodera, Dorylaimus und Tylenchus)," Berlin, 1896.

Visher, Stephen Sargent: "Climatic Laws," John Wiley & Sons, Inc., London, 1924. 95 pp.

WALKOFF, M. I.: Effect of Various Soluble Salts and Lime on Evaporation, Capillary Rise, and Distribution of Water in Some Agricultural Soils, *Soil Sci.*, **9**: 409–436, 1920.

WEAVER, J. E.: Evaporation and Plant Succession in Southeastern Washington and Adjacent Idaho, *Plant World*, **17**: 273–294, 1914.

WEAVER, JOHN E., FRANK C. JEAN, and JOHN W. CRIST: Development and Activities of Roots of Crop Plants: A Study in Crop Ecology, *Carnegie Inst. Wash., Pub.*, 316, 1922. 117 pp., 42 text figs.

WEAVER, J. E., JOSEPH KRAMER, MAUD REED: Development of Root and Shoot of Winter Wheat under Field Environment, *Ecology*, **5**: 26–51, 1924.

WEAVER, J. E., and J. W. CRIST: Direct Measurement of Water Loss from Vegetation without Disturbing the Normal Structure of the Soil, *Ecology*, **5**: 153–171, 1924.

WEISMANN, AUGUST: Neue Versuche zum Saison-Dimorphismus der Schmetterlinge, *Zool. Jahrb., Abt. System., geogr. u. biol. Tiere.*, **8**: 611–613, 1895.

WEISS, H. B., and ERDMAN WEST: Insects and Plants of a Dry Woods in the Pine Barrens of New Jersey, *Ecology* **5**: 241–254, 1924.

WILLIAMS, C. B.: A Short Bioclimatic Study in the Egyptian Desert, *Egypt Min. Agr., Tech. and Sci. Serv. Bull.* 29, 1923.

WILSON, ROBT. E.: Humidity Control by Means of Sulfuric Acid Solutions, with Critical Compilation of Vapor Pressure Data, *Jour. Indus. and Engin. Chem.*, vol. 13, **4**: 326–331, 1921.

ZELENY, ANTHONY: An Electrical Method for the Measurement of the Amount of Moisture in Grain and Other Materials, *Minn. Engin.*, vol. 17, 1909.

ZIMMERMANN, HUGO: Ucber das Auftreten von *Lithocolletis platani* Staudgr. *Insektenbörse* **4**: 28–29, 1904; *Die Chronique der kaukasischen Seidenzucht-Station*, Jahrg. 1892, vol. VI, pp. 1–20, Tiflis, 1899.

APPENDIX TO CHAPTER V

DORMANCY

Dormancy will be used in this connection to cover all cases in which the development of an organism apparently ceases. It will, therefore, include the case of hibernation, or winter sleep; the case of aestivation, or summer sleep; the case of inanition, in which organisms are tiding themselves over a period of lack of food; and certain other cases in which it is impossible, at the present time, to assign a definite cause. Literature abounds in references to this interesting type of lethargy.

Polimonti (1912) summed up the theories of lethargy in an interesting volume entitled "Il Letargo." In 1916, Rasmussen gave a summary of the theories of hibernation. From time to time, almost every possible exciting cause has been taken up and sponsored as the one cause of dormancy. From a theoretical consideration, one may look over a diagram such as Pierce's graph of the effects of temperature and humidity, and see that either temperature or humidity or a combination of the two theoretically might produce dormancy. Similarly we might include all physical factors which may be beyond the limits within which organisms are normally active. It is for this reason that this discussion is entered into at the present time.

Before proceeding further with the discussion, attention will also be called to the fact that almost any physical reaction of an organism may be shown to be due in part to environment, and in part to hereditary constitution. The color of certain insects and, to a certain extent, their form and size may be varied by varying environment. Also, there may be genes which tend to produce certain form, color, and size almost regardless of the environment. The conclusion was reached in this discussion by Weinstein that the characters of an organism, like the area of a rectangle, are due not solely to one dimension. Just as the area of a rectangle varies both with the altitude and the base, so the characters of organisms vary both with environment and heredity. If we will now admit metabolism as a characteristic of an organism and consider, as has been very well demonstrated, that some organisms may have their metabolism proceed almost uninterruptedly and that others may require cessation of metabolism at certain intervals, we have another character, metabolism, which may be affected by both heredity and environment. We have many clearly demonstrated cases of cyclic metabolism, as in the case of reproduction in the oestrous cycle, the length of which has been shown to be an innate hereditary character of given organisms, but which may be influenced to a certain extent by environmental influences. We turn our attention to the vast amount of literature which is before us on this subject, with this viewpoint in mind, granting that there may be cases in which heredity apparently plays the dominant rôle in that the characteristics of metabolism are definitely set down by it and are relatively unaffected by the environment. On the other hand, we will have cases in which environment plays the dominant rôle in determining the length of the period of activities and the length of the period of dormancy. It would seem difficult to draw a hard and fast line between cases of dormancy in which the environmental factors have relatively little influence and those in which they have a great influence, just as it would be difficult to draw the distinction between the effect of temperature in affecting the color of organisms and the influence of heredity in affecting their color; for in many cases the color of an individual may be due to both influences.

If the literature on the subject of dormancy is to be divided into groups on the basis of the types of organisms worked upon, we will find in one group the hibernating homoiothermic organisms which in the winter season might be said to cease to be homoiothermic and become poikilothermic. This is true of certain of the mammals; and Rasmussen (1916) gives a very good review of the various theories that have been proposed to account for this peculiar upset of the temperature regulatory system, and the adoption of a poikilothermic state. The most common theory of the cause of hibernation of these organisms is low temperature, but there are plenty of cases cited in the literature where the animals have not gone into hibernation under experimental conditions when exposed to low temperature. It has been suggested that the carbon-dioxide content of their burrows induces autonarcosis, but the work of Rasmussen on the woodchuck seems to have shown that this is not the case. Abundance of food and lack of food have both been proposed as a cause, and it has also been suggested that it is simply a form of sleep which is very profound. The work of Rasmussen on the woodchuck or marmot, and of Johnson on the striped spermophile are both good examples of the conditions which attend this dormancy in mammals.

Among the poikilothermic animals, the suggestion of the influence of low temperature seems to have carried much more weight, because here it is not necessary to postulate the upset of the mechanism for the control of temperature of the body. Among the insects it is perfectly clear that certain of these species can continue development generation after generation without any imposed dormant period. *Tribolium confusum* is such an insect. On the other hand, we have insects which pass through but one generation per year regardless of the fact that temperature is high enough for development to continue. In the north temperate regions there are many examples of such insects. It happens also that there are certain species which pass through but one generation per year in the northern part of their range, and pass through several generations per year in the southern part of their range. These species have been the subject of a great deal of controversy. It seems evident in the case of many of these that if they were to start a second generation, the winter would catch them at a stage in which they could not endure low temperature, and the species would be wiped out. So we have the very interesting case of species which have either one or two generations per year, many of them without any attempt at an intermediate condition.

Roubaud (1922) proposed the term "holodynamic" for forms which continue their development without interruption, and "heterodynamic" for those which had their development interrupted by periods of dormancy. It seems, however, that the older terms, which have been in use in literature for a long time, of "univoltine" for those which pass through but one generation before dormancy, of "bivoltine" for those which pass through two generations in succession before dormancy, and of "multivoltine" for those with many generations, are more applicable. There is probably no single form which has received more attention from this standpoint than the silkworm, *Bombyx mori*.

Jucci (1924 and 1926) gives a very good statement of the problem in connection with the silkworm, which seems to indicate quite clearly that we have here a combination of environmental and genetic influences. This whole work has to do with the making of a distinction between cases in which environmental temperature is responsible for the oncoming of dormancy, and the cases in which no environmental influence is at least evident in causing the dormancy.

Roubaud (1922) suggested that in the cases where there is no evident environmental factor initiating dormancy, it may be due to an accumulation of waste product, such as urates. However, his theory requires that one conceive of the accumulation of these urates passing over from one generation to another. If they did so pass over, they would have to pass through the egg. It is difficult to conceive, quantitatively, of such an accumulation passing through the egg from one generation to another until the accumulation had reached such proportions that dormancy was induced.

Hormones and enzymes have been suggested as causing the dormancy. Such suggestions are not at all out of harmony with the theory that in many cases dormancy is a genetic factor, for we know perfectly well that in species where the period of the oestrous cycle is a genetic character it is in fact initiated by a hormone, the secretion of which is associated with the genetic factor. In the case of the European corn borer, *Pyrausta nubialis* Hb., there are sections of the country in which there is but one generation a year, other sections where there are two generations a year, and still other sections where there are sometimes one generation and sometimes two generations in a year. Babcock, Barber, Parker, and others have discussed the dormant period of the corn borer. It seems that the only attitude to be taken towards this problem is that many strains of the corn borer are heterozygous for univoltine or bivoltine factors.

Dawson (unpublished thesis) made a study of the polyphemus moth, which has but one generation a year in Minnesota, and two generations a year in Nebraska and points farther south. In this case, certain morphological differences are to be found between the two races, such as size and color of eggs, and other characters. He found, however, that under experimental conditions it was possible to induce the northern univoltine race to pass through many generations in one season, and also to get the southern race to pass through but one generation. However, in all cases there was a certain per cent of the population which did not behave as indicated. Extensive experiments, in which there was an attempt to select pure-line strains of bivoltine stock, indicate quite definitely that there are hereditary and environmental forces operating in this case, just as in nature the races are, to a certain extent, always heterozygous for the character of univoltine or bivoltine metabolism.

Looking at the problem from the standpoint of the general ecology of the organism, it seems evident that the environment is imposing upon the organism a period of dormancy by its selective action in wiping out all organisms which are not capable of enduring dormancy during the cold period of the year. The obvious result of this is the survival of the forms which have some method of passing this cold hibernation period. The question of how these organisms acquire the ability to hibernate is as mute as the question of the acquirement of any character.

Baumberger (1917) concluded that those organisms which could endure dormancy in whatever place the cold weather overtook them did not have a periodic hibernation period, but were controlled very definitely by the temperatures which obtained surrounding them; that those organisms which had to prepare themselves for hibernation by forming a cocoon or digging into the ground or otherwise protecting themselves, were characterized by a periodic dormancy, and that they began to prepare for it at a certain time, quite regardless of the temperatures that obtained at that time. With our present knowledge of the changes of physical factors, it is very difficult to distinguish between cases in which there is a definite periodicity and those in which there is an influence of the environment. At about midsummer, temperature begins its very gradual decline, the angle of incidence of the sun's rays changes, the food plant begins to mature, and a whole series of physical changes is under way though not very evident. A careful analysis of this entire situation with a complete citation of literature would require a volume in itself.

It has been the purpose to insert this little appendix on the subject of dormancy to suggest a viewpoint for the consideration of the whole case of dormancy.

BIBLIOGRAPHY

DORMANCY

BABCOCK, K. W.: The European Corn Borer (*Pyrausta nubilalis* Hubn.): A Discussion of Its Dormant Period, *Ecology*, **8**: 45–59, 1927.

BARBER, GEO. W.: Remarks on the Number of Generations of the European Corn Borer in America, *Jour. Econ. Ent.*, **18**: 496–502, 1925.

BAUMBERGER, J. PERCY: Hibernation: A Periodical Phenomenon, *Ann. Ent. Soc. Amer.*, **10**: 179–188, 1917.

DAWSON, R. W.: "Studies on the Causes of Dormancy among Insects, with Special Reference to the Polyphemus Moth," Univ. of Minn., unpublished Doctor's thesis, 1929.

FINK, D. E.: Physiological Studies on Hibernation on the Potato Beetle, *Leptinotarsa decemlineata*, *Biol. Bull.*, **49**, 381–404, 1925.

HAMLIN, JOHN C.: Seasonal Adaptation of a Northern Hemisphere Insect to the Southern Hemisphere, *Jour. Econ. Ent.*, **16**: 420–423, 1923.

JACKSON, HARTLEY T.: An Apparent Effect of Winter Inactivity on the Distribution of Mammals, *Jour. Mammal.*, **1**: 58–64, 1920.

JOHNSON, GEORGE EDWIN: Hibernation of the Thirteen-lined Ground Squirrel, *Citellus tridecemlineatus* Mitchell, *Jour. Exptl. Zool.*, **50**: 15–30, 1928.

———: Hibernation of the Thirteen-lined Ground Squirrel, *Citellus tridecemlineatus* Mitchell. II. The General Process of Waking from Hibernation, *Amer. Naturalist*, **LXIII**: 171–180, 1929.

JUCCI, CARLO: Su l'eredita del tipo metabolico nei bachi da seta. I. Il Bivoltinismo, *Della R. Scula supp. d'Agric.*, Portici, pp. 1–133, 1924.

JUCCI, C., E D. WEN: Su l'eredita delle capacità di sviluppo dell' uovo. Voltinismo e partenogenesi in incroci tra anormali e bivoltine di bachi da seta, *Estratto dal Rendiconto della quindicesima assemblea ordin. e del convegno dell' Unione zoologica italiana* in Bologna, pp. 26–30, 1926.

PARKER, H. L., and W. R. THOMPSON: A Contribution to the Study of Hibernation in the Larva of the European Corn Borer (*Pyrausta nubilalis* Hubn,) *Ann. Ent. Soc. Amer.*, **20**: 10–22, 1927.

PAYNE, NELLIE M.: "Freezing and Survival of Insects at Low Temperature," Univ. of Minn., Ph.D. thesis, 1925. 88 pp.

———: The Effect of Environmental Temperatures upon Insect Freezing Points, *Ecology*, vol. 7, **1**: 99–107, 1926.

PICARD, F.: L'hibernation des chenilles de *Pieris brassicas* L., *Bull. biol. France et Belg.*, **57**: 98–106, 1923.

PICTET, A.: Nouvelles recherches sur l'hibernation des lepidoptères, *Compt. rend. soc. phys. et hist. nat.*, Genève, **35**: 301–304, 1913.

POLIMANTI, O.: "Il Letargo," Roma, 1912.

RASMUSSEN, ANDREW T.: A Further Study of the Blood Gases during Hibernation in the Woodchuck (*Marmota monax*)—The Respiratory Capacity of the Blood, *Amer. Jour. Physiol.*, vol. XLI, no. 2, 1916.

———: Theories of Hibernation, *Amer. Naturalist*, **50**: 609–626, 1916.

———: The So-called Hibernating Gland, *Jour. Morph.*, **38**: 147–205, 1923.

RAU, PHIL and NELLIE: The Sleep of Insects; an Ecological Study, *Ann. Ent. Soc. Amer.*, IX: 227–274, 1916.

ROBINSON, WM.: Response and Adaptation of Insects to External Stimuli, *Ann. Ent. Soc. Amer.*, vol. XXI, **3**: 407–417, 1928.

————: A Study of the Effect of Surgical Shock on Insects. Determination of the Natural Undercooling and Freezing Points in Insects, *Jour. Agr. Research*, vol. 37, **12**: 743–748, 1928.

ROUBAUD, E.: Étude sur le sommeil d'hiver pré-imaginal des muscides, *Bull. biol. France et Belg.*, **56**: 455–545, 1922.

————: Sur l'hibernation de quelques mouches communes, *Bull. soc. ent. France*, **2**: 24–25, 1927.

ROUBAUD, E., and J. COLAS-BELCOUR: La torpeur hivernale obligatoire et ses manifestations diverses chez nos moustiques indigènes, *Compt. rend. acad. sci.*, Paris, **182**: 871–873, 1926.

SAJO, KARL: Sommerschlaf eines Käfers, *Illus. Wchnschr. Ent.*, **I**: 87–89, 1896.

SHELFORD, V. E.: An Experimental Investigation of the Relations of the Coddling Moth to Weather and Climate, *Ill. Nat. Hist. Survey,Bull.* 16, art. 5, 1926.

SUCKOW, ————: Sur l'hibernation des insectes, *Ztschr. org. Physik.*, p. 597, 1827; rev. in *Bull. Sci. Nat. et Geol.*, **XIV**: 444, 1828.

UDA, HAJIME: On "Maternal Inheritance," *Genetics*, **8**: 322–335, 1923.

WARDLE, ROBERT A.: Seasonal Frequency of Càlliphorine Blowflies in Great Britain, *Jour. Hyg.*, London, vol. 26, 1927.

CHAPTER VI

PHYSICAL CONDITIONS OF ENVIRONMENTAL MEDIA

PRESSURE OF THE ENVIRONMENTAL MEDIA

Introduction.—The force which we measure as pressure of the environmental medium is that of the action of gravity on the superimposed atmosphere or water, although it may very well include the pressure which may be encountered in soil or in any other medium. Atmospheric pressure varies slightly in any given place with the changes in the general atmospheric conditions, but the greatest changes are those associated with altitude. The possibilities for the change of atmospheric pressure which a terrestrial organism may encounter even when going to the highest altitudes are as nothing compared with the pressure which an aquatic organism may experience in going down even to the deepest parts of our lakes, to say nothing of the sea.

Measurements in Recording of Pressure.—Pressure is commonly measured by means of a mercurial barometer which consists essentially of a tube in which the mercury in the vacuum column fluctuates with the atmosphere. The height of the column of mercury is a measure of the atmospheric pressure, when the temperature coefficient has been taken care of. If the instrument is exposed to a complete vacuum, there will be no column of mercury in the tube. If exposed to an ordinary atmosphere at sea-level, the column of mercury will be 760 mm. or practically 30 inches, and is equal to a pressure of 14.696 lb. per square inch, or 1033.3 g. per square centimeter. This is ordinarily stated as one atmosphere of pressure. The aneroid barometer registers the atmospheric pressure on a partially exhausted chamber. It is calibrated to read in the equivalent of inches or centimeters of mercury. These instruments are usually limited to a range of but a few inches, but are portable and require practically no correction for temperature. The more delicate aneroid barometers are often calibrated to read in altitude as well as in inches of mercury. They, therefore, make a very convenient instrument for making rough measurements of altitude when doing field work. The difference in altitude of two points may be calculated when the barometric pressures and the temperatures are known. There are more or less elaborate formulae which are very accurate, but the following approximate formula is practical where the differences of altitude do not amount to more than 1,000 m.

$$H = 1,600,000 \frac{b_1 - b_2}{b_1 + b_2}(1 + 0.004t)$$

128

In this case b_1 and b_2 are the two barometric readings, and t is the mean of the temperature of the two stations. It is often more convenient to determine the altitude directly from the scale of an aneroid barometer so calibrated, or from tables such as may be found in the "Smithsonian Meteorological Tables." Barographs for the recording of pressure usually operate on the principle of the aneroid barometer, which is connected with a lever and pen for writing on a revolving drum. Pressure at various depths and aquatic environments is usually calculated on the basis of the weight of the superimposed column of water, which amounts to one atmosphere for each 10.329 m.

The maintenance of various pressures or vacuums for experimental purposes may be maintained by the use of chambers and pumps. Pumps have now been developed which are capable of producing high pressures or a vacuum down to 0.001 mm. pressure. Some difficulty is experienced, however, in introducing pressure into laboratory experiments and adding it to all the other conditions which it is desirable to maintain at a constant. It is, however, by no means impossible with modern apparatus. The desirability of introducing it in any given experiment must be determined on the basis of the organisms involved and the type of experiment which is to be performed.

PRESSURE AS A FACTOR IN ANIMAL ECOLOGY

Effects of Pressure on Physical Phenomena.—All tables of the constants of physical phenomena designate the temperature under which the determinations were made. There are some physical phenomena which are profoundly affected by even a relatively slight change in barometric pressure. We all know that water boils at 100°C. at a pressure of 760 mm.; but at 775.2 mm. it boils at 100.6°C. At 660.2 mm. it boils at 96.1°C.; and at 431.8 mm. it boils at 84.9°. Therefore at an altitude of 15,430 feet, water will boil at only 84.9°C. It is very evident that evaporation will be greatly affected by such changes of barometric pressure as may be experienced in terrestrial environments.

Effects of Pressure upon Animals.—Knowing the effects of pressure upon the boiling point of water, we are not surprised that animals should be affected by changes in pressure. This is a case, however, in which it is extremely difficult to differentiate between the effects of pressure as such acting directly upon the organism and the effects of pressure upon other factors. It is difficult, if not impossible, to experiment with pressure and leave all other factors unaltered. When we experimentally reduce the pressure, we also reduce the pressure of the gases which are involved in respiration. Most investigations seem to show that metabolism in general is affected by the action of pressure upon the gases involved in respiration.

Herrera and Lope (1899) summarized the results of some experiments on the altitudes at which various organisms were found and were able to survive under equivalent pressures.

Schneider (1921) reviewed the literature on pressure, particularly of mammals, and gives data on the ability of various organisms, and especially man, to survive at different altitudes. It is shown that man becomes unconscious at from 23,000 to 25,000 feet; and this is due primarily to the changes in tension of carbon dioxide and oxygen. Carbon dioxide going from 39.7 mm. at sea-level to 30 mm. at 20,000 feet, and oxygen from 103.2 mm. to 34.8 mm. This allows for a difference in oxygen tension between the blood of capillaries and the alveolar air of only 5 mm., which means that it is no longer possible for the organism to take up sufficient oxygen and give off sufficient carbon dioxide to maintain normal metabolism.

Portier (1928) has arrived at the conclusion that birds are able to endure very much greater altitudes than mammals without suffering any difficulty. He has done this apparently entirely on theoretical grounds. He states that the respiratory mechanism of birds is so arranged that the inhaled air comes directly in contact with the blood capillaries and that the carbon dioxide is swept on ahead of it and is exhaled without mingling with the atmospheric air. In this way he considers that the carbon dioxide and oxygen tensions are balanced between the blood capillaries and the incoming air, whereas in mammals the incoming air mingles with and dilutes the carbon dioxide already present in the lungs. Thus he states that the difference in tension is much greater in birds than in mammals, and for this reason he believes that they are able to fly rapidly without difficulty at high altitudes. This reasoning might be applied to insects, as will be stated later under the consideration of gases.

Greenwood (1906) states that lesions are produced in animals, when they are decompressed, by the escape of nitrogen bubbles in the blood. He states that this would seem to be impossible in the case of insects, for he assumes that the blood performs no respiratory function. He experimented with larvae of *Cossus cossus*, and submitted two larvae to atmospheric pressures which he states as +25 and −30 for 20 minutes in the first case, and for 2 hours 40 minutes in the second case. These larvae pupated normally after being decompressed instantaneously. He concludes that this ability to endure the great change of pressure is due to tracheal respiration.

The literature on the effect of atmospheric pressure upon insects consists of that which is a result of experimental research with controlled pressures and from observations in the field under known barometric pressures. All experimental work seems to indicate that so far as pressure itself is concerned, insects are able to endure a reduction of pressure

EFFECT OF VACUUM VARYING FROM 24 TO 28 INCHES UPON INSECTS IN A CONCRETE VAULT CONTAINING 512 CUBIC FEET

(Back and Cotton, 1925)

Insect	Killed in 3 days, per cent				Killed in 4 days, per cent				Killed in 5 days, per cent				Killed in 6 days, per cent				Killed in 7 days, per cent			
	Eggs	Larvae	Pupae	Adults	Eggs	Larvae	Pupae	Adults	Eggs	Larvae	Pupae	Adults	Eggs	Larvae	Pupae	Adults	Eggs	Larvae	Pupae	Adults
Alphitobius piceus Oliv.		90		86		90		86		100		96		100		98		100		100
Anthrenus fasciatus Hbst.		92	100	100		100	100	100		100	100	100		100	100	100		100	100	100
Attagenus piceus Oliv.		66	100	100		78	100	100		78	100	100		80	100	100		95	100	100
Cryptolestes pusillus Schon.				100				100				100				100				100
Dermestes vulpinus Fab.		100		100		100	100	100		100		100		100		100		100		100
Ephestia kuehniella Zell.		100	100	100		100		100		100		100		100		100		100	100	100
Gnathocerus cornutus Fab.		90		98		100		100		100		100				100				100
Gnathocerus maxillosus Fab.		90		94				100				100				100				100
Necrobia rufipes De Geer				100				65				75				90				100
Oryzaephilus surinamensis L.				50				100				100				100				100
Plodia interpunctella Hbn.				100				100				100				100				100
Silvanus gemellatus Duv.				100				100				100				100				100
Sitophilus oryza L.				100				100		80		100				100				100
Sitophilus granarius L.				100		60		100			100	100		80		100				100
Tenebrio obscurus Fab.		60		100				100		100		100		100	100	100		80		100
Tineola bisselliella Hum.	100	100	100	100		100	100	100		100	100	100	100	100		100			100	100
Tinea pellionella L.		100				100		99	100	100								100		
Tribolium confusum Duv.				98								100				100				100
Tribolium ferrugineum Fab.				99				100				100				100				100
Trogodema tarsale Melsh.		20				20				20				30				30		

which is more than equivalent to the highest altitude that may be experienced on the earth.

Cole (1906) exposed 10 rice weevils, *Sitophilus* (*Calendra oryzae*), which were placed in a vacuum of one inch of mercury with some food. On the fourth day three were dead; the seventh day, one; the twelfth

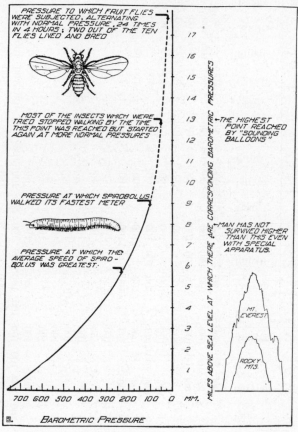

Fig. 52.—Summarizing certain experiments with reduced air pressure. The curved line shows approximately the relation between air pressure (horizontal scale) and height above sea-level (vertical scale) under normal conditions. At the right are human affairs, including diagrammatic representations of the heights of mountains. Entomological facts are given at the left. (*Lutz*, 1929.)

day, one; and the fifteenth day, five were still alive after they were taken from the chamber.

Back, Cotton, and others have shown that insects are capable of withstanding an almost complete vacuum for hours and even days, and that probably evaporation and respiration are responsible for death at the end of this time rather than the reduced pressure as such. The following table from the experiments of Back and Cotton shows how resistant these organisms are. Lutz (1929) experimented with the milliped *Spirobolus* and the fruit-fly, *Drosophila*. Upon measuring the rate of movement of *Spirobolus*, he found it to be most rapid when pressure had dropped as far as nearly 100 mm. In the course of the experiments, flies, beetles, butterflies, and bees were exposed to supervacuum, some being able to survive at 1/10000 mm. for 90 seconds. The general results of the experiments are shown very graphically in Fig. 52. This seems to indicate quite clearly that insects are able to survive at pressures equivalent to altitudes greater than normally might be experienced on the earth.

We turn our attention to aquatic insects, such as *Corethra, Chironomus*, and others which live in the bottoms of our deepest lakes. We find that they are able to endure many atmospheres of pressure and even to emerge from the surface of the water after a rather rapid ascent without any bad effects. Further consideration of the pressures endured in the water will be taken up under the subject of Synecology.

The results of casual observation from the field usually state that flies are affected by a falling barometer. Parman (1920) reports that several species of flies go into a state of nervousness when the barometer is falling. He cites the example of *Stomoxys calcitrans* and the housefly, *Musca domestica*, which were particularly abundant just before the storm in 1916, but which could not be found in any numbers at all after the storm. There is of course no definite evidence that it was the falling barometer alone that affected these flies. Adult insects are said to emerge during times of high barometric pressure; butterflies also are said to migrate during times of high pressure.

Dodds and Hisaw (1925) concluded that the altitudinal distribution of lotic Trichoptera was due primarily to temperature, and that pressure associated with the altitude probably was an insignificant factor if of any importance at all.

We have little direct evidence with regard to the effect of pressure upon the development of insects. Lutz states that some of the *Drosophila* which were exposed to the lowest barometric pressures reproduced and their progeny were apparently normal. Some experimental work with centrifuging developing organisms has shown that it is possible to misplace certain developing tissues, and thereby produce abnormal organisms. This may be of some ecological interest in suggesting that pressure, especially unequal pressures, may be important in influencing the mechanism of development and possibly in extending even to the mechanism of heredity as concerned with genes on chromosomes.

The behavior of insects is undoubtedly affected by pressure, especially as concerned with reactions to gravity. It is common knowledge that many insects are negatively geotropic, *i.e.*, that they react negatively to gravity and crawl upwards on various surfaces.

Loeb (1918), Kanda (1914 and 1916), and others have given attention to the reactions of organisms to pressure. It will not be the purpose at the present time to go into the details of the behavior of organisms, and to discuss the merits of the various views relative to these reactions.

Fielde and Parker (1904) concluded that ants did not react to aerial vibrations, but only to those transmitted to them by the substratum upon which they were resting. They concluded also from their experiments that the reactions did not depend upon the antennae, the head, the abdomen, or any pair or two pairs of legs, but that the organism as a whole reacted and that the stimulus was probably received through the legs. This was in accordance with the belief of Cole (1917), that *Drosophila* reacted to gravity because of the stress of the body as it rested upon the legs, rather than to any chordatonal organs, as suggested by Loeb. The various reactions of contact to vibrations and to pressure might logically be considered under this head. Since, however, it is not the purpose to enter into purely behavioristic or physiological phenomena, they will not be taken up further at this point.

It is difficult to correlate the effect of pressure upon the geographic distribution of insects from our present knowledge. The conclusions of Dodds and Hisaw have already been referred to as showing that altitudinal distribution may be more closely correlated with temperature than with pressure. This would seem to be reasonable, for it is certainly shown by experimental work that insects are able to endure far greater variations of barometric pressure than are ordinarily to be found on the surface of the earth.

BIBLIOGRAPHY

PRESSURE OF THE MEDIUM

BACK, E. A., and R. T. COTTON: The Use of Vacuum for Insect Control, *Jour. Agr. Research*, **31**: 1035–1041, 1925.

CARPENTER, F. W.: The Reactions of the Pomace Fly (*Drosophila ampelophila* Loew) to Light, Gravity, and Mechanical Stimulation, *Amer. Naturalist*, **39**: 157–171, 1905.

COLE, F. J. (1906): The Bionomics of Grain Weevils, *Jour. Econ. Biol.*,**1**: 63–71, 1905–1906.

COLE, W. H.: The Reactions of *Drosophila ampelophila* Loew to Gravity, Centrifugation and Air Currents, *Jour. Anim. Behavior*, **7**: 71–80, 1917.

COOK, WILLIAM C.: Studies on the Flight of Nocturnal Lepidoptera, Minn. State Ent., 18*th Rept.*, pp. 43–56, 1920.

DAVENPORT, C. B.: "Experimental Morphology," chap. V, pp. 112–125; chap. XIV, pp. 376–384, The Macmillan Company, New York, 1908.

DODDS, GIDEON S.: Altitudinal Distribution of Entomostraca in Colorado, *Proc. U. S. Nat. Mus.*, **54**: 59–87, 1919.

DODDS, G. S., and F. L. HISAW: Ecological Studies on Aquatic Insects. IV. Altitudinal Range and Zonation of Mayflies, Stoneflies, and Caddisflies in the Colorado Rockies, *Ecology*, **6**: 380–390, 1925.

FIELDE, A. M., and G. H. PARKER: The Reactions of Ants to Material Vibrations, *Proc. Acad. Nat. Sci.*, Philadelphia, **56**: 642–650, 1904.

FOLSOM, J. W.: "Entomology with Special Reference to its Ecological Aspects," 3d ed., chap. XI, pp. 302–307, P. Blakiston's Son & Co., 1922.

GREENWOOD, M., JR.: The Effects of Rapid Decompression on Larvae, *Jour. Physiol.*, **35**, 1906.

HERRERA, A. L., and D. V. LOPE: "La vie sur les hauts plateaux," Mexico City, 1899. 790 pp.

KANDO, SAKYO: On the Geotropism of Paramecium and Spirostumum, *Biol. Bull.*, **26**: 1–24, 1914.

————: The Geotropism of Freshwater Snails, *Biol. Bull.*, XXX: 85–97, 1916.

LOEB, J.: Ueber Geotropismus bei Thieren, *Pflüger's Arch. Physiol.*, vol. 49, pp. 175–189, 1891.

————: "Forced Movements, Tropisms, and Animal Conduct," J. B. Lippincott Company, Philadelphia, 1918. 209 pp., 42 figs.

LUTZ, FRANK E.: Experiments with "Wonder Creatures," *Nat. Hist.*, vol. XXIX, **2**: 160–168, 1929.

PARMAN, D. C.: Observations on the Effect of Storm Phenomena on Insect Activity, *Jour. Econ. Ent.*, **13**: 339–343, 1920.

PORTIER, P.: Sur le rôle physiologique des sacs aériens des oiseaux, *Compt. rend. soc. biol.*, **99**: 1327–1328, 1928.

RAMSDEN, W.: Die Coagulierung von Eiweisskörpern auf mechanischen Wege, *Dubois-Reymonds Arch. Physiol.*, pp. 517–534, 1894.

SCHNEIDER, E. C.: Physiological Effects of Altitude, *Physiol. Rev.*, **1**: 631–659, 1921.

MOVEMENTS OF THE MEDIA

The movements of the environmental medium, especially the currents of atmosphere and of water, have profound effects upon the distribution of the organisms and upon their immediate environment. The ocean currents affect the temperature of the continents; the prevailing winds influence both the temperature and precipitation of areas, making some favorable and others unfavorable for plants and animals. In the study of autecology, we are most concerned with the effects of the currents of water and atmosphere upon the individual organisms. The effect of the currents of the ocean and of fresh water has attracted much more attention than has the study of the effects of movements of air. We are just beginning to be aware of the great effect which wind has in distributing many of the smaller organisms over the surface of the earth. We now know that the air, like the water, has a great floating population.

Methods of Measuring Currents of Atmosphere and Water.—The measurement of wind is most commonly accomplished by the use of a Robinson cup anemometer (Marvin, 1907; and Humphreys, 1920). Hemispherical cups are mounted on horizontal spokes of a wheel. The open side of the hemisphere will thus face the wind on one side, and the convex side of the cup will be directed toward the wind on the other. The instrument is connected with a recording device, which reads the number of miles of wind which have passed over a period of time. This type of anemometer is not affected by the direction of the wind, but is clumsy to use in the field. The Buram portable anemometer consists of a four-inch fan connected with the dial, which records the passage of wind. It is equipped with a device for starting, stopping, and zero setting. The operator, however, must face it into the wind, as there is no wind vane on it. A watch is used to measure the time. It is, however, a very convenient field instrument.

The pitot tube (Rowse, 1913) may be used for measuring currents of water and also for measuring the speed of air in passing through experimental chambers in laboratory work. This instrument consists of a tube with a dynamic opening facing the wind or water current, and one or more static openings at right angles to it. The dynamic opening is connected with one side of a manometer, and the static opening with the other side. Water may be used as the indicator fluid to show that the difference of level in the two sides of the manometer will be proportionate to the rate of flow. A chart is provided, which is calibrated for either air or water, and from which the rate may be taken when the manometer reading is known. Various instruments have been devised for measuring water currents in the ocean and in large bodies of water. These will be referred to under the subject of Aquatic Synecology. For ordinary aquatic field work and for laboratory work the use of the pitot tube is one of the most convenient methods.

Movements of the Media as Factors in Animal Ecology.—For the present purpose, the action of the wind primarily will be considered under this heading. The action of the currents of water will be referred to in connection with aquatic environments in the section on synecology. Attention has already been called to the importance of wind action as affecting evaporation. Its general effect on the conduction of heat is too well known to require further attention. In all restricted environments, it is of great importance in accelerating the diffusion of gases. There are doubtless many other effects which might be dwelt upon; but in the present treatment of the subject it seems more profitable to consider the cases of distribution of organisms.

The Effect of Wind and Currents of Water on the Distribution of Animals.—The atmospheric air is in almost constant movement horizontally and vertically, on account of differences of temperature and of barometric pressure. In some cases these movements are relatively local and of short duration, while in other cases they are of great magnitude and almost continual. Humphreys (1920) calls attention to certain areas of the world where violent winds blow almost continually because of great differences of altitude, temperature, and barometric pressure. It is only within recent years that we have come to appreciate the great significance of these movements of the air in the distribution of many of the smaller organisms.   Spores of fungi have been found at an altitude of 11,000 feet.

Burgess (1913) and Collins (1915 and 1917) studied the distribution of the gipsy-moth larvae by the wind.   The first instar larvae of this moth have long been known to have specialized hairs which greatly increase their surface ratio.   When the surface-weight ratio of these tiny larvae is compared with that of certain seeds of plants which are known to soar in the air, it is found that they rank among the best, so far as soaring coefficient is concerned.   It is difficult to get an exact measurement of the surface area; but after the first molt the long hairs are no longer present, and the larva is much less subject to transportation by the wind.   When its food is scarce during the early larval life, the caterpillar lifts the anterior part of the body in an effort to find new foliage and is thereby exposed to the action of the wind.   Collins studied the distribution of these larvae by putting out screens covered with adhesive. It was found that they were carried across Cape Cod Bay a distance of 19 to 30 miles; and horizontal screens placed upon meadows showed that large numbers of the larvae were being dropped on every acre of land. Reports from vessels at sea have often recorded insects being found thousands of miles from the shore.

Hurd (1917) records that swarms of grasshoppers were found 1,200 nautical miles at sea, and McCook (1890) states that spiders have been found at a height of from 1,000 to 2,000 feet in the air and 200 miles at sea.

Quayle (1916) showed that the young of the black scale, *Saisettia oleae*, were distributed by the wind from one block of trees in an orchard to another.

Felt (1925) made a study of the distribution of insects by wind in New York State, and used small balloons as an index of the direction and velocity of the winds at various times during the growing season. He states that swarms of mosquitoes have been observed at altitudes of 2,000 and 3,000 feet.   Balloons which were used in these experiments, when inflated for a minimum of buoyancy, were carried by upward currents of the air to elevations of 1,000 feet.   The average velocity of these drifting balloons was approximately 17 miles an hour; but there is a possibility of a speed of 50, 75, or even 100 miles an hour.   Many of these balloons drifted several hundred miles in a period of 24 hours. From the records of southern insects that have been captured far in the north, it seems certain that it is not uncommon for insects to be carried hundreds or even thousands of miles by the wind.   Felt reports *Alabama argillacea* as occurring in Canada, when it is known that it does not breed farther north than in the cotton regions.

Light-trap experiments at the University of Minnesota and in Montana have shown that there are many adult insects which are found at times in the north even though their food plant is at least as far south as the cotton belt.

Elton (1925) reports large numbers of aphids, *Dilachmus piceae*, and a hover fly, *Syrphus ribesii*, which were found after a strong wind in Northeastland, Spitzbergen. These were found all over fresh snow, which indicated that they had recently arrived; and he concluded that they must have been carried by the wind at least 800 miles.

Wadley (1928, unpublished thesis) reports that the green bug, *Toxoptera graminium*, which arrived in Minnesota in 1926, must have been carried by the wind from Oklahoma. This would have required approximately three days of continuous wind with a rate of 200 to 600 miles per day. He tabulated the wind rates from this direction during the spring of the year, and found that in 1918 and 1926 there was sufficient wind to account for such a distribution of the aphids.

At the present time we know very little of the fauna of the upper air. There are, however, several investigations under way at the present time; and doubtless in the near future we shall have more information with regard to the organisms which might be termed the plankton of the air.

This suggests many interesting problems. The limitations of the gas are not very great until a very high altitude has been reached, as has already been referred to. There is, however, a decrease of temperature at a relatively uniform rate of 6° per 1,000 m. from sea-level, to 11,000 m. where the temperature is constant at −55°C. At an altitude of 1,200 or 1,300 m., therefore, the temperature will approach 0°C. The vapor pressure of water also drops off rather rapidly and is reduced by about 20 per cent at 1,000 m. The upper atmosphere is, therefore, not a very favorable environment.

The morphology of animals is probably affected by movements of the medium in much the same way as sessile plants are affected. The pines growing along the seashore, which have been permanently bent by the action of the prevailing wind, are a classical example. We have not many sessile animals, however, which are comparable to these plants. Many aquatic organisms which swim rapidly through the water or which maintain themselves in a constant position in a rapid stream of water have a so-called "streamline form," which seems to offer the least possible resistance to the action of the current.

Clemens (1917) experimented with masses of wax which were molded into different forms, and found that when the wax was molded in the form of a brook trout, it gave a pull of six grams in a constant stream of water; whereas the same quantity of wax in the form of a cone with its apex upstream gave a pull of 50 g. A model of the may-fly, *Chirotonetes*, gave a pull of nine grams. There is nothing to show that the form of these organisms was influenced by the current, but rather that, through selection, the forms living in the rapidly flowing water have body shapes which offer the minimum of resistance. Experiments in aeronautical engineering in connection with aviation have shown that this streamline form offers the minimum amount of resistance to the air. It may be noted that the bodies of the birds of swiftest flight conform more or less to this same streamline form.

Effects of Movements of the Medium on the Behavior of Animals.— Wheeler (1899) observed that some of the Syrphidae (hover flies) oriented themselves to face against a slight breeze and maintained an almost constant position. To this phenomenon he gave the term "anemotropism." There is in this case, however, nothing to indicate that the organism was reacting to the pressure of the air or the movement of the air. It is entirely possible that they were reacting as a result of vision and a sense of relative position. In the case of rheotaxis of aquatic organisms, it is quite clear, in certain cases at least, that the reaction in heading upstream is due to their sense of relative position rather than to a reaction to the current of the water itself. This may be tested in the case of certain fishes by placing them in an aquarium with scenery on each side, which may be moved in one direction. When the scenery is moved, the fish turns to face the direction in which the scenery is moving and swims to maintain his relative position with regard to the scenery.

Allee (1914) has pointed out the ecological importance of the rheotactic reactions of certain stream isopods. The subject matter, however, of the detailed relationships of these organisms to movements of the medium resolves itself into a study of animal behavior of physiological nature.

Lutz (1927) found that the number of insects collected at a light on a side upwind and on the side which was downwind bore a rather consistent relationship. Only about 7 per cent of the total catch was on the windward side, and over 25 per cent was on the leeward side. This must be interpreted as the effect of wind upon the ability of insects to alight, rather than as the effect of wind on the reactions of insects. Many of them undoubtedly are carried beyond the light by the action of the wind, and then return upwind to the trap.

This discussion comes to a close with these fragmentary accounts of the effect of movements of the media. Other references will be found in connection with descriptive synecology, particularly with regard to aquatic environments.

BIBLIOGRAPHY

MOVEMENTS OF THE MEDIA

ALLEE, W. C.: An Experimental Analysis of the Relation between Physiological States and Rheotaxis in Isopods, *Jour. Expt. Zool.*, **13**: 269–344, 1912.

ALLEE, W. C.: The Effect of Moulting on Rheotaxis in Isopods, *Science*, n.s., **37**: 882–883, 1913.

————: The Ecological Importance of the Rheotactic Reaction of Stream Isopods, *Biol. Bull.*, **27**: 52–66, 1914.

BURGESS, A. F.: The Dispersion of the Gipsy Moth, *U. S. Dept. Agr. Bur. Ent. Bull.* 119, 1913. 62 pp.

CLEMENS, W. A.: An Ecological Study of the May-fly *Chirotonetes*, *Univ. Toronto Studies, Biol. ser.* 17, 1917. 43 pp.

COLE, W. H.: The Reactions of *Drosophila ampelophila* Loew to Gravity, Centrifugation and Air Currents, *Jour. Anim. Behavior*, **7**: 71–80, 1917.

COLLINS, C. W.: Dispersion of the Gipsy-moth Larvae by the Wind, *U. S. Dept. Agr. Bur. Ent. Bull.* 273, 1915. 23 pp.

————: Methods Used in Determining Wind Dispersion of the Gipsy Moth and Other Insects, *Jour. Econ. Ent.*, **10**: 170–176, 1917.

ELTON, C. S.: The Dispersal of Insects to Spitzbergen, *Trans. Ent. Soc.*, London, pp. 289–299, 1925.

FELT, E. P.: The Dissemination of Insects by Air Currents, *Jour. Econ. Ent.*, **18**: 152–156, 1925.

HUMPHREYS, WM. J.: "Physics of the Air," J. B. Lippincott Co., Philadelphia, 1920.

HURD, WILLIS E.: Grasshoppers at Sea, *U. S. Monthly Weather Rev.*, **45**: 11, 1917.

————: Influence of the Wind on the Movements of Insects, *U. S. Monthly Weather Rev.*, **48**: 94–98, 1920.

LUTZ, FRANK E.: Wind and the Direction of Insect Flight, *Amer. Mus. Novit.* 291, pp. 1–4, 1927.

McCOOK, H. C.: American Spiders and Their Spinning Work, *Acad. Nat. Sci.*, Philadelphia, 1889–1893.

MARVIN, C. F.: Anemometry, *U. S. Dept. Agr. Weather Bur.* 233, *circular D*, Instrument Division, 1907. 3d ed.

OAMES, A. K.: Measurement of Air Flow, *Jour. Amer. Soc. Heat. and Ventil. Engin.*, **21**: 1–23, 1915.

QUAYLE, H. J.: Dispersion of Scale Insects by the Wind, *Jour. Econ. Ent.*, **9**: 486–492, 1916.

ROWSE, W. C.: Pitot Tubes for Gas Measurement, *Jour. Amer. Soc. Mech. Engin.*, **35**: 1321–1381, 1913.

WADLEY, FRANCIS M.: Ecology of *Toxoptera graminium*, with Special Reference to Northern Outbreaks, Univ. of Minn., unpublished, Ph.D. thesis, 1928.

WEBSTER, F. M.: Winds and Storms as Agents in the Diffusion of Insects, *Amer. Naturalist*, **36**: 795–801, 1902.

WHEELER, WM. M.: Anemotropism and Other Tropisms in Insects, *Arch. Entwickl. Mech. Organ.*, **8**: 373–381, 1899.

THE GASEOUS CONSTITUENTS OF THE MEDIA

Introduction.—The earth is surrounded by an envelope of atmosphere which is relatively uniform near the surface, showing very little change in altitude over a distance covered normally by organisms, and which does not vary greatly from pole to pole, as shown by the following figure taken from Humphreys (1920). In general, the gaseous constituents of various special media, such as soil, water, and others, are in equilibrium with the atmosphere. There are, however, many special restricted environments in which the gases may be present in very limited quantities; and it is into these special limited environments that organisms are often forced by extreme competition which they have to meet. Oxygen and nitrogen appear to be the main constituents of the earth's atmosphere, and it would appear that no others are present in enough quantity to deserve consideration. However, carbon dioxide is very important, for all animals must rid themselves of it; and it is possible that this gas may poison them, even when there is plenty of oxygen present. The vertical distribution of gases in the earth's atmosphere is such that other factors than the lack of oxygen begin to operate before the oxygen has been appreciably reduced. Referring to the discussion upon pressure,

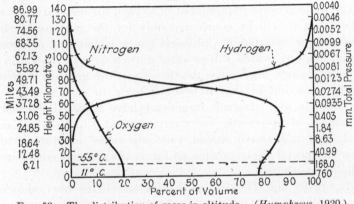

Fig. 53.—The distribution of gases in altitude. (*Humphreys, 1920.*)

it will be noted that the highest point reached by sounding balloons is about the point where oxygen begins to drop off appreciably. Further, temperature approaches a constant value of −55°C. before oxygen has been reduced more than half its value. Consequently, it may be seen that the immediate atmosphere of the earth is everywhere relatively favorable for insect life.

Methods of Measuring the Gases of the Medium.—The methods of measuring the quantity of various gases present in the atmosphere, and the pressure of these various gases may be found in the literature of physiology. Carbon dioxide is normally measured by the use of barium hydroxide as an indicator, and by taking the formation of barium carbonate, which is of milky color, as an index of the presence of carbon dioxide. Various devices have been constructed for measuring carbon dioxide and are described by Thunberg (1905), Lund (1919), Krogh (1919), Fink (1925), and others. The technique of obtaining a fair sample of the gas to be analyzed is important, and must be adjusted to the problem which is in hand.

GASES AS FACTORS IN THE ECOLOGY OF ANIMALS

Effects of Gases on Physical and Chemical Processes.—Oxidation is probably one of the most fundamental phenomena of biotic systems. It is naturally affected by the oxygen. If oxygen is absent, oxidation cannot go on. It may happen that some other gas is present which may combine with the oxygen, and therefore make the oxygen unavailable for a certain reaction, which is the object of investigation. Therefore, in the study of gases we come very close in our biological work to the purely chemical reactions of oxidation, which may occur in any physical system.

The Effects of Gases in the Ecology of Insects on Rates of Biological Processes.—The general requirement of oxygen for respiration is so well established that it will be considered only for the purpose of showing that it is another example of a physical factor which may be present in a minimum amount, which will produce normal activities, or in a maximum amount, which may cause death. Even the greatest necessity of life may be so abundant that it becomes toxic, or so scarce as to be a limiting factor in life. Insects, in general, have adjusted themselves to take advantage of practically every environmental niche which may be inhabited, and they have shown very ingenious adaptation to take advantage of special environments so far as the gaseous constituents of the media are concerned.

Dendy (1919) and Dendy and Elkington (1918) have shown that granary weevils are very definitely limited by the oxygen supply. This is in accordance with our general information. Lund (1921) showed that the flatworm, *Planaria*, was definitely limited by about one-third of the normal saturation of oxygen in water. The experiments of Back and Cotton (1925) with a vacuum tend to indicate that the insects died of oxygen starvation because of the fact that they were able to endure low atmospheric pressure over such long periods of time.

Bodine (1928) has shown that it is possible for insects to endure a paucity of oxygen for a period of time during which a debt of oxygen is built up in the body; but this debt is quickly made up when they return to a normal oxygen. Such conditions can be endured only as emergencies, however, and a long period would end in death. The experiments of Cleveland (1925) have given a much clearer conception of the ranges within which insects are able to endure changes in oxygen pressure. He found that it was possible to kill the protozoan symbionts in the digestive tracts of certain insects by raising the oxygen pressure. He found that high oxygen pressure was over 67 times as toxic for the protozoa as for the hosts. It seemed in this case that it was the oxygen pressure which was operating, for he found that the effect of five atmospheres of ordinary air was the same as the effect of one atmosphere of pure oxygen, which means that in either case the same pressure of oxygen was experienced. The accompanying table shows some interesting relationships to oxygen pressure on symbionts and hosts. It will be noticed that the cockroach was able to endure three and one-half atmospheres of oxygen for twice as long as *Termopsis*, and many times as long as any of the internal symbionts. This seems to indicate that the oxygen tension in the digestive tracts where these parasites normally live must be relatively constant, since the symbionts themselves are so susceptible to oxygen change.

TABLE IX.—THE TIME REQUIRED TO KILL CERTAIN ANIMALS AT VARIOUS PRESSURES OF OXYGEN[1]

Pressure in atmospheres	Time to kill all intestinal protozoa of										To kill trichomonas in culture from			To kill host		
	Termites								Cockroach	Frog	Frog	Rat	Man	Termopsis	Cockroach	Frog
	Rhinotermitidae				Kalotermitidae											
	Leucotermes		Reticulitermes		Termopsis		Cryptotermes									
	Hr.	Min.	Hr.	Min.	Hr.	Min.	Hr.	Min.	Hr.	Hr.	Hr.	Hr.	Hr.	Hr.	Hr.	Hr.
1.0	24		2[2]		72		2[2]							*		
1.5	4	30	9		9		7	30								
2.0	1	35	4		5		4	30								
2.5	1	15	1	40	2		1	55								
3.0		50		50	1	5	1									
3.5		30		30		40		35	3½	28	6	10	11	45	90	65

[1] CLEVELAND, 1925.

[2] Not killed in 10 days.

Cole (1921) experimented with chironomid larvae which were found in the bottom of Lake Mendota, Wisconsin, where the oxygen content of the water for several months of each year is so low that no free oxygen can be detected. The interesting problem as to how the fauna which lives in this environment is able to obtain its oxygen has not been satisfactorily solved. Cole found evidence that some oxidizing material was present, and that this presumably was atomic oxygen; and it was his conclusion that this atomic oxygen must be taken advantage of by the insects living there. Insects, in general, seem to have solved very successfully the problem of making the atmosphere accessible to their tissues.

Lee (1929) gives a good summary of the information on the respiratory mechanism of insects. It seems to be rather generally accepted at the present time that part of the spiracles serve for the inspiratory movement of the air, and another portion of the spiracles for the expiratory movement of air. It seems rather clear, therefore, that the carbon dioxide is forced out of the body and then atmospheric air drawn in. If this is true, the reasoning of Portier (1928) might be used for concluding that the insects would usually have a higher oxygen-tension difference between their tissues and the surrounding air than would other animals; for the air would not be mixed with the carbon dioxide, but would come in as free atmospheric air almost directly in contact with the tissues themselves.

The discussion thus far has dealt very largely with oxygen, but the importance of carbon dioxide must not be overlooked. Haldane (1917) says that there may be plenty of oxygen present, but carbon dioxide may exert its toxic effect nevertheless.

Dendy (1919) showed that while it might be partly lack of oxygen that interfered with the metabolism of insects in air-tight spaces, it was very largely the accumulation of carbon dioxide. The respiratory problems of various special environments involve not only oxygen and carbon dioxide, but even nitrogen. In the case of the respiration of aquatic insects, which will be further considered in connection with synecology, Ege (1915) and others have shown that the bubble of air which is carried below the surface of the water by the insect acts as a mechanism for obtaining oxygen from the water. Since this bubble ordinarily contains four-fifths of its volume in nitrogen, and only one-fifth oxygen, the nitrogen becomes the important factor. As the insect begins to consume the oxygen, the carbon dioxide which is given off diffuses into the water so rapidly that Ege did not take it into account. As oxygen consumption proceeds, the oxygen pressure in the bubble is decreased, and the nitrogen pressure is relatively increased. If we assume that the bubble was in equilibrium with the gas in the water at the start, this change of pressure will lead to a diffusion of oxygen into the bubble and of nitrogen out of the bubble. Since the bubble will continue to exist and act as an air supply until both gases are entirely gone, it is important to know their relative rates of diffusion. Ege compared the rates by the use of a formula and concluded that the oxygen diffused into the bubble over three times as rapidly as the nitrogen passed out. Consequently, the amount of oxygen which would be available from the bubble mechanism would be about 13 times the amount that the bubble originally contained. This applies, of course, to adult insects, which carry bubbles of air below the surface of the water. Nearly all aquatic insect larvae, especially those of the *Diptera*, respire by means of surface respiration and tend to keep the gases in solution in their bodies in equilibrium with those which are in solution in the water.

There are many problems of respiration in special environments of the soil, decaying animal bodies and plant material, which are of special interest to the ecologist, and which require special investigation.

Effects of Gases on the Morphology of Animals.—Here, as in other cases, it is necessary to discriminate between established relationships and assumptions based upon general observations. Purely physiological considerations of conditions which are not known to exist in nature may also be omitted.

Gerould (1924) called attention to the effect of oxygen and temperature in the formation of melanin in the wings of *Colias*. In some experiments he tried shutting off the oxygen supply in certain areas of the wings which developed melanin. He found, however, that his method did not inhibit the formation of the melanin. His general conclusion is that melanin is formed when metabolism is slowed down, whatever the cause of the slowing may be. It is nevertheless true, however, that oxygen is required for the reaction, as he pointed out.

We might conclude that where oxygen is required for the reaction in pigment formation, its absence from the environment would affect color. Further experimentation is required before we shall be able to draw definite conclusions.

Effects of Gases on the Distribution of Animals.—It has already been pointed out that over the various areas of the earth there is very little change in the constitution of the atmosphere. Therefore, we would not expect that the geographic distribution of animals would be greatly affected by the gases of the atmosphere. However, certain local distributions may be very profoundly affected. This is shown to be true in the case of fresh-water lakes and the case of the organisms living in the bottom where oxygen is low or absent, as has already been referred to. It may also be an important factor in the distribution of animals in the soil, as will be taken up under the subject of Synecology. It would seem in general that the distribution of gases and respiration was largely a physiological problem, rather than an ecological one.

BIBLIOGRAPHY

THE GASEOUS CONSTITUENTS OF THE MEDIA

BABAK, E.: Die Mechanik und Innervation der Atmung; in Winterstein, H., "Handbuch der vergleichenden Physiologie," **1**: 362–534, Jena, 1921.

BACK, E. A., and R. I. COTTON: The Use of the Vacuum for Insect Control, *Jour. Agr. Research*, **31**: 1035–1041, 1925.

BAYLISS, W. M.: "Principles of General Physiology," London, New York, Bombay, Calcutta, and Madras, 1918.

BODINE, J. H.: Insect Metabolism, the Anaërobic Metabolism of an Insect (Orthoptera), *Biol. Bull.*, **55**: 395–403, 1928.

CLEVELAND, L. R.: Toxicity of Oxygen for Protozoa in Vivo and in Vitro; Animals Defaunated Without Injury, *Biol. Bull.*, **48**: 455–468, 1925.

COLE, ARCH. E.: Oxygen Supply of Certain Animals Living in Water Containing no Dissolved Oxygen, *Jour. Expt. Zool.*, **33**: 293–320, 1921.

DAVIS, J. G., and W. K. STATER: The Aerobic and Anaërobic Metabolism of the Common Cockroach (*Periplaneta orientalis*), *Biochem. Jour.*, **22**: 331–337, 1928.

DENDY, A.: Report on the Effect of Air-tight Storage upon Grain Insects, *Roy. Soc., London, Grain Pests (War) Comm., Repts.*, Pt. I, Harrison and Sons, 1919.

DENDY, ARTHUR, and H. D. ELKINGTON: Report on the Effect of Air-tight Storage upon Grain Insects, *Roy. Soc., London, Grain Pests' (War) Comm. Rept.* 3, 1918.

EGE, RICHARD: On the Respiratory Function of Air Stores Carried by some Aquatic Insects (*Corixidae, Dytiscidae,* and *Notonecta*), *Ztschr. allg. Physiol.*, **17**: 81–124, 1918.

FINK, DAVID E.: Metabolism during Embryonic and Metamorphic Development of Insects, *Jour. Gen. Physiol.*, **7**: 527–543, 1925.

GEROULD, J. H.: Physiology of the Color Pattern in Butterflies of genus *Colias, Anat. Rec.*, **29**: 93–94, 1924.

HALDANE, J. S.: "Organism and Environment as Illustrated by the Physiology of Breathing," Yale University Press, New Haven, 1917. 138 pp.

HUMPHREYS, C. J.: "The Physics of the Air," J. B. Lippincott Company, Philadelphia, 1920.

JACOBS, M. H.: A Simple Method of Measuring the Rate of Respiration of Small Organisms, *Amer. Naturalist*, **54**: 91–96, 1920.

KNIGHT, H. H.: On the Nature of the Color Patterns in *Heteroptera* with Data on the Effects Produced by Temperature and Humidity, *Ann. Ent. Soc. Amer.*, **17**: 258–272, 1924.

KROGH, A.: On the Composition of the Air in the Tracheal System of some Insects, *Skand. Arch. Physiol.*, **29**: 29, 1913.

————: Mikrorespirometrie, in E. Abderhalden, "Handbuch der biochemischen Arbeitsmethoden," VIII, p. 519, Berlin, 1915.

————: "The Respiratory Exchange of Animals and Man," Longmans, Green and Co., London and New York, 1916. 173 pp.

————: The Rate of Diffusion of Gases through Animal Tissues, with some Remarks on the Coefficient of Invasion, *Jour. Physiol.*, **52**: 391–408, 1919.

LEE, MILTON O.: Respiration in Insects, *Quart. Rev. Biol.*, **4**: 213–232, 1929.

LUND, E. J.: A Simple Method for Measuring Carbon Dioxide Produced by Small Organisms, *Biol. Bull.*, **36**: 105–114, 1919.

————: Oxygen Concentration as a Limiting Factor in the Respiratory Metabolism of *Planaria agilis, Biol. Bull.*, **41**: 203–220, 1921.

PORTIER, P.: Sur le rôle physiologique des sacs aëriens des oiseaux, *Compt. rend. soc. biol.*, **99**: 1327–1328, 1928.

POWERS, EDWIN B.: The Absorption of Oxygen by the Herring as Affected by the Carbon-Dioxide Tension of the Sea Water, *Ecology*, **4**: 307–312, 1923.

SHELFORD, VICTOR, E.: An Experimental Study of the Effects of Gas Waste upon Fishes with Special Reference to Stream Pollution, *Ill. State Lab. Nat. Hist. Bull.*, **11**: 381–412, 1917.

SHELFORD, VICTOR E., and W. C. ALLEE, The Reactions of Fishes to Gradients of Dissolved Atmospheric Gases, *Jour. Expt. Zool.*, **14**: 207–266, 1913.

THUNBERG, TORSTEN: Ein Mikrorespirometer, *Skand. Arch. Physiol.*, **17**: 74–85, 1905.

WELLS, M. M.: The Resistance of Fishes to Different Concentrations and Combinations of Oxygen and Carbon Dioxide, *Biol. Bull.*, **25**: 323–347, 1913.

NEUTRALITY OF THE MEDIA

Introduction.—The neutrality of various media explored from the point of view of hydrogen-ion concentration serves as one of the best examples of a rush of scientific workers into a new field. In 1920 Clark published his first edition on the measurement of hydrogen-ion concentration. In eight years this has been followed by a series of reprints and new editions, until at present we have a volume which is more than twice the size of the original edition. In the introduction to the last edition Clark (1928) called attention to the fact that the number of papers occurring on hydrogen-ion concentration up to 1918 hardly reached the point of 100 per year. In 1927, almost 1,500 papers on this subject were published.

Several factors apparently have contributed to the great popularity of this field. The physiological importance of dissociated ions has been clearly demonstrated. A convenient method of measuring and expressing concentration is available. And last but not least, it has opened up a field in which new facts can be obtained very quickly with very little effort, and there is a great possibility of significance being attached to them. It would be extremely presumptuous in a volume of this nature, with one chapter devoted to the neutrality of the media, to attempt to give such a presentation that the uninitiated might have a clear appreciation of hydrogen-ion concentration, together with a proper conception of its fundamental importance, and in addition to give a summary of examples of the results of the vast amount of investigation. The student is referred to Clark (1928) and to the general textbooks on physiology to form his conception of the importance of hydrogen-ion concentration.

It may be worthwhile to give a brief discussion of the fundamental factors involved in the equilibrium between acids and bases in various systems. Pure, distilled water is often taken as an example of a neutral solution. This contains both hydrogen and hydroxyl ions in accordance with the following formula: $HOH = H^+ + OH^-$. This means that dissociated ions of hydrogen carrying a positive charge may be found free in the water, and that hydroxyl ions carrying a negative charge may also be found. In the case of distilled water, we have a neutral condition, and the system is in equilibrium. This is formally expressed with this equation, $\dfrac{[H^+][OH^-]}{HOH} = K$, in which the dissociated ions are indicated in the numerator, and the undissociated residue in the denominator. As a matter of fact, in the case of distilled water there are so few dissociated ions that the denominator of this fraction may be disregarded for practical purposes. In the case of acid solutions the "strength" of the acid is due to the dissociated ions, which act as electrolytes. Consequently, two acids present in the same per cent of normal solution may have different "strengths" since there are more dissociated ions in the stronger of the two acids. Hydrochloric acid, for instance, is about 90 per cent dissociated in one-tenth of one per cent normal solution. Acetic acid is about 1.3 per cent dissociated in a tenth normal solution. Consequently, we speak of hydrochloric acid as being much "stronger" than acetic acid.

What has been said of acid solutions might also be said of alkaline solutions. In the case of acid solutions, we were speaking of the hydrogen ions; and in the case of alkaline solutions, of hydroxyl ions. Consequently, the acidity, the alkalinity, and the neutrality of a medium will depend upon the balance of the dissociated hydrogen and hydroxyl ions.

Methods of Measuring the Concentration of Ions for Ecological Work. Much of the progress which has been made in biological studies on the effect of neutrality, acidity, and alkalinity has been due to the introduction of new methods of measurement and quite largely to new methods of expression. These new methods have at the same time advantages and disadvantages. The introduction of a simple system of expression has allowed biologists to neglect and even forget the fundamental conceptions upon which the expression is based.

An acid solution may be described in terms of its normality with respect to total acids or with respect to the hydrogen ions. A normal solution of acid is one which contains 1.008 g. of acidic hydrogen in a liter of solution. And a normal solution of hydrogen ions is one containing 1.008 g. of hydrogen ions per liter of solution. These two expressions of normality lead to confusion. Clark (1928) has suggested that we speak of a normal acid solution in the older sense as the "quantity" factor of acidity, and of the hydrogen-ions' normality as the "intensity" factor. It is with the activity of these hydrogen ions that we are concerned at the present time, and attention will now be turned to the expression of the concentration of these hydrogen ions.

Because of the necessity for expressing extremely small fractions of the normal value, the expression of the concentration of hydrogen ions becomes cumbersome, especially to biologists who are not accustomed to thinking in terms of mathematics. Sorensen greatly simplified the notation by adopting a system which is now known as the pH value. At the same time that the notation was simplified by this system of values, the conception of the quantity of hydrogen ions present was greatly complicated. Sorensen's expression was "the logarithm of the reciprocal of the concentration of the hydrogen ions expressed in grams per liter," and may be given formal expression as $pH = \log_{10} \frac{1}{[H^+]}$, or $pH = -\log_{10} H$, so that H may be written $[H^+] = 10^{-pH}$ Here the $-pH$ appears as an exponent, and the term pH literally means the power of hydrogen-ion concentration. In interpreting the pH scale, it is important to keep in mind the fact that the exponent expressing the concentration of hydrogen ions has a negative value, *e.g.*, hydrogen-ion concentration equaling 10^{-7} normal is expressed by the pH scale as 7. The accompanying table shows the relationship between these values for hydrogen-ion concentration, the pH scale and the hydroxyl-ion concentration. The scale of hydrogen-ion concentration or pH goes from one to one one-hundredth trillion normal, whereas the pH scale goes from 1 to 14. There is an enormous advantage in this simplified scale, but a complication in understanding what pH actually means. The fact should be further emphasized that a pH value is an actual value derived from the concentration of hydrogen ions in grams per liter.

RELATIONSHIP BETWEEN VALUES FOR H-ION CONCENTRATION, AND THE 0 H-ION SCALE

pH	Log of H			Log of OH
1	10^{-1}	0.1	0.0000000000001	10^{-13}
2	10^{-2}	0.01	0.000000000001	10^{-12}
3	10^{-3}	0.001	0.00000000001	10^{-11}
4	10^{-4}	0.0001	0.0000000001	10^{-10}
5	10^{-5}	0.00001	0.000000001	10^{-9}
6	10^{-6}	0.000001	0.00000001	10^{-8}
7	10^{-7}	0.0000001	0.0000001	10^{-7}
8	10^{-8}	0.00000001	0.000001	10^{-6}
9	10^{-9}	0.000000001	0.00001	10^{-5}
10	10^{-10}	0.0000000001	0.0001	10^{-4}
11	10^{-11}	0.00000000001	0.001	10^{-3}
12	10^{-12}	0.000000000001	0.01	10^{-2}
13	10^{-13}	0.0000000000001	0.1	10^{-1}
14	10^{-14}	0.00000000000001	1.0	10^{-0}

There is an interesting buffer action of weak acids and their alkali salts, which tends to resist changes in the concentration of ions about the neutral point. When an alkaline solution is added to an acid solution to neutralize it, the ions which were originally undissociated tend to become ionized to maintain the original condition. Thus a solution which is near the neutral point tends to resist any change by dissociating ions to maintain its original ratio of hydrogen and hydroxyl ions. This process is very important in protecting organisms against sudden changes in hydrogen-ion concentration. Henderson (1913) has stressed this point as illustrating how environments tend to adjust themselves to present the conditions most desirable for organisms.

For methods of determining the hydrogen-ion concentration of solutions the student is referred to Clark (1928). There are a number of outfits for field work which use both the colorimetric and electrometric methods of determination. These make it possible to take field readings with very little apparatus and in a short period of time.

Neutrality of the Medium as a Factor in the Ecology of Animals.— The neutrality of the medium is of particular importance in the ecology of aquatic and soil-inhabiting animals. For this reason its significance will be taken up under the chapters on Synecology, which discuss the various environments in which it is concerned. At the present time, attention will be called only to its general ecological importance. Inasmuch as neutrality itself is a condition of equilibrium between the dissociated hydrogen and hydroxyl ions, the conclusion follows that it may be influenced by many of the environmental conditions. Consequently, the hydrogen-ion concentration of a given environment may be looked upon as a sort of a "symptom" rather than a "cause" of any particular condition in the environment. It is very difficult to evaluate any relationship between pH and the environmental conditions. Therefore, it is necessary to look upon the pH value as a sort of algebraic sum of the general condition of the environment rather than as a definite measure of some causal factor.

Effect of Hydrogen-ion Concentration on Physical Processes.—Much of the importance of the hydrogen and hydroxyl ions may be due to their ability to carry electrical charges. The recent literature seems to indicate that many physical phenomena are influenced by these electrical charges, and that very small changes in hydrogen-ion concentration may result in very significant changes in the physical properties of substances, all of which may enter into the functioning of the animal mechanism. The quadrivalent thorium ion is said to be capable of reducing the surface charge of quartz by 50 per cent when it is present in the concentration of only one gram ion in a thousand million grams of water. It is such surprising results as these that have led the great number of investigators to turn to the hydrogen ion as the cause of all sorts of natural phenomena. The index of Clark's most recent edition will lead to a great deal of information on these phenomena.

General Effects of the Concentration of Hydrogen Ions upon Animals.— The sensitiveness of the animal mechanism to changes in the concentration of hydrogen ions is becoming a classic example of the importance of physical factors in animal physiology. It is stated that an addition of 0.00004 per cent solution of hydrochloric acid in the circulating blood of a frog is sufficient to kill the heart. The respiratory center and other tissues are apparently just as susceptible to changes in hydrogen-ion concentration. The permeability of membranes is very markedly affected also by changes in hydrogen-ion concentration. The modern textbooks of physiology are filled with examples, and almost daily new papers are coming into print showing additional effects of changes of hydrogen-ion concentration.

Considering the hydrogen-ion concentration as a physical factor of an environment, it may be compared with the other physical factors which, in general, have some optimum concentration for the existence of animals with a pessimum lying at either side. With all the study which has been devoted to pH in recent years, there are still few authentic cases in which the optimum hydrogen-ion concentration has been definitely demonstrated and where the curves dropping off to the pessimum on either side have been critically marked out. It seems probable that in some organisms such zones of optimum and pessimum may be demonstrated, while other organisms may possibly be able to tolerate great extremes of hydrogen-ion concentration because of either a buffering action of the organism or a great resistance to actual change of hydrogen-ion concentration.

Arrhenius (1921) found that the optimum pH for the survival of earthworms in potted soil was a pH of 7. Above and below this point, the worms died in a shorter period of time. Saunders (1924) found that protozoan, *Spirostomum ambiguum*, was most active at the pH of 7.4, but died at a pH of 8. It had its activity greatly reduced by a pH of 6, though it was not killed at more acid conditions. Saunders believes that the difficulty of keeping a culture of *Spirostomum* in the laboratory has been due mainly to the inability to maintain an aquarium at the required pH rather than to the low oxygen content of the water, as has been previously supposed. Senior-White (1926) states that the neutral waters of Ceylon range from pH 5.4 to 9.2, but that the mosquito larvae, in general, range only from pH 5.8 to 8.6.

It is doubtless true that many other insects have a limiting range of hydrogen-ion concentration. Stickney (1922), however, in experimenting with the dragonfly, *Libellula pulchella*, found that it was indifferent to acidity even to a pH of 1, and lived apparently unharmed in various pH values.

Philip (1927) transferred insects from one part of a lake to another which involved a considerable change of hydrogen-ion value without any noticeable effect whatever. It is probably true in many of these cases that the organisms are capable of buffering the environment and thereby preventing their coming into direct contact with these great changes. We seem to have little dependable evidence of the effect of hydrogen-ion concentration on the rate of the metabolism and development of insects, or upon the form and structure of any of them.

Effects of the Concentration of Ions on the Behavior of Animals.— Shelford and Powers (1915), Wells (1915), Shelford (1918), and others have investigated the reaction of fishes in gradient tanks where various pH concentrations were maintained. It is stated that fish, in general, have a rather definite reaction in choosing an optimum pH, and that, in the Puget Sound region, herrings were found but once in the water above 7.9. They were never found in water below 7.71, and the greatest number were found at pH 7.76 and 7.73. Other species were found to have other optimum pH values varying between 7.98 and 8.08. However, Behre in 1925 stated that in an investigation of Pacific Slope waters, he found them to vary between pH 6.8 and 8.4, and that fish were found to be independent of a considerable variation in pH. All fish which were found in the water of pH 7, were also found in that of pH 8.4. This seems to mean that the pH readings taken, are a measure of certain conditions existing in the environments

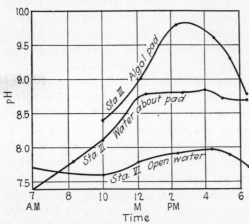

FIG. 54.—Diurnal fluctuations in pH values in Crystal Lake waters during an onshore wind. Station III in shallow water. Station VI at the "drop off." (*Philip*, 1927.)

which affect the equilibrium of ions, and that the organisms themselves are capable of buffering their environmental media. Consequently, it would seem that little significance could be attached to these references in literature to the effect of hydrogen-ion concentration on the distribution of organisms. Shelford (1925) called attention to the difference in hydrogen-ion-concentration readings obtained in various lakes in the western part of the United States.

However, Philip's experience (1927) seems to indicate that a series of readings with as great a variation of pH as Shelford found over the western United States could be found in a single lake even within a single day. This will be referred to later in the subject matter of Synecology.

Hall (1925) presented an interesting example of the combined effect of neutrality and oxygen. Her data, as presented in Fig. 55, furnish another interesting illustration of the combined effects of two factors varying under experimental conditions. The lines are drawn to represent equal times for the development of the short-fin rays of the whitefish. The pH values in the experiment were controlled by CO_2 con-

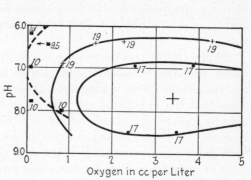

FIG. 55.—Showing equal lines on an oxygen-hydrogen-ion chart. The broken line passes approximately through combinations of oxygen and hydrogen-ion concentration in which the embryos developed a flat tail in ten days, beginning four days after spawning. The solid lines pass through combinations of oxygen and hydrogen-ion concentration in which the embryos developed short fine rays in 17 and 19 days respectively. The general trend of these lines suggests that development may be expected to be more rapid at about 3.4 cc. of oxygen and pH 7.6 to 7.7 where the large cross is placed. This cross is in the center of the ellipse. The center of the ellipse suggested by the flat-tail curve would fall at a higher hydrogen-ion concentration. (*Hall*, 1925.)

centration.   The approximate position of optimum condition for short-fin development is indicated by the large "X" on the diagram. This seems to indicate that the changes of pH within the range shown had a greater effect on the rate of development than did the range of oxygen used in the experiment. However, it is not possible to draw a general conclusion from so few observations. We then conclude that the study of the hydrogen-ion concentration of various environments will furnish interesting supporting evidence in any complete ecological study, but that at the present time we do not have before us evidence to show that hydrogen-ion concentration is a predominant factor in the ecology of animals.

BIBLIOGRAPHY

NEUTRALITY OF THE MEDIA

ARRHENIUS, O.: Influence of Soil Reactions on Earthworms, *Ecology*, **2**: 255–257, 1921.

ATKINS, W. R. G.: The Hydrogen-ion Concentration of Sea Water in Its Biological Relations, *Jour. Mar. Biol. Assoc.*, **12**: 718–771, 1922.

BAYLISS, W. M.: "Principles of General Physiology," London, New York, Bombay, Calcutta, and Madras, 1918.

BEHRE, E. H.: Environmental Factors in Relation to Distribution of Panamanian Fresh-water Fishes, *Anat. Rec.*, **31**: 324, 1925.

BODINE, JOSEPH HALL: Hydrogen-ion Concentration of Protozoan Cultures, *Biol. Bull.*, **41**: 73–78, 1921.

CLARK, W. M.: "Determination of Hydrogen Ions," Williams & Wilkins Co., Baltimore, 1928. 717 pp.

COWLES, R. P., and A. M. SCHWITALLA: The Hydrogen-ion Concentration of a Creek, Its Waterfall, Swamp and Ponds, *Ecology*, **4**: 402–416, 1923.

HALL, ADA, R.: Effects of Oxygen and Carbon Dioxide on the Development of the Whitefish, *Ecology*, **6**: 104–116, 1925.

HENDERSON, L. J.: "The Fitness of the Environment," The Macmillan Company, New York, 1913. 317 pp.

HURWITZ, S. H.: The Reaction of Earthworms to Acids, *Proc. Amer. Acad.*, 46, 1910.

JEWELL, MINNA E.: The Fauna of an Acid Stream, *Ecology*, **3**: 22–28, 1922.

JUDAY, CHANCEY: Behavior of the Larva of *Corethra punctepennis* Say, *Anat. Rec.*, **17**: 340, 1920.

LEEDS, ――――, and NORTHRUP, ――――: "Apparatus for Electrometric Determination of Hydrogen-ion Concentration, Leeds and Northrup Company," Philadelphia, 1921.

PHILIP, CORNELIUS B.: Diurnal Fluctuations in the Hydrogen-ion Activity of a Minnesota Lake, *Ecology*, **8**: 73–89, 1927.

SAUNDERS, J. T.: The Measurement of the Carbon-dioxide Output of Fresh-water Animals by Means of Indicators, *Proc. Cambridge Phil. Soc.*, *Biol. Sci.*, **1**: 43–48, 1923.

SAUNDERS, J. T.: The Effect of Hydrogen-ion Concentration on Behavior, Growth, and Occurrence of *Spirostomum*, *Proc. Cambridge Phil. Soc.*, *Biol. Sci.*, **1**: 189–203, 1924.

SENIOR-WHITE, R.: Physical Factors in Mosquito Ecology, *Bull. Ent. Research*, **16**: 187–248, 1926.

SHELFORD, V. E.: Equipment for Maintaining a Flow of Oxygen-free Water, and for Controling Gas Content, *Ill. State Lab. Nat. Hist. Bull.*, **11**: art. 9, 1918.

———: The Hydrogen-ion Concentration of Certain Western American Inland Waters, *Ecology*, **6**: 270–288, 1925.

SHELFORD, V. E., and E. B. POWERS: An Experimental Study of the Movements of Herring and Other Marine Fishes, *Biol. Bull.*, **28**: 315–334, 1915.

SHOHL, A. T.: Reactions of Earthworms to Hydroxyl Ions, *Amer. Jour. Physiol.*, **34**: 384–404, 1914.

SORENSEN, S. P. L.: Études enzymatiques; II, sur la mésure et l'importance de la concentration des ions hydrogène dans les réactions enzymatiques, *Compt. rend. lab. Carlsberg*, **8**, 1909.

STICKNEZ, FENNER: The Relation of the Nymphs of a Dragonfly *Libellula pulchella* Drury, to Acid and Temperature, *Ecology*, **3**: 250– 254, 1922.

WALTER, E.: Das Gesetz vom Minimum und das Gleichgewicht im Wasser, *Arch. Hydro. u. Planktonkunde*, **4**: 339–366, 1909.

WELLS, M. M.: Reactions and Resistance of Fishes in Their Natural Environments to Acidity, Alkalinity, and Neutrality, *Biol. Bull.*, **29**: 221–257, 1915.

CHAPTER VII

NUTRITION

Introduction.—It cannot be said that nutrition is a purely physical factor of ecology for the reason that no animal, so far as we are able to discern, is able to live upon a diet which does not contain some compounds which have been synthesized by another organism. We have therefore arrived at the point where physical autecology and biotic autecology are merged, and it is an arbitrary matter as to whether this chapter is to be included under physical autecology or biotic autecology. All animals are dependent upon at least one other organism for the preparation of their food. In fact, there has not yet been demonstrated a case in which an animal may be reared in the laboratory on a purely synthetic diet in the sense that every compound involved has been synthesized, independent of the existence of any other organism. There is probably no better example in all nature of the interdependence of organisms than that of nutrition itself.

Nutrition is a broad subject when considered in the present sense. It may be conceived of as including all organic and inorganic chemical compounds which an animal takes into its body from the environment. It includes all materials which go into the upbuilding and maintenance of the animal mechanism and is the direct source of all the energy which is used in its metabolism. From the viewpoint of biochemistry and physiology, it constitutes a great new field of biological science in which enormous progress has been made in the last few years. Its subject matter could not be adequately presented in a smaller space than a large volume. It is not possible in these pages to more than call attention to some of the important literature and to try to point out the ecological significance of the general nutritional relationships of animals.

Method of Measuring Nutrition.—The nutritional value of foods was measured in terms of calories but a short time ago. This gave a physical measurement quite comparable to those in use in connection with all the physical factors of the environment which have just been considered. Within the past few years attention has been called to certain food accessories: vitamines. These are measured only by biological tests. That is, it is necessary to feed the material to animals and note its effect upon the rate of growth, the condition of maintenance, reproduction, and general metabolism of the animal. These measures are all biotic rather than physical and are more or less relative in our present state of knowledge.

This may be considered another reason why it might be more logical to include the factor of nutrition under biotic autecology, because its measurements are all essentially biotic.

Method of Controlling the Nutritive Value of Food.—There are two methods which are generally used in experimental work on nutrition. One is to build up a synthetic food by putting together certain materials, supposedly of known composition. These combinations may be changed, and the corresponding changes in the rates of growth of the organisms noted. This method is well illustrated by the work of Sweetman and Palmer (1928). If it is possible in such work to use pure chemicals, the food requirements may be rather completely analyzed. However, it is usually possible to get no further than the use of some general plant or animal product, the composition of which may not be completely known.

The second method is to start with the normal food of the animal to be studied, and extract certain substances from the food and note the consequences. The difficulty with this method when used alone, is the ability to extract only the one material desired and leave all the others unchanged. Obviously, it is most desirable to combine the two methods of study whenever possible. Examples of the use of these methods are shown in the text in the description of various features of research.

NUTRITION AS A FACTOR IN ANIMAL ECOLOGY

There is probably no other subject under which it will be more necessary to restrict ourselves to the significance with respect to insects as compared with other animals than in the case of nutrition. The general nutritional relationships of animals are so complex, so far reaching, that we must refer to other animals only to get the proper perspectives in our consideration of the insects. In general, the literature before us is purely descriptive, tending to be mere descriptive natural history and quite neglectful of the physiological relationship.

Uvarov (1928), in his excellent consideration of insect nutrition and metabolism, says:

The first glance at the summary, and particularly at the voluminous bibliography, including nearly 600 titles may give the impression that a very large amount of work has been done on the problem of insect nutrition and metabolism, but when all the data available on these particular subjects are put together, it becomes clear that very few points have been touched and the results achieved are but a drop compared with the ocean of unknown phenomena.

In general, literature tells us upon what plants or in what media insects may be found, with the assumption that these plants and media constitute the food, and very little is said of what actually is used by the insect for food.

The Source of Energy in Physical and Chemical Processes.—In the routine treatment of each physical factor of the environment, it has seemed well to call attention first to the action of the factor under consideration upon the physical processes, before taking up its effect upon the animal mechanism. In the case of nutrition, it would have been easier to make this comparison a few years ago when the energy balance had been worked out upon the basis of oxidation, and each animal was described as requiring a certain number of calories per unit weight of its body. In our present information about vitamines and hormones, the subject of nutrition looks more complicated than ever before. We realize that more than proteins, carbohydrates, and fats must be available in order to have a normal functioning of the animal mechanism. If we are to make the classical comparison between an organism and a machine, we must consider the general food, as we usually speak of it, as the fuel for oxidation; while the vitamines and other substances which must be present in small quantities will be comparable to the proper lubrication of the machine to keep it in running order. It is quite possible that, as we obtain new facts and get our information better correlated, the general subject will appear more simple. In the case of insects, we are probably less able to make generalizations than in the case of birds and mammals which have been the object of most of the nutritional research.

The Effect of Nutrition on Biological Processes.—Before proceeding with the ecological consideration of our information about the nutrition of insects, it will be well to get a perspective of the entire field of nutrition by considering the broader groups of organisms in their nutritional relationships. We may distinguish, in general, three great groups of organisms. We have, first of all, the photosynthetic forms which have sometimes been called "autotrophic." These are the green plants which can build up the complicated proteins, polysaccharides, and fats of their tissues from nitrates, phosphates, and sulphates from carbon dioxide and water, with the energy of sunlight. This photosynthetic power is of the greatest importance to the entire organic world; for it is by means of this process that the energy of sunlight is captured and passed on to all living organisms. We cannot conceive of the existence of the organic world, as we know it, without this one great step in nutrition.

There is a second group which is composed of microorganisms which cannot form sugar or starch from carbon dioxide, sunlight, and water, and these organisms, consequently, must be offered more complicated compounds for the synthesis of their carbohydrates. But these forms have the ability to form their proteins from an ammonium salt or a single amino acid. Certain of these microorganisms can even capture the nitrogen of the air and combine it in such a way that it can be made use of by higher organisms. This is a very important function, for available nitrogen constitutes one of the great limiting factors of all organisms. Even the autotrophic organisms must get their nitrogen in the form of nitrates.

The animals, in general, are typical of the third group. They must have their carbohydrates in the form of sugar or starch, and their nitrogen in the form of one or more proteins. These requirements stand in striking contrast to those of the photosynthetic or autotrophic organisms which are capable of capturing the energy of sunlight and combining it with carbon dioxide and water of the atmosphere; and to the second group of microorganisms which is capable of taking the nitrogen from the earth's atmosphere, and so combining it that it can form the basis for all of the protein of the living organic world. The animals, or zootrophic forms, therefore, stand considerably removed from the raw natural resources, so far as their nutrition is concerned. When we add to these requirements the list of all the vitamines required for the normal functioning of the animal mechanism, it seems even more restricted as to its nutritional requirements. There are at least five vitamines which are conservatively accepted as having been demonstrated. Some of these are so complicated that it is proposed to divide them into several factors, and there are many others that have been proposed which are not accepted by the more conservative nutritional physiologists.

We have in general the Vitamine A which is fat soluble; it is found in cod-liver oil, butter, eggs, green vegetables, and fruit. Its absence produces xerophthalmia and widespread weakening of the body. The Vitamine B which is water soluble is found in whole grains, and its absence causes the disease known as beriberi. Vitamine C is found in fresh fruits and vegetables, and its absence produces in mammals the disease known as scurvy. Vitamine D which is found in cod-liver oil as the richest source seems to be affected by the presence of sunlight. The absence of Vitamine D causes rickets and interferes with the calcium phosphorus metabolism at least in the case of vertebrates. Vitamine E is the only one which seems to be fairly abundant in the tissues of animals, and its absence causes sterility.

Our general perspective of the nutritional requirements of insects will be considered further in the general cycle of nutritional substances in nature. The nitrogen cycle has become a classical example of the history of an element in the organic system. Baumberger in 1919 modified Bayliss' diagram of the cycle of nitrogen. The dots and dashes represent the portions of the diagram which have been put in by Baumberger as the result of his investigation of the nutritional requirements of insects. This is one of the best examples of the interdependence of animals. Physiological investigations of nutrition are continually bringing new light upon the various processes involved, and raising new questions as to the limitations of the various forms that appear in the nitrogen cycle. The general scheme of things remains, however, about the same. There may be some question as to the actual restrictions of animals in capturing free nitrogen from the air; but it is, in general, true that the number of organisms which can do this is very greatly limited, and that the entire kingdom of nature looks to relatively few for fixing all the nitrogen. Plant protein is, in general, the supply of animal protein, and animal wastes form a large portion of the source of ammonia which is acted upon by bacteria to be reduced to nitrates, and then to return again to plant protein. Baumberger has shown that the insects with the symbiotic relationship of fungi are able to short-circuit part of this great cycle. Plant and animal residue may be used more or less directly by

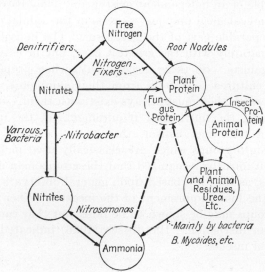

Fig. 56.—Diagram of the nitrogen cycle from the atmosphere through plants and animals. Modified from Bayliss by Baumberger to illustrate the relationship of insects to fungi.

the fungi; and the fungi, by the insect. This, however, does not make any fundamental change in the great nitrogen cycle in nature.

The carbohydrate cycle is no less fundamental than the nitrogen cycle. It is in the course of this cycle that the carbon dioxide of the atmosphere is made use of by plants, which are eaten by animals and carbon dioxide is eliminated by the animals to be returned again to circulation. The insects share the limitations of all animals in respect to these great cycles of nutritive materials in accordance with the laws of nature. For practical purposes, however, many of the insects have developed a system of exempting themselves from the direct action of some of these most stringent restrictions. They have made themselves ecologically independent of some of the physiological restrictions, by associating themselves with microorganisms, in such a way that their symbionts will make up for their own short-comings in the cycles of nitrogen and carbon dioxide. It is this ecological exemption which has led to a great deal of confusion in the description of food habits of insects. There is hardly an organic substance in which insects have not been described as living. They have been able to invade environments of almost pure cellulose where available nitrogen and carbohydrates are not ordinarily considered to be present. They have been able to support themselves in soil and water, and in all the residues of plants and animals. The most recent investigation seems to indicate that they do most of this through their association with symbiotic microorganisms. In some cases, this symbiotic specialization has gone on to such a point that the insects are no longer capable of an independent existence. They become an inseparable part of an ecological unit just as cells in the animal organism have become an inseparable part of the organism. The individual cells may be cultured separately with the greatest care, but in nature they must live in the organism. So these insects may, when proper precautions are taken, be cultured separately from their symbionts, but so far as nature is concerned, they must always exist with them.

In considering the nutritional requirements of the insects for the maintenance of their metabolism, there may be some advantage in dividing them into groups which are classically used in literature. At the same time it must be recognized that the groups may not necessarily be valid groups, as they are based upon general observations as to what seemed to be the food requirement of the insects. When properly analyzed, these groups may be shown to be false, but they can at least form the basis for our discussion. Handlirsch (1926) indicated 29 categories of food habits of insects:

Food Habits of Insects

(English equivalent of Handlirsch's list)

1. No food. (Atrophic.)
2. A very special food. (Monophagous.)
3. Several kinds. (Heterophagous.)
4. Great variety—practically everything. (Pantophagous, omnivorous.)
5. Substance of animal source. (Zoophagous.)
6. Entire animals, especially meat. (Carnivorous.)
7. Prey, either killed or still living. (Predatory.)
8. Dead animals (Zoonekrophagous.)
9. Decaying animals. (Zoosaprophagous.)
10. Sucking blood, which as a rule does not kill the animal. (Haematophagous.)
11. Animal excrements. (Koprophagous.)
12. Liquid secretions, such as spittle, honeydew, etc. (Zoosuccivorous.)
13. Other animal waste, parts of integuments; scales, hair, feathers, wax, silk, etc. (Detritivorous.)
14. On or in a living animal, or its body substances without killing immediately or in fact not killing at all, and staying on or in the host continually, a life time, or at least a long time in one stage. (Ecto- and Endo-parasitic.)
15. Eating each other. (Cannibalistic.)
16. Substance of plant origin. (Phytophagous.)
17. Living plant parts. (Herbivorous.)

18. Algae.   (Algophagous.)
19. Lichen.   (Lichenophagous.)
20. Fungus.   (Mycetophagous.)
21. Woody plant parts.   (Xylophagous.)
22. Fruits and seeds.   (Carpophagous.)
23. Pollen.   (Pollenophagous.)
24. Honey.   (Melliphagous.)
25. Other plant saps.   (Phyto-succivorous.)
26. Dead plant substances.   (Nekrophytophagous.)
27. Decaying plants.   (Saprophytophagous.)
28. In galls.   (Gallivorous.)
29. Soil.   (Geophagous.)

For the sake of the present discussion, we will recognize the phytophagous forms, or plant feeders; saprophagous, or those feeding upon decaying or fermenting organic substances; harpactophagous, or predatory, forms which might also be called carnivorous insects.   We might also recognize parasitic forms.   These would be distinguished from the predatory in that they inhabit but one host during their life cycle. However, this distinction seems to be of relatively little importance for our present consideration.   These categories may be readily harmonized with the physiology of nutrition as may be seen by noting the position they would occupy upon the nitrogen cycle.   More of them are associated with plants than with any other form of food as might be expected, for this is the source of the basic food supply for all organisms.

Weiss (1926 and other papers) has made a study of the number of species found, having the various food habits.   This is a sort of a qualitative measure as we have no right to assume that the number of individuals is directly proportional to the number of species.   However, he found in general that about half the species were phytophagous; about 25 per cent of them, saprophagous; about 15 per cent harpactophagous; and about 10 per cent, parasitic.   Table X gives the comparison of the number of species in these various categories in different parts of America;

TABLE X.—COMPARISON OF THE NUMBER OF SPECIES IN THESE VARIOUS CATEGORIES IN DIFFERENT PARTS OF AMERICA[1]

Habitat	Total species considered	Phytophagous, per cent	Saprophagous, per cent	Harpacto-phagous, per cent	Parasitic, per cent	Pollen feeders, misc. species, per cent
Atlantic coast of North America....	423	45	26	14	11	4
West arctic of North America......	402	47	27	14	10	2
State of New Jersey..............	10,500	49	19	16	12	4
State of Connecticut..............	6,781	52	19	16	10	3

[1] WEISS, 1926.

and it is interesting to note how consistent were the results which Weiss obtained. This seems to indicate that the further removed a species is from the source of food supply, the smaller the number of species will be. This is not consistent with the conclusion of Stunkard (1929), who considered that there were more species of parasites than of all other animals together. He arrived at this conclusion by considering that each species of animal has one or more parasites.

Phytophagous forms vary greatly in their nutritional requirements and may differ as to the choice of host, and the choice of the part of a host. Some insects will eat the foliage of almost any plant, as Japanese beetles, certain grasshoppers, and others do. There are others which are restricted to one species of plant. They will not feed upon any other species, nor can they develop if forced to feed upon another species. There are still others which have a range of host plants but which when started upon one species will not accept one of the alternate food species, but must complete their development upon a species on which they originally started. In some cases the selection of the host plant is made by the female when she deposits her eggs upon the species on which the larvae are to feed. In other cases the larvae make their own selection. There is much of interest to be found in the study of the selection of food plants. Brues (1924, and in other papers) has given consideration to this subject. Craighead (1921) and others have concluded that when a species has been reared for several generations on one of several alternative host plants, the progeny will tend to select the same host plant on which they were reared.[1] There are several possibilities in this connection. It is entirely possible that there may be various strains of each species, some strains feeding upon one host, and other strains feeding upon other host plants. It is also possible that in any given species there may be many heterozygous strains with all the possible combinations of host-plant preferences. If this is the case, there may be a selective action of the environment in eliminating all of the progeny which have a tendency to choose other host plants than those upon which they hatch. This would lead to the progeny which survive choosing again the same host plant on which they were reared. Thorpe (1929) experimented with the small ermine moth, *Hyponomeuta padella* L., which feeds on apple and hawthorn. He concluded from biological, genetic, and morphological evidence that there are two or more biological races within a single species. When the "hawthorn form" was placed on hawthorn and apple, 911 eggs were laid on hawthorn, and 237 on apple in three experiments. When those of the "apple form" were given their choice, 367 eggs were laid on hawthorn and buckthorn, and 3,395 on apple. Thorpe thinks that it is possible that this is an example of an induced situation.

[1] This is sometimes called the "host selection principle."

Every organ of a plant may serve as an environment for an insect. Some species are so closely restricted that they are present only in galls upon flowers, as for instance the famous gall of the oak, which is restricted in its environment not only to a certain species of oak but to the stamens which are present during a few weeks of the year. The physiological conditions represented by these various environments even within a single plant differ greatly. Hering (1926) called attenton to the fact that the nutritive value of the different parts of the leaf may vary greatly. In the extensive work done upon the nutrition of silk-worms, it has been shown that the nutrition of the leaves varies from one time of day to another depending upon whether the contents are essentially starchy or higher in proteins.

Portier (1905) found that the caterpillar, *Nepticula*, which lives on the parenchyma tissue of rose leaves was surrounded by sterile conditions. Baumberger (1919) investigated large numbers of cases of *Prothertri dispar* and found all but a few pathological cases to be sterile. However, the larvae of *Nonagria typhae* which lives in the trunk of the cat-tail, *Typha latifolia*, lives in a symbiotic relationship with a micrococcus and a fungus. It seems possible, therefore, that many supposedly phytopha-gous forms feeding upon green plants are actually living in symbiosis with microorganisms. It seems in general that those forms which live in closed burrows in growing leaves live under sterile conditions; while those forms which live more or less exposed may be associated with micro-organisms. Many questions may well be raised with regard to the nutri-tion of foliage feeders.

Davidson (1923) has concluded that, in the case of the aphids, more attention should be given to the nitrogen requirement. Most of the sap which the aphids draw from the leaves consists of carbohydrates; but he points out that the aphids excrete large quantities of honeydew or carbohydrates. This is probably done during the time that they are concentrating their nitrogen. The nutrient solutions to which the plants have access, undoubtedly affect the organisms feeding upon the leaves. Uvarov suggests that plants may be protected from aphids by the use of acid fertilizers; also Müller (1926) suggests that aluminum sulphate and paraffin solution will keep aphids off the plants if it can be tolerated by the plants, *i.e.*, if it is not injurious. Or we may spray the leaves with nutritive materials in much the same way as we now cover them with poison to kill insects. This would seem to be a fertile field for investigation.

Turning our attention next to the insects which live in the supporting structures, we have the group which is referred to as xylophagous. These insects live in the portion of the plant which is relatively high in carbo-hydrates and low in protein. Haberlandt (1915) concluded that the digestibility of wood was very low and that unless cellulose is changed or destroyed, it has little food value for animals. General observations lead to the conclusion that most insects which live in wood are long-lived. It would seem from this that it requires the ingestion of large quantities of wood in order to accumulate enough protein and other essential materials to complete development. Hubbard (1897), Neger (1908), and many others have shown that most of the insects which apparently feed only upon wood are, in fact, associated with fungi and other microorganisms. The most convincing and complete evidence we have upon this subject is from Cleveland (1923 and 1928) who has studied the symbionts in the intestine of the termites. He states that in some cases half the weight of an adult termite may be due to the protozoan symbionts without which it is unable to live.

It was experimentally demonstrated that when these termites were deprived of their symbionts they could not live on their normal food of cellulose. The symbionts were removed by three methods: by high pressure of gases, by heat, and by starvation. In all cases the results were the same. The six control animals which continued to feed on wood lived normally; while those which were deprived of the protozoan symbiont were unable to live. He found further that all termites which fed upon wood contained these protozoan symbionts. In certain species there are casts which do not possess the symbionts; and these are obliged to feed upon the salivary secretions, or the excrements of the ones which do have the symbionts in order to maintain themselves, even though they continue to feed upon the wood. There seems to be no doubt, after the studies made, both of the termites and their symbionts, that the symbionts digest the cellulose and make it available for the termites. It does not answer the question, however, with regard to how the nitrogen is made available. Heitz (1927) studied a large series of wood-feeding insects and demonstrated that there were symbionts present in all of them, either bacterial or protozoan. In some cases, he found special portions of the digestive tract which were filled with these symbiotic microorganisms. Heitz has suggested that the symbiotic bacteria may be able to fix atmospheric nitrogen, and thus solve the protein problem for these cellulose-feeding insects.

The presence of these symbiotic forms extends further than those merely feeding upon wood; for apparently large numbers of insects which feed upon plant tissues which are low in nitrogen and difficult to digest, have the microorganisms always with them. Escherich (1900) describes the internal symbiont from the beetle, *Anobium paniceum*, a beetle which has often been considered as exceptional in its ability to digest cellulose. Ecologically, we may then regard the cellulose of wood as the environmental medium upon which a fauna of microorganisms lives and maintains the insects which normally are associated with the wood. If we were to define an individual organism as one which was capable of independent existence, we could hardly call some of these forms organisms at all as they are incapable of living without their symbiotic forms. The unit which is capable of maintaining itself consists of the insect with its great fauna and flora, which it is obliged to have with it always.

The insects which live in the reproductive portion of the plant, which is the seed, utilize a portion of the plant in which food materials are stored for the development of the young plant embryo. They live in a medium which is nutritious and which is ordinarily relatively free from micro-organisms. Among this group of organisms we might expect to find

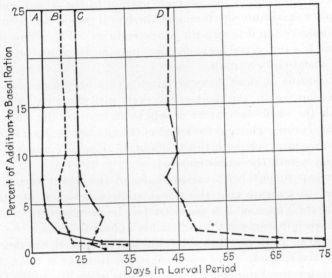

Fig. 57.—Growth of *Tribolium* when a source of Vitamin B is added to a purified basal ration in varying proportions. Addition to basal ration: *A*, wheat embryo; *B*, alcoholi extract equivalent to wheat embryo; *C*, yeast; *D*, alcoholic extract equivalent to yeast Basal ration: casein 28, Osborne-Mendel salts 4, ether extract of wheat embryo 3, dextri 65. (*From Sweetman and Palmer*, 1928.)

insects which were unaided by symbiotic microorganisms. Portier (1919) states that he has been able to rear *Tenebrio* under sterile conditions.

Chapman (1924) reared *Tribolium confusum* on various media and concluded that microorganisms did not play an important rôle. It was found that the slowest growth of the flour beetles took place on flour made from polished rice which might be assumed to contain the smallest amount of vitamine. When synthetic media were used, it was found that the wheat embryo itself gave the greatest acceleration of growth. Sweetman and Palmer (1928) made a critical study of the vitamine requirements of the confused flour beetle, *Tribolium confusum*. Synthetic media were made up which consisted of a basal ration: casein 28 per cent; salts, 4 per cent; fats, 10 per cent; and dextrine to bring it up to 100. To this various other materials were added. Figure 57 shows the result, when (*A*) wheat embryo was added; (*B*) alcoholic extract equivalent to the wheat embryo; (*C*) yeast; (*D*) alcoholic extract of yeast. It is interesting to note the sensitivity of these organisms to the addition of some materials. One-half of 1 per cent of wheat embryo, added to the basal ration, shortened the time of development from 65 days on one-half of 1 per cent to 28 days on 1 per cent. When 3½ per cent had been added, the maximum shortening on the life of larvae was found. Beyond this, up to 25 per cent, there is no change whatever. It is also interesting to note that the larvae are just as sensitive to the addition of the alcoholic extract to the wheat embryo; but even when a maximum shortening of the larval period has been attained, it is still longer than it is with the wheat embryo. This seems to indicate that there is a difference between the Vitamine B content of the extract and the wheat embryo itself.

The addition of yeast, likewise, gives a very abrupt shortening to the life cycle; but, again, the shortest life cycle with the yeast is longer than that with the alcoholic extract of wheat embryo or the wheat embryo itself. Still more striking is the effect of the alcoholic extract of the yeast. The shortest life cycle with this is about 45 days as compared with less than 20 days with the wheat embryo.

Other experiments with various parts of the wheat kernel and with corn seem to indicate that the wheat embryo which is notable for its content of the Vitamine B is necessary for the development of the insect; and that when extracts of this, which are known to contain the Vitamine B are added to a ration which is lacking in Vitamine B, the development is greatly accelerated. This evidence seems to make it clear that these insects require the Vitamine B. Apparently when it is present they can develop normally in the absence of microorganisms.

The insects which live in fruits have not been studied extensively from the standpoint of nutrition. However, Buchner (1928) has shown that many of the flies which live in fruits carry microorganisms with them; and the presumption is that they may feed partly upon the fruit and partly upon the microorganisms. The nectar of flowers is an attractive food for a large number of insects. Its presence is explained teleologically as an attraction for insects to insure the pollenation of the flowers. The honey bee has received more attention from a nutritional standpoint than any of the other insects depending upon nectar. The work of Phillips (1927) and Bertholf (1927) indicates that the adult bees can maintain themselves by the use of pure carbohydrate; but for the rearing of larvae, nitrogen is required which is obtained from the pollen. These pollen grains are passed through the intestinal tract without any alteration unless they are mechanically broken. This is done by the nurse bees preparing the food for the larvae. Many of the butterflies are able to maintain themselves in the adult stage with only the carbohydrates which they obtain from nectar. At least some adult butterflies never feed at all, developing their eggs upon reserves of material which have been stored up during the larval stage. We may thus conclude that in the case of phytophagous insects, some of them are highly specialized as they have types of enzymes which make it possible for them to use certain highly specialized foods. Others associate themselves with microorganisms and thereby make it possible to exist on almost pure cellulose.

We shall next turn our attention to saprophagous insects. These are usually defined as those feeding upon decaying and fermenting matter. It is evident at the start, that these insects live in media which may be teeming with microorganisms. The evidence before us at the present time seems to indicate that in general these insects feed eventually upon microorganisms, and that the decaying material is the medium upon which the microorganisms live. The work of Guyénot (1913

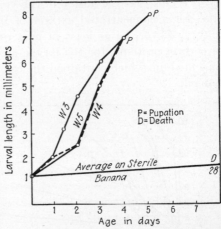

FIG. 58.—Larval growth of *Drosophila* on dead yeast. *W* 3, 4, and 5 show rapid growth on dead yeast; *A* shows slow growth on sterile banana. (*Baumberger*, 1919.)

to 1917), Delcourt and Guyénot (1910 and 1911), Portier (1911), and others seems, to substantiate this. Baumberger in 1919 has given an excellent summary of the work upon these insects and has performed critical experiments with *Drosophila*. This shows that flesh flies, fruit flies, and many others are unable to live on the sterilized medium. It has ordinarily been considered that the banana is the normal food of *Drosophila*. Baumberger, however, demonstrated that the larvae would die after 28 days on sterile banana; while those fed upon yeast completed their life cycles and pupated after five days (Fig. 58).

It was also demonstrated that if larvae were put on sterile banana for a period of 20 to 25 days and at that time yeast was introduced, larvae proceeded to develop in a perfectly normal way.

When media were made up consisting of various percentages of yeast, it was found that the rate of growth was proportional to the percentage of yeast (Fig 59). The greatest size was attained in a medium containing 24 per cent of yeast. As the percentage of yeast was reduced, the ultimate size of the larvae was reduced; and the time required for them to attain maturity was increased. Number 6 was reared on a medium containing yeast nucleoprotein, sugars, and salts. This seems to show that the proteins of the yeast are adequate to support *Drosophila*. Number 8 was reared on a concentrated extract of banana. This was sterile and seems to indicate that concentrated banana may support growth; but the period was about six times as long as on the yeast food. A less concentrated extract of banana was unsuccessful in bringing about pupation; as was also a 1 per cent yeast culture.

It seems that the action of the yeast may be at least partly quantitative, for a concentrated extract of banana can support *Drosophila*. It may, however, be at least in part qualitative through the synthesizing of certain proteins; for the larvae grew more rapidly and to greater size on a medium which contained the nucleoprotein than on the concentrated banana.

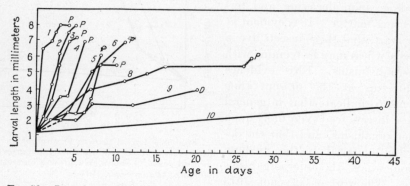

Fig. 59.—Larval growth of *Drosophila* on various media: 1, 24 per cent yeast; 2, maximum 3 to 12 per cent yeast; 3, minimum 3 to 12 per cent yeast; 4, vinegar plant; 5, mushroom; 6, yeast nucleoprotein, sugars, and salts; 7, 2 per cent yeast; 8, hot aqueous extract of banana; 9, 1 per cent yeast; 10, cold aqueous extract of banana. (*Baumberger*, 1919.)

The larvae of *Drosophila* are able to live upon sterile dead yeast which indicates that there is no requirement of living microorganisms. The larvae of Cecidomyid flies living in decaying bark have also been shown to require microorganisms for their food. We may conclude, therefore, that our term, saprophagous, as applied to the insects which we think of as feeding upon decaying plant matter, is misleading in that these actually feed upon the microorganisms; and that the decaying material is merely the stratum on which the fauna of microorganisms exists.

Turning our attention to those forms which feed upon decaying animal matter, we find a situation quite similar to that with those feeding upon decaying plant matter. Guyénot (1906), Bogdanow (1906), and Baumberger (1919) considered that the food of these insects is essentially the same as that of decaying plant matter, *i.e.*, that they feed upon microorganisms. Wollman (1911, 1919, and 1922) contends that he has been able to rear the larvae of the flesh fly under sterile conditions and that they were normal in every way. This seems to indicate that there may be some question as to the absolute requirement of the microorganisms. However, the general proposition seems to be quite clear that this is a group of insects which feed upon a medium which is normally teeming with microorganisms.

We shall next turn our attention to the group which feeds upon the excreta of other animals and which is normally termed "coprophagous." From the evidence which has just been put before us we are at once inclined to feel that these insects may also be feeding upon microorganisms. Critical evidence is lacking in nearly all the cases, and a great deal of research is required in this field. Vaternahn (1924) concluded that microorganisms did not play an important rôle in the nutrition of the dung beetle, *Geotrupes*. However, the excreta of the various organisms vary so much in content and nature that it is quite possible that in some cases microorganisms may play no part at all, and that in other cases they may be very important factors.

Under the heading of carnivorous insects, we might include from the viewpoint of nutrition all those forms which live upon other animals in a living state. Ordinarily we speak of carnivorous forms as those which feed upon organisms smaller than themselves; but from the standpoint of nutrition, there can be little distinction between those which are parasites on other living animals and those which feed directly on smaller animals. Among these insects we seem to find all the categories of food restriction that we find in connection with phytophagous insects. Some of these forms are restricted to a single species and, in the case of parasites, the single organs of single species. Others are nearly omnivorous and range widely in their food habits. It is difficult to make many broad generalizations until more critical physiological work has been done upon the nutrition of these forms. In certain cases, at least, these forms may depend upon symbionts for the digestion of their food. Roubaud (1919) made a study of the tsetse-fly; and it seems in this case that symbionts may be necessary for the digestion of the blood which forms its food.

The large range of food habits of insects from those which are intestinal parasites, to those which are wide-ranging carnivores feeding upon large numbers of minute insects every day, presents a big field for investigation; and we must reserve our broad conclusions until more evidence has been presented. We have a host of insects which feed upon special substances, and these have given rise to many rumors with regard to the peculiar digestive powers of insects. The clothes moth, *Tineola ciselliella*, feeds upon a wide range of organic substances, principally hair. Titschak (1922) has made a very careful study of this insect and has shown that the larvae prefer keratin. Feeding experiments with wool proved that keratin undergoes fermentive digestion. By analysis of the excreta he was able to show that a large portion of it was digested keratin. Albuminoids and carbohydrates were absorbed and other parts were excreted.

The larva of the wax moth, *Galleria melonella*, has been investigated by Sieber and Metalnikov (1904), who showed that the larvae fed not alone upon wax but also upon material containing nitrogenous substances which was found upon the wax in the beehive. It was also demonstrated that they did not grow normally without wax and that much of the wax in the food was digested. It seems that microorganisms are not required in this case, the nitrogen being made up from the molted skins of the bee larvae and other products which are associated with the wax in beehives, the normal environment of this moth. The museum beetle, *Anthrenus museorum*, is known to feed upon a large variety of substances including the dead bodies of insects. Wodsedalek (1917) in a series of interesting experiments demonstrated that it was able to live upon a diet of pure silk in the absence of fats and carbohydrates. The possibility of micro-organisms, however, was not excluded.

Special foods are prepared by many of the social insects, particularly for the feeding of their larvae. This is true of the honey bee, the termites, ants, and many other social insects. In the case of the honey bee, a so-called "royal jelly" is prepared by the workers from predigested pollen. This is fed to all the larvae during the early part of their development, but is fed to the larvae which are destined to be queens throughout their whole development. They are able to differentiate their larvae into those which will be workers and those which will be reproductive forms or queens by controlling the nitrogenous contents of the food. Bertholf (1927) and others have made interesting investigations into the physiology of the nutrition of bees. The case of the termites has already been referred to in connection with the work of Cleveland (1923 and 1925). The nutritional specialization of ants is extremely interesting. They prepare special foods; they cultivate fungi, and in general exert a controlling and selecting activity in connection with their nutrition.

Our general conclusion, with regard to the nutritional requirements of insects for the maintenance of metabolism, may be that they have very much the same physiological limitations as other animals have. Ecologically, however, they have been able to exempt themselves from some of the physiological restrictions. First, by associating themselves with microorganisms which aid in the digestion of substances and make available nitrogen under conditions where other organisms would not be able even to exist. Secondly, the social organisms exercise a selection and combine certain food substances making nutrition of their larval forms possible under conditions where other organisms would not be able to exist. Thirdly, through the specialization of the larval stage for nutrition and growth, certain insects are able to exempt themselves from a food requirement during their brief adult stage. This is true of certain May flies, Lepidoptera, and others.   This great ability of insects to adapt themselves to extreme conditions of nutrition is undoubtedly at least partly responsible for their great success on the earth.

Effect of Nutrition upon the Morphology of Insects.—The specialization in the case of insects requiring the larvae to perform the function of growth makes possible a great adaptation to environmental conditions. Many insects are able to adapt themselves to a small food supply by developing small individuals.   Hunter and Pierce (1912) found that the cotton boll weevil developed into small adults when the larvae were developed in small cotton squares.   Likewise, the bean weevil has been

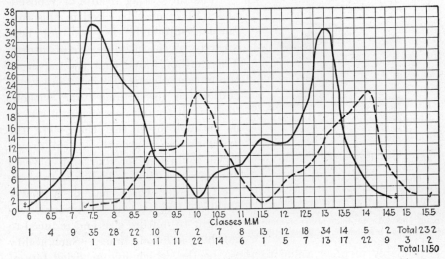

Fig. 60.—Frequency curve of variation in size of male and female of *Dasymutilla bioculata* Cresson.   (*Mickel*, 1924.)

observed by the author to develop into adults of about 8 per cent of the size of the normal adult when they were confined to a small portion of a bean.   This regulatory action with respect to size is not well understood.   Under experimental conditions it was not possible to remove larvae when they had attained a size equal to that at which others were pupating, and leave them entirely without food, and have them transform successfully.   There seems to be some regulatory action for the restriction of food supply.

Mickel (1924) found that a species of *Dasymutilla* which are parasitic upon *Bembix* and *Microbembex*, two genera of wasps, attained a size which is in proportion to the host.   Those individuals which parasitized the larger *Bembix* developed into a large mutillids.   Those which parasitized the small *Microbembex* developed into smaller mutillids.   This accounted for the distribution of size among these mutillids which was found to have a bimodal distribution as shown in Fig. 60.   It will be noticed that the variation in size is almost discontinuous. This might be expected, understanding that the large hosts produce the large individuals, and the small hosts the small individuals which are otherwise identical (Fig 61). Herms (1907) found that the flesh fly, *Lucilia caesar* attained a size which was directly proportional to the number of feeding hours. The larvae at the end of their period, the weight of the pupae, and the weight of the adults were all directly proportional to the feeding time as is shown in Table XI.

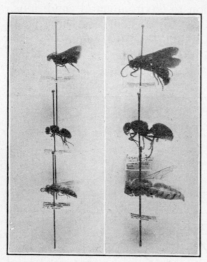

Fig. 61.—Correlation in size between *Dasymutilla bioculata* Cresson and its hosts *Microbembex monodonta* Say (left) and *Bembix pruinosa* Fox (right). In each vertical row: male above, female in the middle, host below. (*Mickel*, 1924.)

The interesting results of Wodsedalek (1917) may be cited in this connection although they do not bear directly on the ultimate size of insects. This author found that the larvae of the museum beetle, *Trogoderma tarsale*, could live for a long time without food, molting and decreasing in size as if catabolism in this case were the exact reverse of growth. A full-grown larva could live for four or five years during which time it decreased to a size even smaller than that of a newly hatched larva. One individual was brought to mature size and reduced to hatching size four times. Such ability is probably of great value to these beetles which live on dried bits of skin and bone, and may at times be called upon to endure long periods of starvation.

TABLE XI.—LARVAE OF SARCOPHAGIDAE WERE REMOVED FROM FISH FLESH AFTER DIFFERENT PERIODS OF FEEDING. THE RESULTING LARVAE, PUPAE AND ADULTS ARE TABULATED ON THE BASIS OF AVERAGE WEIGHT
(Herms, 1907)

Feeding period, hours	Weight, larvae at end of period	Weight, pupae	Weight, adults
60–72	38.183	30.283	22.283
60	35.68	24.76	18.44
54	31.06	22.38	17.54
48	22.14	11.81	8.08
42	17.06	. . . . . .	12.38
36	8.82	9.34	7.15

It is apparently not always true that size is directly proportional to food supply. Chapman (1918) showed that in the case of a confused flour beetle the larvae might attain a large size without being able to transform in foods which were apparently lacking in some essential substance which has to do with the transformation of the pupal stage. Our knowledge of the physiology of control of size in insects is so limited at the present time that we are not warranted in drawing conclusions. It will be sufficient to point out cases cited which are known as the effects of the food and the environment on the size of the insect.

Effect upon the Color of Insect.—From our present knowledge of the pigments which are involved in animals, it seems that they are derived from plant sources already synthesized. A case was investigated by Knight (1924) in which he found that carotinoid pigment of the bug *Perillus* was obtained from its prey, the potato beetle, which in its turn got the pigment from the plant. Toumanoff fed *Dixippus morosus* on carrots and upon white turnips. Those fed upon the carrots showed a yellow color due to the carotinoid pigment. Those fed upon the white turnips showed no yellow color. It is probably well to be conservative in drawing conclusions from the data which are before us as there are metallic colors in insects and also colors which may possibly be synthesized in some other way.

Harrison and Garrett (1926) state that they were able to induce melanism in Lepidoptera by placing twigs of the food plant in a solution of lead nitrate (one gram per liter) before they were fed to the moths, *Selenia bilunaria*. The authors state that these moths have never been taken as normal melanic forms in the wild state, but that they developed melanic forms under the food conditions described, and that a small percentage of this and other species transmitted the melanic character to their progeny. This case raises the perplexing question of the inheritance of an acquired character and therefore may be placed in a debatable class. However, the fact that the pigment of the food plant was incorporated into the insect is nothing surprising and is entirely in accord with our other information.

For the further summary of the physiology of pigments of insects, the student is referred to Uvarov (1928).

The Effect of Nutrition on the Behavior of Insects.—Throughout the class *Insecta*, we apparently have a wide variation in the development of the olfactory senses. Certain insects seem highly sensitive especially to their natural food while others appear to exert very little selective action. Hewitt (1917) summarizes many cases in which it has been possible to attract insects by the use of extracts of their normal food. Minnich (1922) has shown that *Vanessa* is able to detect sugar in a dilution of only one gram-molecular. Richardson (1916) showed that houseflies have some discrimination between nutritious and non-nutritious substances. On the other hand, the confused flour beetle, *Tribolium confusum*, seems to exhibit relatively little olfactory selection. In case of some insects, the selection is exercised by the stage which does the feeding. In others, the female does the selecting; she deposits her eggs and the larvae hatch surrounded by their natural food. In the latter case, there may be a great conservation of the larvae; for when larvae must shift for themselves in seeking their food, large numbers of them are lost without finding a favorable food plant.

Effects of Nutrition on the Geographic Distribution of Insects.— The experimental evidence which is now at hand relative to the food requirements of insects, makes it evident that each insect has certain minimum nutritional requirements for the completion of its life history. It is obvious that any area which is lacking in any one of these required food constituents for any given species will not have that species present in its fauna. An insect which is limited to a single-host plant will of necessity be limited at least to the area of this host plant.

It is even possible that host plants may be able to tolerate deficiencies in certain salts in the soils of certain areas, but that the insects which normally feed upon them may be unable to use the foliage when it is deficient in this particular salt. Such speculation is, of course, without foundation and is of use only as a suggestion for future investigations.

In concluding this chapter on nutrition, it is realized that the usual lists of host plants have been omitted and that no classification of food habits has been given. It has seemed inadvisable, in our present state of knowledge, to go further than to describe the various parts of plants and animals on which insects normally live. When it has been made certain in which cases microorganisms are the essential food and in which cases the substratum is the only food, if there are such cases, we may then proceed to classify food habits on an intelligent basis.

Our chief conclusion may be that, at the end of our consideration of the physical factors of the environment, we are confronted with the fact that insects are unable to use nutrient materials without some materials which have been synthesized by other organisms.

The subject matter of nutrition furnishes us with an excellent example of the inter-relationship of physical and biotic factors, and of physiological and ecological subject matter. We may logically conclude that nutrition is a biotic factor of the environment, inasmuch as none of these animals are able to live without the use of some material which has been synthesized by another organism. We find also that the nutrition of many of the insects is largely an ecological problem in that these insects have associated themselves with symbionts which exempt them from certain physiological requirements of their own class; or that they have formed social organizations in which certain individuals are specialized for performing the function of preparing food for the others. This vast subject will merit the preparation of a critical volume presenting the information which has been prepared from various sources of investigation. For further consideration, the student is referred to the paper of Uvarov, and to various other papers listed in the bibliography, which will lead him to the original results of investigations.

BIBLIOGRAPHY

NUTRITION

ABDERHALDEN, EMIL: Beitrag zur Kenntnis der synthetischen Leistungen des tierischen Organismus—Hoppe-Seyler, *Ztschr. Phys. Chem.*, **142**: 189–190, 1925.

BACOT, A. W., and A. HARDEN: Vitamin Requirements of *Drosophila I.* Vitamins A, B, and C, *Biochem. Jour.*, **16**: 148–152, 1922.

BAUMBERGER, J. P.: The Food of *Drosophila melanogaster* Meigen, *Proc. Nat. Acad. Sci.*, **3**: 122–126, 1917.

————: A Nutritional Study of Insects, with Special Reference to Microorganisms and Their Substrata, *Jour. Exptl. Zool.*, **28**: 1–81, 1919.

BERTHOLF, L. M.: The Utilization of Carbohydrates as Food by Honey-bee Larvae, *Jour. Agr. Research*, **35**: 429–452, 1927.

BOGDANOW, E. A.: Über das Züchten der Larven der gewöhnlichen Fleischfliege (*Calliphora vomitoria*) in sterilisierten Nährmitteln, *Pflüger's Arch. Physiol.*, **113**: 97–105, 1906.

————: Über die Abhängigkeit des Wachstums der Fliegenlarven von Bakterien und Fermenten und über Variabilität und Vererbung bei den Fleischfliegen, *Arch. Anat. u. Physiol.*, Physiol. Abt., p. 173, 1908.

BÖRNER, C.: Über den Einfluss der Nahrung auf die Entwicklungsdauer von Pflanzenparasiten nach Untersuchungen an der Reblaus, *Ztschr. angew. Ent.*, **13**: 108–128, 1927.

BRUES, CHAS. T.: The Selection of Food Plants by Insects with Special Reference to Lepidopterous Larvae, *Amer. Naturalist*, **54**: 313–332, 1920.

————: Correlation of Taxonomic Affinities with Food Habits in *Hymenoptera* with Special Reference to Parasitism, *Amer. Naturalist*, **55**: 134–164, 1921.

————: Choice of Food and Numerical Abundance Among Insects, *Jour. Econ. Ent.*, **16**: 46–51, 1923.

————: The Specificity of Food Plants in the Evolution of Phytophagous Insects. *Amer. Naturalist*, **58**: 127–144, 1924.

BRUES, C. T., and R. E. GLASER: A Symbiotic Fungus Occurring in the Fat Body of *Pulvinaria innumerabilis* Rath, *Biol. Bull.*, **40**: 299–324, 1921.

BUCHNER, P.: "Tier und Pflanze in intrazelluläre Symbiose," Gebrüder Bornträger, Berlin, 1921.   462 pp.

————: "Holznahrung und Symbiose," Berlin, 1928.   64 pp.

CHAPMAN, R. N.: Observations on the Life History of *Agrilus bilineatus*, *Jour. Agr. Research*, **3**: 283–294, 1914-1915.

————: The Confused Flour Beetle (*Tribolium confusum* Duval), *Minn. State Ent. Rept.*, pp. 73–94, 1918.

————: Nutritional Studies on the Confused Flour Beetle, *Tribolium confusum* Duval, *Jour. Gen. Physiol.*, **6**: 565–585, 1924.

CLEVELAND, L. R.: Symbiosis between Termites and Their Intestinal Protozoa, *Proc. Nat. Acad. Sci.*, **9**: 424–428, 1923.

————: Correlation between the Food and Morphology of Termites and the Presence of Intestinal Protozoa, *Amer. Jour. Hyg.*, **3**: 444–461, 1923.

————: The Physiological and Symbiotic Relationships between the Intestinal Protozoa of Termites and Their Host, *Biol. Bull.*, **46**: 177–227, 1924.

————: The Method by Which *Trichonympha campanula*, a Protozoan in the Intestine of Termites, Ingests Solid Particles of Wood for Food, *Biol. Bull.*, **48**: 282–288, 1925.

————: The Ability of Termites to Live Perhaps Indefinitely on a Diet of Pure Cellulose, *Biol. Bull.* **48**: 289–293, 1925.

————: The Feeding Habit of Termite Castes and Its Relation to Their Intestinal Flagellates, *Biol. Bull.*, **48**: 295–308, 1925.

————: The Effects of Oxygenation and Starvation on the Symbiosis between the Termite, *Termopsis*, and Its Intestinal Flagellates, *Biol. Bull.*, **48**: 309–326, 1925.

————: Toxicity of Oxygen for Protozoa in Vivo and in Vitro; Animals Defaunated without Injury, *Biol. Bull.*, **48**: 455–468, 1925.

————: Some Possible Uses of Oxygenation, *Science*, **63**: 168–170, 1926.

————: Further Observations and Experiments on the Symbiosis between Termites and Their Intestinal Protozoa. *Biol. Bull. Mar. Biol. Lab.*, Woods Hole, **54**: 231–237, 1928.

CRAIGHEAD, F. C.: Hopkins' Host-selection Principle as Related to Certain Cerambycid Beetles, *Jour. Agr. Research*, **30**: 189–220, 1921.

DAVIDSON, J.: Biological Studies on *Aphis rumicis* Linn. The Penetration of Plant Tissues and the Source of the Food Supply of Aphids, *Ann. Appl. Biol.*, **10**: 35–54, 1923.

DELCOURT, A., and E. GUYÉNOT: Biologie expérimentale—De la possibilité d'étudier certains Diptères en milieu défini, *Compt. rend. acad. sci.*, Paris, **151**: 255–257, 1910.

————: Génétique et milieu; nécessité de la détermination des conditions. Sa possibilité chez les Drosophiles; technique, *Bull. sci. France et Belg.*, **45**: 249–332, 1911.

DOTEN, S. B.: Concerning the Relation of Food to Reproductivity, Activity, and Longevity in Certain Hymenopterous Parasites, *Nev. Agr. Expt. Sta. Tech. Bull.* 78, pp. 1–30, 1911.

ELY, C. R.: Recent Entomological Chemistry and Some Notes Concerning the Food of Insects, *Proc. Ent. Soc.*, Wash., **20**: 12–18, 1918.

ESCHERICH, K.: Über das regelmässige Vorkommen von Sporspilzen in dem Darmepithel eines Käfers, *Biol. Zentralbl.*, vol. 20, pp. 350–358, 1900.

EYRE, JOHN R.: Rearing Anthomyid Root Maggots on Artificial Media, *Ent. News*, **32**: 215–216, 1921.

FORBES, S. A.: Food of Illinois Fishes, *Ill. State Lab. Nat. Hist. Bull.* 2, pp. 71–86, 1878.

————: Studies of the Food of Birds, Insects and Fishes, *Ill. State Lab. Nat. Hist. Bull.* 3, pp. 1–160, 1880.

————: Food Relations of the Carabidae and Coccinellidae, *Ill. State Lab. Nat. Hist. Bull.* 6, pp. 33–64, 1883.

GLASER, R. W.: The Effect of Food on Longevity and Reproduction in Flies, *Jour. Exptl. Zool.*, **38**: 383–412, 1923.

————: The Relation of Microorganisms to the Development and Longevity of Flies, *Amer. Jour. Trop. Med.*, **4**: 85–107, 1924.

GREGORY, LOUISE H.: The Effect of Starvation on the Wing Development of *Microsiphum destructor*, *Biol. Bull.*, **33**: 296–303, 1917.

GUYÉNOT, E.: Sur le mode de nutrition de quelques larves de mouches, *Compt. rend. soc. biol.*, Paris, **61**: 634–635, 1906.

————: "Études biologiques sur une mouche, *Drosophila ampelophila* Löw," I. Possibilité de vie aseptique pour l'individu et la lignée, *Compt. rend. soc. biol.*, **74**: 97–99; II. Rôle des levures dans l'alimentation, *Compt. rend. soc. biol.*, **74**: 178–180;

III. Changement de milieu et adaptation, *Compt. rend. soc. biol.*, **74**: 223–225; IV. Nutrition des larves et fécondité, *Compt. rend. soc. biol.*, **74**: 270–272; V. Nutrition des adultes et fécondité, *Compt. rend. soc. biol.*, **74**: 332–334; VI. Résorption des spermatozoides et avortement des oeufs, *Compt. rend. soc. biol.*, **74**: 389–391 [Paris, 1913].

————: Recherches expérimentales sur la vie aseptique et le développement d'un organisme (*Drosophila ampelophila*) en fonction du milieu. Analyse et précision des facteurs externes. Leur importance dans l'étude de l'hérédité et de l'évolution, *Bull. biol. France et Belg.*, **51**: 1–330, 1917.

HABERLANDT, G.: The Nutritive Value of Wood, *Sitzber. Preuss. Akad. Wiss.*, vol. 14, pp. 243–257, 1915.

HANDLIRSCH, A.: Biologie (Ökologie-Ethologie). Die Nahrung, "Handbuch der Entomologie," von Ch. Schröder, **2**: 35–52, 1926.

HARGUE, J. S.: A Study of the Proteins of Certain Insects with Reference to Their Value as Food for Poultry, *Jour. Agr. Research*, **10**: 633–637, 1917.

HARRISON, J. W. H., and F. C. GARRETT: The Induction of Melanism in the Lepidoptera and Its Subsequent Inheritance, *Proc. Roy. Soc.*, London, ser. B, **99**: 241–263, 1926.

HEITZ, E.: Über intrazelluläre Symbiose bei holzfressenden Käferlarven, *Ztschr. Morph. Ökol. Tiere*, **7**: 279–305, 1927.

HERING, M.: Die Oligophagie der blattminierenden Insekten in ihrer Bedeutung für die Klärung phytophyletischer Probleme (Unter Berücksichtigung der modernen Ergebnisse der botanisch-serodiagnostischen Forschung). *Verhandl. III. Internatl. Ent. Kongr.*, pp. 216–230, Zurich, 1926.

————: "Die Ökologie der blattminierenden Insektenlarven," Berlin, 1926. 256 pp.

————: "Biologie der Schmetterlinge," Julius Springer, Berlin, 1926. 480 pp.

HERMS, W. B.: An Ecological and Experimental Study of *Sarcophagidae* with Relation to Lake Beach Débris, *Jour. Exptl. Zool.*, **4**: 45–83, 1907.

HEWITT, C. G.: Insect Behavior as a Factor in Applied Entomology, *Jour. Econ. Ent.*, **10**: 81–91, 1917.

HOPKINS, A. D. (1916): Economic Investigations of the Scolytid Bark and Timber Beetles of North America, "U. S. Dept. Agr. Program of Work," p. 353, 1917.

HUBBARD, H. G.: The Ambrosia Beetles of the United States, *U. S. Dept. Agr. Bur. Ent. Bull.* 7, pp. 9–35, 1897.

HUNGERFORD, H. B.: Notes Concerning the Food Supply of Some of our Water Bugs, *Science*, n. s., **45**: 336–337, 1917.

HUNTER, W. D., and W. D. PIERCE: The Mexican Cotton Boll-weevil, *U. S. Dept. Agr. Bur. Ent. Bull.* 114, 1912.

KIANIZIN, I.: The Effect on Higher Animals of the Sterilization of the Inhabited Medium, the Air, and the Food, *Jour. Physiol.*, **50**: 391–396, 1916.

KLEIST, FRANK VON: Nahrungsaufnahme und Kälte beim Bienenvolk, *Arch. Bienenk.*, pp. 1–4, 1919.

KNAUER, FRIEDRICH: Die Symbiosis der Ambrosenkäfer mit Pilzen, *Zentralbl. Gesamm. Forstw.*, pp. 498–501, 1908.

KNIGHT, H. H.: On the Nature of the Color Patterns in *Heteroptera* with Data on the Effects Produced by Temperature and Humidity, *Ann. Ent. Soc. Amer.*, **17**: 258–274, 1924.

KOPEČ, S.: Studies on the Influence of Inanition on the Development and the Duration of Life in Insects, *Biol. Bull.*, **46**: 1–21, 1924.

————: Über die Entwicklung der Insekten unter dem Einfluss der Vitaminzugabe, *Biol. Generalis*, **3**: 375–384, 1927.

KŘÍŽENECKÝ, J.: Über die beschleunigende Einwirkung des Hungers auf die Metamorphose, *Biol. Zentralbl.*, **34**: 46–59, 1914.

KŘÍŽENECKÝ, J., and PODHRADSKÝ: Studien über die Funktion der im wassergelösten Nährsubstanzen im Stoffwechsel der Wassertiere, *Pflüger's Arch. Physiol.*, **203**: 129–140, 1924.

KUNKEL, B. W.: The Effects of the Ductless Glands on the Development of the Flesh-flies, *Jour. Exptl. Zool.*, **26**: 255–264, 1918.

LARSON, A. O., and C. K. FISHER: Longevity and Fecundity of *Bruchus quadrimaculatus* Fab. as Influenced by Different Foods, *Jour. Agr. Research*, **29**: 297–305, 1924.

LEACH, J. G.: The Relation of the Seed-corn Maggot (*Phorbia fuscips* Zett.) to the Spread and Development of Potato Black Leg in Minnesota, *Phytopathology*, **16**: 149–177, 1926.

LOEB, J.: The Salts Required for the Development of Insects, *Jour. Biol. Chem.*, **23**: 431–434, 1915.

————: The Simplest Constituents Required for Growth and Completion of the Life Cycle in an Insect (*Drosophila*), *Science*, **41**: 169–170, 1915.

LOEB, J., and J. H. NORTHROP: Nutrition and Evolution, *Jour. Biol. Chem.*, **27**: 309–312, 1916.

————: On the Influence of Food and Temperature upon the Duration of Life, *Jour. Biol. Chem.*, **32**: 103–121, 1917.

McCOLLOCK, J. W.: Longevity of the Larval Stage of the Cadelle, *Jour. Econ. Ent.*, **15**: 240–243, 1922.

MANZEN, K.: The Woolly Apple Aphis (*Eriosama lanigera* Hausm.) in Japan, with Special Reference to Its Life-history and the Susceptibility of the Host-plant, *Verhandl. III. Internat. Ent. Kongr.*, pp. 249–275, Zurich, 1926.

MICKEL, C. E.: An Analysis of a Bimodal Variation in Size of the Parasite *Dasymutilla bioculata* Cresson (Hymen.: Mutillidae), *Ent. News*, **35**: 236–242, 1924.

MINNICH, DWIGHT E.: A Quantitative Study of Tarsal Sensitivity to Solutions of Saccharose in the Red-admiral Butterfly, *Pyrameis atalanta* L., *Jour. Exptl. Zool.*, **36**: 445–457, 1922.

MÜLLER, A.: Die innere Therapie der Pflanzen, chap. VIII, "Monog. angew. Ent.," 1926. 206 pp.

NEGER, F. W.: Die Pilzkulturen der Nutzholzborkenkäfer, *Vorl. Mitt. Cent. Bakt. Par.*, Abt. II, vol. 20, p. 279, 1908.

————: Die pilzzüchtenden Bostrychiden, *Naturw. Ztschr. Forst- u. Landw.*, vol. 6, p. 274, 1908.

NENJUKOV, D. V.: On some Peculiarities in the Nutrition of Lepidoptera (in Russian), *La Défense des Plantes*, **4**: 12–14, 1927.

NEWSTEAD, R.: Guide to the Study of Tsetse-flies, *Liverpool School Trop. Med. Mem.*, n.s., 1924. 268 pp.

NORTHROP, J. H.: The Effect of Prolongation of the Period of Growth on the Total Duration of Life, *Jour. Biol. Chem.*, **32**: 123–126, 1917.

————: The Rôle of Yeast in the Nutrition of an Insect (*Drosophila*), *Jour. Biol. Chem.*, **30**, 181, 1917.

NUTTALL, G. H. F.: Symbiosis in Animals, *Brit. Assoc. Adv. Sci. Rept.*, 91, pp. 203–207, 1923.

PALMER, L. S., and H. H. KNIGHT: Carotin—the Principal Cause of the Red and Yellow Colors in *Perillus bioculatus* Fab., and Its Biological Origin from the Lymph of *Leptinotorsa decemlineata* Say, *Jour. Biol. Chem.*, **59**: 443–449, 1924.

————: Anthocyanin and Flavone—Like Pigments as Cause of Red Colorations in the Hemipterous Families Aphididae, Coreidae, Lygaediae, Miridae, and Reduviidae, *Jour. Biol. Chem.*, **59**: 451–455, 1924.

PASSERINI, N.: Influenza della qualita delli agrumi sull' accresscimento delle larve e sul metabolismo del Tenebrio molitor, Atti r. accad. naz. Lincei, *Rend. Cl. Sci. Fis., Mat. e Nat.*, **611**: 58–59, 1925.

PEARL, RAYMOND: Starvation Curves, *Nature*, **114**: 854, 1924.

PHILLIPS, E. F.: The Utilization of Carbohydrates by Honeybees, *Jour. Agr. Research*, **35**: 385–428, 1927.

PICTET, A.: Influence des changements de nourriture sur les chénilles et sur l' information du sexe de leur papillons, *Arch. Sci. Nat.*, 1 (4) **15**: 98–100, 1903; same as **16**: 586–588.

POPOVICI-BOZNOSANU, H.: Rélation entre la taille de l'adulte et la quantité de nourriture absorbée par les larves chez l'*Osmia rufa* et l'*Osmia cornuta*, *Compt. rend. soc. biol.*, Paris, **68**: 480*ff.*, 1910.

PORTIER, P.: La vie dans la nature à l'abri des microbes, *Compt. rend. soc. biol.*, Paris, **58**: 605–607, 1905.

——: Digestion phagocytaire des chénilles xylophages des lepidoptères, exemple d'union symbiotique entre un insecte et un champignon, *Compt. rend. soc. biol.*, Paris, **70**: 702–704, 1911.

——: Symbiose chez les larves xylophages. Étude des microörganismes symbiotiques, *Compt. rend. soc. biol.*, Paris, **70**: 857–859, 1911.

——: Passage de l'asepsie à l'envahissement symbiotique humoral et tiussulaire par les microörganismes dans la série des larves des insectes, *Compt. rend. soc. biol.*, Paris, **70**: 914–917, 1911.

——: Développement complet des larves de *Tenebrio molitor*, obtenu au moyen d'une nourriture stérilisée à haute température (130°), *Compt. rend. soc. biol.*, Paris, **82**: 59–60, 1919.

PREST, W.: On Melanism and Variation in Lepidoptera, *Entomologist*, **1**: 129–131, 1877.

RICHARDSON, C. H.: The Response of the House Fly (*Musca domestica* L.) to Ammonia and Other Substances, *N. J. Agr. Expt. Sta. Bull.* 292, pp. 3–19, 1916.

——: The Attraction of Diptera to Ammonia, *Ann. Ent. Soc. Amer.*, **9**: 408–413, 1916.

——: A Physiological Study of the Growth of the Mediterranean Flour Moth (*Ephestia kuehniella* Zeller) in Wheat Flour, *Jour. Agr. Research*, **32**: 895–929, 1926.

ROUBAUD, E.: Les particularités de la nutrition et la vie symbiotique chez les mouches tsétsés, *Ann. Inst. Pasteur*, **33**: 489–536, 1919.

SAVASTIANO, L.: Rapporti biopatologici della mosca delle arance (*Ceratitis capitata* Wied) e gli agrumi, *Ann. r. staz. sper. agrumic e fruttic. Acireale*, **2**: 97–128, 1914.

SCHULTZE, P.: Entwicklung von *Drosophila rubrostriata* Becker in formol; ein Beitrag zur Kenntnis der Lebensweise der Drosophilalarven, *Zool. Anz.*, **39**: 199–202, 1912.

SHINODA, OSAMU: Einige Beobachtungen über die Ernährungsbiologie der wilden Seidenraupe, *Dictyoploca japonica* Moore, *Mem. Col. Sci., Kyoto Imp. Univ.*, ser. B, vol. II, no. 2, 1926.

SHULTZ, N.: Die Verdauung der Raupe der Kleidermotte (*Tinea pellionella*), *Biochem. Ztschr.*, **156**: 124–129, 1925.

SIEBER, N., und S. METALINKOW: Ueber Ernährung und Verdauung der Bienenmotte (*Galleria melonella*), *Pflüger's Arch. Physiol.*, **102**: 269–286, 1904.

SINGH-PRUTHI, H.: Studies on Insect Metamorphosis. III. Influence of Starvation, *Brit. Jour. Exptl. Biol.*, **3**: 1–8, 1925.

SNODGRASS, R. E.: "Anatomy and Physiology of the Honey-bee," New York, 1925. 327 pp.

STUNKARD, HORACE W.: Parasitism a Biological Phenomenon, *Sci. Monthly*, **28**: 349–362, 1929.

SWEETMAN, M. D., and LEROY S. PALMER: Insects as Test Animals in Vitamine Research, *Jour. Biol. Chem.*, **77**: 33–52, 1928.

TEBBUTT, H.: On the Influence of the Metamorphosis of *Musca domestica* upon Bacteria Administered in the Larval Stage, *Jour. Hyg.*, London, **12**: 516–526, 1913.

THORPE, W. H.: Biological Races in *Hyponomeuta padella* L., *Jour. Linn. Soc.* (London) *Zool.*, **36**: 621–634, 1929.

TITSCHAK, E.: Beiträge zu einer Monographie der Kleidermotte, *Tineola biselliella, Ztschr. Tech. Biol.*, **10**: 1–168, 1922.

———: Untersuchungen über das Wachstum, den Nahrungsverbrauch und Eiererzeugung, II. *Tineola biselliella, L. C.*, **128**: 509–569, 1926.

TOWER, D. G.: Comparative Study of the Amount of Food Eaten by Parasitized and Non-parasitized Larvae of *Cirphis unipunctata, Jour. Agr. Research*, **6**: 455–458, 1916.

TOWNSEND, C. H.: A General Summary of the Known Larval Food Habits of the *Acalyptrate Muscidae, Canad. Ent.*, **25**: 10–16, 1893.

UVAROV, B. P.: Insect Nutrition and Metabolism—A Summary of the Literature, *Trans. Ent. Soc.*, London, **31**: 255–343, December, 1928.

VATERNAHN, TH.: Zur Ernährung und Verdauung unserer einheimischen *Geotrupesarten, Ztschr. wiss. Insektenbiol.*, **19**: 20–27, 1924.

VESTAL, A. G.: Local Distribution of Grasshoppers in Relation to Plant Associations, *Biol. Bull.*, **25**: 141–180, 1913.

VINOKUROV, S. I.: "Physiology of Nutrition of the House-fly," pp. 74–78 (in Russian), *memoir* publ. for V. G. Korolenko, Kharkov, 1922.

WEISS, H. B.: A Summary of the Food Habits of North American *Coleoptera, Amer. Naturalist*, **56**: 159–165, 1922.

———: Insect Food Habits and Vegetation, *Ohio Jour. Sci.*, **24**: 100–106, 1924.

———: Ratios between the Food Habits of Insects, *Ent. News*, **35**: 362, 1924.

———: Notes on the Ratios of Insect Food Habits, *Proc. Biol. Soc.*, Wash., **38**: 1–4, 1925.

———: Insect Food Habit Ratios in Death Valley and Vicinity, *Ohio Jour. Sci.*, **25**: 253–254, 1925.

———: The Similarity of Insect Food Habit Types on the Atlantic and Western Arctic Coasts of America, *Amer. Naturalist*, **60**: 102–104, 1926.

WODSEDALEK, J. E.: Five Years of Starvation of Larvae, *Science*, n.s., **46**: 366–367, 1917.

WOLLMAN, E.: Sur l'élevage des mouches stériles. Contribution à la connaissance du rôle des microbes dans les voies digestives, *Ann. Inst. Pasteur*, **25**: 79–88, 1911.

———: Élevage aseptique des larves de la mouche à viande (*Calliphora vomitoria*) sur milieu stérilise à haute température, *Compt. rend. soc. biol.*, Paris, **82**: 593, 1919.

———: Larves de mouche (*Calliphora vomitoria*) et vitamines, *Compt. rend. soc. biol.*, Paris, **82**: 1208–1212, 1919.

———: Biologie de la mouche domestique et des larves des mouches à viande, en élevages aseptiques, *Ann. Inst. Pasteur*, **36**: 784–788, 1922.

ZABINSKI, J.: Élevages des blattides soumis à une alimentation artificielle, *Compt. rend. soc. biol.*, Paris, **98**: 73–77, 1928.

———: Nouvelles recherches sur l'élevage des blattides soumis à une alimentation artificielle. Influence de la composition du régime, *Compt. rend. soc. biol.*, Paris, **93**: 78–80, 1928.

ZWEIGELT, F.: Blattlausgallen, unter besonderer Berücksichtigung der Anatomie und Aetiologie, *Centralbl. Bakt.*, Abt. 2, **47**: 408–535, 1917.

CHAPTER VIII

BIOTIC FACTORS IN AUTECOLOGY

The preceding discussion of physical autecology has followed the usual lines of physiological investigations. Attention is now turned to the biotic factors which are the ones more usually associated with ecological studies. Naturalists have always been attracted by the biotic factors which have not lent themselves so readily to the quantitative treatment used in connection with physical autecology. An attempt will be made to treat the subject of biotic autecology, so far as is possible, in the same quantitative way as was used in the subject of physical autecology. In so doing there is no implication that qualitative observations of biotic factors are not of value; for, in fact, they represent the very foundation upon which all quantitative work must rest.

The primary object of this quantitative attempt in the treatment of biotic autecology is to bring together the widely divergent results of physical autecology of the physiological type, and the biotic autecology of the naturalist. The results in these two fields have proceeded quite independently of each other with a great gulf fixed between them. We have had, on the one hand, a school of ecologists who have been essentially physiological, who have been concerned with temperature coefficients and responses to various physical features of the environment. On the other hand, we have had a school of naturalistic ecologists who have propounded the sound doctrines, that the necessity for food, shelter from the physical factors of the environment, and protection from natural enemies were the most important dynamic factors of nature so far as the survival of the individual was concerned; and that reproduction and distribution were the most dynamic factors so far as the welfare of the species was concerned. This school of natural history has been inclined to feel that the general physical factors operating in the universe were fixed and omnipresent, and were of relatively little concern as compared with the organism's ability to survive against them; and that the chief concern of the ecologists was the study of the ways and means through which the organism was able to maintain itself.

Physical barriers have been considered of relatively little importance because every species has some way to get around each physical barrier. It seems that if progress is to be made in the field of ecology, both of these two attitudes must be brought together and made use of. In accordance with the laws of nature, if two things of divergent character are to be brought together, they must be placed over a common denominator; and it would seem that that common denominator would have to be a quantitative expression of mathematical nature. Fourier says of mathematics,

It seems to be a faculty of the human mind destined to supplement the shortness of life and the imperfection of the senses; and what is still more remarkable, it follows the same course in the study of all phenomena; it interprets them by the same language, as if to attest the unity and simplicity of the plan of the universe, and to make still more evident that unchangeable order which presides over all nature.

In the field of physical autecology, it has been pointed out that the technique of the physiologists may be followed, and that the limitatioins of our knowledge are due not so much to the unsurmountable difficultaes of technique, as to the lack of data and crucial experiments to demonstarte the fundamental effects of the various factors. In the field of quantitative biotic autecology, there is not only a lack of quantitative data with regard to the fundamental effects of the biotic factors, but there also exist unsolved technical difficulties in the way of accumulating such data and expressing them quantitatively. The transition from physical to biotic autecology might be likened to the transition from arithmetic to calculus and trigonometry. It is necessary to superimpose upon the quantitative effects of physical factors a quantitative expression of all the complicated biotic functions and characteristics. On a quantitative basis, biotic autecology should be destined to develop into one of the highest branches of science. It is not to be denied that there are many difficulties in the way, nor that the relationships to be dealt with are extremely complicated. If this were not true, the future development of this field would be circumscribed. At the present stage of development, the pathway of progress through this field is ill-defined and insecure. Its chief attribute seems to be that it promises to lead to a goal of importance.

Biotic Characteristics of Species.—It is necessary to know something of the biotic characteristics of the organisms which appear as factors in the environment before considering the organism as a factor. It has already been pointed out (Chapman, 1928), that organisms themselves have certain inate biotic characteristics which are at least analogous to the characteristics of physical compounds. These characteristics have been summed up in the general term "biotic potential." This has been defined as the inherent property of an organism to reproduce and to survive; *i.e.*, to increase in numbers. It is a sort of algebraic sum of the number of young produced at each reproduction, the number of reproductions in a given period of time, the sex ratio of the species, and their general ability to survive under given physical conditions. It is the potential power that an organism has to reproduce and survive in its environment.

The Significance of Biotic Potential.—The biotic potential of the species is a quantitative expression of the dynamic power of the species which is pitted against the resistance of the environment in which it lives in its struggle for existence. Organisms which encounter a great resistance from the environment must have a high biotic potential in order that there may be survivors to replace required organisms. Nature has required that organisms which live in environments that offer great resistance, possess a high biotic potential in order that, after all the resistance of nature has been met, there may still be survivors to maintain the population. In the event that the biotic potential was high with reference to the resistance of the environment, the population of the species would increase until it became out of all proportion to the rest of nature. If the biotic potential was relatively low, as compared with the resistance of the environment the numbers of the species would gradually be reduced until it became extinct. The fact that our present fauna has survived down through the ages is evidence that biotic potential and environmental resistance have tended to maintain a balance, just as the various types of physical pressure tend to maintain a balance. Parasitic forms whose life cycles expose them to various hazards of the environment are classically known to have large numbers of eggs produced. Those organisms which live in relatively constant and secure environments produce very few young at each reproduction. Those organisms which have a high biotic potential are able to increase their numbers very rapidly at any decrease in the resistance of the enviroment. The history of economic biology contains the records of many biotic explosions in nature where there has been a sudden change in environmental resistance; and the biotic potential of the organism has been fully expressed; and populations have shot up to enormous proportions.

Biotic potential is just as definite a characteristic of a species as is the valence of carbon a characteristic of that element. Our common fruit fly *Drosophila*, for instance, is very distinctly characterized by its ability to reproduce rapidly; and its usefulness in genetical experiments has been due to this biotic characteristic. It is obvious that a species like the 17-year cicada, while it might have contained better genetic characters than *Drosophila* would be much less useful in genetical experiments because of the difference in biotic potential. One can pass through a generation in a few days' time; the other requires years of time.

Quantitative work in ecology will require a knowledge of the biotic potential of the species, just as quantitative work in chemistry requires a knowledge of the valence of elements which go into compounds. The reaction of an element may be predicted on the basis of its valence; and the reaction of a species in an environment may be predicted on the basis of its biotic potential, provided the characteristics of its biotic potential are fully understood. It would seem that the general situation of the biotic potential as an inherent characteristic of the organism on the one hand, and the resistance of the environment on the other hand, should be rather clear. The species is continually reproducing. In this respect it is sometimes very extravagant of individuals; while the environment is continually taking an enormous toll from its numbers. The result is that the population remains relatively constant because such great numbers are produced. Further examples are to be given in the subsequent discussion. For the present, the main object is to make clear the general picture.

It may add to the appreciation of this general situation with respect to the biotic potential of the organism and the resistance of the environment, if we cite a few examples from literature illustrating the capacities of organisms to reproduce. Huxley (1858) cited an example which has become almost a classic in biological literature, showing that a single parthenogenetic female aphid could give rise in a year's time to a population of progeny whose total protoplasms would be equal to that represented by the inhabitants of the Chinese empire. Herrick (1926) tested this calculation using the common cabbage aphid, *Brevicoryne brassicae*, which he had shown to be capable of producing twelve generations between March 31 and Aug. 15. A single stem mother could give rise on an average to 41 young. On this basis, the progeny, if they all lived, would number 564,087,257,509,154,652. He determined the average weight of four aphids as 1.4 mg. Therefore, this number of aphids would weigh 1,645,254,501,068 lb., which seems to substantiate the statement of Huxley.

Woodruff (1922) calculated that it was possible for a single infusorian to produce a cubic meter of protoplasm in 60 days' time with 1,000 individuals to the cubic millimeter. In 7 years' time, the progeny of this single infusorian would be represented by a mass of protoplasm 10,000 times greater than the mass of the earth itself, and that in a few hundred years it would exceed the whole visible universe including the sun and all of its planets.

Lefroy (1909) calculated that a single pair of fruit flies, *Drosophila*, would in one year's time produce 30 broods; and if each brood consisted of 40 eggs, half females; and if all came to maturity, their numbers would be appalling. He said:

If they were packed tightly together so that each cubic inch of space contained a thousand of them, they would very easily cover the whole of India, from Kashmir to Cape Comorin, from Karachi to Calcutta, with a solid cake of flies a hundred million miles thick, or would coat the whole world with a layer of insects a million miles in depth. And yet as it is we do not particularly notice them.

It would be possible to continue to cite similar incidents based upon general observations and general citations in literature. Such calculations usually are not taken seriously. They are considered to represent fantastic numbers. It is perfectly obvious that these potential numbers are never realized because the various actions of the environment inhibit the reproduction. However, it is just as obvious that they are true potential numbers.

A species without the ability to reproduce rapidly could not produce a large population in a short period of time. The history of economic biology gives the examples of numerous species which have been moved accidentally from one environment to another and in the new environment the population level has been entirely different from that in the natural environment, due to the difference in resistance in the two environments. Tropical species go north until the resistance of the environment overcomes their biotic potentials. Species from the lowlands move up the mountains until their biotic potential is overcome by the environmental resistance.

This general picture does not solve problems, but it may aid in clear thinking as to the relationship of organisms to their environment. To be of use in research in analyzing complicated situations it is necessary to proceed further and analyze more minutely the constitution of biotic potential. It is interesting to note that there are hardly any economic species in which the data are available to determine their potential rate of reproduction. With the hundreds of volumes which have been written on various species it seems surprising that so elemental a fact as the potential reproductive rate should have been overlooked. With the limited information now before us it would be disastrous to make dogmatic statements as to the minute details of biotic potential. Inasmuch as the entire value of the conception depends upon the contributions which it can make to research, it is necessary to proceed cautiously and not to adopt dogmatic definitions on the basis of insufficient evidence. It will probably be necessary to continually make revisions, just as in the tables of atomic weights of chemicals it has been necessary to make revisions.

The Constants of Biotic Potential.—It is necessary to give biotic potential a quantitative expression in order that it may be used in measuring the effect of the environment. In giving it such quantitative expression it is of primary importance that the expression be simple, easily understood, and easily standardized. It is also essential that it should not be prematurely dogmatized and made subject to a series of definitions and revisions which lead to controversy and confusion. The conception of biotic potential pitted against environmental resistance leaves the biotic potential as the absolute optimum of the rate of reproduction of the species when there is no environmental resistance. This conception postulates the condition in which any action of the environment will bring about a reduction of the potential number, or the rate of increase of the population. The situation is therefore simplified in one respect, the measure of environmental resistance will be the reduction of the rate of reproduction below the optimum of potential.

A rather serious difficulty is presented however in the matter of determining this optimum or absolute biotic potential. It involves both the technical difficulties of making the determination, and the assurance that the determination made is the absolute biotic potential, and not some close approximation to it. If the work on the biotic potential of each species must be held up until this difficult determination is made, it will be a serious interference with progress. For this reason there is a practical advantage in introducing the term "partial potential" to represent the biotic potential of a species under a given set of conditions. We may therefore speak of a partial potential of *Tribolium confusum* at 27°C., 75 per cent of relative humidity, and a nutrient medium of pure whole-wheat flour. It may be advantageous to establish a series of partial potentials along the temperature scale, or along the humidity scale, or over a series of nutrient media.

The absolute biotic potential may then remain a hypothetical number of theoretical value just as the absolute zero on the temperature scale of physical chemistry remains a real but hypothetical value of great theoretical importance. Similarly in the study of a field-crop insect, it is possible by a careful field study to make the determination of the partial potential of an insect for a given year under the field conditions of a specified geographic area. The partial potential quoted becomes of value when comparing different areas and different years and in evaluating the effect of the various environmental factors in reducing the partial potential. A careful investigation of the change in population numbers throughout the life cycle compels attention to the facts which it concerns us to know; *i.e.*, the action of the environment in reducing the population numbers.

In accordance with this hypothesis, biotic potential is a constant; and if environmental conditions were to remain constant the population should also be constant. Such conditions have been brought about under certain limited laboratory conditions (Chapman, 1928). In this series of experiments the environmental resistance was ultimately due to the size of the environment which was measured by the number of grams of wheat flour. Environments of various sizes forming a geometric series were used and they varied from 4 g. to 128 g. Populations of newly emerged adult beetles were introduced into each of these environments to provide one beetle to each 2 g. flour. The numbers of eggs, larvae, pupae, and adults were recorded at various times and the flour was changed at each observation to maintain a uniform nutritive value of the environment. Table XI gives the results of the various counts over a period of over 156 days. In Table XII these counts have been reduced to numbers of individuals per gram of flour.

TABLE XI.—TOTAL NUMBER OF INDIVIDUALS IN EACH ENVIRONMENT. *Tribolium confusum* IN WHOLE-WHEAT FLOUR AT 27°C. AND UNIFORM MOISTURE[1]

Days	4 Grams				8 Grams				16 Grams				32 Grams				64 Grams				128 Grams			
	Eggs	Larvae	Pupae	Adults	Eggs	Larvae	Pupae	Adults	Eggs	Larvae	Pupae	Adults	Eggs	Larvae	Pupae	Adults	Eggs	Larvae	Pupae	Adults	Eggs	Larvae	Pupae	Adults
0	…	…	…	2	…	…	…	4	…	…	…	8	…	…	…	16	…	…	…	32	…	…	…	64
15	41	17	0	2	62	71	0	4	127	187	0	8	263	280	0	16	631	686	0	32	854	1,543	0	64
30	44	74	0	2	30	168	0	3	103	314	0	8	188	509	0	16	369	1,118	2	32	393	2,371	99	61
50	42	45	21	31	47	75	51	90	89	178	79	167	383	310	114	332	402	792	220	639	1,265	1,204	503	1,405
64	64	20	14	59	107	47	12	144	205	78	36	220	497	180	58	414	1,145	400	157	842	2,215	541	198	1,832
78	60	10	6	65	114	11	20	144	330	16	39	158	636	14	91	428	1,254	67	159	875	2,705	230	256	1,857
101	89	5	1	66	185	30	0	156	390	46	1	174	861	94	3	445	2,086	146	1	928	2,672	318	21	1,906
114	125	2	0	66	180	20	7	156	368	21	13	174	846	56	20	449	1,530	97	16	904	2,943	218	481	1,914
134	81	0	0	66	257	3	0	159	460	24	1	174	842	13	0	452	2,143	32	4	908	3,805	63	41	1,905
156	89	0	0	65	236	2	0	157	544	8	6	173	837	6	4	445	1,912	45	7	902	4,097	63	101	1,882

[1] CHAPMAN, ROYAL N., *Ecology*, vol. IX, No. 2, 1928.

TABLE XII.—BEETLES (*Tribolium confusum*) PER GRAM OF FLOUR[1]

Days	4 Grams	8 Grams	16 Grams	32 Grams	64 Grams	128 Grams
	0.5	0.5	0.5	0.5	0.5	0.5
15	15	17	20	17	21	19
30	30	25	26	22	24	23
50	35	33	32	35	32	34
64	39	39	34	39	40	37
78	35	41	39	36	37	39
101	40	46	38	44	49	39
141	48	45	36	43	40	40
134	37	50	41	41	48	45
156	38	49	46	44	45	47
171	46	49	46	43	42	40

[1] *Ibid.*

After a period of approximately 100 days, the number of individuals, as expressed in beetles per gram of flour, becomes constant at about 43.97 individuals per gram and fluctuates about this number.

It will be noted that comparing the number of beetles per gram in each of the environments on any one day, and comparing the number of individuals per gram in any one environment over a series of days, from 100 to 150, the fluctuations are of about equal magnitude. This seems to indicate that it makes little difference whether an environment is as small as 4 g. or as large as 128 g. The number of beetles per gram of flour is about constant. Referring back to the table which gives the numbers of the various stages found in each count it will be noted that thousands of eggs may be present every day but that the populations do not change.

A complete analysis of all the resistance which is met by the biotic potential of these beetles is complicated and difficult. It has, however, been shown that the adults and larvae eat the eggs of their own species. There is apparently no selective action in the eating of the eggs, it being merely an accident, whether an adult or a larva encounters an egg while it is eating flour. However, the incidence of these active forms with the eggs and also the pupae is a matter of the concentration of the beetles in the flour. At low concentration, eggs and pupae escape and develop to become adult beetles. When many of them have developed into adult beetles, the concentration is then so high that relatively few eggs or pupae are able to escape; and the population then remains constant. When the resistance of the environment was experimentally reduced by placing the population in a large environment, the numbers increased rapidly, as might be expected from the presence of thousands of eggs.

It has often been postulated that populations reach a limit due to the accumulation of toxic substances in the environment. In this case the medium was renewed according to a schedule and such an accumulation was impossible. It seems, therefore, that the limitation is simply an accumulation of numbers in a limited environment.

Biotic Constants of Potential.—Attention will now be turned to the factors which go to make up biotic potential. Theoretically we may divide biotic potential into *reproductive potential* and *survival potential;* and each of these may be again subdivided. There may be some question as to the practicability of the use of these divisions in making quantitative calculations with our present amount of knowledge; but a discussion of these various factors will at least contribute to the understanding of the significance of biotic potential.

The reproductive potential is a measure of the ability of the organism to produce large numbers. The survival potential is the ability of the organism to maintain the high numbers. It seems to be a general law in nature that if the reproductive potential is high, the survival potential may not be so high and *vice versa*. Many species produce relatively few young but exercise parental care to see that the few produced actually survive. On the other hand, many species produce enormous numbers of young and leave them to take their own chance in nature, which means that the survival potential is not high.

The question of practicability may be raised in considering the relationship between survival potential and environmental resistance. The calculation of environmental resistance as the reduction of the reproductive potential is relatively simple, as compared with introducing another factor to represent survival potential. It is not possible with the present amount of experience to predict what will be the most practical method of handling these conceptions in making calculations. It is certain that various species differ in their ability to endure severe environmental conditions. This means that the same amount of environmental resistance produces different effects upon different species. This may be explained as being due to the difference of the survival potential of the different species. For example, the lowering of temperature acts as an increase of resistance to all species. However, the point on the temperature scale where the different species encounter the absolute minimum temperature, differs just as the freezing points for various chemicals do, although it is true that low temperature approaches the freezing point of all.

It is possible, therefore, to conceive of survival potential as representing the actual position on the temperature scale where a species would experience its optimum and pessimum conditions. This has furnished the basis for the comparison of various species in the same environment. The difference in the reduction of the potential number of organisms of various species by the same environmental resistance would be a measure of the survival potential of these different species. For practical procedure, therefore, the question may be raised as to whether it is more advantageous to conceive of the environmental resistance as being a unit for any given set of conditions, and its differential action on different species be conceived of as a characteristic of each species, representing a survival potential; or whether it is better to calculate the environmental resistance for each species separately.

It is under these categories of biotic potential that all the facts of natural-history observation come to find a place and to be analyzed quantitatively. All the intricate adaptations, all the protective habits and reactions if they are of significance to the species must contribute, at least some small amount, to the ability of the organism to reproduce and maintain its numbers. When the welfare of a species is viewed in terms of the population it is able to maintain, all these facts should be able to find their place and be evaluated. It seems likely that many controversies over protective coloration, mimicry, and resemblance might find the solution if they were investigated from the viewpoint of their contributions to the maintenance of the population of the species. Thus, this quantitative approach to the subject anticipates a new light on the observations of natural history.

Reproductive Potential.—The reproductive potential of a species may be divided into the factors of the sex ratio of the population; *i.e.*, the number of females which are going to reproduce, and the number of young produced per each female in a unit of time. If reproductive potential is to be used as a constant in making calculations, it is obviously necessary to search for something constant with regard to the number of young produced. There are theoretically two possibilities in this connection. One is the attempt to demonstrate that there is a constant number of primary oocytes for any given species. Such a demonstration involves many technical difficulties, but a knowledge of the subject would be of fundamental importance. The second is to demonstrate a mean value for the number of eggs produced. It is known, however, that the number of eggs produced is constant within certain limits; but in some species at least the variation within these limits is great. The shad, for instance, is said to lay from 30,000 to 100,000 eggs per season, and the carp from two to four million. Among the insects we may also find examples of very wide discrepancy in the number of eggs produced.

Pemberton and Willard (1918) state that the parasites which they studied, often died with eggs left in the oviduct. Parker (1930) found that under laboratory conditions where an attempt was made to maintain the environment as near the optimum as possible, certain grasshoppers laid more eggs than under field conditions. This would seem to indicate that, in certain species at least, the potential number of eggs is never laid under the conditions of nature. It is interesting in this connection to note that Parker found the increased number of eggs in species which are often pests, and that he did not find such an increase in certain other species which are not of economic importance. This seems to indicate that of the many species of grasshoppers, it is only the few which are of economic importance which have the potential ability to produce a larger number of eggs under optimum conditions.

Among parasitic organisms in general, there are cases cited where enormous numbers of eggs are produced in order to overcome the enormous resistance of the environment which is experienced before the individuals become established in new hosts. Raillet (1895) states that the tapeworm, *Taenia*, will have at least 8,800 eggs in a single proglotus and may discharge as many as 13 or 14 proglotids per day. These are literally spread broadcast in the environment on the chance that a few will come to rest in the proper hosts.

The phenomenon of polyembryony is found among certain of the parasitic insects; and in this case the female places the eggs within the host and thereby practically insures the development of the egg that is so placed. The egg which is placed, then proceeds to produce many individuals instead of just one. This amounts to an increase in the number of young produced and brings about the increase, after the hazard of environmental resistance in passing from one host to another has been overcome.

Many of the social insects have made the matter of reproduction a social affair rather than an individual affair. The case of the honey bees is arranged to have one individual represent the reproductive power of a colony. The individuals of the colony are specialized as to reproduction, care of the young, and the providing of food, so that reproductive potential and survival potential both become social functions rather than individual functions.

The sex ratio becomes an important factor in reproductive potential because it is the rate of increase of the population rather than that of certain individuals which is of ecological importance. The simplest sex ratio of adult insects is an equal number of males and females which may be expressed as a sex ratio of 0.5. In certain cases the females may greatly outnumber the males, and in some of the aphids and other insects there may even be parthenogenesis. In such a case the sex ratio becomes 1.0 so far as the adult insects are concerned. Holdaway (unpublished thesis) found evidence that under certain environmental conditions there may be a change of sex ratio in *Tribolium confusum*.

For the purpose of population studies one may distinguish between the true sex ratio and the effective sex ratio. The former designates the actual percentage of females in the population and is usually applied to the adult population. The effective sex ratio designates the percentage of the total population capable of producing eggs or young. For all purposes of calculation, it is necessary to know the ratio of the number of reproducing females to the entire population. The expression of

Thompson (1922) may be adopted to represent the reproductive potential of a given generation of individuals: $fs = z$. f represents the sex ratio and s the number of young produced at each reproduction. The product of these two values equals z which will be the value for the reproductive potential. The advantage in using the expression lies in the fact that it makes it possible to evaluate any adaptation either for the production of an increased number of young or an increase in the relative number of females. This factor then represents the increase in one reproduction and is the factor by which the population must be multiplied to raise the number to the population value at the end of one reproductive period.

The practicability of the use of these expressions may be greatly increased by adopting the partial biotic potential for any given set of conditions, as has been already suggested. While the number of young produced and the sex ratios may vary, it has been shown in the case of *Tribolium confusum* that under a standard condition of temperature, humidity, and nutrition these numbers are relatively constant. Therefore we may assign a partial potential for *Tribolium confusum* at 27°C., 73 per cent of relative humidity with a standard whole-wheat flour as a nutrient medium, and obtain results which may be duplicated in a series of experiments without wide variation.

Survival Potential.—A survival potential represents the place in the scale of environmental resistance which an organism can endure. We may compare the action of two different environments upon a given species on the basis of environmental resistance. When we wish to compare the effect of an environment on two different species, we may find that the same conditions offer high resistance for one species and low resistance for the other. It represents a sort of buffering ability on the part of the organisms against environmental resistance. It is possible that the chapters on Physical Autecology would have had much greater ecological significance had they been treated in such a way as to represent the survival potential of the various organisms under various conditions of environmental resistance. This has not been done for the reason that the effects of the environmental factors are represented by very well-established physiological results; while the biotic-potential principle is still in the state of a hypothesis. It has, therefore, seemed best to let the physiological facts stand upon their own foundation rather than to involve them with a theory which demands further support.

It is possible to further subdivide survival potential into nutritive potential and protective potential. Nutritive potential represents the ability of the organism to utilize environmental materials for the support of its own metabolism. An organism which has a potential power of synthesizing food materials in a few compounds in the presence of sunlight, carbon dioxide, and water, has an enormous advantage over those organisms which require their food to be already synthesized. The chapter on Nutrition has called attention to the fact that all animals, at least those above certain protozoa, require that their protein be in the form of amino acids at least, and that their carbohydrates be sugars or starches. This is due to their limited potential powers of synthesis. There is evidence that certain animals and possibly some insects are able to absorb nutrient materials from solutions in the water. Matheson (1929) has suggested that this is possible in the case of mosquito larvae.

Ecologically the nutritive potential of a species may be greatly increased by symbiosis. An organism which lacks the mechanism for synthesizing in its own organs, may acquire another organism which possesses the mechanism and thus makes itself the equivalent of an organism with these powers. A high nutritive potential may therefore be due to fundamental physiological properties, as in the case of certain plants; or it may be due to fundamental ecological relationships in the case of certain termites which are able to live on cellulose by being associated with microorganisms. We thus have an illustration of emergent evolution in the nutrition of organisms which makes it possible for a highly organized insect, which is actually an association of organisms rather than an individual, to have the potential nutritive ability of a microorganism.

Protective Potential.—Reproductive potential and nutritive potential are concerned with the dynamic properties of the organism in bringing other organisms into existence, and in utilizing the raw materials of the environment to build up protoplasm and maintain metabolism. The protective potential of an organism is concerned with the potential ability to protect itself against the dynamic forces of the environment. Individual organisms exhibit adaptations varying all the way from what seems to be pure chance in surviving to the most intricate protective structures and habits. It is impossible to dwell upon these in detail in the present discussion. In a qualitative way the descriptions and generalizations concerning such adaptations form the subject matter of much of our present-day ecology. Undoubtedly the future is going to see these generalizations translated into quantitative terms which will be a measure of the advantages which the species derives from such adaptations. It will undoubtedly be shown that certain species which do not have the high reproductive potential may yet survive in large numbers due to their ability to protect themselves against the organic and inorganic environmental resistance.

Social insects have made the matter of protection a social function rather than an individual function. Special castes have been developed in various of the social insects such as the soldiers among the ants and termites, whose function it is to protect the social organization against the organisms of the external environment. These soldiers are produced to sacrifice themselves for the protection of the colony in general. Social insects offer some of the most enticing opportunities for study of the quantitative value of protection.

Environmental Resistance.—There is a great practical advantage in being able to consider both the physical and biotic factors of the environment in the same quantitative way and to measure them with the same scale.   In the chapters on Physical Autecology, the physical factors were dealt with in a purely physiological way, although it was recognized that the results were not of the greatest ecological value.   However, the biotic factors have not been measured in the same physical terms that are used in connection with physical factors.   What is more, they are not susceptible to such measurement, at least not to the same degree that the physical factors are.   For this reason, a departure must be made in the method of measurement rather than an attempt to evaluate the biotic factors in terms of physical resistance.   The biotic potential of the organism will be taken as the standard of measurement.   The environment will be represented as resistance to the biotic potential.   The difference between the potential number of organisms as indicated by the biotic potential, and the actual number of organisms as observed in the environment, will be the measure of the resistance of the environment. This method of measuring the resistance of the environment suggests an analogy to the methods used by Fourier in measuring the transmission of heat through solids, and by Ohm in measuring the resistance of a system to the transmission of an electric current.   In both cases the resistance was measured in terms of the energy which was being dealt with.

Ohm stated that the amount of current which could be measured at any point in a system depended upon two factors: first, the potential amount of current; and second, the amount of resistance which was offered to that current.   If the potential was high and the resistance low, the measurable amount of current would be high.   If the potential was low and the resistance was high, the observed amount of current would be small.   In any event, the only current which could be observed and measured was the amount which was left in the system after the resistance had been satisfied.

There are two important points for the student of ecology in connection with Ohm's generalization.   Ohm did not understand the nature of resistance to an electric current when he formulated his statement which is now recognized as a law of physics.   Without understanding resistance he did correctly state the relationship between the potential amount of current, the actual amount of current to be observed along the circuit, and the nature of the circuit through which it passed.

The second important point in Ohm's generalization is the fact that it led to the definition of resistance in terms of the resistance offered to an unvarying electric current by a standard-unit circuit which was chosen arbitrarily. It is known as the "Ohm"; and the actual unit circuit which it represents is of little consequence now that it has been adopted. Its existence as an accepted unit makes possible the measurement of resistance; and by the use of Ohm's law it is possible to calculate the current which will pass through a circuit when the resistance of the circuit and the potential amount of current are known. It is also possible to calculate the resistance of the circuit when the potential amount of current at one end of the circuit and the actual amount at the other end are known.

It is possible to calculate the potential number of individuals that a species will produce if we assign a partial biotic potential to the species as the result of an investigation of its sex ratio and the number of young produced in a unit of time under given conditions. It is also possible to measure the number of individuals which are actually present in the environment at any time. The difference between the two numbers thus obtained must represent the reduction of the potential number of individuals by the resistance of the environment, in much the same way that the resistance of an electric circuit reduces the current from its potential to its actual value.

Since the biotic potential of a species is balanced by the environmental resistance, certain biologists have concluded that it is of no importance because it is always nullified by the resistance of the environment. If the state of equilibrium was absolutely stable this would be true. However, the oscillations of the population are a function of the biotic potential and these oscillations are the important variables. They are perhaps most important in environments in which the physical resistance is subject to wide and extreme fluctuations. In the case of a species which is moved from one environment to another the biotic potential is important in determining the trend of the population of the new species.

The Measurement of Environmental Resistance.—It will not be possible or practical to review the attempts to express the effects of the environment in diminishing the potential number of organisms in an environment. It is still too early in the history of these attempts to be able to select the most promising methods.

Lotka (1925) has devoted considerable attention to the consideration of equations to express the various conditions of equilibrium. In his chapter on "Analysis of the Growth Function," this author uses the terms "birth rate" and "force of mortality" in somewhat the same way that biotic potential and environmental resistance are used here. Lotka presents many ingenious and suggestive formulae for expressing the various conditions of equilibrium which may be found in nature. It is interesting to note the application of these formulae, primarily from the field of physical chemistry, to systems composed of living organisms. The advent of such methods in the field of chemistry led to a great advance in our knowledge of the structure and energy relationships of chemical systems; and it is possible that they may be a great aid in the understanding of the relationships of systems composed of living organisms.

It is possible that too much stress on analogies drawn from afar may confuse the situation. Proof will not come from the contemplation of analogies unless such contemplation stimulates investigation which results in the accumulation of significant facts.

The statement that the ratio of the actual number of individuals to the potential number of individuals is a measure of the resistance of the environment may serve as a hypothesis. The resistance of the environment consists of many factors which may be classified as physical and biotic. Each of these may in turn be divided into individual factors. For the purpose of a general statement with regard to the measurement of environmental resistance, it will be permissible to treat the total resistance rather than the individual factors, just as Lotka (1925, page 162) has done in a similar computation.

The essential point of the hypothesis presented here is that it proposes the measurement of environmental resistance in terms of the potential number of organisms. By using these three values, biotic potential, the actual number of organisms present in the environment, and the resistance of the environment, we have two values which may be determined by examination. The biotic potential may be determined as previously stated. The actual number of organisms, present in the environment, should be subject to determination. The ratio of the number of organisms which should be present because of the inherent ability of the organisms to reproduce themselves (the biotic potential) and the number which are present may be considered as the measure of the resistance of the environment. If it were not for the environment, the potential number would be reached. In an environment in which all of the factors were at the optimum, the potential number would be realized. In an environment in which the conditions were all near the minimum of toleration, the numbers would depart very far from the potential number of organisms.

Thus when the biotic potential is constant and the number of individuals is high, environmental resistance must be low, and when the number of individuals is low, the environmental resistance must be high.

An example of the relationship of actual numbers of individuals to the potential number may be taken from the results of the bird census taken by the U. S. Biological Survey (Cooke, 1923). There were 11 nesting pairs of English sparrows to each 100 acres of land in the North Central states during the period from 1916 to 1920. The smallest number in any year was nine and the largest 13. It was originally estimated that a single pair of English sparrows would give rise to 275,716,983,698 individuals in 10 years' time (Barrows, 1889). Yet under the conditions in the North Central states, the number has been 11 nesting pairs to each 100 acres of land; and the fluctuation has only been between nine and 13 during this five-year period.

Adopting the rate of increase just cited, each 100 acres of land should have given rise to 575 sparrows each year, but the number remained constant. This difference between the potential number of sparrows and the actual number must be a measure of the toll taken by the environment; or, stated in the terms of the present hypothesis, the resistance of the environment. In the North Eastern states the resistance of the environment seems to be greater; for the average number of nesting pairs was only five; and it varied between three and seven.

The equilibrium of nature is in general a moving equilibrium as cited by Lotka (1925), with fluctuating numbers rather than absolutely constant numbers. If numbers were to be absolutely constant it would be expected that all environmental conditions were also constant, which obviously does not happen in usual cases. Additional examples of such equilibria will be cited under the subject of physical resistance and biotic resistance.

Physical Resistance.—In the chapters on Physical Autecology, the effects of the various factors were considered in much the same way as they would be treated in general physiology. The measurements of the various factors are in terms of physical systems. When considered as environmental resistance, the effect of these factors must be measured in terms of the reduction of the potential number of organisms. This furnishes a good example in making the distinction between physiology and ecology. In the consideration of temperature as a physical factor, the coefficient for the various processes of metabolism in organs or in individual organisms was considered. As pointed out in that chapter, many of these are not of direct ecological importance.

Ecology is concerned with the groups of organisms; and it is the effect of temperature upon the population which is of ecological importance. The effect of temperature upon the rate of hatching of an egg is of indirect importance to ecology, just as the effect of temperature on surface tensions or any other physical phenomena is of fundamental importance to physiology. The interest of ecology is centered upon the trend of the population, just as the interest of the physiologists is centered upon the metabolism which is a summation of all the physical phenomena involved.

Table XIII represents the resistance of temperature to the development of *Tribolium confusum*. It will be noted that the change in the rate of the hatching of the eggs, development of larvae, and the development of pupae, each has its own coefficient. It is also evident that the per cent of mortality changes with temperature. Each contributes to the general rate of increase of population; but it is the algebraic

Table XIII.—Biotic Constants for *Tribolium confusum*

Stage	17°				22°				27°				32°			
	Time	Per cent	Average numbers A.	B.	Time	Per cent	Average numbers A.	B.	Time	Per cent	Average numbers A.	B.	Time	Per cent	Average numbers A.	B.
Eggs	38.8	27.5	100	100	14.09	77	100	100	6.04	90.0	100	100	4.41	92.5	100	100
Larvae	...	...	25	30	60.00	77	78	76	22.42	93.5	88	92	17.35	84.0	93	92
Pupae	...	...	...	...	17.20	80	64	54	8.64	82.0	88	86	5.37	86.0	78	76

sum of these as represented in the rate of population increase that becomes the center of interest for ecology.

The table also gives the history of two series of experiments starting with 100 eggs each. In this case there is an accumulation of time and mortality for the death rate in each stage, as applied to the number of individuals which have survived the former stages. At 22° the percentage of mortality, which represents an unknown resistance factor, is 23 per cent in both the egg stage and in the larval stage; however 23 of the original population died in the egg stage; while the average deaths in the two larval populations was only 17.71.

This is an example of the chain-resistance reaction which is characteristic of organisms with specialized stages in their life cycle. A study of the resistance in one stage does not necessarily give a true value of the resistance to the life cycle. Chains of resistance will be considered further in connection with synecology.

A study of the time, required for the complete stage, shows that the effects of temperature are in essential agreement with the principles of Krogh and Van t'Hoff as described in the chapter on Temperature. When attention is turned to the population increase during a period of time, it becomes evident that one cannot make an approximation on the basis of temperature coefficients.

Figures 62 and 63 indicate the rates of increase of population at the temperatures indicated, covering the time from the first oviposition of the original population to the beginning of oviposition by the first progeny. It seems obvious that the refinement of the expressions of Q_{10} and various other temperature coefficients is of relatively little direct importance to the ecologist as compared with the study of the rates of increase of population under various conditions of environmental resistance.

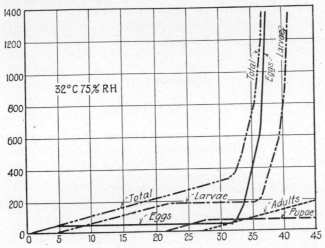

Fig. 62.—Population trends for *Tribolium confusum* from first oviposition of original population to the first oviposition of the first progeny. Number of individuals on the ordinate and days on the abscissa.

In considering the effects of physical resistance and the operation of the total physical and biotic resistance on the life of an individual, it

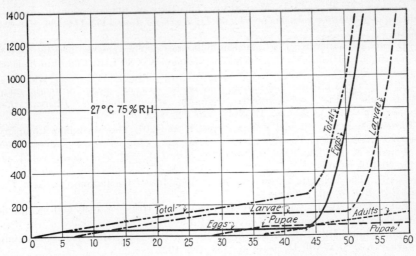

Fig. 63.—Population trends for *Tribolium confusum* from the first oviposition of the original population to the first oviposition of the first progeny (27°C. and 75 per cent of relative humidity). Compare with Fig. 62 for the effect of a difference of 5° in the temperature of the environment.

is necessary to take into consideration the limiting of individual factors which are near the limits of toleration, as the effect of the relative importance of various other factors operating contemporaneously. Our present knowledge of these total effects is very limited. We are in about the same relative position that general physiology was, when it began to realize the importance of the various phenomena of physical chemistry which contribute to the rates of metabolism.

BIBLIOGRAPHY

BIOTIC AUTECOLOGY

BAIRD, A. B.: Some Notes on the Natural Control of the Larch Sawfly and the Larch Case Bearer in New Brunswick in 1922, *Proc. Acadian Ent. Soc.*, No. 8, pp. 158–171, 1922.

BARROWS, W. B.: The English Sparrow in North America, *U. S. Dept. Agr.* (Div. Econ. Ornithol. and Mammal.) *Bull.* 1, p. 29, 1889.

CHAMBERLIN, THOMAS R.: Introduction of Parasites of the Alfalfa Weevil into the United States, *U. S. Dept. Agr. Circ.* 301, 1924. 9 pp.

CHAPMAN, R. N.: The Confused Flour Beetle, *Minn. Agr. Expt. Sta. Paper* 154; *Minn. State Ent. Rept.*, **17**: 73–94, 1918.

———: The Quantitative Analysis of Environmental Factors, *Ecology*, **9**: 111–122, 1928.

CHATELIER, LE, M. H.: Sur un énoncé général des lois des équilibres chimiques, *Compt. rend.*, **99**: 786–789, 1884.

COOKE, M. T.: Report on Bird Censuses in the United States 1916 to 1920, *U. S. Dept. Agr. Bull.*, 1923, 1165 pp.

CUTLER, D. W., and L. M. CRUMP: The Rate of Reproduction in Artificial Culture of *Colpidium colpoda;* pts. I and II, *Biochem. Jour.*, **17**: 174–186, 878–886, 1923.

D'ANCONA, UMBERTO: Del' influenza della stasi peschereccia del periodo 1914–18 sul patrimonio ittico dell' Alto Adriatico, *Memoria* CXXVI, R. Comitato Talassografico Italiano.

——— : Intorno alle associazioni biologiche e a un saggio di teoria matematica sulle stesse con particolar riguardo all' idrobiologia, *Internat. Rev. Gesamm. Hydrobiol. u. Hydrog.*, **17** (**314**): 189–225, 1927.

ELTON, CHARLES: "Animal Ecology," pp. 17 and 207, The Macmillan Company, New York, 1927. 8 pl.

FORBES, S. A.: The Food of Birds, *Ill. State Lab. Nat. Hist. Bull.*, vol. I, no. 3, pp. 80–148, 1880.

———: The Regulative Action of Birds upon Insect Oscillations, *Ill. State Lab. Nat. Hist. Bull.* 6, pp. 1–33, 1883.

FOURIER, J. B. J.: "The Analytical Theory of Heat," transl. with Notes by Alexander Freeman, Cambridge University Press, 1878. 466 pp.

FRIEDERICHS, DR. K.: Grundsätzliches über die Lebenseinheiten höherer Ordnung, *Naturwissenschaften*, vol. 15, no. 8, pp. 153–186, 1927.

GIBBS, WILLARD: On the Equilibrium of Heterogeneous Substances, *Trans. Conn. Acad. Arts & Sci.*, **3**: 380–400, 1874–1878.

HERRICK, G. W.: The "Ponderable" Substance of Aphids (*Homop.*), *Ent. News*, **37**: 207–210, 1926.

HOLDAWAY F. G.: Unpublished thesis.

HOWARD, L. O.: The House Fly and How to Suppress It, *U. S. Dept. Agr. Farmers, Bull.* 1408, 1924.

HOWARD, L. O., and W. F. FISKE: The Importation into the United States of the Parasites of the Gypsy Moth and the Brown-tail Moth, *U. S. Dept. Agr. Bur. Ent. Bull.* 91, 1912. 344 pp.

HUXLEY, T. H.: On the Agamic Reproduction and Morphology of Aphis, *Trans. Linn. Soc.*, London, **22**: 193–220, 221–236, 1858.

LEFROY, H. M.: "Indian Insect Life," reference on p. 624, W. Thacker and Co., London, 1909. 786 pp.

LOTKA, A. J.: "Elements of Physical Biology," Williams & Wilkins Co., Baltimore, 1925. 460 pp.

MATHESON, ROBERT, and E. H. HINMAN: Further Studies on *Charasp.* and Other Aquatic Plants in Relation to Mosquito Breeding, *Amer. Jour. Trop. Med.*, **9**: 249–266, 1929.

MUIR, F.: Presidential Address, *Proc. Hawaii Ent. Soc.*, vol. 3, **1**: 28–42, 1914.

MYERS, EVERETT CLARK: Relation of Density of Population and Certain Other Factors to Survival and Reproduction in Different Biotypes of *Paramecium caudatum, Jour. Exptl. Zool.*, **49**: 1–45, 4 figs., 1927.

OHM, G. S. (1827): "The Galvanic Circuit Investigated Mathematically," transl. by W. Francis, D. Van Nostrand Company, Inc., New York, 1905. 2d ed. 269 pp.

PARKER, J. R.: Some Effects of Temperature and Moisture upon *Melanoplus mexicanus, Mexicanus saussure,* and *Camnula pellucida* Scudder (Orthoptera), *Mont. Univ. Agr. Expt. Sta. Bull.* 223, p. 132, 1930.

PEARL, R.: "The Biology of Population Growth," especially chaps. I and VI, Alfred A. Knopf, Inc., New York, 1925. 260 pp.

PEARL, R., S. L. PARKER, and B. M. GONZALES: Experimental Studies on the Duration of Life. VII. The Mendelian Inheritance of Duration of Life in Crosses of Wild Type and Quintuple Stock of *Drosophila melanogaster, Amer. Naturalist,* **57**: 153–192, 1923.

PEMBERTON, C. E., and H. F. WILLARD: Interrelations of Fruit-fly Parasites in Hawaii, *Jour. Agr. Research,* **12**: 285, 1918.

―――: A Contribution to the Biology of Fruit-fly Parasites in Hawaii, *Jour. Agr. Research,* **15**: 419, 1918.

PÉRÈS, JOSEPH: Une application nouvelle des mathématiques à la biologie: La théorie des associations biologiques, *Rev. gén. sci.,* **37**: 295–300, 337–341, 1927.

RAILLET, A.: "Traité de zoologie médicale et agricole," 2d ed., Assilin and Houzeau, Paris, 1895. 239 pp.

ROACH, B. MURIEL: On the Relation of Certain Soil Algae to Some Soluble Carbon Compounds, *Ann. Bot.*, **60**: 149–199, 1926.

THOMPSON, W. R.: Théorie de l'action des parasites entomophages. Accroissement de la proportion d'hôtes parasites dans le parasètisme cyclique, *Compt. rend. acad. sci.,* Paris, **175**: 65–68, 1922.

―――: Étude de quelques cas simples de parasitisme cyclique chez les insectes entomophages, *Compt. rend. acad. sci.,* Paris, **174**: 1647–1649, 1922.

―――: La théorie mathématique de l'action des parasites entomophages, *Rev. gén. sci.,* **34**: 202–210, 1923.

―――: La théorie mathématique de l'action des parasites entomophages et le facteur du hasard, *Ann. facult. sci.,* Marseilles, 11e série, tôme 11, fascicule 11, pp. 68–89, 1924.

―――: A Method for the Approximate Calculation of Introduced Parasites of Insect Pests, *Bull. Ent. Research,* **17**: 273–277, 1926.

―――: On the Effect of Methods of Mechanical Control on the Progress of Introduced Parasites of Insect Pests, *Bull. Ent. Research,* **18**: 13–16, 1927.

―――: A Contribution to the Study of Biological Control and Parasite Introduction in Continental Areas, *Parasitology,* **20**: 90–112, 1928.

————: On the Relative Value of Parasites and Predators in the Biological Control of Insect Pests, *Bull. Ent. Research*, **19**: 343–350, 1929.

————: On the Effect of Random Oviposition on the Action of Entomophagous Parasites as Agents of Natural Control, *Parasitology*, **21**: 180–188, 1929.

————: On Natural Control, *Parasitology*, **21**: 269–281, 1929.

————: On the Part Played by Parasites in the Control of Insects Living in Protected Situations, *Bull. Ent. Research*, **20**: 457–462, 1929.

TOTHILL, J. D.: The Meaning of Natural Control, *Proc. Ent. Soc. Nova Scotia No. 4*, pp. 10–14, 1918.

————: Some Notes on the Natural Control of the Oyster Shell Scale, *Lepidosaphes ulmi* L., *Bull. Ent. Research*, **9**: 183–196, 1919.

VOLTERRA, V.: Variazioni e fluttuazioni del numero d'individui in specie animali conviventi, *Mem. accad. Lincei*, ser. VI, vol. II, 1926.

————: Sulle fluttuazioni biologiche et leggi delle fluttuazioni biologiche, *Rend. r. a. Lincei*, ser. VI, vol. VI, Jan., 1927.

WARDLE, ROBERT A.: "The Problems of Applied Entomology," p. 587, Manchester Univ. Press, 1929.

WOODRUFF, L. L.: "Foundations of Biology," reference on p. 375, The Macmillan Company, New York, 1922.

CHAPTER IX

SYNECOLOGY

Introduction.—The discussion will be interrupted at this point, only to call attention to the fact that the transition is now being made from autecology to synecology. In autecology individual physical factors and individual organisms were considered. Now individual organisms are to be combined into the populations; and individual physical factors into weather, climate, soil, and other environmental media. In the treatment of the subject matter of autecology, physical factors were given first consideration. In the treatment of synecology the population systems will be given first consideration. Ordinarily the combinations of physical factors which make up weather, which is a study of the variations of these physical factors in time, and the combinations which make up climate, or climatology, representing the distribution of these physical factors over geographic areas, are considered as separate subject matter. In the present consideration there is no separate chapter devoted to weather or to climate. Climatology is considered under chorology or distribution in space, and weather, is considered under both the subject of Chorology and Chronology. It is possible that this division of the subject matter will not be the most satisfactory to students who are particularly interested in weather and climate. However, for those who are interested in the distribution of insects, in space and time, it may prove more convenient.

In considering the populations of animals there are several possible viewpoints. From the viewpoint of biocenology the population, or biocenose, may be classified on the basis of the bond which is of primary importance in holding the population together as an ecological unit. In many cases this bond may be primarily physical, *i.e.*, the organisms may be forced to associate with each other because they have a similar toleration of physical conditions of the environment. In this case the biotic relationships are secondary. These biotic relationships are forced upon the organism as a result of their aggregation on the basis of a physical factor.

In other cases the primary bond may be biotic, *i.e.*, it may be an association of organisms on the basis of some biotic bond such as a social aggregation. Here we could classify the social insects with their parasites and symbionts. Here also could be classified the groups of organisms which have common host plants. It is this phase of ecology that appeals to the naturalist. It represents a serious branch of science with great possibilities as illustrated by Wheeler's "The Social Insects" (1928). However, in the present volume there will be no special chapters devoted to these subjects. They will be referred to in connection with the populations of various areas and in connection with the chorology involved. Possibly any scheme of handling the subject matter of synecology will prove unsatisfactory to students interested in particular subjects. An attempt will be made to treat it with a dynamic viewpoint with particular reference to methods which may aid in furthering our information of the general subject matter. Under each of the principal headings the main literature will be cited. It is probably true that the student will find more satisfactory information if he will follow these main citations than by using the present treatment alone.

Biotic Potential, Environmental Resistance, and Population Equilibrium.—Biotic systems may be considered as in equilibrium when the populations remain approximately stationary over a considerable period of time. Lotka (1925) prefers to use the term quasi-equilibria for such systems because there is a continual dissipation or degradation of energy involved in maintaining the stationary state. This, he believes, makes a proper distinction from the true equilibrium of physical systems in which all forces are balanced and velocity vanishes.

The relatively stable state of biotic systems resembles the static equilibrium in that the point or line about which it oscillates is itself stationary. It is, however, like a dynamic system in that the population is moving about a stationary point, but it is nevertheless moving. It is, therefore, necessary to be clear as to the conditions to be considered. A population may be treated, in a general way, as in a stationary state in which its biotic potential is balanced against the environmental resistance.

Individual organisms are continually being produced to replace those which are eliminated by the resistance of the environment. At times the trend of the population is slightly upward, and at times it is slightly downward. This represents the stationary state of equilibrium, or the state of quasi-equilibrium of the oscillating population. On this basis, the general situation of a population may be considered as balanced with its biotic potential equal to the environmental resistance; but the statement does not apply to the population as it follows its oscillation above and below the level which may be called its stationary state.

The economic entomologist becomes impatient to apply a formula for the solution of his problems. However, the present state of our knowledge is too immature for such applications. It is evident that a species of high biotic potential has the ability to increase its population very rapidly if there is a reduction of environmental resistance. Similarly, if the population is reduced artificially, it has the ability to return to the original population in a very short period of time, because of its high biotic potential.

It may be concluded from the above that, when the population remains constant with a low physical resistance, the biotic resistance must be high. Conversely, when the biotic resistance is low, the physical resistance must be high if the same state of equilibrium is to exist. This is in accordance with experience in the biotic control of pests. In countries where physical factors are moderate and relatively constant, pests have often been successfully controlled by parasites and predators; while such control has been difficult in countries where physical conditions fluctuate greatly and often become extreme.

For a consideration of the calculation of the trends of the populations, the student is referred to the Appendix by Dr. Volterra.

Biotic Resistance.—When we approach the subject of biotic resistance, particularly in connection with the equilibrium of populations, we are in the borderground between autecology and synecology. The discussion will be continued from the consideration in the last chapter on Autecology. It is perfectly clear that we are analyzing the effects of organisms upon each other, and this may very logically be the subject matter of synecology.

The history of economic entomology contains the records of many unintentional experiments in which organisms have been carried to new environments which contained no biotic resistance in the way of predators, parasites, or competitors. In many cases the physical resistance has been about the same as in the original environment, but the absence of the biotic resistance has been enough to permit the biotic potential to express itself and the populations to rise to unprecedented numbers. In such cases it has seemed obvious that the most promising method of control is to examine the original environment to determine the nature of the biotic resistance, with a view to introducing it into the new environment and thus reestablish the equilibrium of the original environment.

When the sugar-cane leaf hopper, *Perkinsiella saccharicida*, was introduced into the Hawaiian Islands, it apparently came without biotic resistance in the form of parasites; and the new environment presented a minimum of physical resistance. As a consequence, its rate of reproduction was practically that of the unimpeded biotic potential. Later, parasites were introduced and, in the presence of this biotic resistance, the hoppers were reduced to a minimum which is no longer of economic importance.

Environmental resistance must necessarily be determined for each stage in the life cycle of an organism. Thompson (1928) has called attention to the necessity of properly evaluating resistance factors which function as a part of a chain series of resistances, each operating in a different stage of the life cycle. He calls the mortality of a population as expressed in the per cent of the total individuals in a given stage the "apparent mortality." The real mortality is defined as the per cent of the egg population of the life cycle which dies. To illustrate the relative importance of apparent and real mortality, he gives a hypothetical illustration of an insect depositing 100 eggs for whose control a 98 per cent mortality is required. The chain of factors are given by Thompson (1928) as follows:

Stage	Factor	Apparent mortality, per cent	Real mortality, per cent
Eggs at deposition................	Sterility	5.00	5.00
Eggs after deposition.............	Egg parasites	10.00	9.50
Young larvae....................	Intrinsic factors	80.00	68.40
Mature larvae	Larval parasites	60.00	10.20
Pupae	Pupal parasites	10.00	0.47
Adults..........................	Meteorological factors	54.86	2.30

The fact that a mortality of 54.86 per cent among the adults should make a difference of only 2.3 per cent in the population of the cycle is striking.

Thompson then proceeds to calculate the effect of removing the parasites which caused a 10 per cent mortality among the eggs, a 60 per cent mortality of the larvae and a 10 per cent mortality of the pupae. While the sum of these three amounts to 80 per cent, it makes only a difference of 4 per cent in the total mortality of the cycle. From this he concludes: "The absence of the parasites would allow the escape for reproduction of only two additional females per hundred." It is worthwhile to note that these two extra females would give rise to an extra 200 eggs, making a total of 300 eggs to start the next life cycle instead of the 100 with which he started his calculation.

In many cases the measurement of the total resistance may be of the greatest importance and in certain cases it would be impossible to calculate the total resistance on the basis of any measurement of the resistance to the different stages of the life cycle. Obviously the greatest progress is to be made by combining analytic work in a laboratory where resistance is determined down to the finest point both from the standpoint of the environment and the organism, and observations and measurements in the field where the total conditions are to be met with. When the results of these two types of investigation are in harmony, it may be assumed that the essential facts of the situation are known. When there is a discrepancy between the two types of information, it may be assumed that there is some unknown resistance which has not yet been determined.

Attention may now be turned to the consideration of the various types of biotic resistance which may be encountered in the environment. Attention has been called by some authors to the practical value of various organisms in regulating populations of insects (Forbes, 1883, and others).

This work has had a tendency towards certain more or less quantitative field observations and the formulation of general principles. There has been a tendency towards the production of generalizations with regard to the balance of nature on the one hand, and the attempt at the control of numbers of organisms of economic importance on the other. The general situation in regard to the balance of nature in connection with mammals has recently been emphasized by Grinnell (1928), and has been given a rather full treatment by Elton (1927).

The problem has also received attention from those interested in a more formal mathematical expression. The authors have been both mathematicians and biologists, such as Muir (1914), Thompson (1922 to 1924), Lotka (1925), D'Ancona (1927), Pérès (1927), and Volterra (see Appendix). These authors have been interested primarily in the mathematical theory of population change, and the state of moving equilibria in natural systems. All of these various attempts have, in general, recognized the necessity for accepting a potential rate of increase for a species, and expressing the action of the environmental factors in terms of the change of the trend of population. The biologists have used simple arithmetical formulae having to do with the number of generations of organisms, while the mathematicians have been inclined to use the compound interest law, or some modification of it, to follow the trend of population.

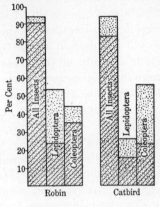

FIG. 64.—The food of birds from an infested orchard compared with the usual food during the month of May. There is a slight increase in the percentage of all insects in the total food and a significant increase in the percentage of Lepidoptera and Coleoptera in the food of the birds from the infested orchard. (*Forbes*, 1883.)

Mathematically, one of the simplest cases which we have is that of one species which feeds upon another. This may represent the relationships of predator and prey, or of insect parasites and insect hosts. In the case of insects, the distinction is usually made on the basis of whether the predator attacks one host or many hosts; but if it attacks a single host for the support of its entire life cycle, it is usually classed as an insect parasite. Forbes (1883) turned his attention to the action of predators in maintaining the state of equilibrium in nature. He made a comparison of environments in which the numbers of insects were normal, so far as could be determined, and conditions in which there were outbreaks of insects. A study was made of the food which was consumed by birds in these two types of environments (Fig. 64). The accompanying histograms show the general nature of the results, which tend to show that the total per cent of insects in the food is higher in orchards in which there were outbreaks of insects than in other environments; and also that the various birds tended to consume more of the abundant species than they did of the others. Forbes considered that this showed that the birds should have a considerable regulatory action in that they would eat the largest numbers of species which were abundant and thus permit species which were low in numbers to increase, while those that were high in numbers would be brought down towards an equilibrium stage. Bryant (1912) made a study of the grasshoppers eaten by birds in areas where there were different grasshoppers populations known to be present. He found that birds ate 120,453 grasshoppers per square mile, when the population of grasshoppers was 20 or 30 per square yard or 635,000,000,000 per square mile. This represents 0.019 per cent of the population eaten by the birds per day.

Muir (1914) considered a theoretical example which postulates a constant number of the total of three species present in an environment, and also a differential action of a predator on the three species so that during the larval stage of species A none of the larvae were destroyed; 25 per cent of those of species B; and 50 per cent of the larvae of species C. In his calculation he maintained the sum total of species A, B, and C as a constant number, and followed the trend of each individual species to show the rate at which species A would supplant species B and C. The following graph illustrates the trend which he found from his calculation (Fig. 65). This is, of course, a case of unstable equilibrium which is tending rapidly to the establishment of one species and the exclusion of others. It may, however, be taken to represent a species which has been introduced into an environment, and has the advantage over two native species in that it is exempt from predators.

Muir (1914) has also represented the case of unstable equilibrium with a parasite and a host. The rates of reproduction are assumed to be the same in both parasite and host; and the assumption is made that each parasite destroys a host and that there is no duplication of parasitism. The accompanying graph follows the trend of the population of the host and parasite, starting with the host free from parasites for the first four generations (Fig. 66). After this the parasite is introduced, and the rate of reproduction in the parasite is the same as that of the host. Seven generations after the parasite is started, it equals the host in numbers; but, nevertheless, the host population tends to increase up to within two generations of the time when it entirely disappears. This is interesting as a case of unstable equilibrium in which the effect on the host is not superficially noticeable up to the time when it is about to be entirely eliminated. It is possible that certain sudden fluctuations in numbers in nature are due to actions of this kind, where the significance of relative numbers of host and parasite are not realized, until the point is passed in which the parasite equals the number of its host and the sudden change comes about. Such conditions, however, are probably the exception rather than the rule in nature. A more stable equilibrium is undoubtedly the rule.

There is some advantage in following these theoretical considerations of the actions of parasites and hosts if for no other reason than that they can call attention to the relative value of the various factors which must

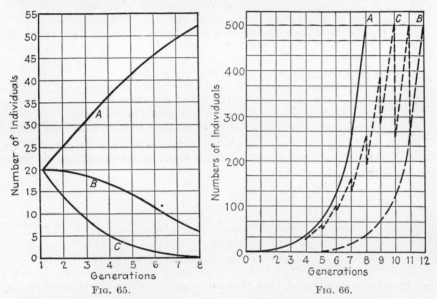

Fig. 65.

Fig. 66.

Fig. 65.—The theoretical trend of three species whose total population remains constant at 60; 50 per cent of the larvae of species *C* are destroyed by predators in each generation, 25 per cent of species *B*, and none of species *A*. (*Adapted from Muir*, 1914.)

Fig. 66.—A hypothetical case of the effect of a parasite on the population of a host. *A*, host; four young and sexes equal. Population trend without parasites. *B*, parasite; four young and sexes equal. Each one causes the death of one mature host. *C*, trend of the host population as a result of the action of the parasites. The parasite starts at the fourth generation of the host and lays four eggs with the result that only 28 out of a possible 32 hosts develop. If this continued the host would become extinct very suddenly in the eleventh generation. (*Muir*, 1914.)

be involved in the expressions, and thus to an appreciation of the advantages of various adaptations.

Thompson (1922 and 1924) has proposed a formula for the calculation of the number of generations required for the termination of such an unstable state of equilibrium as is indicated above. Such calculations are as yet theoretical, but they have great possibilities.

A slight modification of Thompson's formula for calculating the number of generations required for a parasite to overtake a host is presented. The example is as follows:

n = the original population of the host.
l = the sex ratio of the host.

l = the number of young produced by each female host.
p = the original population of the parasite.
f = the sex ratio of the parasite.
s = the number of young produced by each female parasite.

The calculation may be simplified by combining the sex ratio and the number of young produced as a sort of expression of the biotic potential and thus have one character to handle rather than two.

$lh = w$ = rate of reproduction (reproductive potential) of the host.
$fs = z$ = rate of reproduction (reproductive potential) of the parasite.
nw = the number of hosts after the first reproduction.

Then

pz = the number of parasites after the first reproduction.
$nw - pz$ = the number of surviving hosts after the first generation.
pz^2 = the number of parasites after the second reproduction.
$(nw - pz)(w)$ = the number of hosts after the second reproduction.
$(nw^2 - pzw) - pz^2$ = the number of surviving hosts after the second generation.

To solve for $(nw^{k-} \text{———}) - pz^k$, where k = the number of generations until the population of parasites will equal the number of hosts, the calculation may be simplified and reduced to the following:

$$O = \frac{w}{z}$$

$$B = \frac{zp}{n(z - w) + zp}$$

$$k = \frac{\log B}{\log O}.$$

In this case it is assumed that there is no duplication in parasitizing the host. It is also assumed that each egg of the parasite is laid in a host and that each host is killed after being so parasitized.

The formula thus represents the increment of difference in the biotic potential of the host and the parasite, and will obviously hold for conditions in which the value for reproductive potential of the parasite is greater than the reproductive potential of the host. If the converse were true, it would be impossible for a time to come when the parasite population would equal the host population. In a case where the two potentials are equal, the increment of difference in the two values for the biotic potential is reduced to zero; and the number of generations required for the host to overtake the parasite may be determined by dividing the host population by the parasite population.

In this simple case we have been able to calculate the value of the parasite as environmental resistance to the biotic potential of the host. It is true that we have made certain assumptions as to the lack of duplication on the part of the parasite, but this and similar factors may be taken care of by determining the per cent of duplication which normally takes place. It also assumes that the host population is continually increasing, which is contrary to the normal condition of equilibrium.

Thompson (1924) has made considerable progress in calculating the value of hazards in the life of the parasite. As stated above, however, the formula as presented does not take care of the case of stable equilibrium between the parasite and host. There is a great practical value even in this calculation. According to Thompson it would require 19 generations for 1,000 individuals of the parasite, *Liparis dispar*, to exterminate 1,000,000,000 hosts when the parasite is reproducing twice as fast as the host. Even under these conditions, 10 per cent or less of the host would be attacked up to the 16th generation. Without a method of calculation, there would be no way of knowing whether the parasite was making satisfactory progress when, after 15 generations the per cent of parasitism was still below 10 per cent.

From our study of insects of economic importance, we now know very well that there are many cases in which the numbers of parasites do not reach a large per cent of those of the host. They seem to come to an equilibrium, when the numbers of the host have not been materially affected. Attention has been called to this by Chamberlin in the case of the alfalfa weevil; and there are many other cases now well known which seem to substantiate the hypothesis that in nature, ordinarily, things come to a state of at least semi-stable equilibrium.

Lotka (1925) illustrates a state of stable equilibrium by the use of the population of the United States and the population of sheep which it uses for part of its food. This example has been chosen because the quantitative data were at hand and it seemed to satisfy the conditions of such an equilibrium. Lotka gave this formal expression in the following way:

$$\frac{X_f}{X_i} = \frac{V_{if}u_i}{\alpha_{if}v_f}, \text{ or } X_f = \frac{V_{if}u_i}{\alpha_{if}v_f}X_i.$$

The human population which consumes the sheep is represented by $X_i = 103,587,955$ individuals. The population of sheep which serves as food is represented by $X_f = 48,873,000$ individuals. The quantity of sheep eaten by each human individual per year is represented by $V_{if}u_i = 0.1096$ individual sheep. The per cent of the standing population of sheep slaughtered each year is represented by $\alpha_{fi}v_i = 0.2322$.

The state of equilibrium would, therefore, be represented by:

$$X_f = \frac{0.1096}{0.2322}X_i$$
$$= 0.4718X_i.$$
$$X_i = 103,587,955,$$

Hence

$$X_f = 0.4718(103,587,955),$$
$$X_f = 48,873,000.$$

The population of the predators is, therefore, multiplied by a coefficient which expresses the ratio of the number of individuals of the prey consumed by each individual predator, to the per cent of the standing population of prey consumed by the entire population by predators. If the product of this coefficient and the population of the predators is not equal to the population of the prey, the condition is not that of stable equilibrium.

It will be noticed that two ratios are involved. One is the number of individuals of the prey consumed by each individual predator; *i.e.,* the number of sheep eaten by each individual of the human population. The other is the per cent of the population of the prey which is eaten each year by the entire population of the predator or the human population. We may then translate his formula into an expression where we will write as the numerator of the fraction the number of prey eaten by each individual predator in a unit of time, and as the denominator the per cent of the population of prey eaten by the total population of the predators in a unit of time. If we then multiply the total population of the predator by this fraction, the product should be equal to the population of the prey. If it is not equal to the population of the prey, it indicates that there is an unstable state of equilibrium: either that the predator is eating a larger portion of the prey than it should in a case of equilibrium, or else it is eating a smaller portion than it should at equilibrium. No account is taken of the increase of the sheep population.

Volterra (see Appendix) has developed the mathematical theory of equilibrium between host and parasite, competitors for the same food, and for any relationship which one species may have to any other which is living in the same habitat with it.

THE ACTION OF COMPETITORS

The action of competitors is not as simple to handle with our present information as that of prey and predator, or parasite and host. However, its significance in biotic communities may be just as great or even greater. There may be many manifestations of competition. It may result in competition for food, or for space, or for mates. The individuals or species which succeed in competition may do so because of sheer numbers, because of their ability to overpower their competitors, because of their ability to develop more rapidly than their competitors, or because of a whole series of biological functions which may result in their superiority. Careful studies of the analysis of definite cases of competition are necessary in order to determine whether we have general principles applying in all cases.

Competition has been considered one of the most important factors in determining the composition of plant associations (Clements, 1916). From the time of Malthus it has been considered that the populations of nations were to be limited by the competition of the individual components for space and food. Pearl (1925) studied the populations of

Drosophila in a milk bottle, and considered the nature of the rate of population growth to be fundamental to the growth of all populations, and superimposed the growth curves of the populations of nations on the curve for *Drosophila* in a milk bottle.

There are many factors involved even in the increase of the population of a *Drosophila* culture; for the flies are dependent upon a population of microorganisms, which are in turn dependent upon certain physical conditions of the environment. Yet the condition is one of competition; and it is interesting to note that the rate of increase is slowed as the population grows and the competition becomes greater. The curve approaches an asymptote which represents a condition of starvation.

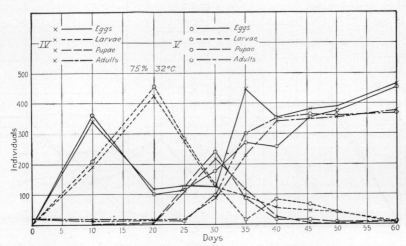

Fig. 67.—Population trend of *Tribolium confusum* at 32°C. and 75 per cent of relative humidity.

Pearl *et al* (1923) found that the different mutants of *Drosophila* had different abilities as to the concentration which they might attain in a milk bottle.

The case of competition in the limited environment of individuals of the same species, *Tribolium confusum*, has already been referred to. This case is simple in many ways, yet complicated in the calculation of the incidents of the larvae and adults with the pupae and eggs. The constancy of the general result of this competition, however, is attested by the following graphs, each of which represents duplicate experiments. One set run at 32°C. and 73 per cent of relative humidity, and the other at 27°C. with the same relative humidity. The fact that duplicate populations follow so closely the same course indicates that they must be following definite laws (Figs. 67 and 68).

The fundamental regularity of this competition is very striking. These curves, however, represent merely the attainment of the state of equilibrium. During this early stage of population growth, the events may be calculated on the basis of the physical factors. The appearance of eggs, larvae, pupae, and adults all follows as would be expected. As the saturation point is reached and the population begins to oscillate about the state of equilibrium, the biotic factors become of primary importance. The results of the study of this state of equilibrium are not yet available for consideration.

Another example of the action of competitors is furnished by the work of Pemberton and Willard (1918a and b) on the parasites of the Mediterranean fruit-flies, *Ceratitis capipata*. Of a number of species of

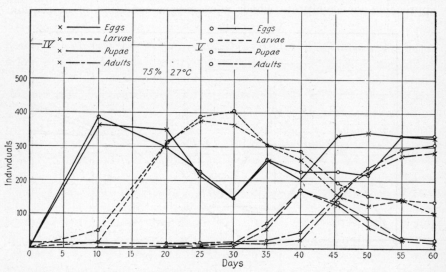

FIG. 68.—Population trend of *Tribolium confusum* at 27°C. and 75 per cent of relative humidity.

parasites which were introduced into the Hawaiian Islands for the control of the fruit fly, *Opius humilis*, demonstrated that it was the most efficient parasite as measured by the per cent of hosts which it was able to parasitize. Another parasite, *Dichasma tryoni*, was less efficient than *Opius*, so far as the number of hosts which it was able to reach was concerned. It was found that these two parasites oviposited in the same hosts in many cases which resulted in competition between the larvae of the two species. In case of such competition, *Dichasma* was able to overcome *Opius*. The result was that when these two parasites competed, the less efficient of the two survived. Thus efficiency in survival and efficiency in destroying hosts were not the same. In discussing the results of their study of these parasites the authors say:

If one species of larval parasite when working alone parasitizes 60 per cent of the host, and another species not strikingly different from the first and working the same in every known respect parasitizes 40 per cent of the host when working alone, there is no reason to assume that both combined can exceed a parasitism of 60 per cent. All overlapping by the species capable of only 40 per cent parasitism can only serve to reduce the total effect to a point below 60 per cent of parasitism

Further results on the study of these parasites are to be watched with interest. Smith (1929) takes exception to the conclusion that the combination of the two parasites will either reduce or retard the control of the host. He does not believe that the per cent of parasitism will be lower at equilibrium with the two than with *Opius* alone. The question can be settled only by careful observation and experimentation. Studies are also being made on many other forms of economic importance; and it may be expected that we shall revise many of our views of the action of organisms in biotic equilibrium on the basis of the practical results which shall be gathered. The study of the equilibrium of biotic systems is undoubtedly one of the most fertile in the field of ecology, and the results which will be obtained from the methods of observation in the field and from theoretical calculation are going to contribute much to our knowledge. It will be necessary to maintain an open mind, and to accept both types of information with the hope that the coordination of these types of information is going to contribute to the progress of our understanding of such phenomena.

Attention must now be called to the various papers by Volterra which are cited in the Bibliography and the Appendix, which give a general summary of the work. Becoming interested in the theory of biotic equilibrium through the statistics gathered by D'Ancona in the study of the ratios of various predatory fish in the Adriatic Sea, Volterra came to develop a series of equations representing the various phases of biotic equilibrium (see Appendix). Putting aside for the moment the practicability of the use of such calculations in determining the relative abundance of organisms in the field, it is interesting to note the development of the theory beginning with the biological association of two species which depend on the same food, and proceeding to the association of two species one of which feeds upon another. He adds one complication after another to the association, until he eventually deals with the association of any number whatever of species some of which contend for the same food and some of which feed upon others.

In the course of these theorems he develops what he calls the fundamental laws of fluctuations of two species living together which are, First, the law of periodic cycle—*The fluctuations of two species are periodic; and the period depends solely upon the coefficients of increase and decrease, and the initial conditions.* Second, the law of the conservation of the averages—*The averages of the number of individuals of two species are constant whatever may be the initial values of the numbers of individuals of the two species, just so long as the coefficient of increase and decrease of the two species and that of protection and offense remain constant.* Third, the law of the disturbance of the averages—*If an attempt is made to destroy the individuals of two species uniformly and in proportion to their numbers, the average of the number of individuals of the species that is eaten increases, and that of the individuals feeding upon the other diminishes.*

The author devotes a special section of his paper to a consideration of the limitations of the last law of the disturbance of averages. It is interesting to note, however, the possibility that the destruction of a whole section of a population of hosts and parasites may result in a subsequent relative increase of the host, and a relative decrease of the parasite. Another fundamental consideration to be drawn from these deductions is that there may be fluctuations in the biotic systems which are due solely to the components of the biotic system. Biologists usually look to the outside for great physical catastrophes to account for fluctuations in the population. It is undoubtedly true that such fluctuations in the physical factors of the environment are often causes of biotic fluctuation, but the fact must not be overlooked that the biotic system itself may set up a series of fluctuations which are entirely characteristic to itself.

The publication of these mathematical considerations seems quite analogous to the publications of Willard Gibbs in the field of physical chemistry in which he gave a purely mathematical treatment to the phenomena of physical systems. At the time of his publication it was not considered that his theories had any practical value; however, they subsequently formed the foundation of the science of physical chemistry.

Similarly, today, biologists in general find little of practical importance in these theoretical considerations, but undoubtedly in the course of the quantitative development of ecology, they are going to form a very firm part of the foundation for our future science. There seem, therefore, to be three great necessities for advancement in our understanding of the equilibrium of biotic systems: first, the collection and bringing together of facts from nature giving the quantitative expression of the relative abundance of animals and their inter-relations; second, the following of the mathematical theory of the possibilities of biotic systems; and, third, and possibly most important, the coordination of the mathematical theory with the facts as gathered from nature. When the foundation has been properly laid and the fundamental generalizations are before us, we will probably enter upon one of the most important fields of biological science which will be highly theoretical, highly quantitative, and highly practical.

In the conclusion of the section on biotic potential and environmental resistance, it may be said that our present knowledge seems to extend to the frontier between the descriptive matter of the naturalists' observations, and the quantitative data which are susceptible to calculation by the mathematician. The field of descriptive observation has been so well surveyed that we have spent little time on it in this volume, which is concerned largely with the borderlines of knowledge. In the field of quantitative knowledge and calculation which lies just ahead of us, the facts now known are so few and so widely scattered that our discussion of it cannot be complete. In fact, as we look from one isolated piece of work to another, they seem so far apart that we are inclined to wonder whether they all belong to the same field. It has been felt that the various attempts at quantitative methods which have been presented and others which are scattered through the literature do belong to the same field and that the day will come when new facts will have been assembled to fill in the interspaces and the entire field of ecology will appear as a unit to us. The inherent ability of a species to reproduce and maintain itself, on the one hand; and the adverse physical and biotic conditions of the environment, which involve temperature extremes, food, enemies, and other factors which have been portrayed by naturalists in their descriptions of the struggle for existence, on the other hand, are just the beginnings of quantitative considerations.

We have now come to the period when the potential of the organism and the resistance of the environment are to be measured, and predictions of future conditions are to be calculated on the basis of these measurements. This does not mean that the descriptive results which have been gleaned by the naturalists are to be discarded. It is quite the contrary. They are to form the very foundation upon which the quantitative knowledge will be built. In fact, many of our quantitative methods are nothing more than refinements to be used in evaluating the observations which naturalists have made.

BIBLIOGRAPHY

SYNECOLOGY

BAIRD, A. B.: Some Notes on the Natural Control of the Larch Sawfly and the Larch Case Bearer in New Brunswick in 1922, *Proc. Acadian Ent. Soc.*, No. 8, pp. 158–171, 1922.

BRYANT, H. C.: Some Insects and Other Arthropods in the Diet of the Western Meadowlark, *Jour. Ent. and Zool.*, **4**: 807–809, 1912.

CHAMBERLIN, THOMAS R.: Introduction of Parasites of the Alfalfa Weevil into the United States, *U. S. Dept. Agr.*, *Circ.* 301, 1924. 9 pp.

CLEMENTS, F. E.: "Plant Succession," Carnegie Inst., Wash., 1916. 512 pp.

D'ANCONA, UMBERTO: Intorno alle associazioni biologiche e a un saggio di teoria matematica sulle stesse con particolar riguardo all' idrobiologia, *Internat. Rev. Hydrobiol. u. Hydrog.*, **17** (**314**): 189–225, 1927.

ELTON, CHARLES: "Animal Ecology," pp. 17 and 207, 8 pl., The Macmillan Company, New York, 1927.

FORBES, S. A.: The Food of Birds, *Ill. State Lab. Nat. Hist. Bull.* 3, **1**: pp. 80–148, 1880.

————: The Regulative Action of Birds upon Insect Oscillations, *Ill. State Lab. Nat. Hist. Bull.* 6, pp. 1–33, 1883.

GRINNELL, JOSEPH: Presence and Absence of Animals, *Calif. Univ. Chron.*, pp. 429–450, October, 1928.

IMMS, A. D.: The Biological Control of Insects and Injurious Plants in the Hawaiian Islands, *Ann. Appl. Biol.*, **13**: 402–423, 1926.

LOTKA, A. J.: "Elements of Physical Biology," Williams & Wilkins Company, Baltimore, 1925. 460 pp.

MUIR, F.: Presidential Address, *Proc. Hawaii. Ent. Soc.*, **3**: 28–42, 1914.

MYERS, EVERETT CLARK: Relation of Density of Population and Certain Other Factors to Survival and Reproduction in Different Biotypes of *Paramecium caudatum, Jour. Exptl. Zool.*, **49**: 1–45, 4 figs., 1927.

OHM, G. S. (1827): "The Galvanic Current Investigated Mathematically," transl. by W. Francis, D. Van Nostrand Company, Inc., New York, 1905. 2d ed., 269 pp.

PEARL, R.: "The Biology of Population Growth"; especially chaps. I and II, Alfred A. Knopf Inc., New York, 1925. 260 pp.

PEARL, R., S. L. PARKER, and B. M. GONZALEZ: Experimental Studies on the Duration of Life. VII. The Mendelian Inheritance of Duration of Life in Crosses of Wild Type and Quintuple Stock of *Drosophila melanogaster, Amer. Naturalist*, **57**: 153–192, 1923.

PEMBERTON, C. E., and H. E. WILLARD: Interrelations of Fruit-fly Parasites in Hawaii, *Jour. Agr. Research*, **12**: 285, 1918.

————: A Contribution to the Biology of Fruit-fly Parasites in Hawaii, *Jour. Agr. Research*, **15**: 419, 1918.

PÉRÈS, JOSEPH: Une application nouvelle des mathématiques à la biologie: La théorie des associations biologiques, *Rev. gén. sci.*, **37**: 295–300, 337–341, 1927.

SMITH, H. S.: Multiple Parasitism: Its Relation to the Biological Control of Insect Pests, *Bull. Ent. Research*, pt. 2, **20**: 141–149, August, 1929.

THOMPSON, W. R.: Théorie de l'action des parasites entomophages. Accroissement de la proportion d'hôtes parasites dans le parasitisme cyclique, *Compt. rend. acad. sci.*, Paris, **175**: 65–68, 1922.

————: Étude de quelques cas simples de parasitisme cyclique chez les insectes entomophages, *Compt. rend. acad. sci.*, Paris, **174**: 1647–1649, 1922.

————: La théorie mathématique de l'action des parasites entomophages, *Rev. gén. sci.*, **34**: 202–210, 1923.

————: La théorie mathématique de l'action des parasites entomophages et le facteur du hasard, *Ann. facult. sci.*, Marseilles, 11e série, tôme 11, fascicule 11, pp. 68–89, 1924.

————: A Contribution to the Study of Biological Control and Parasite Introduction in Continental Areas, *Parasitology*, **20**: 90–112, 1928.

————: On the Relative Value of Parasites and Predators in the Biological Control of Insect Pests, *Bull. Ent. Research*, pt. 4, **19**: 327–437, 1929.

————: On the Effect of Random Oviposition on the Action of Entomophagous Parasites as Agents of Natural Control, *Parasitology*, nos. 1 and 2, **21**: 180–188, 1929.

————: On Natural Control, *Parasitology*, no. 3, **21**: 269–281, 1929.

————: On the Part Played by Parasites in the Control of Insects Living in Protected Situations, *Bull. Ent. Research*, pt. 4, **20**: 457–462, 1929.

TOTHILL, J. D.: The Meaning of Natural Control, *Proc. Ent. Soc. Nova Scotia*, no. 4, pp. 10–14, 1918.

————: Some Notes on the Natural Control of the Oyster Shell Scale, *Lepidosaphes ulmi L., Bull. Ent. Research*, **9**: 183–196, 1919.

VOLTERRA, VITO: See Appendix.

WHEELER, W. M.: "The Social Insects," 1928.

CHAPTER X

CHOROLOGY, DISTRIBUTION IN SPACE OR ZOOGEOGRAPHY

Animal chorology or zoogeography concerns itself with the distribution of faunas over the face of the earth. The accumulation of facts and general principles in this branch of zoology in the last quarter of a century well justifies this special category in the field of general zoology to cover this subject. The student is referred to the recent publication of Dahl (1921), Olbricht (1923), Hesse (1924), and Elton (1927) for general consideration of the field and an introduction to its literature. The student of ecology will find his viewpoint particularly well represented in Hesse's volume. No attempt will be made to include in this discussion all that Hesse has considered in his 600 pages, or to include in the bibliography the hundreds of books and journals which he has so well summarized.

The earliest attempts of the study of a geographic distribution of animals were concerned with continental areas and followed the genetic development of faunas. The classical work of Wallace (1876) was dominated by an interest in the phylogeny of animal groups. This author divided the world into six great regions which are probably still the best-known faunal areas, and are widely used by taxonomists describing the distribution of species of all groups of animals (Fig. 69). A study of the map, and the terms applied to these regions and sub-regions, will show that the method of division of the world into these areas was not a purely ecological one. The great physical barriers of continental areas, mountain ranges, and seas often determine the possibility of animals being present to occupy favorable environmental conditions. The centers from which phylogenetic groups of animals have been distributed also determine the possibilities of various species being forced to occupy certain favorable environments. Attention has been called to this by Adams (1905). The influence of glaciation at successive epochs in the history of the earth also imposed certain great faunal restrictions which are still evident in the composition of the fauna of various areas.

Kennedy (1928) believes that there is a correlation between the evolutionary level of species and the type of environment which they may occupy. He believes that primitive insects usually have a low rate of metabolism, while very modern insects have a high rate. He says:

We can classify environments by their energy intensities. A hot sun-baked environment has a greater energy intensity than a cold, lightless one. The

219

tropics have a greater energy intensity than the boreal regions. The hot and light middle of the day has a greater energy intensity than the cool dark night. The series of insects, from the slow with low metabolism to fast with high metabolism, tends to be found in environments of parallel-energy intensities. The slow insects, usually primitive, occur in cool environments of low-energy intensity, in environments that are cool and shady, or even dark, while the fast insects— usually modern types—occur in the light, hot environments of high-energy intensity, such as the tropics, the mid-summer, or the mid-day.

The next step in the study of animal geography was the consideration of the distribution and significance of climatic factors, such as the physical

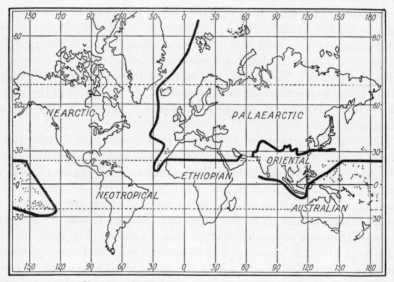

FIG. 69.—Wallace's faunal regions of the world.

factors of temperature, moisture, etc. It may be permissible to pass over the early history of this work in which temperature received the main consideration, and to cite as more or less typical of these attempts the work of Merriam (1898, and subsequently). The geographic distribution of various temperature areas is very obvious from the mere fact that the earth is a sphere, and that it receives more energy from solar radiation at the equator than at the poles. To this must be added the modifying influence of the seas, with their currents of warm water which warm the shores of temperate and even polar continents.

Merriam (1898) formulated certain principles which he designated as the laws of temperature control of the distribution of animals as follows:

Animals are restricted in their northern distribution by the total quantity of heat during the season of growth and reproduction. The southern range:

animals are restricted in their southern range by the mean temperature of a brief period covering the hottest part of the year.

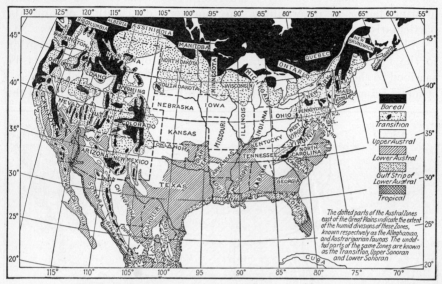

Fig. 70.—Life zones in the United States. (*After Merriam.*)

After a study of the conformity of groups of animals to the temperate conditions in North America, Merriam divided the area into regions and zones which he characterized by their temperatures as follows:

Regions	Zones	Governing temperatures	
		Northern limit, sum of normal mean daily temp. above 43°F.[1]	Southern limit, normal mean temp., 6 hottest weeks, °F.
Boreal..................	Arctic	......	50.0
Boreal..................	Hudsonian	......	57.2
Boreal..................	Canadian	......	64.4
Austral.................	Transition	10,000	71.6
Austral.................	Upper austral	11,500	78.8
Austral.................	Lower austral	18,000	
Tropical................	....	26,000	

[1] A precaution must be used in making calculations as described by Merriam (1894) in computing the normal mean temperature above 43°F. for the various zones. Merriam took the mean temperature in degrees Fahrenheit per day, beginning in the spring with the first day which was above 43°F., and continuing until fall, when the temperature of the day dropped below 43°. He consequently used the total mean temperature of the day, and not the daily temperature minus 43°F., as might be interpreted from his statement. The sum of the temperatures, therefore, can not be transferred directly into degrees centigrade as was done by Merriam; for in so doing, he neglected the fact, that the centigrade scale starts at the freezing point of water, and the Fahrenheit scale, 32° below this.

It will be noticed that no account is taken of the extremes of low temperature in controlling the northern distribution of organisms. This, as has been pointed out by Sanderson (1908), may be an important limiting factor in determining the northern distribution of animals, particularly poiklortherms, to which the insects belong.

The plant and animal ecologists have been quick to call attention to the fact that the geographic distributions of organisms cannot be ascribed to the influence of temperature alone. The plant ecologists and others, Livingston and Schreve (1921), and Ward (1925), have stressed the

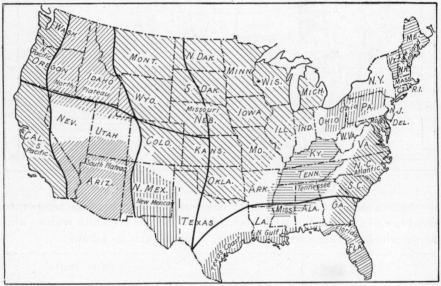

Fig. 71.—Ward's rainfall types of the United States. (*Adapted from Ward, 1925, by F. G. Holdaway.*)

importance of moisture in influencing the distribution of vegetation (Fig. 71). This is particularly true on the continent of North America, as one goes over the central plains from either coast.

Shelford (1911) emphasized the importance of various factors and the necessity for recognizing the operation of the law of minimum, whereby one factor might limit the distribution of a species. It may be recognized that, other things being equal, the distribution of animals may be an expression of the physical factors of the environment including in these physical factors all those reactional factors due to the effect of the biotic environment. Therefore, if we understood fully the distribution of the physical factors of the environment and the ecological valence of an organism we could place it for its geographic distribution, and if we knew its biotic potential we could determine its relative abundance.

Hopkins (1918, 1919, 1920, 1921) has given particular attention to the effects of latitude, longitude, and altitude on the occurrence of periodic phenomena. His interest in this problem was aroused while studying bark beetles in the south eastern part of the United States. The study of periodic phenomena or phenology is very old. Hopkins (1918) gives a brief review of the subject in which he says that Pliny credits Caesar with having issued a calendar of periodic events for the guidance of farmers.

The main conclusions of Hopkins (1918) are as follows:

1. The periodical phenomena of plants and animals are in response to the influence of all of the complex factors and elements of the climate as controlled, primarily, by the motions of the earth and its position relative to the influences of solar radiation.

2. The variations in the climate and consequent variations in the geographic distribution and periodical activities of plants and animals of a continent are controlled by the modifying influences of topography, oceans, lakes, large rivers, and of other regional and local conditions, and the amount and character of daylight, sunshine, rain, snow, humidity, and other elements and factors of a general and local nature.

3. There is a tendency toward a constant rate of variation in the climatic and biological conditions of a continent, as a whole in direct proportion to variation in geographical position as defined by the three geographical coordinates: latitude, longitude, and altitude.

4. Other conditions being equal, the variation in the time of occurrence of a given periodical event in life activity in temperate North America is at a general average rate of four days to each 1° lat., 5° long. and 400 feet altitude, later northward, eastward and upward in the spring and early summer, and the reverse in late summer and autumn.

5. Owing to the fact that all conditions are never exactly equal in two or more biological or climatic regions of the continent, and rarely alike in two or more places within the same region or locality, there are always departures from the theoretical time constant.

6. The departures, in number of days from a theoretical time constant, are in direct relation to the intensity of the controlling influences. Therefore the constant, as expressed in the time coordinates of the low, is a measure of the intensity of the influences.

From this statement it appears that there are two applications to be made. One may calculate the time when a periodical event may be expected to take place by starting from another point where the time of the event is known, and applying the rule with respect to latitude, longitude, and altitude. It is also possible to measure the influence of local factors, since it is assumed that all departures from the calculated dates are due to such local factors.

To facilitate the use of the "law," Hopkins (1918) has prepared maps with isophanes (lines of equal periodical events) which proceed across North America from the Atlantic to the Pacific in a northwestward curve at the rate of 1° lat. to 5° long. Their position and numbers correspond to latitude on the 100th meridian of longitude. Phenomeridians are also drawn at intervals to represent 1° or more of longitude, according to the intervals of the isophanes on the map to which they are applied at the rate of 5 to 1. An arbitrary base for the phenological meridians lies at the intersection of the 125th meridian of longitude which is at the intersection of the northern border of the United States and the Pacific Coast. This phenological meridian is designated as zero, and from it the others are numbered both east and west (Fig. 72).

Adjustable and computing calendars and tables for making corrections for altitude have been devised for use in predicting the dates for planting

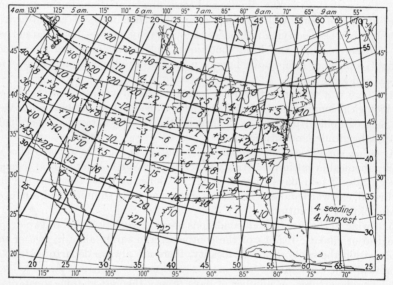

Fig. 72.—Isophanes and phenological meridians for the United States. The figures in the quadrangles indicate the departures of the calculated dates from the actual dates for the time of seeding wheat (upper figure) and of harvesting (lower figure). (*Hopkins*, 1918.)

crops and controlling insects. Practical use of this "law" has been made in computing the "fly-free date" for planting wheat to escape the Hessian fly.

It would seem that the trend of the isophanes in a northwestern and southeastern direction across the United States reflected the influence of the warm ocean currents of the Pacific, and the cool waters of the North Atlantic Coast.

In animal ecology we are further removed from the physical factors than in the case of plant ecology. In natural environments at least, animals are largely controlled by the plant communities in which they live. They are either directly dependent upon the plants for food, or they experience the physical conditions which are brought about by the reaction of a plant community. The animal ecologists may, therefore, turn some attention to the results of the students of plant geography. Maps showing not only the distribution of temperature, of rainfall, evaporation, and the ratio of evaporation and rainfall but also showing the distribution of plants (Shelford, Jones, and Dice, 1926) form a valuable background to the beginning of the study of the distribution of animals.

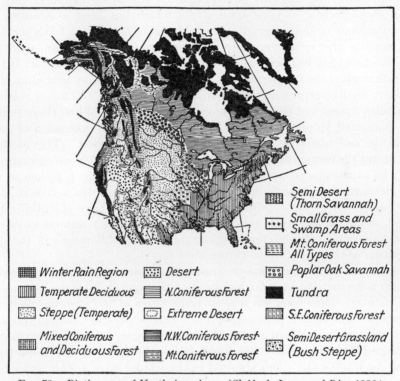

Fig. 73.—Biotic areas of North America. (*Shelford, Jones, and Dice, 1926.*)

Dahl (1921) has divided the world into regions and provinces on the basis of environmental and faunal characteristics. When such wide areas are considered there are many factors of local distribution which must necessarily be disregarded. For instance, he has divided the world into four regions for the land and fresh-water animals, and has included all of Europe, Asia, and North America in one region which he terms *Arktogaisches Reich.* To this he has added the distribution of environmental conditions, such as wooded and agricultural lands, deserts, steppes and tundra, tree steppes, and mountainous regions over 2,000 m.

Olbricht (1923) considered the effect of climate both with respect to the present geographic distribution of animals and to the phylogeny of faunas. He follows Huntington (1922) in the descriptions of climatic energy and proposes the term *Isobionen* to designate the lines of equal decrease of climatic energy which he has drawn over the maps of the earth. The "ophelothermal" region of the northern continents is described by Olbricht as being a region which, because of its climatic conditions, has brought about the greatest development of higher organisms. This region he believes represents the biotic height of the earth.

Ball (1910) introduced a new method for the measurement of climate as a characteristic of geographic areas which has been a stimulus to investigations of the geographic distribution of organisms. His method of plotting the mean monthly temperature and the mean monthly relative humidity has been called the climograph method (Taylor, 1916). In this method the temperature is plotted against relative humidity, and a point used to represent the mean temperature and the mean relative humidity for each of the twelve months of the year. When these points are connected up and labeled, it is possible to see the succession of temperature and humidity conditions throughout the year. The method facilitates the comparison of one climate with another, for one climograph may be superimposed upon another; and it is possible at a glance to see the similarities and dissimilarities in the temperature, the moisture, and the succession of the conditions. Localities which have essentially the same mean annual temperature and the same mean annual moisture may have strikingly different climographs due to differences in the distribution of these conditions throughout the year.

In a study of conditions of human settlement in Australia, Taylor (1916) constructed a standard white-race climograph from the average of the monthly conditions for several large cities of the eastern, western, southern, and northern hemispheres. This white-race climograph was then used as a standard of comparison, by superimposing upon it the climograph of any locality which was to be studied as a possible environment for white men. This resulted in the setting up of a standard measure of physical environments for a given species.

Taylor (1919) proposed the term "hythergraph" for a similar diagram of temperature and monthly precipitation. The term "hyther" was originally proposed by Walker to mean "comfort" and was used in connection with a comfort scale. Inasmuch as Taylor does not refer to Walker and the previous use of the term "hyther," it seems possible that he re-invented the word for his own purpose. There may be some question therefore as to the standing of the term "hythergraph" and the question may also be raised as to whether it is necessary to have one term for a graph using temperature and relative humidity, and another term for a graph using temperature and precipitation. It is obviously necessary to label the two dimensions of every graph in degrees Fahrenheit and inches precipitation or percent of relative humidity, which does away with the necessity for a special term.

In Taylor's study of the suitability of various areas for growing certain economic plants, he has called attention to the value of the climograph in that it indicates the portions of the year which are comparable in the two environments being examined. In the study of the wheat areas of the world, for example, it was found that in the tropical wheat areas the conditions which obtain during the winter are similar to those which obtain during the early spring in temperate wheat areas. It is during these two comparable periods that the wheat is raised in the two climates, regardless of the times of the year in which these comparable conditions may occur. The climograph has rapidly come into general use for the description of the physical conditions of an environment. It is possible to make a theoretical climograph to represent the optimum or normal conditions for a species, another to represent the zone of rare occurrence, and then to outline the limits beyond which the species theoretically will not be found.

In making such studies, it is necessary to know rather well the ecology of the species concerned, and to make sure whether the distribution is coincident with its host plant or whether it is directly affected by the physical conditions which are measured by the climograph. It is also necessary to pay particular attention to certain critical periods of the year, such as the period of flight of the adult insects for mating, during the period of the development of the egg; and that of the development of the larva, anyone of which may be of more importance than all of the rest of the year together. A slight deviation from the ideal conditions during the critical period may be of extreme importance, while large deviations during other periods of the year may have no significance whatever.

Attention will be called to the following examples of the use of this method. Cook (1923) adopted a curve representing the optimum temperature and precipitation for the pale western cutworm, *Porosogrotis orthogonia*, superimposed this on climographs, and used it as the standard of comparison of climatic conditions in different areas. This curve was adopted as representing, theoretically, the necessary balance between temperature and precipitation to maintain a constant soil moisture representing the optimum conditions for the pale western cutworm. Since the soil moisture is dependent to a considerable extent upon the evaporating power of the air, and since the vapor pressure of water at various temperatures follows an exponential curve when plotted against temperature, it has seemed that a curve of this same nature would express the moisture condition of the soil.

In Fig. 74 of the accompanying graph, this curve is shown superimposed upon the climographs of various other localities. From a study of these climographs, a map was constructed on the basis of the conformity of the climate to the curve of optimum conditions for the pale western

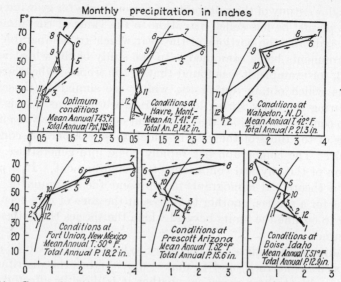

Fig. 74.—Curve of optimum temperature and moisture condition for the pale western cutworm (*Porosagrotis orthogonia*) superimposed on the climographs of various regions. (*Cook*, 1924.)

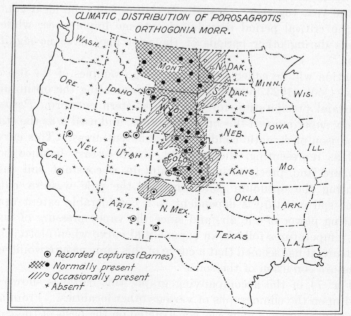

Fig. 75.—Map showing the distribution of the pale western cutworm, based on the climographs shown in Fig. 74.

cutworm.   This map is reproduced below with characters to represent the
results of actual collections of *Porosogrotis* which were made for a comparison with the theoretical results of the climographs.   It will be noted that
there are but seven recorded captures outside of the areas in which the
climographs would indicate the possible presence of the cutworms.

Cook (1924 and 1929) made a comparative study of the pale western
cutworm, *Porosagrotis orthogonia*, the variegated cutworm, *Lycophotia
margaritosa*, and the army worm, *Cirphis unipunctata*.   In Fig. 76 the
curves representing the optimum conditions of these three species are

superimposed on the climographs of
Glasgow, Mont.; Ithaca, N. Y.; and
Jacksonville, Fla.   It can readily be
seen that in the climograph none of
the species correspond with that of
Jacksonville.   This is in accordance
with the facts, for none of the species
is found there.   It is also evident that
the pale western cutworm should be
found only in Glasgow, which is again in
accordance with the facts of the case.

The variegated cutworm is normally
present at Ithaca, and not at Glasgow.
The army worm is not normally present
at Ithaca, but it was pointed out by
Fitch (1860) that it does occur there
following dry years; *i.e.*, the climate of
Ithaca is slightly too wet for the army
worms to be abundant.   However, a

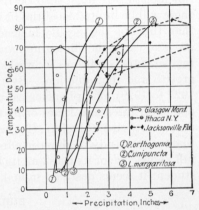

Fɪɢ.   76.—Climatological relations
of certain Noctuidae.   A curve representing the long axis of the ideal
climograph of each of three species is
compared with the climographs of
Ithaca, N. Y., Glasgow, Mont., and
Jacksonville, Fla. (*Cook*, 1923.)

year of dry weather may produce conditions which approach the optimum
for the species, and they may then become abundant.

Bodenheimer (1927) and Vayssière (1926) found that the scale insect,
Guerinia serratulae, is limited to a region along the Mediterranean Sea.
The limits of its distribution, Bodenheimer finds to agree very closely with
the distribution of temperature sufficient for the completion of its life
cycle.   In Palestine it has two generations a year, while farther north it
has but one.

Bodenheimer (1924) has also applied the same reasoning to the distribution of the Mediterranean fruit fly, *Ceratitis capitata*, and has
tabulated the areas of its possible distribution and the number of generations in a year.

It is possible to develop many refinements of these methods by a
careful study of the species and the environments in which it lives.   When
sufficient information is at hand, it may be possible to construct the climograph representing the various conditions of abundance of the species.

One may then turn attention to the climatological data of various geographic areas, and construct the climographs for all the points for which data are available. Next by a comparison of climographs, one may map out the areas of normal abundance, of rare occurrence, and the areas in which the organism theoretically would not be present at all. In any such procedure it must be clearly recognized that there may be local conditions which are quite at variance with the general climatological conditions. This is true especially in areas where there is a great difference of elevation. In the case of all forms which are dependent upon soil moisture it must also be recognized that in every geographic area there will be limited localities in which the soil moisture is higher or lower than that for the locality in general. In many cases it may be advantageous to carry the climograph analysis down to the point of following the temperature conditions by weeks or even days during the season of active growth and reproduction. By the use of Shelford's principle (Shelford, 1927 to 1929), of a phenological unit, we may be able to assign the developmental rates and times of maturity on the basis of the climatological data. It seems, therefore, that we have in the climograph a very valuable tool for the study of climatic effects. Like all tools it must be used with full knowledge of its uses and its limitations. In the hands of the careful student it seems destined to make important contributions.

BIBLIOGRAPHY

CHOROLOGY

Adams, C. C.: Postglacial Dispersal of the North American Biota, *Biol. Bull.*, **9**: 53–71, 1905.

Ball, John: Climatological Diagrams, *Cairo Sci. Jour.*, vol. 4, no. 50, 1910.

Bodenheimer, F. S.: On Predicting the Development Cycles of Insects, L. *Ceratitis capitata* Wied., *Bull. Roy. Soc. Ent. Egypte*, pp. 149–157, 1924.

———: Über die für das Verbreitungsgebiet einer Art bestimmenden Faktoren, *Biol. Zentralbl.*, **47**: 25–44, 1927.

———: Les frontiers écologiques d'une cochénille le *Guerinia serratulae* Fab., *Bull. soc. ent. France*, pp. 195–198, 1927.

Cook, W. C.: Studies in the Physical Ecology of the Noctuidae, *Minn. Agr. Expt. Sta. Tech. Bull.*, 12, 1923. 38 pp.

———: The Distribution of the Pale Western Cutworm, *Porosogrotis orthogonia* Morr: A Study in Physical Ecology, *Ecology*, **5**: 60–69, 1924.

———: Weather and Probability of Outbreaks of the Pale Western Cutworm in Montana and Near-by States, *U. S. Monthly Weather Rev.*, **56**: 103–106, 1928.

———: A Bioclimatic Zonation for Studying the Economic Distribution of Injurious Insects, *Ecology*, **10**: 282–293, 1929.

Dahl, Friedrich: "Grundlagen einer ökologischen Tiergeographie," 113 pp., Jena, 1921.

Elton, Charles: "Animal Ecology," 207 pp., London, 1927.

Fitch, Asa: Sixth Report on the Insects of New York, *Weather and the Army Worm*, 121 pp., 1860.

Friederichs, K.: Der Kaffeebeerenkäfer in Niederländisch-Indien, *Ztschr. angew. Ent.*, **11**: 325–385, 1925.

HESSE, RICHARD: "Tiergeographie auf ökologischer Grundlage" 613 pp., Jena, 1924.

HOPKINS, A. D.: Periodic Events and Natural Law as Guides to Agricultural Research and Practice, *U. S. Monthly Weather Rev.*, supp. 9, 1918.

————: The Bioclimatic Law as Applied to Entomological Research and Farm Practice, *Sci. Monthly*, **2**: 496–513, 1919.

————: The Bioclimatic Law, *Jour. Wash. Acad. Sci.*, **10**: 34–40, 1920.

————: The Bioclimatic Law and Its Application to Research and Practice in Entomology, *Jour. Wash. Acad. Sci.*, **11**: 141–142, 1921.

————: International Problems in Bioclimatics with Special Reference to Natural and Artificial Distribution of Plants and Animals, *Jour. Wash. Acad. Sci.*, **11**: 223–227, 1921.

————: Bioclimatic Zones of Continents; With Proposed Designations and Classification, *Jour. Wash. Acad. Sci.*, **11**: 227–229, 1921.

HUNTINGTON, ELLSWORTH: "World Power and Civilization," Yale University Press, 287 pp., 1919.

KENNEDY, C. H.: Evolutionary Level in Relation to Geographic, Seasonal, and Diurnal Distribution of Insects, *Ecology*, **9**: 367–379, 1928.

LIVINGSTON, B. E., and FORREST SHREVE: The Distribution of Vegetation in the United States, as Related to Climatic Conditions, *Carnegie Inst. Wash. Pub.* 284, 1921.

MCDOUGALL, ERIC: The Moisture Belts of North America, *Ecology*, **6**: 325–332, 1925.

MERRIAM, C. HART (1894): The Geographic Distribution of Animals and Plants in North America, *U. S. Dept. Agr. Yearbook*, pp. 203–214, 1894–1895.

————: Life Zones and Crop Zones of the United States, *U. S. Dept. Agr. Bur. Biol. Survey* No. 10, p. 79, 1898.

OLBRICHT, K.: "Klima und Entwicklung," p. 74, Jena, 1923.

SANDERSON, E. D.: The Influence of Minimum Temperature in Limiting the Northern Distribution of Insects, *Jour. Econ. Ent.*, **1**: 245–262, 1908.

SHELFORD, V. E.: Physiological Animal Geography, *Jour. Morph.*, **22**: 551–617, 1911.

————: An Experimental Investigation of the Relations of the Coddling Moth to Weather, *Ill. Nat. Hist. Survey Bull.* 16, pp. 311–440, 1927.

————: "Laboratory and Field Ecology," 608 pp., Williams & Wilkins, Co., Baltimore, 1929.

SHELFORD, V. E., L. JONES, and L. R. DICE: Descriptive List of North American Biota (South to Central America), in "Naturalist's Guide to the Americas," pp. 60–74, Williams & Wilkins Co., Baltimore, 1926.

TAYLOR, G.: Control of Settlement by Humidity and Temperature, *Comm. Bur. Met. Bull.* 14, 1916. 33 pp.

————: The Settlement of Tropical Australia, *Geogr. Rev.*, **8**: 84–115, 1919.

UVAROV, B. P.: "Weather and Climate in Their Relation to Insects," p. 20, Conf. of Empire Meterologists, Agr. Sect., London, 1929.

VAYSSIÈRE, P.: Contribution à l'étude biologique et systématique des Corcidae, *Ann. des epiphytics*, **12**: 197–382, 1926.

WALLACE, A. R.: "The Geographic Distribution of Animals," London, 1876. 2 vols.

WARD, ROBERT DE COURCY: "The Climates of the United States," p. 518, Ginn & Company, New York, 1925.

WILLIAMS, C. B.: A Third Bio-climatic Study of the Egyptian Desert, *Egypt. Min. Agr. Bull.* 50, 1924. 32 pp.

CHAPTER XI

CHRONOLOGY

Distribution in Time.—If it were possible to turn time backwards, and make a critical review of the past events which have to do with the development of environments and the parallel course which animals have followed in their evolution, we should no doubt find the answer to some of the most perplexing questions of biology. Since this is not possible, we probably can do no better than to make a division of the subject matter of the distribution of animals through time, and consider on the one hand the subject matter of paleochronology, or the distribution of animals in past time where the evidence is not directly available to us, but which has to be pieced together from fragmentary facts and conjecture; and on the other hand, neochronology, or distribution in recent time, when facts are available both as to progress of the environment and the distribution of the animal associations.

PALEOCHRONOLOGY

It seems to be the inevitable conclusion of all students of the distant past that the earth has not always been as we now know it. During its development it has presented a series of environmental conditions. As these conditions change, the flora and fauna of the earth also change. The evidence for these changes is fragmentary. It has had to be pieced together by the best of scholars, but it now presents a history which must be more or less accurate. Part of the evidence has been physical, based upon the formation of the earth's surface and the evident modifications which have come about from time to time. Much of it is biological, being based upon the remains of plants and animals that are found in various places and at various levels in the present surface of the earth. The finding of the remains of plants and animals which resemble our present tropical forms in the far North is taken as evidence that those northern regions once enjoyed a tropical climate; and the time at which those tropical climates were experienced can be fixed more or less definitely by the deposits of material which bury those tropical forms. We may be justified in assuming that during a succession of environmental conditions, the evolution of plants and animals was going on. The inter-relationship between genetic constitutions of the organism and effects of the environment probably existed in the past much as it does today, though the quantitative relationships may have been slightly different. The records

TABLE OF EVENTS IN PALEOCHRONOLOGY[1]

Eras	Epochs or periods	Advances in life	Dominant life	General climatic conditions
Archeozoic, 25 per cent of total geologic time		First life	No known fossils Age of unicellular life	Little known; probably cold at first; later warm enough for first appearance of simplest life
Early proterozoic, 15 per cent			First known fossils	Began with glacial period, temperate to tropical; closed with frigid climate, glacial action
Late proterozoic, 15 per cent			Age of primitive marine invertebrates	
Paleozoic, 28 per cent	Cambrian	First known marine fauna; dominance of trilobites; rise of shelled animals	Age of higher invertebrates	Warm uniform climate world over
	Ordovician	Rise of land plants and corals; rise of armored fishes; rise of nautilids		Warm uniform climate
	Silurian		Age of fishes	Warm first half; colder and local glaciation at close
	Devonian	Rise of amphibians; first known land flora		Cool at opening of period; warm during most of period
	Mississippian	Rise of ancient sharks; rise of echinoderms	Age of amphibians and lycopods	Uniformly mild
	Pennsylvanian	Rise of primitive reptiles and insects		Relatively mild or even subtropical; high humidity
	Permian	Rise of land vertebrates; rise of modern insects; extinction of ancient life		Cool glacial action
Mesozoic, 12 per cent	Triassic	Rise of dinosaurs	Age of reptiles	Variable; cool to subtropical
	Jurassic	Rise of birds and flying reptiles		Cool at polar regions; warm to subtropical in temperate and equatorial
	Comanchian	Rise of flowering plants		Warm temperate
	Cretaceous	Extreme specialization of reptiles; extinction of great reptiles; rise of archaic mammals		Warm uniform climate, cooler at close of period
Cenozoic, 5 per cent	Paleogene	Vanishing of archaic mammals	Age of mammals	Temperate
		Rise of higher mammals		South temperate
	Neogene	Culmination of mammals		Warm in early part; cooler during middle and late Miocene; arid locally
		Rise of man		Temperate, semi-arid locally
Psychozoic, (30,000 years?)	Glacial	Extinction of great mammals	Age of man	Period of glacial action, variable
	Recent	Rise of world civilization		

[1] Compiled from various sources.

of paleontology disclose a series of animal forms representing, in at least an abbreviated way, the evolutionary series of animals; and the order of their appearance must have been profoundly affected by the environmental conditions to which they were subjected. The alternate conditions of warmth and cold which apparently existed over various parts of the surface of the earth, must have called forth and eliminated various species of animals; for we had the age of reptiles and the age of mammals. This was partly due to the genetic constitution of the fauna that was then present and partly due to the environmental conditions that were present on the earth (see table on page 233).

The evidence of paleochronology from the standpoint of the plant ecologist was summed up by Clements (1916), and it will also be found in the various texts of paleontology and climatology. The accompanying figure has been assembled from various sources to give a diagrammatic picture of these influences on the faunas which probably accompanied them. These matters are of more than historical interest when considering the present distribution of the various species of plants and animals.

NEOCHRONOLOGY

Distribution in Recent Times or Ecological Succession.—In turning our attention to the succession of environmental and faunal conditions of recent times, we have the advantage of more tangible evidence. In the first place, we may follow the history of an environment and population back into the more recent times by the use of well-preserved evidence of what has just taken place; or secondly, we may follow the history of an environment and its population forward by observational or experimental methods. Either of these methods has the advantage of tangible evidence which may be found in duplicate. The recent history of many different associations may be studied and compared, and many observations made.

Ecological succession may be defined as the natural and orderly sequence of organic communities in which the organisms of any given stage tend to be replaced by another group of inhabitants which is to be dominant during the succeeding stage. The normal course of ecological succession is from conditions of relative instability to a condition of relative stability. It represents the fundamental dynamic principle of nature which results in the development of organic communities, just as growth results in the development of individual organisms. The life cycles of these communities may be compared with the life cycles of individual organisms, in that they develop, attain to maturity with the power to reproduce, and eventually give way to young communities of another stage. The general conception of ecological succession is probably one of the most fundamental contributions which ecology has yet made to general biology. The views of the various students of ecological succession have varied from the conception of Clements (1916):

The developmental study of vegetation necessarily rests upon the assumption that the unit of climax formation is an organic entity. As an organism the formation arises, grows, matures, and dies. Its response to the habitat is shown in the processes or functions and in structures which are the record as well as the result of these functions . . . The life history of a formation is a complex but definite process, comparable in its chief features with the life history of an individual plant . . .

The essential nature of succession is indicated by its name. It is a series of invasions, a sequence of plant communities, marked by the change from lower to higher forms . . . It is the basic, organic process of vegetation which results in the adult or final form of the complex organism. All the stages which precede the climax are stages of growth. They have the same essential relations to the final stable structure of the organism that the seedling and growing plant have to the adult individual.

Few ecologists would grant that conditions are as definite and uniform as just indicated by the quotation from Clements. The dominant physical conditions at which succession takes place are themselves variable. The communities themselves which consist of individual organisms are more complex than individual organisms. Consequently, it may be well expected that the course of succession is much more complicated than the course of growth of an individual organism.

Gleason (1927) says

The successional phenomena of vegetation include all types of change in time, whether they are merely fluctuating or produce a fundamental change in the association. Vegetational change is constant and universal, but varies greatly in its rate. It is caused by environmental change, or by change in the plant population independently of environment, through migration and evolution.

Different causes of succession may act simultaneously but at different rates or in different directions. In such cases the effects of the slowly acting causes may be obscured by the more conspicuous or by the different effects of the rapidly acting factors. The actual direction of succession may be likened to a resultant of forces . . .

1. *Ecological Plant Succession.*—The background for the consideration of animal succession may be laid by a brief review of what has been done in the field of plant succession. Long ago, botanists gathered the first evidence of an orderly sequence in the development of plant communities from the study of bogs (King, 1685; Degner, 1729; and Buffon, 1742). In the digging of peat from bogs for fuel, it was found that layers of vegetation were well enough preserved to identify the plants, and that they gave evidence that aquatic plants were succeeded by bog plants. Rennie (1810) gave a comprehensive account of the formation of bogs

and recognized the fact that if the peat was dug from the bog, the bog would repeat its former history and again develop peat.

Hult (1885 to 1887) first fully recognized that the vegetation of any area could be studied from the developmental standpoint; and that the development proceeded, from either bare soil on the one hand or from open water on the other hand, to a final climax. Warming, in his text (1891 to 1907), treated of the subject of succession as a whole and included an account of the succession on sand dunes. Since this time we have had the investigations of Cowles (1899) on sand dunes, Shantz (1911) on grass land, and many others covering practically all of the

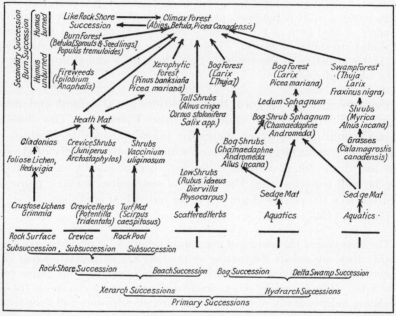

Fig. 77.—Diagram of development of the climax forest on Isle Royal. (*From Cooper,* 1913.)

various types of plant communities. Clements (1916) summarized the literature and the general subject matter of plant succession in a comprehensive way.

Clements (1916 and 1928) gives a summary of the work on plant succession and an analysis of the processes. He has divided the process of plant succession into: (1) nudation, (2) migration, (3) ecesis, (4) competition, (5) reaction, and (6) stabilization. The factors which may actually create bare areas on which plant succession may start from the beginning, are considered as physical and biotic. All of the other processes have to do with the interaction of the plants and their environment. These processes involve moving into the area; becoming established under the conditions that exist; competition among the various inhabitants which ultimately determines which are to be dominant; reactions to the general conditions and eventually a stabilization. The work on plant succession as compared with that of animal succession has the great advantage of working with organisms which are sessile. Therefore quantitative methods have been possible. It has been possible to stake out a definite area or quadrat, and to follow its development over a period of years. It has also been possible to examine the soil of a definite area; and, on the basis of the plant remains, to reconstruct its history over a period of the past. With all these advantages the students of plant succession have been able to map out not only the general course of events, but in certain cases to study quite in detail also the variations which come about in the general process of succession.

The accompanying diagram gives a good illustration both of the various types of plant succession, and also the variations which may occur in the course of succession (Fig. 77). The bare areas in general may be designated as xerarch or dry surfaces, and hydrarch or open water. Succession may proceed from this to a relatively stable climax or it may be interrupted at various times and start over as secondary succession. Of this general process, Gleason (1927) has said,

All phenomena of succession depend upon the ability of the individual plant to maintain itself and to reproduce its kind. The individualistic concept of succession is directly related to the individualistic concept of association. Since succession depends upon the behavior of the individual plant, since its causes are complex; and since each casual factor may act independently of the others at a different rate and in a different direction, a logical classification of seres has not been developed. The usual grouping of seres, and the common correlation of spacial distribution with succession, are of practical value when approximations are sufficient.

Gleason says further,

Since the rate of successional causes varies, there appear in vegetation time phases of slow change and relatively high stability, alternating with others of rapid change. Retrogressive succession represents the reappearance of an earlier time phase caused by the recurrence of an earlier environmental complex. Climax associations represent time phases of great stability, in which we cannot observe the action of successional causes and for which we cannot predict the future. All time phases of a single habitat constitute a sere. Each time phase of a sere is independent of the preceding one, except as the vegetation of the older phase contributes to the determination of the environment of the latter one or as certain species persist. The sere is not a genetic series in vegetation, and does not necessarily follow an orderly sequence in its development.

The general course of plant succession gives rise to a series of plant entities beginning with herbaceous forms on bare soil passing through shrubs to forests. In a broad way the general conditions of various climatic areas permit succession to proceed to a certain point, where it stops at a climax or sub-climax, which as Gleason has pointed out, is a relatively stable condition. We have thus areas which are prairies and areas which are forests. This is due presumably to the fact that the physical conditions of the particular area permit succession to proceed to the point which gives the most stable conditions. This, in a general way, determines the environmental conditions to which animals must adjust themselves.

2. *Ecological Animal Succession.*—The brief consideration of plant succession has shown us two things: first, something of the nature of ecological succession in plants, from which we may gain some insight into the possible succession of animals; secondly, it has shown us that the result of plant succession is a series of communities to which animals must adjust themselves. The example set by the plant ecologists, like any other example in the field of science, may be a handicap or an advantage. If we are prejudiced by the method of attack employed by the plant ecologists and attempt to apply it without any original knowledge of the animal problem, it may prove a handicap. On the other hand, if we will take the information from their field and, realizing the possibilities of this natural phenomenon, proceed to an investigation of animal communities, it may be a great advantage to us.

Considering the subject matter of succession of animals from the viewpoint of the activity of the animals, it is at once evident that there may be a succession of animals in an area in which the animals themselves may be entirely passive, and the changes may be due to physical and floristic changes. It is also perfectly evident that there may be cases in which the animals themselves are active and themselves bring on the changes. On the other hand, we may also have cases in which the animals act simply to modify the physical or floristic conditions and thus bring about the changes. We may consequently outline animal succession as:

> Animals passive;
> > Initial or reactional causes physical,
> > > Physiographic changes,
> > > Climatic changes,
> > > Seasonal changes;
> > Initial or reactional causes biotic,
> > > Floristic changes;
> Animals active:
> > Animals themselves causing the changes.

In the case of passive animal succession the environment changes are due to physical or biotic causes, and the animals have to adjust themselves to the new order of things. When these changes are severe, the animals must either migrate from the environment or perish. Thus, in the ordinary course of plant succession as outlined above, a series of environmental conditions is presented; and each stage may be represented by a characteristic fauna which must leave and be replaced by another, as the next stage of plant succession comes on.

It is not possible to say that the animals play absolutely no part in the reactions which bring about these changes. However, it is true that the animals are usually not predominant in these reactions. Person (unpublished thesis for the Master's degree) investigated the action of the larch sawfly in connection with the succession of trees in bogs, and concluded that this insect was largely responsible for the disappearance of larch and its replacement by other trees in certain bogs. There are also many plants which owe their existence to pollination by insects, and the seeds of many plants are distributed by animals, so that their very entrance into an environment is conditioned by the presence of these animals. Perhaps the largest portion of the studies of animal succession has been of such situations. But brief consideration will be given to the cases in which animals are passive. Physiographic changes have been referred to in connection with chorology. The climatic changes have been referred to also. Seasonal changes are very evident from temperature conditions. Allee (1911) studied the succession of organisms in forest ponds during the progress of the seasons, as did Peterson (1926). Blackman (1918) made a study of the seasonal succession of insects which visited certain flowering plants; and literature contains many citations of similar studies.

The empirical generalization, which has already been referred to (page 223) as "Hopkins' bioclimatic law," has to do with the appearance of seasonal phenomena. It is, however, concerned primarily with the time of occurrence of periodic phenomena with respect to their occurrence in other places. For this reason the discussion of this principle is included in the chapter on Chorology.

Shelford (1911 and 1912) published a series of papers on the subject of animal succession which were concerned with cases in which the animals were passive. Various aquatic and terrestrial habitats were described, together with the lists of the organisms found. The animal communities were designated by the names of the dominant forms in much the same manner that plant communities are designated by the names of the predominant plants. This subject matter will be returned to in the chapters on Descriptive Synecology. Attention at the present time is to be centered upon the phenomenon of succession as such, rather than on the details of the organisms which are found with the various stages of plant succession in the different communities.

ACTIVE ANIMAL SUCCESSION

From the standpoint of the phenomenon of succession itself, the most interesting cases are those in which the animals themselves are active in causing the changes. It has already been pointed out that it is not possible to say that animals are not active in the cases which have just been cited.

First of all it is necessary to recognize that an animal habitat need not be a geographic area. A community of animals may live in a very restricted environment: it may be a pool of water, a prairie, or a forest; it may be a plant or even a portion of a tree, or the dead body of another animal. In a broad and general way, it may be said that plant succession is constructive beginning with bare soil or open water and proceeding to a mesophytic forest. In much the same way it may be said that animal succession is destructive, in that it accomplished the breaking down of materials which have been built up by plants. This, however, is a very important function in the balance of the energy of nature, for it is returned to the soil in order that another cycle of material may begin. Thus restricted environments may be set up to illustrate certain successions which can be studied experimentally in the laboratory. One of the first of these experiments was reported by Woodruff (1912). He set up hay infusions in the laboratory and studied the sequence of microorganisms that were found on the surface of these cultures. He determined the sequence of the dominant types of protozoa in the order of their abundance as follows: *Monad, Colpoda, Hypotrichida, Paramoecium, Vorticella*, and *Amoeba*. These infusions were left to run their course under ordinary laboratory conditions. Woodruff believed that the maxima of the various species of protozoa were probably determined by certain biological characteristics of these species which had to do with their rates of development. Since it is necessary to assume that all forms are present at the start of the experiment, he believes that their rates of development will determine the times at which they reach their maxima. The case, however, is not a simple one; many factors are involved, such as the physical conditions which exist at the beginning of the experiment and their cycle as influenced by the biotic conditions of the population. Therefore, the mere fact that the environments can be set up in a dish in the laboratory does not mean that it is simple.

More recently, Eddy (1928) has made an experimental study of such cultures. In all, 15 series of cultures were set up. Each series represented the influence of some factor having to do with the original conditions of the environment, or with the temperature, or other conditions under which the experiment was run. Under such conditions it was possible to compare cultures which were run in the same environmental conditions, and also to compare these cultures with another series run under different environmental conditions. As the result of these experiments, Eddy says,

In a group of similar cultures existing under similar conditions, a very noticeable regularity occurs. In each culture of a series the same organisms were always dominant simultaneously, so that each culture, at any period of its life, contained a community of protozoa, similar to that found in any other culture of the same age and composition, and existing under the same conditions. The oganisms generally appeared and reached their maxima at approximately the same period, so that an average sequence represented closely the sequence of any single culture of the series.

As to the factors which influenced the occurrence of the dominants, Eddy does not agree with Woodruff. He believes that the occurrence of the dominants is probably due to a favorable response to the conditions of the habitat and not to any rate of development, and that the maximum is determined by the establishment of a proper condition for growth and reproduction rather than by the rate of development of the form which comes to the maximum. He believes that the amount of dissolved oxygen, present in the infusion, is a much more important factor than light, temperature, or hydrogen-ion concentration, since the oxygen content of the culture is very largely the result of biotic reactions in the culture. This author concludes that biotic reactions are an extremely important factor in this type of succession.

In comparing the succession which is found in one of these cultures of protozoa with that of plants on geographic areas, Eddy states that every line of succession ultimately ends in a stage in which the dominants are not replaced by succeeding dominants. This reminds us again of plant succession. This climax is the final stage of the life of the community as an organic unit. However, the final stage of the hay infusion depends upon physical factors surrounding it, and he therefore calls it an edaphic or local climax. He believes that if the infusion were maintained forever against evaporation, it would go the way of so many organic communities and end by deposition in a land series. After six months, most of the series had reached their old-age or climax stage; and in this stage conditions were more suitable for the growth of algae which replaced protozoa as dominants. It would seem that the study of such cultures offers great possibilities in the understanding of animal succession.

Active animal succession may also be studied to advantage in trees. The tree itself represents an ecological unit environment for certain animals. Graham (1925) has called attention to the fact that the fauna and flora comprising the living population of a log are distinctly characteristic of this environment. The tree trunk is a deliminated-unit environment, and the fauna that is found in it is as well adapted to it as any other fauna is adapted to its environment. There is a definite succession of faunas which may be found in trees: the first stage is in the living tree; the second, in the dying tree; and the following stages while decay takes place. Blackman and Stage (1924) studied the hickory and followed through many of the stages from the time that the tree was killed until it was decayed. Graham (1925) points out that there is a definite succession of organisms as the chemical and physical character of the wood changes during the process of disintegration and decay, and states that there is a regular succession from truly woody forms toward an association of organisms characteristic of the substrata of forest soil.

Chapman (1915) studied some of the buprestid beetles which attack living oak trees and kill them. The larvae of the two-lined chestnut borer, *Agrilus bilineatus*, live in the cambium between the bark and the wood. They are active for but a few weeks during which time the tree is killed and the larvae then construct cells out in the bark in which they pupate the following spring. The tree is not killed until it is infested with a large number of beetles of this species. Isolated larvae which accidentally work in advance of the others are unable to survive in the living cambium. Likewise those which are left behind die in the dry dead cambium.

Following close upon the buprestid bettles are certain members of the family, *Cerambycidae*. These beetles lay their eggs in the crevices of the dying trees. Their larvae enter the dead cambium and feed among the narrow burrows which were left by the buprestids. The buprestids are highly specialized for making narrow burrows, while the cerambycids are less highly specialized and leave relatively wide burrows and occasional tunnels into the wood. The buprestids are legless, but some of the species of cerambycids have small thoracic legs.

The next stage is dominated by less specialized beetles which have thoracic legs. Some of the pyrochroid and temebrionid beetles are common. They come to the cambium layer after it has been partly loosened by the cerambycids; and they leave it with large spaces between the bark and the wood filled with decaying material.

The course of the succession from this point is determined to a certain extent by certain physical conditions, particularly those influencing the moisture content of the wood. The larvae of elaterid beetles come in at this time if the wood is not too dry; and these burrow into the wood, carrying with them wood-rotting microorganisms. From this time on, the wood is reduced to a culture bed of microorganisms. Under the bark, spiders and even small vertebrates may seek shelter.

The wind usually blows the tree down during one of the latter stages; and then the decay proceeds until the wood has been reduced essentially to soil. Thus a living organism has been attacked and reduced to earth by a process dominated by a series of animals, each of which has lived in it for a short period, and so modified it that it has become more fit for the animals of the succeeding stage. A physical agent or some other biotic agent might cause the death of the tree, and make it possible for the other stages of insects to come in in the same order, as if the initial attack had been by the buprestids as outlined above.

Graham (1925) has pointed out that in the first or initial stage the insects and fungi hold the center of the stage, and the other organisms play a minor rôle, whereas in the last stages of decomposition bacteria are probably of major importance. From the standpoint of the tree as an ecological unit, the action of these animals in active succession may be considered a destructive one; but, from the broader aspect of nature, it will be seen that their rôle is that of bringing back to the soil materials with which it had once been built up, thereby insuring the continuance of the balance of nature. A visit to a primeval wood which had not been disturbed will disclose many of the areas in which tree trunks have fallen and decayed. In the later stages of decay, seedlings of various other plants and trees may be found springing into growth; and still later there will be little to indicate where the decaying tree trunk lay, other than possibly a slight elevation of the surface of the ground. This individual series of succession then has been complete, ending in the soil as a climax stage.

Seeds of plants also form restricted environments in which ecological succession may go on, activated by animals. This type of succession is interesting because it also lends itself easily to laboratory study. Experiments may be set up with the various species of insects introduced into wheat, and only those which are capable of initiating the succession will be able to establish themselves; but later the changes will come on, so other species can get started.

There are relatively few insects which can attack sound wheat as has been demonstrated by Barnes and Grove (1916), Dendy (1918), and others. The granary weevil, *Sitophilus granarius*, and the rice weevil, *Sitophilus oryzae*, and a few others are adapted to feeding on the sound wheat berries. The confused flour beetle, *Tribolium confusum*, the Mediterranean flour moth, *Ephestia kuhniella*, and certain others cannot live on the sound wheat for the reason that their mouth parts are not adapted to attacking large hard pieces of food.

The weevils are able to burrow into the wheat and lay their eggs within the wheat berry. The larvae which hatch are legless and simply eat about themselves until the entire inner portion of the wheat berry has been consumed, when they pupate in the shell which is composed largely of the bran. In case, one of these larvae is accidentally displaced, it dies, for it has no method of locomotion outside of its natural environment. Consequently sound wheat is essential to these weevils. The adults may feed in wheat from which larvae have emerged or even in flour, but they never reproduce, unless they encounter hard masses of flour which are similar in consistency to wheat itself (Chapman, 1921).

The flour beetles and flour moths scatter their eggs about and the larvae crawl about in search of food. These larvae are structurally quite different from those of the weevils as they have legs and mouth parts which are adapted for eating small particles which may be taken between the mandibles. They feed readily upon the wheat from which weevils have emerged or upon flour which has been ground from wheat. It is occasionally possible for these larvae to eat a portion of the embryo from moist wheat, but in general they cannot.

Active succession may also be found in the study of animal bodies. An animal may be killed by the action of an animal parasite, which thus acts to initiate the succession. Shortly after death, flesh flies oviposit on the body, and for a period it is dominated by the maggots of these flies. The carrion beetles come in and contribute to reducing the body. Last of all, the dermestid beetles appear and feed upon the dry tissues of the bone.

Fabre (1922) made a study of the action of these scavengers. Motter (1898) published a review of literature on the study of the insect fauna of human bodies that had been interred for different periods of time, and concluded that there was a definite succession, but that conditions were very complicated and that no two histories could be considered alike. Therefore, the faunas would not be expected to be exactly alike. Dahl (1896) trapped the beetles which were attracted to carrion, and concluded that there was a regular animal succession in which the tissues of the animal were gradually reduced to essentially the conditions of soil; so that again we have an active animal succession which is destructive so far as the tissues of the organism acting as environment is concerned.

So far as the general cycle of matter in nature is concerned, this is a fundamental and important step in bringing the compounds which are built up from the highly specialized bodies, back to soil. It would seem then, that in the light of our limited knowledge, we will have to think of the succession of animals as passive in cases where they follow along after physical and biotic changes which bring about a succession of environment; and as active in certain cases where they themselves initiate and are dominant in causing the various stages of succession to appear. The latter cases seem to be mostly restricted to environments in which they utilize, as a unit environment, the body of some animal or plant.

BIBLIOGRAPHY

DISTRIBUTIONAL SYNECOLOGY

ADAMS, C. C.: Postglacial Dispersal of the North American Biota, *Biol. Bull.*, **9**: 53–71, 1905.

ALLEE, W. C.: Seasonal Succession in Old Forest Ponds, *Trans. Ill. Acad. Sci.*, **IV**: 126–132, 1911.

BALL, JOHN: Climatological Diagrams, *Cairo Sci. Jour.*, vol. 4, no. 50, 1910.

BARNES, J. H., and A. J. GROVE: The Insects Attacking Stored Wheat in the Punjab and the Methods of Combating Them, Including a Chapter on the Chemistry of Respiration, *Mem. India Dept. Agr.*, **4**: 165–280, 1916.

BLACKMAN, M. W.: On the Insect Visitors to the Blossoms of Wild Blackberry and Wild Spiraea. A Study in Seasonal Distribution, *N. Y. State Col. Forestry, Syracuse Univ., Tech. Pub.*, **18**: no. **10**: 119–143, 1918.

BLACKMAN, M. W., and H. H. STAGE: On the Succession of Insects Living in the Bark and Wood of Dying, Dead, and Decaying Hickory, *N. Y. State Col. Forestry, Syracuse Univ., Tech. Pub.*, **24**: no. **17**: 1–269, 1924.

BUFFON, G. L. L.: "Mémoire sur la Culture des Forêts," *Hist. Acad. Roy. Sci.*, p. 233, 1742.

CHAPMAN, R. N.: Observations on the Life History of *Agrilus bilineatus*, *Jour. Agr. Research*, **3**: 283, 1914–1915.

————: Insects Infesting Stored Food Products, *Minn. Agr. Expt. Sta. Bull.* 198, 1921.

CLEMENTS, F. E.: "Plant Succession," Carnegie Inst., Wash., 1916. 512 pp.

————: "Plant Succession and Indicators," p. 453, H. W. Wilson Co., New York, 1928.

COOPER, W. S.: The Climax Forest of Isle Royal, Lake Superior, and Its Development, *Bot. Gaz.*, **55**: 1, 1913.

COWLES, H. C.: The Ecological Relations of the Vegetation on the Sand Dunes of Lake Michigan, *Bot. Gaz.*, **27**: 95–117, 1899.

DAHL, F. T.: Vergleichende Untersuchungen über die Lebensweise wirbelloser Aasfresser, *Sitzungsber. d. K. Akad. d. Wissensch.*, Berlin, vol. I, pp. 17–30, 1896.

————: "Grundlagen einer ökologischen Tiergeographie," G. Fischer, Jena, 1923 2 vols., 117 pp.

DEGNER, H. J.: "Dissertatio physica de turfis," (1729).

DENDY, A.: Experiments with Two Secondary Grain Pests, Showing Their Inability to Attack Sound Wheat, *Roy. Soc. Grain Pests (War) Com. Rept.* 3, pp. 15–16, 1918.

DuRIETZ, G. E. (1921): "Zur methodologischen Grundlage der modernen Pflanzensoziologia," Vienna.

EDDY, SAMUEL: Succession of Protozoa in Cultures under Controlled Conditions, *Trans. Amer. Micros. Soc.*, **47**: 283–319, 1928.

FABRE, J. H.: "More Beetles," transl. by Mattos, 1922; reference chaps. II and III, Dodd, Mead & Company, New York.

FITCH, ASA: Weather and the Army Worm, Sixth Rept. on the Insects of New York, p. 121, 1860.

GLEASON, H. A.: Further Views on the Succession-concept, *Ecology*, **8**: 299–326, 1927.

GRAHAM, S. A.: The Felled Tree Trunk as an Ecological Unit, *Ecology*, vol. VI, no. 4, 1925.

HOPKINS, A. Q.: Periodical Events and Natural Law as Guides to Agricultural Research and Practice, *U. S. Monthly Weather Rev.*, Supp. 9, 1918.

————: The Bioclimatic Law as Applied to Entomological Research and Farm Practice, *Sci. Monthly*, pp. 496–513, June, 1919.

————: Intercontinental Problems in Bioclimatics; with Special Reference to Natural and Artificial Distribution of Plants and Animals, *Jour. Wash. Acad. Sci.*, **11**: 223–227, 1921.

HULT, R.: Blekinges vegetation. Ett bidrag till växtoformationeronas utvecklings-historie, *Medd. Soc. Fenn.* **12**: 161, 1885; *Bot. Cent.*, **27**: 192, 1886.

————: Die alpinen Pflanzenformationen des nördlichsten Finnlands, *Medd. Soc. Fenn.*, **16**: 153, 1887; Bot. Cent., **36**: 207, 1888.

HUNTINGTON, E.: "Civilization and Climate," Yale University Press, New Haven, 2d ed., 1922. 432 pp.

KING, W.: On the Bogs and Loughs of Ireland, *Phil. Trans. Roy. Soc.* [London], **15**: 948, 1685.

MERRIAM, C. H.: Life Zones and Crop Zones of the United States, *U. S. Dept. Agr. Bur. Biol. Survey Bull.* 10, 1898.

MOTTER, M. G.: A Contribution to the Study of the Fauna of the Grave, *Jour. N. Y. Ent. Soc.*, **6**: 201–231, 1898.

OLBRICHT, K.: "Klima und Entwicklung," G. Fischer, Jena, 1923.   74 pp.

PEARSON, G. A.: A Meteorological Study of Parks and Timbered Areas in the Western Yellow Pine Forests of Arizona and New Mexico, *U. S. Monthly Weather Rev.*, **41**: 1615–1629, 1913.

PERSON, H. L.: "An Ecological Study of the Larch Sawfly (*Lygaeonematus erichsonii* Hartig)," *Univ. of Minnesota*, unpublished thesis.

PETERSON, WALBURGA: Seasonal Succession of Animals in a Chara-cattail Pond, *Ecology*, **7**: 371–377, 1926.

RENNIE, R.: "Essays on the Natural Historie and Origin of Peat Moss," 1810.

SANDERSON, DWIGHT: The Influence of Minimum Temperatures in Limiting the Northern Distribution of Insects, *Jour. Econ. Ent.*, vol. I, pp. 245–262, 1908.

SHANTZ, H. L.: Natural Vegetation as an Indicator of the Capabilities of Land for Crop Production in the Great Plains Area, *U. S. Dept. Agr. Bur. Plant Indus. Bull.* 201, 1911.

SHELFORD, V. E.: Physiological Animal Geography, *Jour. Morph.*, **22**: 551–619, 1911.

————: Ecological Succession. I. Stream Fishes and the Method of Physiographic Analysis, *Biol. Bull.*, **21**: 9–35, 1911.

————: Ecological Succession. II. Pond Fishes, *Biol. Bull.*, **21**: 127–151, 1911.

————: Ecological Succession. III. A Reconnaissance of Its Causes in Ponds with Particular Reference to Fish, *Biol. Bull.*, 22, 1911–1912.

————: Ecological Succession. IV. Vegetation and the Control of Land Animal Communities, *Biol. Bull.*, **23**: 59–99, 1912.

————: Ecological Succession. V. Aspects of Physiological Classification, *Biol. Bull.*, **23**: 331–370, 1912.

————: Physiological Life Histories of Terrestrial Animals and Modern Methods of Representing Climate, *Trans. Ill. Acad. Sci.*, **13**: 257–270, 1920.

TAYLOR, GRIFFITH: Geographical Factors Controlling the Settlement of Tropical Australia, *Queensland Geogr. Jour.*, **32–33**: 1–67, 1918.

————: The Settlement of Tropical Australia, *Geogr. Rev.*, **8**: 84–115, 1919.

TRANSEAU, EDGAR N.: The Relation of the Climatic Factors to Vegetation, *Amer. Naturalist*, **43**: 487–489, 1909.

WARMING, E.: "Oecology of Plants," 1891–1907.

WINTERBOTTOM, D. C.: Weevil in Wheat and Storage of Grain in Bags, Govt. Printer, Adelaide, South Australia, 1922.   122 pp.

WOODRUFF, L. L.: Observations on the Origin and Sequence of the Protozoan Fauna of Hay Infusions, *Jour. Exptl. Zool.*, **12**: 205–264, 1912.

CHAPTER XII

AQUATIC SYNECOLOGY

The Historical Events.—The discovery of the microscope was a stimulus to the study of minute aquatic organisms. Early explorations, mostly marine, gathered miscellaneous material for museums. The Challenger Expedition stimulated great interest in oceanography (see Murray and Hjort, 1912). The publication of Darwin's "Origin of Species" brought out the scientific value of the lower forms of aquatic organisms.

In 1846, Johannes Müller took several of his students, including Ernst Haeckel, to Heligoland and demonstrated the minute free-floating organisms which he obtained from the North Sea by the use of a fine net. This was the beginning of a now extensive study of what Hensen (1887) later called plankton (Planktos-drifting). (See Hentschel, 1923, and Johnstone, 1924.)

Forel and his school founded limnology by the publication "Le Leman, monographie limnologique," 1892 to 1904, and his work, associated with Chrystal, Halbfass, Wedderburn, and others demonstrated that an environment might be studied with the same exactness as an organism. In America, the studies of Birge and Juday on the Wisconsin lakes have made outstanding contributions to our knowledge of aquatic environments and the dynamic relationships between the fauna and the physical environment.

The introduction of quantitative methods for the study of aquatic organisms by Hensen (1887), Peterson (1911 to 1918), Ekman (1910), Birge and Juday (1922), Adamstone (1924), and others served to differentiate ecological work from that of observational natural history. They furnish examples which may well be given serious consideration by the students of terrestrial ecology.

General References to Literature on Hydrobiology.—The general works present much good biological information on the ocean: Murray (1885 and 1912), Johnstone (1908 and 1924), Steuer (1910), Hess (1924), and others; and on inland waters: Stokes (1896), Needham and Lloyd (1915), Brauer (1900 to 1912), Whipple (1927), Ward and Whipple (1918), Thienemann (1925), and others. However, the real advances have been made by those who have employed quantitative methods and who have

247

made it possible to arrive at new facts. Such publications as those of Hensen (1887) and Forel (1892 to 1904) have contributed to the advancement of ecology; and they have been followed by such works as those of Helland-Hensen (1912), Birge and Juday (various papers), Pearse (1921), Clemens (1924), and others.

Institutions Devoted to the Study of Hydrobiology.—Anton Dorn established the Zoological Station at Naples in 1870, and this laboratory has since been a mecca for students of general biology as well as for those with a special interest in marine life.

Louis Agassiz established a laboratory on the island of Penikese in 1872, of which the present Marine Biological Laboratory at Woods Hole, Mass., is a descendant (Lillie, 1913). Many laboratories have been established since, in all parts of the world. (See *Internat. Rev. der Gesamm. Hydrobiol. u. Hydrog.*) There are some 30 laboratories in the United States situated on fresh or salt water, and devoting themselves to teaching and research work with aquatic organisms. Interest in evolution brought about the establishment of field laboratories by universities. Economic pressure stimulated the Bureau of Fisheries to investigate the possibilities of increasing our food resources. (*Bull., U. S. Bur. Fisheries.*) Sanitary conditions surrounding large cities made it necessary to investigate lakes and rivers as sources of water for human consumption (Whipple, 1927). All of these agencies have contributed to our knowledge of aquatic organisms. Some of them have made contributions to our knowledge of ecology in its present sense.

WATER THE PHYSICAL ENVIRONMENT

The Characteristics of Water as an Environment.—There is no other substance which has all of the properties essential to life that water has. This may be expected because animals are composed very largely of water. (Henderson, 1913; Bayliss, 1918.) It is for this reason that we shall turn our attention to it before taking up the consideration of bodies of water.

It is the standard for many physical measurements, such as density, heat capacity, and other properties. It is the most universal chemical agent. It is the most important geological agent. The ancient philosophers looked upon it as the agent of all energy and the cause of all action.

It is difficult to explain the properties of water and their variation in response to temperature upon the assumption that water is simply H_2O with an atomic weight of 18. Dyclaux (1912) points out that a simple compound of this formula should have a freezing point of about $-150°C.$, and a boiling point of about $-100°C.$ It seems likely that it is polymerized; *i.e.*, a number of molecules are associated together. But by comparing formaldehyde CH_2O, which is liquid at $20°C.$, with trioxymethylene, $C_3H_6O_3$, which is solid at $150°C.$, it is found that great changes take place when three molecules are combined. From this it may be computed that while H_2O ought to boil at $-100°$, H_6O_3 might well boil at 100°C.

Sutherland (1900) has proposed the names hydrol, dihydrol, and trihydrol. Trihydrol is present in the greatest concentration in the solid state; dihydrol is the main constituent at ordinary temperatures; and monohydrol or steam increases in proportion as the temperature approaches the boiling point. These three may be distinct chemical substances which are easily convertible from one to the other, and which exist together in certain ratios at each temperature. Heat may then have to do three things: decompose polymeres, heat polymeres, and heat monomeres.

THE PHYSICAL PROPERTIES OF WATER

Heat capacity is measured in terms of the response of water to temperature. Water has the highest heat capacity or specific heat of all solids and liquids under ordinary conditions. The small calorie is the amount of heat required to raise the temperature of 1 g. of water from 0°

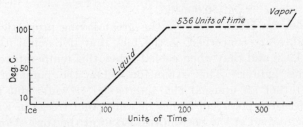

Fig. 78.—Diagram to illustrate the possibilities of the thermostatic action of water due to its latent heat. One unit of time represents a change of one small calorie.

to 1°C. The law of Dulong and Petit states that the specific heat of a substance varies inversely as the atomic weight. Therefore, it follows that substances which have a low atomic weight will have a high specific heat. A compound containing much hydrogen can be expected to have this high specific heat. The function of water in an environment, for the maintenance of constant temperature alone, makes it a very important substance.

Latent Heat.—Water has three phases: solid, liquid, and gas. The latent heat is the amount of heat required to change it from one state to another without changing its temperature. Eighty small calories are required to convert 1 g. ice at 0°C. to 1 g. water without changing its temperature at all. Five hundred and thirty-six small calories are required to convert 1 g. water at 100° to 1 g. vapor at the same temperature without raising its temperature at all. This means that the heat units required to vaporize one gram of water are equal to the amount required to raise the temperature of 536 g. water from 0° to 1°C.

The latent heat of water is greater than that of all other liquids except ammonia. The latent heat of evaporation is greater than that of any other liquid not even excepting ammonia. The heat of the sun evaporates water from streams, lakes, and the ocean; and this heat is again recovered when the vapor condenses to form rain, equalizing temperature, distributing water, and giving rise to all of the water power of the earth.

The possibilities of water as a thermostat in nature are great. If we had a theoretical environment of water in which the temperature had a constant rate of rise and fall, we might plot it as in Fig. 78.

The diagram is further complicated by the fact that the evaporation goes on at temperatures lower than 0°, and that it is greater at the higher temperatures. This means that the more extreme a high temperature becomes, the more evaporation tends to modify the extreme condition.

Conduction of Heat.—Water is a poor conductor of heat when compared with metals, but when it is compared with other liquids it is found to be higher than all others. With silver at 1.0, water is but 0.0125. Alcohol, however, is only 0.00046.

Expansion by Heat.—One of the great saving properties of water, so far as lakes are concerned, is the fact that it reaches its maximum density at 4°C., and that when cooled below this temperature it expands and becomes lighter. This expansion below the point of maximum density is rather an unusual characteristic. If water did not expand above the freezing point, all bodies of water that freeze in winter would have the ice formed at the bottom instead of at the top. Consequently, it is very fortunate that water has this unusual property.

Surface Tension.—Water has a surface tension of 75 dynes, which is greater than that of any other liquid save mercury. When we consider the relation of aquatic organisms to the surface film and to air inclusions in the water, we find that this property is what makes it possible for adult insects to live in the water.

Transparency.—Water in the liquid state is practically transparent, to some extent at least, to all rays of the visible spectrum. The fact that water, at a great depth, appears blue means that it absorbs more of the waves of longer length than those of shorter length. The waves of longer length, heat waves, are comparatively more absorbed, and water makes a good heat screen.

Viscosity.—The viscosity of water increases, as the temperature lowers, and this makes it about twice as great at the freezing point as at ordinary summer temperatures.

Compressibility.—Water is but slightly compressible. It contains more molecules per unit volume than any other known liquid except fused metals. Consequently, there is little space between the molecules for compression.

THE CHEMICAL PROPERTIES

Stability.—It is usually stated that, with the exception of hydrolytic and electrolytic dissociation, the action of water on solutes is practically *nil* because of its chemical inertness and stability. Kendall (1927), however, states, "Instead of being a substance which can be neglected, water is perhaps the most reactive of all substances." Be this as it may, it is possible to recover solutes from water in practically their original conditions. So the reactions which take place when substances go into solution in water are apparently reversible, and the substances come out of solution unchanged.

Solubility.—More substances are soluble in water than in any other substance. Practically all of the inorganic salts are soluble in water and many of them in no other liquid. Organisms, therefore, find more of the essential substances in solution in water than would be possible in any other medium.

BIBLIOGRAPHY

WATER THE PHYSICAL ENVIRONMENT

ADAMSTONE, F. B.: The Bottom Fauna of Lake Nipigon, *Univ. Toronto Studies,* publ. by Ontario Fish. Research Lab., no. 24, 1924.

BAYLISS, WILLIAM MADDOCK (1918): "Principles of General Physiology," chap. VIII, pp. 226–245, Longmans, Green and Co., New York and London, 1915, 1918 and 1920. 850 pp.

BIRGE, EDWARD E., and CHANCEY JUDAY: The Inland Lakes of Wisconsin. The Plankton. I. Its Quantity and Chemical Composition, *Wis. Geol. and Nat. Hist. Survey Bull.* 641, ss. no. 13, 1922.

BRAUER, A.: "Die Süsswasserfauna Deutschlands," publ. by Prof. Dr. A. Brauer, booklets 1 to 19 (Taschenformat), 1909–1912.

CLEMENS, WILBERT A.: The Limnology of Lake Nipigon in 1923, *Univ. Toronto Studies,* publ. by Ontario Fish. Research Lab., no. 22, 1924.

COMSTOCK, J. H.: "An Introduction to Entomology," Comstock Publ. Co., Ithaca, N. Y., 1920. 1042 pp.

DUCLAUX, JACQUES: La constitution de l'eau, *Rev. gén. sci.,* **23**: 881–887, 1912.

EKMAN, SVEN: Neue Apparate zur qualitativen und quantitativen Erforschung der Bodenfauna der Seen, *Internat. Rev. gesamm. Hydrobiol. u. Hydrog.,* **3**: 553–561, 1910.

ESSIG, E. O.: "Insects of Western North America," The Macmillan Company, New York, 1926. 1035 pp.

FOREL, F. A.: "Le Leman monographie limnologique," Lausanne, 1892–1904. 3 vols.

HELLAND-HANSEN (1912): The Ocean Waters, an Introduction to Physical Oceanography. I. General Part, *Internat. Rev. Gesamm. Hydrobiol. u. Hydrog.,* Hydrographisches suppl., **1**: 1–84, 1911.

HENDERSON, LAWRENCE J.: "The Fitness of the Environment," chap. III, Water, pp. 72–132, The Macmillan Company, New York, 1913. 317 pp.

HENSEN, VICTOR: Ueber die Bestimmung des Plankton, *Ber. 5, Komm. wissensch. Untersuch. d. deutsch. Meere,* Berlin, 1887.

————: Die Biologie des Meeres, *Arch. Hydrobiol. u. Planktonkunde,* **1**: 330–377, 1906.

HENTSCHEL, ERNST.: "Grundzüge der Hydrobiologie," G. Fischer, Jena, 1923. 221 pp.

JOHNSTONE, J.: "Conditions of Life in the Sea," Cambridge, Eng., 1908.

JOHNSTONE, JAMES, ANDREW SCOTT, and HERBERT C. CHADWICK: "The Marine Plankton," London, 1924. 194 pp.

KENDALL, JAMES: The Abuse of Water, *Science* n.s., vol. LXVI, pp. 610–611, 1927.

KNAUTHE, KARL: "Das Süsswasser," Neudamm, 1907. 663 pp.

LILLIE, FRANK R.: The Marine Biological Laboratory at Woods Hole, *Internat. Rev. Gesamm. Hydrobiol. u. Hydrog.*, **5**: 583–589, 1913.

MURRAY, SIR JOHN: "Summary of Oceanography in Challenger Report," Edinburgh, vol. 1, 1873–1876.

MURRAY, SIR JOHN, and JOHAN HJORT: "Depths of the Ocean," The Macmillan Company, New York, 1912.

NEEDHAM, J. G., and J. T. LLOYD: "Life of Inland Waters," Comstock Publ. Co., Ithaca, N. Y., 1915. 438 pp.

PEARSE, A. S.: The Distribution and Food of the Fishes of Three Wisconsin Lakes in Summer, *Wis. Univ. Studies Sci.*, no. 3, 1921.

PETERSON, C. G. T. Valuation of the Sea, I. *Rept. Danish Biol. Sta.*, **20**: 1–76, 1913; Valuation of the Sea, II. *Rept. Danish Biol. Sta.*, **21**: Pl–68, 1918; The Sea Bottom and Its Production of Fish Food, *Rept. Danish Biol. Sta.*, **25**: 1–62, 1918.

SHELFORD, V. E.: Determination of Hydrogen-ion Concentration in Connection with Fresh-water Biological Stations, *Nat. Hist. Survey*, **14**: 379–394, 1923.

STEUER, A.: "Planktonkunde," Leipzig, 1910. 723 pp.

STOKES, A.: "Aquatic Microscopy for Beginners," 3d ed., 1896, 326 pp.; 4th ed., 1918, 324 pp.; John Wiley & Sons, Inc., New York.

SUTHERLAND, WM.: The Molecular Constitution of Water, *Phil. Mag.*, **50**: 460–489, 1900.

THIENEMANN, AUGUST: Hydrobiologie als selbständige Wissenschaft und die Gründung einer Anstalt für die Hydrographie der Binnengewässer, Biol. suppl., *Internat. Rev. Hydrobiol.*, **6**: 1–14, 1914.

———: "Die Binnengewässer Mitteleuropas," p. 255, Stuttgart, 1925.

WALTHER, J.: Einleitung in die Geologie als historische Wissenschaft. I. Bionomie des Meeres; II. Die Lebensweise der Meeresthiere; III. Lithogenesis der Gegenwart. Jena, 1893–1894.

WARD, HENRY B., and GEORGE C. WHIPPLE: "Fresh-water Biology," John Wiley & Sons, New York, 1918. 1,111 pp.

WESENBURG-LUND: Über die süsswasserbiologischen Forschungen in Dänemark, *Internat. Rev. Gesamm. Hydrobiol. u. Hydrog.*, **3**: 128–135, 1910.

WHIPPLE, G. C.: The Microscopy of Drinking Water, p. 586, pl. 19, John Wiley & Sons, Inc., New York, 1927.

ZACHARIAS, OTTO: Die staatliche Sanktion der biologischen Unterrichts, *Arch. Hydrobiol. u. Planktonkunde*, **4**: 233–266, 1909.

———: Ziele und Wege der biologischen Unterrichts, *Arch. Hydrobiol. u. Planktonkunde*, **8**: 321–327, 1913.

———: Neue Ziele und Aufgaben der Gewässerbiologie, *Arch. Hydrobiol.*, **9**: 389–410, 1914.

———: Zur Frage der Einführung des Planktons als selbständigen Unterrichts Gegenstandes an höheren Schulen, *Arch. Hydrobiol. u. Planktonkunde*, **5**: 47–61, 1910.

THE CHARACTERISTICS OF AQUATIC COMMUNITIES—MARINE COMMUNITIES

General Characteristics of Marine Communities.—Seventy per cent of the surface area of the earth is covered by the ocean to an average depth of two and one-half miles. When this great three-dimension space is compared with the terrestrial environment, it is found to bear a ratio of about 1000:1 on the basis of available space for organisms to live in. While not directly concerned with marine environments, we cannot ignore the earth's largest continuous environment and greatest storehouse of the energy of solar radiation. Aside from its magnitude as an environment, it deserves consideration for its influence upon the distribution of moisture and temperature in the terrestrial environment.

The bottom of the ocean, like the exposed surface of the earth, is of an uneven contour. The continents are surrounded by relatively shallow water causing the continental shelves, beyond which the continental slopes lead to the greater depths over the extensive abyssal plains of the ocean's bottom. The great "Deeps," like the earth's great mountains, have been located and named. There are nearly 60 of them known, 32 of which occur in the Pacific Ocean. The deepest sounding is in the "Challenger Deep," and is over 6,265 fathoms (37,590 feet).

Morphometry.—The following data compiled from the various writings of Sir John Murray and others give the area of various depths of the ocean.

Depth, fathoms	Area	Square miles	Percentage of total ocean
0 to 100	Continental shelf	9,750,650	7.00
100 to 1,000	Continental slope	11,974,350	8.59
1,000 to 2,000	Abyssal plain	26,915,000	19.34
2,000 to 3,000	Abyssal plain	91,381,000	58.42
3,000 to 4,000	Deeps	9,058,000	6.50
Over 4,000	Deeps	216,000	0.15

The bottom of the ocean has been formed partly by material of inorganic origin and partly by material of organic origin. In the littoral zone the deposits are coral rock, sand (partly coral), gravel, and mud. Beyond the continental shelf (hundred-fathom line), there is mud, partly from land, containing coral and various volcanic materials and ooze of organic origin, called Radiolarian ooze, Diatom ooze, Globigerina ooze, and Pteropod ooze, depending upon the organisms which are involved in its formation.

Hygrometry.—Sea water is characterized by its salinity. However, it is not merely the quantity of salts which distinguishes it from fresh water, but also a difference in the proportions of the salts. The following table from Helland-Hansen (1911) gives a comparison of the salts in sea water and fresh water.

Salts	Sea water, per cent	River water, per cent
Chlorides................	88.64	5.2
Sulphates................	10.80	9.9
Carbonates..............	0.34	60.1
Various.................	0.22	24.8
Total.................	100.00	100.00

The salinity is not uniformly distributed throughout the ocean, but is influenced by the inflow of fresh water from rivers, the melting of ice in the arctic, and evaporation in the equatorial regions. In general, it is lowest at or near the poles, and highest at the Tropics of Capricorn and Cancer. Along the continental shelves the salinity may be greatly influenced by the ocean currents which mix the inflowing river water with that of the sea.

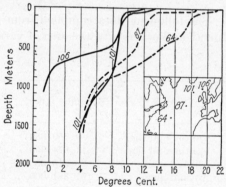

Fig. 79.—The distribution of temperature at four different stations in the summer of 1910. Position of stations shown on inset map. (*Murray and Hjort, 1912.*)

The temperature of the ocean varies greatly with latitude and depth, and is profoundly influenced by ocean currents. The surface temperature may be represented by a relatively smooth curve; starting with temperatures below zero Centigrade at either pole and rising to a maximum just north of the equator.

The distribution of temperature in depth is illustrated in Fig. 79. There is a rather rapid fall in temperature in the first 100 m. at all stations shown, followed by more or less uniformity down to 500. At station 106 there is a sudden drop in temperature between 500 and 700 m. This is similar to the thermocline to be described in connection with fresh-water lakes.

The density of sea water is influenced by both salinity and temperature. In general, salinity is least in the north when temperature is the lowest, and greatest near the tropics when temperature is the highest.

The gases of the ocean may be considered briefly. Sea water contains less oxygen than fresh water, for the solubility of oxygen decreases as salinity increases. Consequently, the amount of oxygen present in the warm and very salty waters of the tropics is very little.

Temperature, °C.	Salinity		
	0 per thousand	20 per thousand	35 per thousand
	Oxygen in c.c. per liter	Oxygen in c.c. per liter	Oxygen in c.c. per liter
0	10.29	9.01	8.03
10	8.02	7.10	6.40
20	6.57	5.88	5.35
30	5.57	4.96	4.50

Ocean currents and winds also influence the distribution of oxygen in the sea. Biotic conditions also contribute to the control of the oxygen

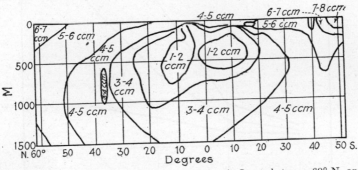

FIG. 80.—The distribution of oxygen in the Atlantic Ocean between 60° N. and 50° S. and from the surface to 1,500 m. Amount given in cubic centimeters per liter of water. (*Murray and Hjort*, 1912.)

content of the water. The actual oxygen content of sea water is, therefore, the result of a complicated set of factors (Fig. 80). As in freshwater lakes, there are cases of enclosed seas in which the bottom water becomes stagnant in the summer and the oxygen is exhausted. The Black Sea, for instance, may contain oxygen in only the upper 100 m. of water (Murray and Hjort, 1912). In certain "threshold fjords"and "oyster polols," a similar condition may exist in late summer.

Carbon dioxide may be present in the sea to the extent of 50 c.c. to the liter of water, but only a few tenths of this will be free and the majority will exist in the form of carbonates with which McClendon (1918) found the sea water to be supersaturated. Thus, if carbon dioxide is added to the water, more carbonates will be formed; while, if some is withdrawn, as in the case of photosynthesis, more will precipitate. Krough concluded that the sea acted as a great regulator of the carbon dioxide of the earth's atmosphere, containing 30 times as much carbon dioxide as the air (McClendon, 1916).

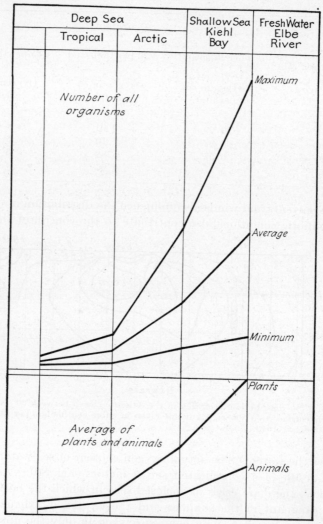

Fig. 81.—Diagrams showing the average relative numbers of Plankton organisms in fresh water, a bay, and the deep sea. (*Lohman's data adapted from Hentschel,* 1923.)

The waters of the sea are usually slightly alkaline and this condition is maintained in spite of all the changes which are constantly taking place in connection with the metabolism of its flora and fauna. The mean value is a pH 8.1 in the far North, or 8.2 near the equator. This is maintained through the "buffer action" of the salts in solution.

Biotic Characteristics of the Sea.—Since the present outlines are concerned mainly with insects, which are not marine organisms, it is necessary to pass over the vast faunas of the sea with a mere mention of them. The student is referred to Steuer (1910) and Johnstone (1924), Hentschel (1923), Murray and Hjort (1912), the *Reports of the Challenger Expedition* and the papers cited in the bibliographies of these works for information on these interesting and too little known ecological groups. The average student of zoology in his laboratory work comes into contact with more marine animals than those from fresh water. The marine biological laboratories specialize in the study of this group, and a great contribution has been made to the general conceptions of ecology by such work as that of Möbius.

We have almost no marine insects. The small water striders of the genus, *Halobetes*, are truly plagic and live on the surface of the ocean, and are said to be found hundreds of miles from land.

Quantitative studies in ecology began in the sea and the general results will be discussed in connection with the biotic characteristics of fresh-water communities. In general, the quantity of life in the sea is not as great as in fresh water, and it tends to be greater near the poles than near the equator (Fig. 81).

BIBLIOGRAPHY

MARINE COMMUNITIES

ALLEN, W. E.: Some Work on Marine Phytoplankton in 1919, *Trans. Amer. Micros. Soc.*, **40**: 177–181, 1921.

———: The Investigation of Ocean Pasturage, *Ecology*, **11**: 215–219, 1921.

———: Problems of Floral Dominance in the Open Sea, *Ecology*, **11**: 26–31, 1921.

———: Observations on Surface Distribution of Marine Diatoms between San Diego and Seattle, *Ecology*, **III**: 140–145, 1922.

———: Recent Work on Marine Microplankton at the La Jolla Biol. Station, *Trans. Amer. Micros. Soc.*, **42**: 180–183, 1923.

ATKINS, W. R. G.: The Hydrogen-ion Concentration of Seawater in Its Biological Relation, *Jour. Mar. Biol. Assoc.*, **12**: 717–780, 1922.

BORRADAILE, L. A.: "The Animal and Its Environment," chap. VIII, The Fauna of the Sea, pp. 200–212; chap. IX, Food and Subfaunas in the Sea, pp. 216–246, Froude and Hodder & Stoughton, London, 1923.

BRANDT, K. (1899): Ueber den Stoffwechsel im Meere, "Wissensch. Meeresuntersuchungen," herausgegeben v. d. Kommission zur wissensch., Untersuch. d. deutschen Meere, in Kiel. N. F. Abth., Kiel, vol. IV, pp. 493–506, 1899; 2d Abhandl. vol. VI, pp. 23–79, 1902.

BROOKS, W. K.: Salpa in Its Relation to the Evolution of Life, *Johns Hopkins Univ. Stud. Biol. Lab.*, **V**: 129–211, 1893.

CAMERON, A. T. and IRENE MOUNCE: Some Physical and Chemical Factors Influencing the Distribution of Marine Flora and Fauna in the Straits of Georgia and Adjacent Waters, *Contr. Can. Biol.*, n.s., **1**: 41–70, 1922.

CLARK, AUSTIN H.: On the Deep Sea and Comparable Faunas, *Internat. Rev. Gesamm. Hydrobiol. u. Hydrog.*, **6**: 17–30, 133–146, 1913.

CORI, CARL J.: Über die Meeresverschleimung im Golfe von Trieste während des Sommers von 1905, *Arch. Hydrobiol. u. Planktonkunde*, **1**: 385–391, 1906.

COWLES, R. P.: The Distribution of Water Density and Salinity in Chesapeake Bay, *Internat. Rev. Gesamm. Hydrobiol. u. Hydrog.*, **12**: 392–395, 1925.

FISH, CHARLES J.: Seasonal Distribution of the Plankton of the Woods Hole Region, *U. S. Bur. Fisheries Bull.*, Doc. 975, vol. XII, pp. 91–179, 1925.

GALTSOFF, PAUL S.: Seasonal Migrations of Mackerel in the Black Sea, *Ecology*, **V**: 1–6, 1924.

GEBBING, J.: Über den Gehalt des Meeres an Stickstoffnährsalzen Untersuchungs-ergebnisse der von der deutschen Südpolar Expedition (1901–3) gesammelten Meerwasserproben, *Internat. Rev. Gesamm. Hydrobiol. u. Hydrog.*, **3**: 50–67, 1910.

GRABAU, A. W.: "Zoology: Marine Invertebrates," A. W. Grabau, and J. E. Woodman, editors, 1898.

————: The Relation of Marine Bionomy to Stratigraphy, *Bull. Buffalo Soc. Nat. Sci.*, **VI**: 319–367, 1899.

HAUSMAN, LEON AUGUSTUS: Fresh-water and Marine Gymnostominian Infusoria, *Trans. Amer. Micros. Soc.*, **40**: 118–143, 1921.

HELLAND-HANSEN, BJÖRN: The Ocean Waters, an Introduction to Physical Oceanography. I. General Part (Methods, with the assistance of Adolph H. Schröder and other collaborators), *Internat. Rev. Gesamm. Hydrobiol. u. Hydrog.*, suppl., **1**: 1–84, 1912.

————: Eine Untersuchungsfahrt im Atlantischen Ozean mit dem Motorschiff "Armauer-Hansen," *Internat. Rev. Gesamm. Hydrobiol. u. Hydrog.*, **7**: 61–83, 1914.

HENSEN, VICTOR: Organic Matter in the Baltic, *U. S. Bur. Fisheries Bull.*, **5**: 267–269, 1885.

————: Ueber die Bestimmung des Planktons oder des im Meere treibenden Materials an Pflanzen u. Thieren; nebst Anhang; Ber. 5 der Kommission zur wissensch. Untersuch. d. Deutschen Meere in Kiel für die Jahre 1882–1886, pp. 1–107, 1887.

————. Die Biologie des Meeres, *Arch. Hydrobiol. u. Planktonkunde*, **1**: 360–377, 1906.

HENTSCHEL, ERNST: "Grundzüge der Hydrobiologie," G. Fischer, Jena, 1923. 221 pp.

HESSE, RICHARD: "Tiergeographie auf ökologischer Grundlage," Fischer, Jena, 1924. 613 pp.

HIRSCH, ERWIN: Vorläufige Mitteilung über die Ergebnisse einer biologischen Untersuchung des versalzenen Flussgebiets der Wupper, *Arch. Hydrobiol. u. Plank-tonkunde*, **12**: 82–121, 1918.

HJORT, JOHANN: Die Tiefsee Expedition des "Michael Sars" nach dem Nord-atlantik im Sommer 1910, *Internat. Rev. Gesamm. Hydrobiol. u. Hydrog.*, **4**: 152–173, 335–362, 1911.

JOHNSTONE, J.: "Life in the Sea," Cambridge, Engl., pp. 206–298, 1908.

KNIEP, HANS: Über die Assimilation und Atmung der Meeresalgen, *Internat. Rev. Gesamm. Hydrobiol. u. Hydrog.*, **7**: 1–38, 1914.

KOEHLER, M. R.: Sur un Hemiptère marin, *Aepophilus bonnairei* Sign, *Compt. rend. acad. sci.*, Paris, **110**: 126–128, 1885.

KOFOID, CHARLES A.: Contributions of Alexander Agassiz to Marine Biology, *Internat. Rev. Gesamm. Hydrobiol. u. Hydrog.*, **4**: 39–43, 1911.

LLOYD, BLODWEN: The Technique of Research on Marine Phytoplankton, *Jour. Ecology*, **13**: 277–288, 1925.

LOHMANN, H.: Über die Quellen der Nahrung der Meerestiere und Pütter's Untersuchungen hierüber, *Internat. Rev. Gesamm. Hydrobiol. u. Hydrog.*, **2**: 10–30, 1909.

————: Beiträge zur Charakterisierung des Tier- und Pflanzenlebens in den von der "Deutschland" während ihrer Fahrt nach Buenos Aires durchfahrenen Gebieten des Atlantischen Ozeans, *Internat. Rev. Gesamm. Hydrobiol. u. Hydrog.*, I. Teil **4**: 407–432, 1912; II. Teil, **5**: 186–225; 343–372, 1913.

LORENZ, J. R.: "Physikalische Verhältnisse und Verteilung der Organismen im Quärnerischen Golfe," Wien, 1863. 379 pp.

LUTZ, F. E.: "Field Book of Insects," G. P. Putnam's Sons, New York, 1918. 509 pp.

McCLENDON, J. F.: The Composition, Especially the Hydrogen-ion Concentration, of Sea-water in Relation to Marine Organisms, *Jour. Biol. Chem.*, **28**: 135–152, 1916.

———: The Hydrogen-ion Concentration CO_2 Tension, and CO_2 Content of Seawater, *Carnegie Inst. Wash. Pub.* 251, pp. 23–69, 1917.

———: On Changes in the Sea and Their Relation to Organisms, *Carnegie Inst. Wash. Pub.* 252, pp. 213–258, 1918.

McEWEN, GEORGE F.: The Distribution of Ocean Temperatures along the West Coast of North America Deduced from Ekman's Theory of the Upwelling of Cold Water from the Adjacent Ocean Depths, *Internat. Rev. Gesamm. Hydrobiol. u. Hydrog.*, **5**: 243–285, 1912.

MATTHEWS, D. J.: A Deep Sea Bact. Waterbottle, *Jour. Mar. Biol. Assoc.*, **9**: 525–529, 1913.

MAYOR, A. G.: Hydrogen-ion Concentration and Electrical Conductivity of the Surface Water of the Atlantic and Pacific, *Carnegie Inst. Wash. Pub.* 312, pp. 61–86, 1912.

MICHAEL, E. L., and W. E. ALLEN: Problems of Marine Ecology, *Ecology*, **II**: 84–88, 1921.

MIALL, L. C.: "The Natural History of Aquatic Insects," The Macmillan Company, New York, 1895. 395 pp.

MURRAY, JAMES: The Observation of Tides and Seiches in Frozen Seas, *Internat. Rev. Gesamm. Hydrobiol. u. Hydrog.*, **4**: 129–135, 1911.

NANSEN, FRIDTJOF: The Waters of the North-eastern North Atlantic. Investigations made during the Cruise of the *Fridtjof* of the Norwegian Royal Navy in July 1910, *Internat. Rev. Gesamm. Hydrobiol. u. Hydrog.*, Hydrographisches Suppl., **II**: 1–139, 1913.

NEEDHAM, J. G., and J. T. LLOYD: "The Life of Inland Waters," Comstock Publ. Co., Ithaca, N. Y., 1916. 438 pp.

NEEDHAM, J. G., and P. R. NEEDHAM: "A Guide to the Study of Fresh-water Biology," The American Viewpoint Society, Inc., New York and Albany, 1927. 88 pp.

PACKARD, A. S., and P. R. UHLER: Insects Inhabiting Salt Water, *Stillman's Amer. Jour. Sci.*, 1871; i (3); rev. in *Ann. Mag. N. H.* (4) **VII**: 230 soc.

PETERSON, C. G. JOH. (1911): Über einige in Angriff genommene Untersuchungen über Menge und Nahrung der niederen Tiere am Meeresboden, mit besonderer Berücksichtigung der Ernährung der Scholle im Limfjord, *Internat. Rev. Gesamm. Hydrobiol. u. Hydrog.*, **3**: 3–5, 1910.

PETERSON, C. G. JOH., and P. B. JENSEN: Valuation of the Sea. I. Animal Life of the Sea Bottom, Its Food and Quantity, *Rept. of Danish Biol. Sta.* to Bd. of Agr. **XX**: 1–76, 1911. *Trans. Fisherei-Beretnung*, Copenhagen, 1910.

POWERS, EDWIN B.: The Variation of the Condition of Seawater, Especially the Hydrogen-ion Concentration, and Its Relation to Marine Organisms, *Puget Sound Biol. Sta. Pubs.*, **2**: 369–385, 1920.

———: Experiments and Observations on the Behavior of Marine Fishes Toward the Hydrogen-ion Concentration of the Sea Water in Relation to Their Migratory Movements and Habitat, *Puget Sound Biol. Sta. Pubs.*, **3**: 1–22, 1921–1925.

———: The Absorption of Oxygen by the Herring as Affected by the Carbon Dioxide Tension on the Sea Water, *Ecology*, **IV**: 307–312, 1923.

RITTER, W. E.: "The Marine Biol. Sta., San Diego," circ. by the Sta. at La Jolla, Calif., 1910.

ROUSSEAU, E.: "Les Larves et Nymphes aquatiques des Insectes d'Europe," Office de Publicité, Anc. Établis J. Lebèque et Cie., Éditeurs, 36 rue Neuve, Bruxelles, 1921. 967 pp.

SAUNDERS, L. G.: Some Marine Insects of the Pacific Coast of Canada, *Ann. Ent. Soc. Amer.*, **21**: 521–545, 1928.

SCHWARTZ, E. A. (1921): Preliminary Remarks on the Insect Fauna of the Great Salt Lake, Utah, *Canad. Ent.*, **23**: 235–241, 1891.

SERNOW, S. A.: Grundzüge der Verbreitung der Tierwelt des Schwarzen Meeres bei Sebastopol, *Internat. Rev. Gesamm. Hydrobiol. u. Hydrog.*, Abt. II, **3**: 299–305, 1910.

STEUER, A.: Veränderungen der Nordadriatischen Flora u. Fauna während der letzten Dezennien, *Internat. Rev. Gesamm. Hydrobiol. u. Hydrog.*, **3**: 6–16, map, 1910.

————: Einige Ergebnisse der 7. Terminfahrt S.M.S. *Najade* in Sommer 1912 in der Adria, *Internat. Rev. Gesamm. Hydrobiol. u. Hydrog.*, **5**: 551–570, 1913.

————: Horizontale und vertikale Verteilung der Copepoden nach den Ergebnissen der deutschen Tiefsee-Expedition, *Internat. Rev. Gesamm. Hydrobiol. u. Hydrog.*, **7**: 205–213, 1914.

SUMNER, F. B.: An Intensive Study of the Fauna and Flora of a Restricted Area of the Sea-bottom, *U. S. Bur. Fisheries Bull.*, vol. XXVIII, pp. 1225–1263, 1910.

THIENEMANN, AUGUST: Der Zusammenhang zwischen dem Sauerstoffgehalt des Tiefenwassers und der Zusammensetzung der Tiefenfauna unsere Seen, *Internat. Rev. Gesamm. Hydrobiol. u. Hydrog.*, **6**: 243–249, 1913.

————: Untersuchungen über die Beziehung zwischen dem Sauerstoffgehalt des Wassers und der Zusammensetzung der Fauna in Norddeutschen Seen, *Arch. Hydrobiol. u. Planktonkunde*, **12**: 1–65, 1918.

————: Biologische Seetypen und die Gründung einer hydrobiologischen Anstalt am Bodensee, 1921–1922.

VERNADSKI, V.: Living Matter and Marine Chemistry, *Rev. gén. sci.*, **35**: 13–15, 46–54, 1924.

WALKER, J. J.: One of the Genus Halobates Esch., and Other Marine *Hemiptera*, *Ent. Monthly Mag.*, **29**: 227–232, 1893.

WARD, H. B., and G. C. WHIPPLE: "Fresh-water Biology," John Wiley & Sons, Inc., New York and London, 1918. 1111 pp.

WARMING, B., C. WESENBERG-LUND, etc.: Sur les "vads" et les sables maritimes de la Mer du Nord, *Kon. Danske Vid. Selsk. Skrift*, vol. VII, R. II, pp. 48–56, 1904.

WILSON, O. T.: Some Experimental Observations of Marine Algal Successions, *Ecology*, **VI**: 303–311, 1925.

WOLFF, MAX: Die Pütter'schen Untersuchungen über die Nahrung der Marinen Tiere und über den Stoffhaushalt des Meeres, *Arch. Hydrobiol. u. Planktonkunde*, **4**: 193–202, 1909.

YENDO, K.: On the Cultivation of Seaweeds with Special Accounts of Their Ecology, *Proc. Roy. Dublin Soc. Econ.* **2**: 105–122, 1914; rev. *Jour. Ecology*, **II**: 126–129, 1914.

ZACHARIAS, OTTO: Über Periodizität, Variation und Verbreitung verschiedener Planktonwesen in südlichen Meeren, *Arch. Hydrobiol. u. Planktonkunde*, **1**: 498–575, 1906.

ZSCHAKKE, F.: Leben in der Tiefe der sub-alpinen Seen. Ueberreste der eiszeitlichen Mischfauna, *Arch. Hydrobiol. u. Planktonkunde*, **8**: 109–138, 1913.

CHAPTER XIII

PHYSICAL CHARACTERISTICS OF AQUATIC COMMUNITIES

There are few environments which are so definitely circumscribed, and which lend themselves to exact physical measurement as lenitic environments do. It is for this reason that they are of special interest not only as aquatic environments, but as objects of study for the better understanding of environments in general.

Birge and Juday (1911) say of their work on the Wisconsin Lakes:

Perhaps the chief interest which our work has had for us has been the fact that its progress has revealed to us the existence of physiological processes in lakes as complex, as distinct, and as varied as those of higher animals. The processes which we have studied are intricately bound up with physical, chemical, and biological processes of every kind, of which limnologists are still in large measure ignorant.

These relationships and processes are to be found everywhere in nature, though they may be less susceptible to analysis in other environments. The student of terrestrial synecology may do well to study the results of the aquatic synecologists.

Forel, Halbfass, Birge and Juday, Thienemann, and others demonstrated that the form and size of lenitic environments are of first importance in determining the physical conditions within them. This is particularly true with regard to the penetration of solar radiations, and the action of the wind which distributes heat and gases, and erodes the shore line. The form of the lake basin determines not only the physical conditions, but also the biotic conditions through the materials which may be carried into the lake by streams, and which may remain in solution or accumulate as sediment in the bottom.

The distinction between lakes and ponds is a matter of size, or specifically the ratio of surface and bottom to volume, which may be measured by depth. Temporary ponds are distinguished from permanent ponds by the fact that there is no water present during a part of the year. The water may evaporate because the surface area, which is exposed, is so great in proportion to its volume that, in the absence of an adequate source, all of the water evaporates. In climates where evaporation exceeds rainfall, there are many such temporary ponds. Again, the water may be absent because it has all been frozen, due to the great surface exposed to low temperature. In northern climates there are many such temporary ponds.

The classification of lakes (Whipple, 1927; Birge, 1914; Thienemann, 1925; and others), which is of greatest ecological significance, is based directly or indirectly on depth, which is the measure of the ratio of surface to volume. The proportion of the total volume of water which receives energy from solar radiation (Birge, 1914), depends upon the size and shape of the lake basin. The extent to which the wind is able to distribute this heat (Birge, 1914), depends partly on the lake itself and partly on the physiography of its environs. The presence or absence of oxygen in the lower water is immediately dependent upon biotic phenomena which are in turn dependent upon the form of the lake basin and the materials in solution in the water.

Morphometry.—Methods of studying the morphometry of inland lakes have been described by Birge and Juday (1914) and more recently by Whipple (1927). Many of the methods used in physical oceanography (Helland–Hansen, 1911; Murray and Hjort, 1912; and others) may be adapted to fresh water.

In northern climates such studies may be made while the surface is frozen. The outline may then be accurately made with a plane table, and the depth determined with some of the simpler sounding apparatus (Whipple, 1927) at regular intervals. By using cross-section paper on the plane table, an accurate record may be made in a short time.

The mean depth of a lake may be calculated from the following formula: $\frac{V}{A} = DM$: V = volume, A = area; DM = mean depth. Planimeter measurements of areas are the most rapid and reliable.

Volume is computed from the following formula.

$$V = \frac{h}{3}(S_1 + S_2 + \sqrt{S_1 S_2});$$

where

h = thickness of stratum,
S_1 = area of upper surface of stratum,
S_2 = area of lower surface of stratum.

This is Penk's formula, and Halbfass has shown that all of the formulæ give about the same results. (See Juday, 1914.)

Hygrometry.—It has been stated above that depth is a most important characteristic of a body of water because it determines the proportion of the volume of water which may receive solar radiation in the form of heat and chemical energy. The former determines the thermal stratification and stability of the lake, and the latter furnishes the energy for photosynthesis which in turn forms the basis for all biological processes in the water.

Methods of Measuring Physical Characteristics of Lenitic Environments.—Light is measured directly at various depths both as to the actinic and heat rays by certain methods (Klugh, 1925); and the transparency of the water is measured by other means. Sechi's disc (Sechi, 1866) is a white or black and white metal disc which may be used for a comparative measure of the transparency of water. It has probably been used more widely than any other method. Typical results, as given by this disc which is lowered into the water to obtain the mean of the depths at which it disappears, and the depth at which it reappears when drawn up, are given by Needham and Lloyd (1916).

Depths	Meters
Pacific Ocean	59
Mediterranean Sea	42
Lake Tahoe	33
Lake Geneva	21
Cayuga Lake	5
Fure Lake, March	9
Fure Lake, August	5
Fure Lake, December	7
Spoon River under ice	3.65
Spoon River at flood	0.013

The Geneva Commission incandescent lamp gives a measure of transparency. When the light is lowered, it gives the appearance of a bright spot surrounded by a halo. The point at which the spot disappears is taken as the limit of clear vision, and the point at which the halo disappears is taken as the limit of diffused light.

The photographic method is a standard of measurement which gives a much better value than the above methods which are more or less comparisons of transparency. It measures the actinic end of the spectrum. Klugh (1925) gives a summary of the attempts with photometers. Forel (1877) introduced this method, which has since been refined by the use of various filters in order to determine the quality of the light present at various depths. Shelford (1922) used a photo-electric cell. Klugh's photometer (Klugh, 1925) has been discussed in connection with the subject of light.

The heat of the sun's rays as it penetrates the water of a lake was measured by Birge and Juday (1921) by a pyrlimnometer (Birge, 1922) which consists of a series of black and white silver discs mounted over iron-constantin thermocouples, by means of which the temperature is read and calculated in calories per square centimeters per minute.

The color of water as affecting the transparency is due to the substances which are in solution. All methods of measuring the color values of water depend upon the same principle—the comparison of the water with an arbitrary standard. The platinum cobalt, the Natural Water

Standard, and the Nesler Water Standard are the ones commonly used (Whipple, 1927).

There are two seasons of maximum color values, one in the early summer, May or June, and one in the early winter, November or December. Whipple (1927) states that he found that in some of his experiments the water at the surface will be bleached as much as 20 per cent in 100 hours of bright sunlight. Bleaching is said to be independent of temperature and dependent entirely upon the amount of sunlight. It is difficult, however, to distinguish between bleaching and color changes due to chemical and biotic processes which may be going on in the water.

Turbidity of the Water.—The method of measuring turbidity which has been employed by Hazen at the Lawrence Experiment Station is by means of a platinum wire lowered into the water. A bright wire 1 mm. in diameter and projecting at right angles from the rod was lowered into the water, and the depth at which it disappeared from view was noted. Water in which this wire disappeared from view at a depth of one inch was taken as the standard of measurement, and its turbidity was designated at 1.0. The rod to which the wire was attached was graduated in inches, and the degrees of turbidity were read off in percentage of the unit of turbidity. Water in which the wire disappeared from view at five inches has a turbidity of 0.2. The U. S. Geological Survey turbidity rod is graduated in millimeters, and readings may be converted to turbidity in parts per million by the use of a table (Whipple, 1927). It is obvious that this method does not make any distinction between color and turbidity.

Temperature of water has been measured by various thermometers (Juday, 1916; Helland-Hansen, 1911; Murray and Hjort, 1912; Whipple, 1927), which act as minimum or maximum recording instruments. The Richter reversing thermometer (Murray and Hjort, 1912) is so made that a column of mercury is broken off from the volume of mercury in the bulb, at the time that a reading is desired, by reversing the ends of the thermometer. This gives a column of mercury of a given length at the temperature which is to be determined. By comparison with a thermometer mounted in the same case, a correction is applied in the reading of the temperature, making the accuracy as great as 1/100°C. Resistance thermometers and thermocouples have been used (Birge, 1922; Whipple, 1927), but instruments requiring galvanometers for reading are difficult to use in boats; consequently, the thermophone which employs an interrupter to detect the presence of a current has been devised (Whipple, 1927).

Water samples, especially when well insulated, may be used for determining the temperature of the water when brought to the surface. The "Peterson-Nansen" water bottle (Murray and Hjort, 1912) has thus been used.

The mean temperature of a body of water is computed as follows: Multiply the mean temperature of each stratum of a lake by the per cent of that stratum in the whole volume of the lake and add the several products. The result will show the mean temperature of the water.

$$[(Tm\ 1)(\%\ 1)] + [(Tm\ n)(\%\ n)] = Tm \text{ of whole lake.}$$

The thermal stratification of water in lakes and ponds is due in part to the manner in which the sun's energy is transmitted below the surface, and partly to the conduction and convection capacities of the water as well as to its relative viscosity. Birge and Juday (1921) have shown that in Seneca Lake about 70 per cent of the sun's energy is absorbed by the first meter of water and that only about 1 per cent of it reaches the tenth meter. In a more recent investigation (Birge and Juday, 1929), a series of lakes has been studied by the thermopile method of measuring the transmission of solar radiation. Lakes which have a large amount of material in suspension, such as plankton, or highly colored water due to material in solution, transmit the least solar radiation. In general, the shallower lakes transmit the least radiation through the first meter; and in none of them is there more than 40 per cent left below the first meter. Shelford and Gail (1922) used the photo-electric cell in a study of light penetration in Puget Sound and showed a transmission of about 60 per cent of the light through the first meter by their method. Klugh (1927) measured the transmission of light into the Bay of Fundy and found 40 per cent of red, 78 per cent of green, and 55 per cent of blue at the end of the first meter. In Chamcook Lake he found 58 per cent of the total light at the end of the first meter, and 10 per cent at 10 m. The agreement of the results from these various methods is close enough to indicate that most of the light is absorbed in the first 3 m. of water. The water of a pond may, therefore, take up as much of the sun's energy as a deep lake, for the latter will receive it only in its surface layers. The pond will transmit little of the sun's radiation because of the color of the water and the amount of suspended material.

The further distribution of this heat is dependent upon the conduction of convection capacities, with the exception of the action of the wind, which will be treated later. The conduction capacity of water is low, as has already been stated. The convection capacity is important and is dependent upon the relative density of the water at different temperatures. This may best be appreciated by a study of the accompanying table modified from Birge (1910).

The relative difference of density of water at 4 and 5°C. is taken as one. On this basis the relative difference of density at 29 and 30°C. is 37.25 times as great as at 4 and 5°C. Stating the facts in terms of resistance which this water will offer to mixing, it may be said that it takes 37.25 times as much energy to mix two volumes of water, one at

TABLE XIV.—TEMPERATURE AND DENSITY OF WATER[1]

Temperature, °C.	Density	Difference in density for 1°C.	Relative difference for 1°C.	Work done in mixing. Ergs.
0	0.999868	+0.000059	7.38	0.0491
1	0.999927	+0.000041	5.12	0.0342
2	0.999968	+0.000024	3.00	0.0200
3	0.999992	+0.000008	1.00	0.0067
4	1.000000	−0.000008	1.00	0.0067
5	0.999992	−0.000024	3.00	0.0200
6	0.999968	−0.000039	4.88	0.0325
7	0.999929	−0.000053	6.62	0.0441
8	0.999876	−0.000068	8.50	0.0566
9	0.999808	−0.000081	10.12	0.0675
10	0.999727	−0.000095	11.18	0.0791
11	0.999632	−0.000107	13.38	0.0891
12	0.999525	−0.000121	15.12	0.1008
13	0.999404	−0.000133	16.62	0.1108
14	0.999271	−0.000145	18.12	0.1208
15	0.999126	−0.000156	19.50	0.1299
16	0.998970	−0.000169	21.12	0.1408
17	0.998801	−0.000179	22.38	0.1491
18	0.998622	−0.000190	23.75	0.1583
19	0.998432	−0.000202	25.25	0.1683
20	0.998230	−0.000211	26.38	0.1758
21	0.998019	−0.000222	27.75	0.1849
22	0.997797	−0.000232	29.00	0.1993
23	0.997565	−0.000242	30.25	0.2016
24	0.997323	−0.000252	31.50	0.2099
25	0.997071	−0.000261	32.62	0.2174
26	0.996810	−0.000271	33.88	0.2257
27	0.996539	−0.000280	35.00	0.2332
28	0.996259	−0.000288	36.00	0.2399
29	0.995971	−0.000298	37.25	0.2482
30	0.995673			

[1] Birge, 1910.

29°C. and one at 30°C., with the warmer lighter water lying above the cooler heavier water, as would be required if these volumes were at 4 and 5°C. in the same respective positions. The graph from Birge (1910) presents these facts in a way that facilitates comparison (Fig. 82).

By comparing the graph of the transmission of the sun's radiation (Fig. 97) with that of resistance to mixing, it will be seen that 90 per cent of the heat of solar radiation is received and retained in the upper 3 m. of water and that the more heat this water receives and retains, the less possibility there will be of its being mixed with that below it. We have here the basis for explaining the fundamental difference between ponds and lakes.

Ponds are but a meter or two deep and the heat of solar radiation penetrates to the bottom. The surface area exposed to the wind is large as compared with the volume, and the water may be mixed whenever the wind blows. Lakes are deep and the ratio of the surface area to volume

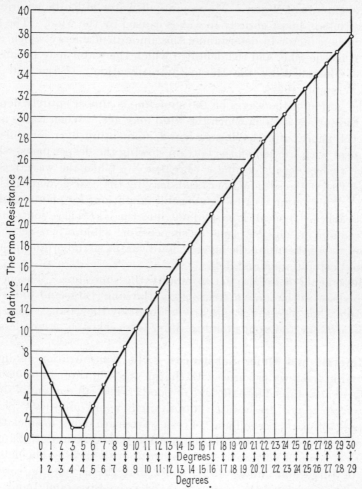

Fig. 82.—The relation of 1° of temperature difference to the resistance to mixing of water. Relative thermal resistance on the ordinate, the resistance at 3° − 4° and 5° − 4° being taken as unity. (*Birge*, 1910.)

is small as compared with this ratio for ponds. Consequently, the heat absorbed in the surface layers builds up a resistance to mixing which cannot be overcome by the wind. Having made this distinction between lakes and ponds, the temperature phenomena in lakes will be postponed to the chapter on Lakes.

Pressure.—The pressure in a body of fresh water increases at the rate of one atmosphere for 10.328 m. with a slight increase due to the

compression at greater pressure. It follows that a lake 100 m. deep will
have a pressure of approximately 10 atmospheres. Again ponds and
lakes differ, in that the extreme conditions of pressure are to be found only
in lakes.

Movements of Water.—Movements of water in lenitic environments
are restricted almost entirely to waves caused by the wind. The surface
exposed is a factor in determining the amount of energy which may be
applied to the lake, and the depth to which the water may be affected is
largely controlled by the thermal stratification. (Birge and Juday,
1914; Whipple, 1927.)

The action of the waves on the shoreline is almost entirely dependent
upon the surface area on which the wind may act. When waves advance
upon the shore, after having gathered momentum over long distances,
they meet with friction on the bottom slowing the deeper parts, while the
surface rushes ahead forming a "breaker." When the wave recedes, it
carries with it the silt and finer sand, leaving the coarser materials on the
beach. This action creates unfavorable conditions for plants, and leaves
open beaches. The silt is carried out into the lake where some materials
may remain in solution, some in suspension; while others settle to the
bottom to contribute to the layer of mud that is so important in supporting the bottom fauna and flora.

Movements of ice also act to modify the shore line. This occurs on
its expansion at the times of freezing and thawing (Birge and Juday, 1914),
and later when pieces of ice are driven about by the wind. Again surface
area is a factor and ponds tend to differ from lakes in having less severe
conditions.

Minerals and Other Substances.—The concentration of inorganic
material in fresh water varies with that of the soil, through or over which
the water has drained into the lake or pond. The salt content of sea water
differs from that of fresh water in both quality and quantity. Sea water
averages 350 parts per million. Fresh waters are richer in silica than sea
waters. Forel considered the composition of lake waters to be uniform
both as to time of year and as to the strata of the lake. The determinations of Birge and Juday (1914) show that this is not the case. The
diagram of Beasley Lake (Fig. 83) taken from Birge and Juday (1911),
shows the variations with depth. When compared with the graph of
plankton distribution, it will be seen that the greatest fluctuations occur
at the depth of maximum plankton abundance (Fig. 84). This indicates
that many of the materials are present in organisms rather than in suspension or solution in the water.

A general conception of the results of mineral analysis of lake waters
may best be obtained by the study of the following table from Birge and
Juday (1911).

TABLE XV.—MINERAL ANALYSES OF WISCONSIN LAKES[1]

(In parts per million)

Lake	Date	Depth, meters	SiO_2	$Fe_2O_3 + Al_2O_3$	Ca	Mg	Na	K	CO_3	HCO_3	SO_3	Cl
Bass.......	9/07	0	5.0	5.0	0.6	1.2	0.3	0.6	0.0	4.9	1.4	2.5
		0	13.3	1.7	46.6	27.8	2.4	2.0	2.0	104	10.3	2.8
	9/9/07	8	21.6	0.8	43.5	27.8	2.2	2.1	0.0	118	9.4	2.5
		14	33.0	4.0	47.1	28.0	2.6	1.9	....	121	11.8	2.0
		0	6.9	0.8	16.2	19.5	3.8	2.4	8.0	107	10.7	6.0
Elkhart	9/12/07	10	8.5	1.1	10.1	24.8	3.9	1.9	4.0	121	12.7	5.0
		21	9.4	1.8	24.1	26.8	4.3	2.2	0.0	129	10.6	5.2
		33	10.8	2.6	24.9	26.0	4.5	2.4	0.0	136	12.4	6.5
		0	6.1	1.5	16.9	9.0	3.6	0.8	11.0	88	12.8	6.0
Garvin.....	9/5/07	6	7.6	1.8	23.0	23.0	...	...	0.0	117	11.4	5.0
		9	16.9	9.1	28.4	25.1	2.0	1.4	....	153	11.5	5.6
		0	7.8	0.7	18.3	25.8	4.6	2.5	11.0	94	12.5	5.0
Geneva.....	9/26/07	15	....	0.7	20.0	27.0	4.4	2.5	0.0	111	13.0	5.0
		30	....	1.1	21.8	27.3	4.1	2.2	0.0	113	....	5.0
		41	11.1	2.0	22.8	27.5	4.2	2.8	0.0	114	14.1	3.5
		0	8.4	1.6	16.4	25.9	3.0	3.1	8.0	87	16.0	6.0
Green......	9/14/07	15	8.4	2.0	23.8	26.0	3.5	2.8	0.0	109	15.8	5.5
		40	10.3	2.1	24.0	....	3.4	2.9	0.0	110	16.3	6.2
		65	10.4	2.2	21.7	25.3	3.6	3.1	0.0	112	18.6	5.5
		3	14.6	1.7	39.1	24.1	...	...	...	...	3.7	2.3
Knights....	8/27/09	4	14.3	1.1	32.5	22.7	...	...	...	...	4.0	2.5
		4.5	13.6	0.7	29.3	22.7	...	...	...	...	4.1	2.3
		5	18.6	1.4	38.8	23.8	...	...	...	...	3.4	1.9
		0	9.2	1.6	17.4	21.8	2.7	2.6	10.0	74	15.2	3.0
Mendota...	9/18/07	14	8.5	1.6	17.6	20.0	...	...	0.0	108	15.4	
		17	9.0	1.8	17.6	20.2	...	...	0.0	116	15.7	3.0
		22	21.2	2.8	22.2	21.5	4.6	1.8	0.0	132	15.1	3.0
		0	2.5	0.5	31.3	30.0	...	...	8.0	99	12.5	3.0
		6.5	2.6	...	46.2	32.0						
N. W. part.	8/10/05	8	9.1	0.8	49.1	27.5	...	...	0.0	131	14.4	2.5
		15	9.7	1.1	49.2	26.4	...	...	....	127	12.1	4.0
		22	11.5	...	49.3	27.4	...	...	....	128	10.2	2.5

[1] Birge and Juday, 1911.

Certain of the minerals are found in greatest abundance at the bottom of lakes and at the end of summer stagnation in the hypolimnon. Silica is carried down in the shells of diatoms as they die and sink to the bottom. Iron goes into solution in the absence of oxygen in the hypolimnon and is precipitated out again when oxygen is distributed at the time of the overturn.

A comparison of the Wisconsin lakes with Borradaile's (1923) data for the ocean is as follows:

CONCENTRATION IN PARTS PER MILLION

Salt	Ocean	Wisconsin lakes
Na............................	306.4	3.23
Mg...........................	37.6	19.63
Ca............................	12.0	26.92
K.............................	10.9	2.05
Cl............................	552.1	3.28
SO_4........................	77.0	9.84
CO_3........................	2.1	2.23

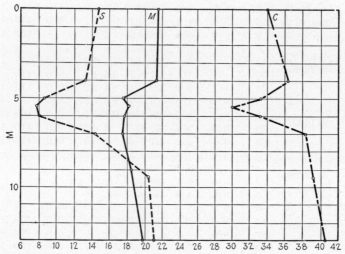

FIG. 83.—Beasley Lake, August 3, 1908. *S*, silica, *M*, magnesium; and *C*, calcium. The vertical spaces represent depth in meters and the horizontal spaces parts per million. (*Birge and Juday*, 1911.)

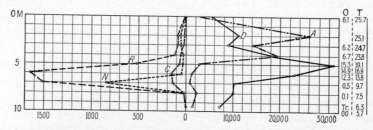

FIG. 84.—Vertical distribution of plankton organisms in Beasley Lake, August 3, 1908. Scale, 1 horizontal space = 100 crustacea, nauplii, and rotifers per liter of water, and 2,000 algae and diatoms. Predominant forms: *Aphanocapsa, Fragilaria, Dinobryon, Uroglena, Polyarthra,* and *Cyclops.* The large number of rotifers at 6 m. and 7m. consisted almost wholly of *Polyarthra.* (*Birge and Juday*, 1911.)

Such comparisons are apt to be misleading if we do not keep in mind the fact that both the ocean and the lakes vary in the amounts of the different materials. The calcium, for instance, was found to be 49.6 parts per million in certain parts of Lake Mendota during the fall. Lake water may, therefore, exceed sea water in the concentration of certain materials, but in others it may be far below it.

The Gases in the Water.—The study of the Wisconsin lakes has contributed much to our knowledge of gases in lenitic environments; and it is doubtful if there is a more comprehensive treatment of the subject than in Birge and Juday's (1911) volume on the dissolved gases in these lakes and Whipple (1927). Oxygen and carbon dioxide are the most important of these gases, though nitrogen, methane, hydrogen sulphide, and ammonia demand consideration.

Atmospheric air is ordinarily composed of 79.2 per cent of nitrogen, 20.5 per cent of oxygen, 0.03 per cent of carbon dioxide, and small traces of the other gases. Water absorbs them from the air in the following percentages: oxygen, 34.91; and nitrogen, 65.09; on account of the fact that the solubility of these gases bears a very different ratio from their relative percentages in the air as shown in the following table from Birge and Juday (1911). This table also illustrates the effect of temperature in reducing the solubility of the gas.

Cubic Centimeters of Gas per Liter of Water from a Pure Atmosphere of the Gas at 760 mm. Pressure

Temperature	Oxygen	Carbon dioxide	Nitrogen
0°C.	.41.14	1796.7	20.35
20°C.	28.38	901.4	14.03

Each gas is absorbed from the air independently of all others and in proportion to its own pressure. The volume of gas absorbed is influenced by pressure because the volume of a gas is decreased by increased pressure. Consequently, when measured at a standard pressure of 760 mm., the gas absorbed at twice this pressure gives twice the volume; and the gas absorbed at half the pressure gives half the volume.

The Winkler method of determining the quantity of dissolved oxygen and the Seyler methods for carbon dioxide are described by Birge and Juday (1911); Shelford (1929); and Powers (1927). Various methods have been used in obtaining the samples of water.

The distribution of gases in time and space in a lenitic environment presents an interesting example of the mutual relationship between organisms and their environment in determining conditions for existence. Purely physical processes govern the intake of oxygen and carbon dioxide at the surface where the water is in contact with the atmospheric air, and in and on the surrounding soil as the ground and surface waters come into the lake.   This is also true of the mixing of the waters by the winds which may circulate them daily in ponds or semi-annually in the larger lakes of the temperate regions.   However, there are biological processes which create a supply and demand for oxygen and carbon dioxide, which much of the time are more in accord with the distribution of these gases than are the physical factors involved.

The surface of a lake is exposed to the atmosphere and tends to come into equilibrium with it.   But in the great volume below the surface, diffusion plays a relatively small rôle in maintaining the oxygen supply. Whipple (1928) says that Hüfner calculated that over a million years would be required for the Bodensee, which is 250 m. deep, to restore its O_2 if deprived of it; *i.e.*, by diffusion alone.   However, lakes are not dependent upon the atmospheric air for their oxygen supply.   The respiration of a body of water may produce a net excess of oxygen.   The subject of the oxygen conditions in lakes will be returned to in connection with the classification of lakes.

Pütter (1924) says that in summer the surface plankton in Kiel harbor liberates 2.34 ± 0.07 mg. O_2 per liter of H_2O per day.   This implies sugar formation at the ratio of 2.27 mg. per liter per day and O_2 liberation of about 400 mg. per square meter per hour of daylight.

In the respiration of the planktonic organisms, we have a reciprocal relationship in the production of oxygen and consumption of carbon dioxide, in photosynthesis on the part of the plants and in the respiration of the animals.   In the bottom of the lake the process of decay in the dead bodies of plants and animals often exhausts the oxygen supply and creates an excess of CO_2.   What effect these biological processes may have on the quantities and distribution of these gases in a lake may best be seen in the following diagrams (Figs. 85 and 86) of Knights Lake (Birge and Juday, 1911).

This is an extreme case in which the oxygen content is a saturation to a depth of two meters and then mounts to more than 350 per cent of saturation at $4\frac{1}{2}$ m. and again falls off to only a trace at 7 m. and entire absence, so far as determinations could ascertain, at a little over 8 m. The increase of oxygen is correlated with 100,000 algae and 20,000 diatoms to the liter of water in the third to the fifth meters.   In the zone in which we find the sudden drop of oxygen, we find 900 rotifers and more than 200 crustaceans, including the nauplii.   The curves for carbon dioxide and mono-carbonates indicate a great demand for carbon dioxide by the photosynthetic forms.

A comparison of the first 2 m. which are stirred by the winds with the strata below where biological processes are in control, furnishes a good comparison of the potential importance of the physical and biological phenomena.

It is seen that when the water is shallow, mixing by the winds may keep conditions fairly stable, in vertical distribution as in ponds, and that in lakes there may be great gradients in vertical distribution but stability over periods of time.

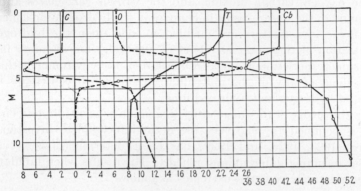

Fig. 85.—Knights Lake, August 25, 1909. *T*, temperature; *C*, carbon dioxide; *O*, oxygen; *cb*, carbonates. Note the correlation in depth of high alkalinity, excess oxygen, and increase of fixed carbon dioxide. (*Birge and Juday*, 1911.)

The situation with carbon dioxide is complicated by its existence in three states. It may be present in chemical union as normal or monocarbonates, $CaCo_3$ or $MgCo_3$. This is fixed carbon dioxide and its presence is dependent upon the presence of a base. One liter of pure H_2O dissolves only 0.0131 g. of $CaCo_3$ at 16°. It is also found as bicarbonates

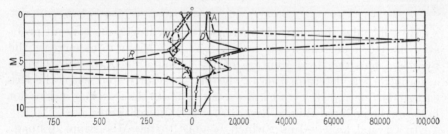

Fig. 86.—Vertical distribution of plankton organisms in Knights Lake, August 25, 1909. Scale, 1 horizontal space = 50 crustacea, nauplii, and rotifers per liter of water, and 4,000 algae and diatoms. The maximum quantity of dissolved oxygen is correlated in depth with the maximum number of diatoms, but the maximum number of other algae is 1 m. above this depth. (*Birge and Juday*, 1911.)

or half-bound carbon dioxide. Its presence is indicated as $Ca(HCO_3)_2$ ($CaCo_3 + H_2O + CO_2$). It is not as stable as the normal and the algae are able to make use of a large part of it in their photosynthetic activities.

Free carbon dioxide is also found. The degree of alkalinity of the water may be measured by the amount of CO_2 which would be required to convert the normal carbonates into bicarbonates and thus restore the water to the neutral condition. If there are 32.3 c.c. of normal and 27 c.c.

of bicarbonates in the surface water, the difference is 5.3 c.c., which is the amount of CO_2 which would have to be added to the water to make it neutral. This is the amount of free CO_2 used by the plants.

The Neutrality of the Medium.—Many of the complex relationships between oxygen, carbon dioxide, and the various carbonates and salts to be found in the water, result in changes in the hydrogen-ion concentration. Some investigators are inclined to look upon the hydrogen-ion concentration of the water as a sort of algebraic sum of many factors, which sum is more important as a measure of the environment than the measurement of any of the individual factors which contribute to the balance of hydrogen and hydroxyl ions.

Our knowledge of the range of hydrogen-ion concentration in environments is confined to relatively recent and incomplete investigations. Shelford (1923, 1925, and 1929) has made determinations in various localities including different watersheds. His results when tabulated lie between relatively constant extremes as follows:

Locality	Maximum pH	Minimum pH
Illinois lakes and streams............................	8.5	6.7
Puget Sound and Columbia River basins............	8.5	6.5
Salt Lake, and Colorado and Rio Grande drainage basins..	8.4	6.5
Mississippi and Great Lakes drainage basins.........	8.2	4.4
(If the single case of Vincent Lake is omitted the above values are).....................................	8.2	6.5

He concludes that altitude increases the hydrogen-ion content probably due to a decreased salt content and that heavy rains increase the hydrogen ions due to a dilution of the buffer. Shelford (1925) gives a graph for the determination of the pH value of water, when the free carbon dioxide and HCO_3 are known but states in the text that it does not hold for the polluted Illinois River or for certain well-water, etc.

In Crystal Lake, Minn., which belongs to the Mississippi drainage basin, C. B. Philip and the author obtained readings varying from pH9.4, in a shallow bay, over a bed of marl, to 7.1 at the bottom of the lake in 37 feet of water. In the shallow bay the values varied from pH 7.6 in the early morning to 9.4 in the late afternoon of a bright warm day. It seems from the evidence now at hand, that the hydrogen-ion concentration as expressed by the pH value may be a measure of general conditions in the environment including certain physical and biotic factors. It would therefore, be difficult to distinguish cause from effect in measuring an environment by this factor alone.

Cowles and Schwitalla (1923) made a study of a creek, 1,376 feet in length, including several small ponds. These authors found variations between pH 6.5 and 7.2. The graph in Fig. 87 shows the distribution of these values in space and time.

Cowles and Schwitalla remark about the diurnal variation of the pH values and consider it in harmony with the free carbon-dioxide content.

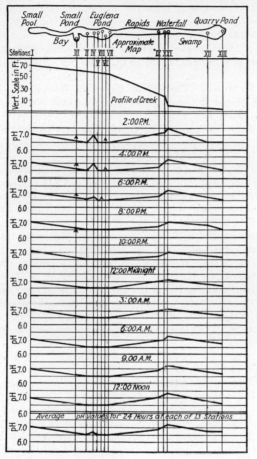

Fig. 87.—Gradients of pH during 24 hours at all stations in relation to the map and profile of a creek (pH at stations aside from the main stream indicated by inverted V when it does not correspond with the curve for the main stream line). (*Cowles and Schwaitalla,* 1923.)

They also conclude that a large population of Euglena is confined to sections of the water course where the water is stagnant and has a low but uniform pH.

Further discussions of physical factors will be included with the descriptions of the various aquatic environments.

BIBLIOGRAPHY

PHYSICAL CHARACTERISTICS OF AQUATIC COMMUNITIES

ATKINS, W. R. G.: The Hydrogen-ion Concentration of Sea Water in Its Biological Relation, *Jour. Mar. Biol. Assoc.*, **12**: 717–780, 1922.

ATKINS, W. R. G., and M. V. LEBOUR: The H.-ion Concentration of the Soil and of Natural Waters in Relation to the Distribution of Snails, *Proc. Roy. Dublin Soc. Sci.*, n.s., **17**: 233–240, 1923.

BIRGE, E. A.: I. An Unregarded Factor in Lake Temperatures. II. On the Evidence for Temperature Seiches, *Trans. Wis. Acad. Sci., Arts and Letters*, XVI: 989–1016, 1910.

———, and C. JUDAY: The Inland Lakes of Wisconsin. The Plankton. I. Its Quantity and Chemical Composition, *Wis. Geol. and Nat. Hist. Survey Bull.* 64, sci. ser. 13, 1922. 219 pp.

BIRGE, E. A., and C. JUDAY: The Inland Lakes of Wisconsin. The Dissolved Gases of the Water and Their Biological Significance, *Wis. Geol. and Nat. Hist. Survey Bull.* XXII, sci. ser. 7, 1911. 259 pp.

———: The Inland Lakes of Wisconsin. The Hydrography and Morphometry of the Lakes, *Wis. Geol. and Nat. Hist. Survey Bull.* XXVII, sci. ser. 9, 1914. 137 pp.

———: Further Limnological Observations on the Finger Lakes of New York, *U. S. Bur. Fisheries Bull.*, vol. XXXVII, Doc. 905, 1919–1920. pp. 211–252, Oct. 1921.

———: Transmission of Solar Radiation by the Waters of Inland Lakes, *Trans. Wis. Acad. Sci., Arts and Letters*, **24**: 509–580, 1929.

BODINE, JOSEPH HALL: Hydrogen-ion Concentration of Protozoan Cultures, *Biol. Bull.*, vol. XLI, **1**: 73–77, 1921.

BODINE, JOSEPH HALL, and DAVID E. FINK: A Simple Micro Vessel with Electrodes for Determining the Hydrogen-ion Concentration of Small Amounts of Fluid, *Jour. Gen. Physiol.*, vol. VII, **6**: 735–740, 1925.

BORRADAILE, L. A.: "The Animal and Its Environment," H. Froude and Hodder & Stoughton, London, 1923.

BRAUER, A.: "Die Süsswasserfauna Deutschlands," Hrsg. von Prof. Dr. A. Brauer, booklets 1–19 (Taschenformat), 1909–1912.

BROCHER, F.: Les phénomènes capillaires, leur importance dans la biologie aquatique, *Ann. biol. lacustre*, IV: 89–138, 1910.

BRÖNSTED, J. N., and WESENBERG-LUND: Chemisch-physikalische Untersuchungen der Dänischen Gewässer nebst Bemerkungen über ihre Bedeutung für unsere Aufassungae der Temporalvariation, *Internat. Rev. Hydrobiol.*, **4**: 251–290, 437–492, 1911.

CHAMBERS, C. O.: The Relation of Algæ to Dissolved O_2 and CO_2, with Reference to Carbonates, *Missouri Bot. Gard.*, **23**: 171–207, 1912.

CHIDESTER, F. E.: Studies on Fish Migration. II. The Influence of Salinity on the Dispersal of Fishes, *Amer. Naturalist*, **56**: 373–380, 1922; abst. *Ecology*, vol. IV, **1**: 85, 1923.

CHRYSTAL, GEORGE: The Hydrodynamical Theory of Seiches, *Trans. Roy. Soc.*, Edinburgh, vol. XLI, pt. III, p. 599, *Internat. Rev. Gesamm. Hydrobiol. u. Hydrog.*

COKER, R. E.: Observations of Hydrogen-ion Concentration and of Fishes in Waters Tributary to the Catawba River, North Carolina (with Supplemental Observations in Some Waters of Cape Cod, Massachusetts), *Ecology*, vol. VI, **1**: 52–66, 1925.

COWLES, R. P., and A. M. SCHWITALLA: The Hydrogen-ion Concentration of a Creek, Its Waterfall, Swamp and Ponds, *Ecology*, vol. IV, **4**: 402–417, 1923.

FOREL, F. A.: "Le Leman, monographie limnologique," p. 190, Lausanne, 1877.

GEBBING, J.: Über den Gehalt des Meeres an Stickstoff-nährsalzen. Untersuchungsergebnisse der von der deutschen Südpolarexpedition (1901-1903) gesammelten Meerwasserproben, *Internat. Rev. Gesamm. Hydrobiol. u. Hydrog.*, **3**: 50–66, 1910.

HALL, ADA R.: Effects of Oxygen and Carbon Dioxide on the Development of the White-fish, *Ecology*, vol. VI, **2**: 104–117, 1925.

HELLAND-HANSEN: The Ocean Waters, an Introduction to Physical Oceanography. I. General Part (Methods) with the Assistance of Adolph H. Schröder and Other Collaborators, *Internat. Rev. Gesamm. Hydrobiol. u. Hydrog., suppl.*, **1**: 1–84, 1912.

JEWELL, MINA E.: The Fauna of an Acid Stream, *Ecology*, III: 22–28, 1922.

JUDAY, CHANCEY: Limnological Apparatus, *Trans. Wis. Acad. Sci., Arts and Letters*, **18**: 566–592, 1916.

———: Limnological Methods, *Arch. Hydrobiol.*, **22**: 517–524.

———: A Third Report on Limnological Apparatus, *Trans. Wis. Acad. Sci., Arts and Letters*, **22**: 299–314, 1926.

JUDAY, CHANCEY, E. B. FRED, and FRANK C. WILSON: The Hydrogen-ion Concentration of Certain Wisconsin Lake Waters, *Trans. Amer. Micros. Soc.*, vol. XLIII, **4**: 177–188, 1924.

KEMMERER, GEORGE, J. F. BOVARD, and W. R. BOORMAN: Northwestern Lakes of the United States: Biological and Chemical Studies with Reference to Possibilities in Production of Fish, *U. S. Bur. Fisheries Bull.*, vol. XXXIX, doc. **944**: 51–140, 1923.

KERB, H.: Über den Nährwert der im Wasser gelösten Stoffe, *Internat. Rev. Gesamm. Hydrobiol. u. Hydrog.*, **3**: 496–505, 1910.

KLUGH, A. BROOKER: Ecological Photometry and a New Instrument for Measuring Light, *Ecology*, vol. VI, pp. 203–237, 1925.

———: Light Penetration into the Bay of Fundy and into Chamcook Lake, New Brunswick, *Ecology*, **8**: 90–93, 1927.

LEGENDRE, R.: "La Concentration en ions hydrogène de l'eau de mer le pH.," Paris, 1925. 291 pp. (General considerations and discussion and bibliography.)

LOHMANN, H.: Über die Quellen der Nahrung der Meerestiere und Pütter's Untersuchungen hierüber, *Internat. Rev. Gesamm. Hydrobiol. u. Hydrog.*, **2**: 10–30, 1909.

McCLENDON, J. F.: The Composition, Especially the Hydrogen-ion Concentration, of Sea Water in Relation to Marine Organisms, *Jour. Biol. Chem.*, vol. XXVIII, pp. 135–152, 1916.

———: The Standardization of a New Colorimetric Method for the Determination of the H.-ion Concentration, CO_2 Tension, and CO_2 and O_2 Content of Sea Water, of Animal Heat and of CO_2 of the air, with a Summary of Similar Data on Bicarbonate Solutions in General, *Jour. Biol. Chem.*, vol. XXX, pp. 265–288, 1917.

———: The Use of the Van Slyke CO_2 Apparatus for the Determination of Total CO_2 in Sea Water, *Jour. Biol. Chem.*, vol. XXX, pp. 259–263, 1917.

———: On the Changes in the Sea and Their Relation to Organisms, *Carnegie Inst. Wash. Pub.* **252**: 213–258, 1918.

MARSH, M. C.: The Effects of Some Industrial Wastes on Fishes, *U. S. Geol. Survey Water-Supply Paper* 912, The Potomac River Basin, pp. 337–348, 1907.

———: Notes on the Dissolved Content of Water in Its Effect on Fishes, *U. S. Fisheries Commission Bull.*, 1908; *Internat. Fisheries Congress Bull.*, 1910.

MAYER, A. G.: Hydrogen-ion Concentration and Electrical Conductance of the Surface Waters of the Atlantic and Pacific, *Carnegie Inst. Wash. Pub.* **312**: 61–86, 1912.

MINDER, LEO: Studien über den Sauerstoffgehalt des Zürichsees, *Arch. Hydrobiol. u. Planktonkunde, suppl.*, **III**: 107–155, 1923.

MURRAY, SIR JOHN, and JOHAN HJORT: "The Depths of the Ocean," Macmillan & Co., Ltd., London, 1912.

NEEDHAM, J. G., and J. T. LLOYD: "Life of Inland Waters," Comstock Publ. Co., Ithaca, N. Y., 1916.

PEREIRA, J. R.: Influence of Hydrogen-ion Concentration upon the Oxygen Consumption in Sea Water Fishes, *Biochem. Jour.*, **18**: 1294–1296, 1925.

PHILIP, C. B.: Diurnal Fluctuations in the Hydrogen-ion Activity of a Minnesota Lake, *Ecology*, vol. VIII, no. 1, 1927.

POWERS, E. B.: Influence of Temperature and Concentration on the Toxicity of Salts to Fishes, *Ecology*, vol. I, **2**: 95–112, 1920.

———: A Simple Colorimetric Method for Field Determinations of the Carbondioxide Tension and Free Carbon Dioxide, Bicarbonates and Carbonates in Solution in Natural Waters. I. A Theoretical Discussion, *Ecology*, vol. VIII, no. 3, 1927.

PÜTTER, A.: Der Umfang der Kohlensaeurereduktion durch die Planktonalgen, *Pflüger's Arch. Physiol.*, **205**: 293–312, 1924.

REED, GUILFORD, and A. BROOKER KLUGH: Correlation between Hydrogen-ion Concentration and Biota of Granite and Limestone Pools, *Ecology*, vol. V, **3**: 272–276, 1924.

SECCHI, (1866): See Needham and Lloyd, 1916.

SHELFORD, V. E.: The Hydrogen-ion Concentration of Certain Western American Inland Waters, *Ecology*, vol. VI, **3**: 279–287, 1925.

———: "Laboratory and Field Ecology," Williams & Wilkins Co., Baltimore, 1929.

SHELFORD, V. E., and W. C. ALLEE: The Reaction of Fishes to Gradients of Dissolved Atmospheric Gases, *Jour. Exptl. Zool.*, **XIV**: 207–266, 1913.

SHELFORD, V. E., and F. W. GAIL: A Study of Light Penetration into Sea Water Made with the Kunz Photo-electric Cell with Particular Reference to the Distribution of Plants, *Puget Sound Biol. Sta. Pubs.*, **3**: 141–176, 1921–1925.

SMITH, FRANK (1925): Variation in the Maximum Depth at Which Fish Can Live during Summer in a Moderately Deep Lake with a Thermocline, *U. S. Bur. Fisheries Bull.*, vol. XLI, doc. 970, pp. 1–7, 1925.

THIENEMANN, AUGUST: Der Zusammenhang zwischen dem Sauerstoffgehalt des Tiefenwassers und der Zusammensetzung der Tiefenfauna, *Internat. Rev. Gesamm. Hydrobiol. u. Hydrog.*, **6**: 243–249, 1913.

———: Untersuchungen über die Beziehung zwischen dem Sauerstoffgehalt, des Wassers und der Zusammensetzung der Fauna in Norddeutschen Seen, *Arch. Hydrobiol.*, **12**: 1–65, 1918.

———: "Die Binnengewässer Mitteleuropas," E. Schweizerbart'sche Verlagsbuchhandlung (Erwin Nägele), G.m.b.H., Stuttgart, 1925.

WESENBERG-LUND, C.: Über die praktische Bedeutung der jährlichen Variationen in der Viskosität des Wassers, *Internat. Rev. Gesamm. Hydrobiol. u. Hydrog.*, **2**: 231–233, 1909.

———: Über einige eigentümliche Temperaturverhältnisse in der Litoralregion der baltischen Seen und deren Bedeutung nebst einem Anhang über die geographische Verbreitung der zwei Geschlechter von *Stratoides aloides*, *Internat. Rev. Gesamm. Hydrobiol. u. Hydrog.*, **5**: 287–316, 1913.

WHIPPLE: "The Microscopy of Drinking Water," John Wiley & Sons, Inc., New York, 1927.

WHIPPLE, G. C., and H. N. PARKER: On the Amount of Oxygen and Carbonic Acid in Natural Waters and the Effect of These Gases on the Occurrence of Microscopic Organisms, *Trans. Amer. Micros. Soc.*, **23**: 103–144, 1901.

WINKLE, W. VAN: Quality of the Surface Waters of Washington, *U. S. Geol. Survey Water-Supply Paper* 339, Qual. of Oregon, 1914.

WINKLER, L. W.: Sauerstoffschätzung mit Adurol, *Ztschr. angew. Chem.*, vol. 26, pt. 1, pp. 134–135, 1913.

————: Über die Bestimmung des im Wasser gelösten Sauerstoffes, *Ztschr. analyt. Chem.*, **53**: 665–672, 1914.

————: Über die Bestimmung der freien Kohlensäure in Tink- und Natzwässern, *Ztschr. analyt. Chem.*, **53**: 746–755, 1914.

————: Über die Bestimmung des gelösten Sauerstoffs in verunreinigen Gewässern. *Ztschr. Untersuch. Nahr.-u. Genussmitteln*, **29**: 121–128, 1915.

WOLFF, MAX: Ein einfacher Versuch zur Pütterschen Theorie von der Ernährung der Wasserbewohner, *Internat. Rev. Gesamm. Hydrobiol.*, **2**: 715–736, 1909.

WOLFF, MAX: Die Pütterschen Untersuchungen über die Nahrung der marinen Tiere und über den Stoffhaushalt des Meeres, *Arch. Hydrobiol. u. Planktonkunde*, **4**: 193–202, 1909.

CHAPTER XIV

BIOTIC CHARACTERISTICS OF AQUATIC COMMUNITIES

The population of lakes and ponds may be classified on the basis of their position in the water: as *pelagic*, living in the water independent of the bottom; and *benthic*, living on the bottom. The pelagic forms may be subdivided into *plankton* and *nekton*, the former being the free-floating forms which have no directive swimming activity; and the latter, the larger forms which swim directively.

The ecological categories were first defined for the ocean and have since been applied to fresh-water communities. Steuer (1910) has given the following diagram of these categories (Fig. 88):

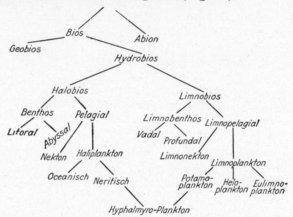

Fig. 88.—Steuer's ecological categories of aquatic organisms.

Hensen used the term "plankton" to designate the forms which floated freely. Haeckel (Johnstone, 1924) proposed the terms "benthos" (*benthos*—bottom) and "nekton" (*nektos*—swimming). These terms have come into general use and Johnstone (1924) has sought to define them in accordance with this general usage.

The following types of plankton are now recognized (Steuer, 1910): potomoplankton, of running water; heloplankton, of ponds; eulimnoplankton, of lakes; cryptoplankton, the plankton of the perpetual ice and snow; nannoplankton, the minute plankton which escape the ordinary methods of filtration and which are to be detected by centrifuging.

A comprehensive study of this independent, self-supporting ecological unit is as broad as biology itself, as may be seen from a study of Steuer (1910), Hentschel (1923), or Johnstone (1924).

For qualitative studies, identifications of fresh-water organisms may be made from Ward and Whipple (1918); for the phytoplankton, from Smith (1920).

For quantitative studies, the first method was that of Hensen with his quantitative net and pipet. The most common method has been by the use of the Sedgwick-Rafter counting apparatus (Whipple, 1927). The sample of water may be obtained by the use of a pump and a hose extending to the desired depth or by the use of a water bottle (Steuer, 1910; Birge, 1922; Birge and Juday, 1922).

The Sedgwick-Rafter filter concentrates a sample from 500 c.c. to 5 c.c. The standardized sand in the filter is then rinsed and the number of organisms counted in a cell which is 1 mm. thick and contains 1 c.c. An eyepiece micrometer is used to count the individuals and estimate their quantity in "standard units." The standard unit of Whipple is an area 20 microns on a side, or 400 square microns. Twenty squares, under the micrometer eyepiece, each representing 1 c.mm., are counted from various parts of the cell and the number of standard units in the entire cell estimated by the use of the following formula:

$$50t = \left(\frac{t}{20} \times 1{,}000 \right) \text{number in 1 c.c. of concentrated plankton.}$$

$$\frac{50t}{100} = \left(\frac{t}{2} \right) \text{number in 1 c.c. of unconcentrated plankton.}$$

t = number of organisms in 20 squares.

Steuer (1910), Whipple (1927), Johnstone (1924), and others describe various methods of estimating the quantity of plankton, but the centrifuge method seems the most satisfactory. Birge and Juday (1922) have used a continuous centrifuge which has made it possible to make determinations based on large quantities and to analyze for various organic compounds.

Birge and Juday (1922) have used a pump for obtaining the water while we have used a modified Kemmerer sampler made by Arthur Hertig of the University of Minnesota (unpublished).

Certain general conditions of the existence of the plankton will be considered at this time, while special conditions within the various environments will be postponed until discussion of the environments.

Since planktonic organisms are characterized by their ability to exist as free floating, the factors involved in floatation must be of importance. The distribution of sunlight in the upper layers of water determines that photosynthetic organisms must live near the surface. Other organisms are attracted to the zone in which the primary process of food manufacture is going on.

We shall now consider the physical factors which may be concerned with the sinking of planktonic organisms.

Ostwald (1903) and Steuer (1910) proposed a formula for calculating the rate of sinking of planktonic organisms under various conditions. One may get a measure of the value of the various factors involved by applying Stokes's law.

Stokes's law for the settling of particles may be expressed as follows:

$$V = \frac{2R^2(S - S_1)G}{9N}.$$

V = velocity of settling.
R = radius of the particle in centimeters.
S = specific gravity of the particle.
S_1 = specific gravity of the liquid.
G = gravity (988 dynes).

Dyne = force which, acting upon 1 g., will impart a velocity of 1 cm. per second or about that of 1 mg. weight acting under the influence of gravity.
N = viscosity of the liquid.

The velocity of settling will be zero for a free-floating plankton. The radius of the particle is introduced for the factor of size. The planktonic organisms, however, are usually radiate either as individuals or as colonies with a consequent increase in surface as compared with volume. Since the formula provides for taking twice the square of the radius, it may be seen that size or surface is very important. Wesenberg-Lund called attention to the fact that many planktonic organisms belonging to different phyla were found to have longer processes in warm water, where viscosity and density of the water are both reduced. In the following table the data for Bosmina have been taken from Wesenberg-Lund (1910) and the length of beak is given in per cent of the body length, and this value is compared with the viscosity of the water at the various temperatures given.

Temperature, °C.	Relative viscosity	Length of beak, per cent of body length
1	2.15	122
6	1.84	188
12	1.53	211
15	1.42	220
22	1.19	227

The length of the beak is not a true measure of the surface change, yet it does show that when viscosity was lowered 80 per cent the beak ratio increased 86 per cent.

The comparison of the specific gravity of the particle and the liquid next appears in the formula. The specific gravity of the water increases very rapidly at the thermocline because of the change in temperature (Eyden, 1924). However, the specific gravity of planktonic organisms likewise changes rapidly as they settle into the cooler water. Being composed largely of water, the change of specific gravity of its protoplasm must closely parallel that of the water. Needham and Lloyd (1916) point out that there are many droplets of fat and oil which seem to decrease the specific gravity of planktonic organisms.

Gravity is a constant force in the formula of settling and consequently needs no discussion, so long as the organisms swim with random movements only. In the case of many, however, this is hardly true as they often overcome the action of gravity by swimming upward.

Viscosity is an important factor appearing in the denominator as nine times its measurable value. Consequently, the retardation of settling of particles at the thermocline is very great. In shallow lakes and ponds where stratification is absent and the water is in circulation whenever the wind blows, the currents of water assume an important rôle in controlling the distribution of planktonic organisms.

While planktonts as a group are characterized by their lack of direction in swimming, there are, however, diurnal movements on the part of certain of the crustacea especially, which tend to migrate to the surface at night. Birge (1896), Juday (1903), and others have advanced various explanations for such phenomena.

In fresh-water environments it is not easy to draw a definite line between the plankton of the littoral and of the abyssal zones. In general, the littoral zone may be taken as the outer limit of rooted vegetation, or the margin of the thermocline in stratified lakes. Ponds may be distinguished from lakes on this basis, by the fact that they have no abyssal zone.

The plankton organisms may have eggs or encysted stages which are, for a time at least, benthonic. Likewise many of the insects may be said to have benthonic and nektonic, and even planktonic, phases. *Corethra* has been considered as a planktonic insect (Needham and Lloyd, 1916) and as a benthonic insect (Juday, 1922). Similarly the Coleoptera and Hemiptera as adults pass to the nektonic phase because of the necessity of obtaining air at the surface of the water, although they are predominantly benthonic.

The Distribution of Plankton in Time.—"Plankton pulses" are of the greatest importance as ecological phenomena. They represent fluctuations in populations which are undoubtedly far more complicated than the early students thought.

Whipple gives the seasonal distribution of organisms in Lake Cochituate in the following diagram (Fig. 89).

Transeau has classified the plankton algae under the following heads: spring annuals, summer annuals, autumn annuals, winter annuals, perennials, and ephemerals.

Thienemann (1925) compares the seasons of the year as Muttkowski does for Lake Mendota.   It has been the tendency to consider that the great changes in population are due to the physical changes which occur at the different seasons of the year.   However, there are certain great fluctuations which occur when physical conditions are relatively constant. At least some of these changes may be due to the biotic relationships of the members of the population with each other.

Needham and Lloyd (1916) call attention to plankton pulses as examples of fluctuating supply and demand in this relatively self-supporting assemblage of organisms.   At times certain of the diatoms increase in

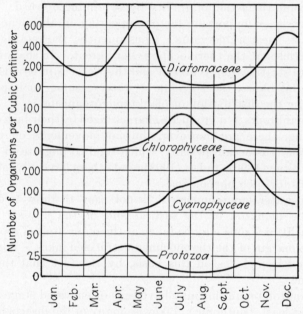

FIG. 89.—Seasonal distribution of microscopic organisms in Lake Cochituate.   (*Whipple*, 1910.)

numbers geometrically, doubling every 24 hours.   Huff (1923) found that the enormous fluctuations in numbers of zoo-plankton continued even after copper sulphate had been introduced and the algae killed.   Consequently, he concluded that the demand and supply of food were not the controlling factor.

Nekton.—Nektonic animals are those which swim with actively directed movements and are essentially independent of the bottom. These organisms are nearly all fishes, so far as lenitic environments are concerned.   However, they are not all nektonic throughout their lives, for the majority of them lay their eggs on the bottom and are thus benthonic in this stage.   Shelford (1911) believes that the character of the bottom for egg laying is the limiting factor in certain ponds.   We thus have nektonic adults limited in their distribution by their benthonic egg stages.

The "fry" of many fishes resemble the plankton in that their swimming is hardly more directive than that of some of the crustacea, such as *Daphnia*. Indeed, it may almost be said of some of these that they are benthonic, planktonic, and nektonic in the course of their life histories.

Nektonic organisms are characteristic of lakes rather than of ponds. Shelford states that in a series of ponds which were separated from Lake Michigan at various times there is an increase in the number of animals as the ponds get older, with the exception of the fish which decrease with the age of the ponds.

Pearse (1921) found the greatest number of fish per unit area in the shallowest lake which he studied, which was hardly more than four meters in depth. The best development of fish, however, was found in Lake Mendota with its deep water and varied bottom. Lake Michigan had the smallest number of fish per unit area, but it also contained the largest individuals. Quantitative methods are described by Pearse (1921).

Benthos.—Benthos has been defined by Johnstone (1924) in his definition of the categories of life habits in the sea as:

. . . all those organisms which live on the sea bottom either on the foreshore between tide-marks or below low-water mark down to the greatest depths known. . . . In general, by the Benthos we mean all those marine species that are bottom-living or "demersal" in habit, that are rooted, stalked or attached in other ways to the rocks, stones, or other solid objects on the sea floor; that are sedentary, or nearly so in habit; that burrow in the deposits, that crawl about sluggishly on the bottom or, at the best, have only a limited migration.

Steuer (1910) did not limit the term to marine organisms, but used the term "limnobenthos" to designate the forms that live on the bottom of fresh-water lakes. Steuer also made a division of the benthos, both marine and fresh-water, on the basis of depth, using the terms "littoral" (*litoralis* = shore) and "abyssal" (*abyssus* = deep) for the marine environments, and the German terms "vadal" and "profund" for the fresh water. The terms littoral and abyssal will be used here for both marine and fresh water, although it is realized that the littoral zone of the ocean may extend to depths greater than the abyssal zone in certain lakes. Further consideration will be given to the communities under the description of the different types of aquatic environments.

Quantitative methods for the study of benthonic organisms have made important contributions to our knowledge of the quantity of life in lenitic environments (Juday, 1922; Adamstone, 1924). The Ekman dredge (Ekman, 1910; Birge, 1922) makes it possible to obtain a sample of a given area of the bottom. This may then be washed and the organisms weighed. Juday (1922) has thus obtained dry weights and had the material analyzed.

BIBLIOGRAPHY

BIOTIC CHARACTERISTICS

ABDERHALDEN, E.: "Handbuch der biologischen Arbeitsmethoden," pt. 9, p. 115, Urgan and Schwarzenberg, Berlin, 1923.

ADAMSTONE, F. B.: Distribution and Economic Importance of the Bottom Fauna of Lake Nipigon, *Univ. Ontario Studies*, publ. by Ontario Fisheries Research Lab., **24**: 35–100, 1924.

ALLEN, W. E.: A Brief Study of the Range of Error in Micro-enumeration, *Trans. Amer. Micros. Soc.*, **40**: 14–25, 1921.

————: Some Work on Marine Phytoplankton in 1919, *Trans. Amer. Micros. Soc.*, vol. XL, **4**: 177–182, 1921.

————: Observations on Surface Distribution on Marine Diatoms between San Diego and Seattle, *Ecology*, III: 140–146, 1922.

————: Recent Work on Marine Microplankton at the La Jolla Biological Station, *Trans. Amer. Micros. Soc.*, **42**: 180–183, 1923.

AMBERG, OTTO: Untersuchungen einiger Planktonproben vom Sommer 1902, *Forschungsberichte aus der biologischen Station zu Plön.*, **10**: 86–89, 1903.

AMMAN, HANS: Temporalvariationen einiger Plankton ten in Oberbayrischen Seen, 1910–1912, *Arch. Hydrobiol. u. Planktonkunde*, **9**: 127–147, 1914.

————: Zum Formenkreis von *Ceratium hirundinella* O. F. Mund *Aneuraea cochlearis*, *Arch. Hydrobiol. u. Planktonkunde*, **13**: 92–96, 1921–1922.

BACHMANN, H.: Das Phytoplankton des Süsswassers mit besonderer Berücksichtigung des Vierwaldstättersees, G. Fischer, Jena, 1911. 213 pp., 15 plates.

BIGELOW, HENRY B.: A New Closing Net for Horizontal Use, with a Suggested Method of Testing the Catenary in Fast Towing, *Internat. Rev. Gesamm. Hydrobiol. u. Hydrog.*, **5**: 576–580, 1913.

BIRGE, E. A.: Plankton Studies of Lake Mendota, *Trans. Wis. Acad. Sci.*, *Arts and Letters*, **10**: 421–484; **11**: 274–448, 1895–1896.

————: A Second Report on Limnological Apparatus, *Trans. Wis. Acad. Sci.*, *Arts and Letters*, XX; Biol. Lab. Notes XIX, pp. 533–553, 1922.

BIRGE, E. A., and CHANCEY JUDAY: The Inland Lakes of Wisconsin. The Plankton. I. Its Quantity and Chemical Composition, *Wis. Geol. and Nat. Hist. Survey Bull.* 64, sci. ser. 13, 1922. 219 pp.

BLACKMAN, F.: "Die mikroskopische Tierwelt des Süsswassers," pt. I, Protozoa, Hamburg, 1895.

BREHM, V.: Einige Beobachtungen über das Zentrifugenplankton, *Internat. Rev. Gesamm. Hydrobiol. u. Hydrog.*, **3**: 173–177, 1910.

————: Beobachtungen über die Entstehung des Potomo-Planktons, *Internat. Rev. Gesamm. Hydrobiol. u. Hydrog.*, **4**: 311–314, 1911.

CALKINS, G. N.: Marine Protozoa of Woods Hole, *U. S. Fish Comm. Bull.* 21, 1901.

CHIDESTER, F. E.: A Simple Apparatus for Studying the Factors Influencing Fish Migration, *Soc. Exptl. Biol. and Med. Proc.*, vol. XVIII, pp. 175–177, 1921.

CLEMENT, HUGUES: Quelques phénomènes dus à la centrifugation, *Lyon ann. soc. Linn.*, **60**: 147–152, 1913.

CLEMENTS, F. E.: "Research Methods in Ecology," Neb. State Univ. Publ. Co., Lincoln, 1905.

CONN, H. W.: The Protozoa of the Fresh Waters of Connecticut, *Conn. State Geol. and Nat. Hist. Survey Bull.* 12, 1905. 69 pp., 34 pls.

————: A Preliminary Report on the Protozoa of the Fresh Waters of Connecticut, *Conn. State Geol. and Nat. Hist. Survey Bull.* 2.

DOOLITTLE, A. A.: Notes on the Plankton Environment of Connecticut Lakes, *U. S. Bur. Fisheries Bull.*, Doc. 633, July 6, 1908.

EDDY, SAMUEL: The Distribution of Marine Protozoa in the Friday Harbor Waters (San Juan Channel, Wash. Sound), *Trans. Amer. Micros. Soc.*, **44**: 97–108, 1925.

EDMONOSON, CHARLES HOWARD: Protozoa of the Devil's Lake Complex, North Dakota, *Trans. Amer. Micros. Soc.*, **39**: 167–198, 1920.

EKMAN, SVEN: Neue Apparate zur quantitativen und qualitativen Erforschung der Bodenfauna der Seen, *Internat. Rev. Gesamm. Hydrobiol. u. Hydrog.* **3**: 553–561, 1910.

ESTERLY, C. O. : Reactions Underlying the Diurnal Migrations of Various Plankton Animals, *Calif. Univ. Pubs.*, Zool., April 4, 1919.

EYDEN, D.: Specific Gravity as a Factor in the Vertical Distribution of Plankton, *Proc. Cambridge Phil. Soc.*, vol. I, pp. 49–55, 1924.

FISH, CHARLES J.: Seasonal Distribution of the Plankton of the Woods Hole Region, *Bull., Bur. Fisheries*, Doc. 975, pp. 91–179, 1925.

FORBES, S. A.: On Some Entomostraca of Lake Michigan and Adjacent Waters, *Amer. Naturalist*, **16**: 640, 1882.

FREIDENFELT, T.: Neue Versuche zur Methodik der quantitativen Untersuchung der Bodenfauna der Binnenseen, *Arch. Hydrobiol. u. Planktonkunde*, **14**: 572–584, 1923.

GRAN, H. H.: Preservation of Samples and Quantitative Determination of Plankton, *Cons. perm. int. pour l'expl. de la mer*, Publ. 62, 1912. 15 pp.

HAECKEL, ERNST: "Planktonic studies," 1889–1891, transl. by G. W. Field, *Rept. U. S. Comm. of Fish and Fisheries*, pp. 565–641, 1893.

HARRING, H. K., and F. J. MYERS: The Rotifers of Wisconsin, *Trans. Wis. Acad. Sci., Arts and Letters*, vol. XX, pp. 553–656, pl. XLI–LXI, 1922.

———: The Rotifer Fauna of Wisconsin II, *Trans. Wis. Acad. Sci., Arts and Letters*, vol. XXI, pp. 415–549, pl. XVI–XLIII, 1924.

HAUER, J.: Neue Rotatorien des Süsswassers, *Arch. Hydrobiol. u. Planktonkunde*, **13**: 693–695, 1921–1922.

HAUSMANN, LEON AUGUSTUS: Fresh Water and Marine Gymnostominian Infusoria, *Trans. Amer. Micros. Soc.*, **40**: 118–143, 1921.

HELLAND-HANSEN: The Ocean Waters—an Introduction to Physical Oceanography, I. General Part. (Methods with the Assistance of Adolph U. Schröder and Other Collaborators), *Internat. Rev. Gesamm. Hydrobiol. u. Hydrog.*, Hydrogr. Suppl. I, pp. 1–84, 1912.

HENSEN, VICTOR: Organic Matter in the Baltic, *U. S. Bur. Fisheries Bull.* 5, pp. 267–269, 1885.

———: Ueber die Bestimmung des Planktons oder des im Meere treibenden Materials an Pflanzen und Thieren; nebst Anhang, 5. *Ber. der Komm. zur wissensch. Untersuch. d. Deutschen Meere in Kiel, für die Jahre*, 1882–1886, pp. 1–107, pl. III–XVIII, Berlin, 1887.

HENTSCHEL, ERNST: "Grundzüge der Hydrobiologie," G. Fischer Jena, 1923. 221 pp.

HERDMAN, W. A. (1910): Note on the Factors Affecting Variations in the Quantity of Marine Plankton, *Internat. Rev. Gesamm. Hydrobiol. u. Hydrog.*, **2**: 124–125, 1909.

———: Note on the Distribution of the Plankton on the West Coast of Britain in 1911, *Internat. Rev. Gesamm. Hydrobiol. u. Hydrog.*, **4**: 433–436, 1912.

HUFF, L. N.: Observations on the Relation of Algae to Certain Aquatic Animals of Vadnais Lake, *Minn. Univ. Studies, Biol. Sci.*, **4**: 185–198, 1923.

JASCHNOV, W. A.: Das Plankton des Baikalsees nach dem Material der Expedition des Zoologischen Museums der Moskauer Universität im Jahre 1917, *Russ. Hydrobiol. Jour.*, **1**: 225–241, 1922.

JENNINGS, H. S.: The Rotatoria of the United States, *Bull. U. S. Fish. Comm.* XX, pp. 67–104, 1899.

JOHANNSEN, O. A., and J. T. LLOYD: "Genera of Plankton Organisms of the Cayuga Lake Basin," Ithaca, N. Y., 1915.

JOHNSTONE, JAMES, ANDREW SCOTT, and HERBERT C. CHADWICK: "The Marine Plankton," London, 1924.   194 pp.

JUDAY, CHANCEY: The Plankton of Turkey Lake, *Ind. Acad. Sci. Proc.*, pp. 287–296, 1 map, 1896.

――――: The Diurnal Movement of Plankton Crustacea, *Trans. Wis. Acad. Sci., Arts and Letters*, vol. XIV, pp. ·534–568, 1903.

――――: The Cladocera of the Canadian Arctic Expedition, *Rept. Canad. Arctic Exped.*, 1913–1918; vol. VII, pt. H, 1920.

――――: Limnological Apparatus, *Trans. Wis. Acad. Sci., Arts and Letters*, **18**: 566–592, 1916.

――――: Quantitative Studies of the Bottom Fauna in the Deeper Waters of Lake Mendota, *Trans. Wis. Acad. Sci., Arts and Letters*, vol. XX, pp. 461–493, 1921.

KAMMERER, PAUL: Über Schlammkulturen, *A⅃ch. Hydrobiol. u. Planktonkunde*, **2**: 500–526, 1907.

KEISSLER, VON K.: Untersuchungen über die Periodizität des Phytoplankton des Leopoldsteiner Sees, in Steirmark, in Verbindung mit einer eingehenderen limnologischen Erforschung dieses Seebeckens, *Arch. Hydrobiol. u. Planktonkunde*, **6**: 480–485, 1911.

KENT, W. S.: "A Manual of the Infusoria," London, 1880–1882.   913 pp., 51 pl.

KING, L. A. L., and S. RUSSELL: A Method for the Study of the Animal Ecology of the Shore, *Proc. Roy. Phys. Soc.*, Edinburgh, vol. XVII, no. 6, pp. 225–253, 1909.

KNAUTHE, K.: "Das Süsswasser, chemische, biologische und bakteriologische Untersuchungsmethoden unter besonderer Berücksichtigung der Biologie und der fischereiwirtschaftlichen Praxis," Neudamm, 1907.   663 pp.

KNÖRRICH, W.: Studien über die Ernährungsbedingungen einiger für die Fischproduktion wichtiger Mikro-organismen des Süsswassers, *Forschungsberichte aus der biologischen Station zu Plön*, **10**: 152, 1901.

KNUDSEN: Plankton of Northern Europe, *Bulletin des résultats acqui pendant les cours périodique publié par le bureau du conseil avec l'assistance de M. Knudsen*, Copenhagen, 1903–1904.   No. 1, 66 pp.   ·

KOFOID, C. A.: Plankton Studies II, *Ill. State Lab. Nat. Hist. Bull.*, **5**: 273, 1897–1901.

――――: Plankton Studies III.   On Platy-dorina, a New Genus of the Family Volvocidae, from the Plankton of the Illinois River, *Ill. State Lab. Nat. Hist. Bull.* **5**: 419–440, pl. XXXVIII, 1899.

――――: The Plankton of Echo River, Mammoth Cave, *Trans. Amer. Micros. Soc.*, **XXI**: 113–126, 1899.

――――: A Preliminary Account of Some of the Results of the Plankton Work of the Illinois Biological Station, *Science*, **XI**: 255–258, 1900.

――――: The Plankton of Lake Winnebago and Green Lake, *Wis. Geol. and Nat. Hist. Survey Bull.* 12, sci. ser. 3, 1903.

――――: The Plankton of the Illinois River, *Ill. State Lab. Nat. Hist. Bull.*, **8**: 360 pp., 1908.

――――: A New Horizontal Self-closing Plankton Net, *Internat. Rev. Gesamm. Hydrobiol. u. Hydrog.*, **5**: 91–92, 1912.

KOLKWITZ, R. (1912): Plankton und Seston Berichte d. deutschen bot. Gesellsch., **30**: 334–346, 1912; rev. in *Jour. Ecology*, **I**: 177–178, 1913.

KROGH, AUGUST: Ethyl Urethane as a Narcotic for Aquatic Animals, *Internat. Rev. Gesamm. Hydrobiol. u. Hydrog.*, **7**: 42–47, 1914.

LIST, THEODOR: Über die Temporal- und Lokalvariationen von *Ceratium hirundinella* O.F.M. aus dem Plankton einiger Teiche in der Umgegend von Darmstadt und einiger Kolke des Altrheins bei Erfelden, *Arch. Hydrobiol. u. Planktonkunde,* **9**: 81–126, 1914.

LOHMANN, H.: Über das Nannoplankton und die Zentrifugierung kleinster Wasserproben zur Gewinnung desselben im lebenden Zustande, *Internat. Rev. Gesamm. Hydrobiol. u. Hydrog.*, **4**: 1–38, 5 colored pl., 1911.

LUDWIG, F.: Der Moschpilzen, ein regularer Bestandteil des Limnoplanktons, *Forschungsberichte aus der biologischen Station zu Plön*, **7**: 59–63, 1899.

McCLENDON, J. F.: The Standardization of a New Colorimetric Method for the Determination of the Hydrogen-ion Concentration, CO_2 Tension, and CO_2 Content of Sea Water of Animal Heat and of CO_2 of the Air, with a Summary of Similar Data on Bicarbonate Solutions in general, *Jour. Biol. Chem.*, XXX: 265–288, 1917.

———: The Use of the Van Slyke CO_2 Apparatus for the Determination of Total CO in Sea Water, *Jour. Biol. Chem.*, **XXXI**: 259–263, 1917.

MACKAY, HECTOR H.: A Quantitative Study of Lake Nipigon, *Univ. Toronto Studies*, **26**: 169–222, 1924.

MANN, ALBERT: The Dependence of the Fishes on the Diatoms, *Ecology*, vol. II, **2**: 79–83, 1921.

MARSHALL, WM. S., and N. C. GILBERT: Notes on the Food and Parasites of some Fresh-water Fishes, from the Lakes at Madison, Wis., *U. S. Bur. Fisheries Bull.*, pp. 513–517, 1908.

MATTHEWS, D. J.: A Deep-sea Bacteriological Waterbottle, *Jour. Mar. Biol. Assoc.*, **9**: 525–529, 1913.

MEUNIER, A.: "Microplankton des Mers de Barents et de Kara, Duc d'Orleans Campagne Arctique de 1907," Brussels, 1907.

MOBERG, ERIK G.: Variation in the Horizontal Distribution in Devil's Lake, N. D., *Trans. Amer. Micros. Soc.*, **37**: 239–268, 1918.

MONTI, RINA: Un nouveau petit fillet pour les pêches planktoniques de surface à toute vitesse, *Internat. Rev. Gesamm. Hydrobiol. u. Hydrog.*, **3**: 548–553, 1910.

MÜLLER, FRIEDRICH C. G.: Apparat zum Schöpfen von Wasserproben aus der biologischen Station zu Plön., **15**: 189–190, 1903.

NAUMANN, EINAR: Über die photographische Darstellung der Planktonformationen, *Internat. Rev. Gesamm. Hydrobiol. u. Hydrog.*, **7**: 56–60, 1914.

———: Quantitative Untersuchungen über die Organismenformationen der Wasserfläche, *Internat. Rev. Gesamm. Hydrobiol. u. Hydrog.*, **7**: 214–221, 1914.

———: Über die photographische Darstellung der Planktonformationen. II. Die Aufnahme in direkt-positivem Bild, *Internat. Rev. Gesamm. Hydrobiol. u. Hydrog.*, **7**: 443–447, 1916.

———: Die Sestonfärbungen des Süsswassers, *Arch. Hydrobiol. u. Planktonkunde*, **13**: 647–692, 1921–1922.

———: Einige Gesichtspunkte betreffs der Fettproduction des Süsswasser-Zooplankton, *Arch. Hydrobiol. u. Planktonkunde*, **13**: 307–312, 1921–1922.

NEEDHAM, J. G., and J. T. LLOYD: "Life in Inland Waters," Comstock Publishing Company, Ithaca, 1916.

OSTENFELD, C. H.: Immigration of a Plankton Diatom into a Quite New Area within Recent Years, *Internat. Rev. Gesamm. Hydrobiol. u. Hydrog.*, **2**: 262–374, 1909.

OSTWALD, WOLFGANG: Über eine neue theoretische Betrachtungsweise in der Planktologic, insbesondere über die Bedeutung des Begriffs der inneren Reibung des Wassers für dieselbe, *Forschungsberichte aus der biologischen Station zu Plön*, **10**: 1–49, 1903.

———: Theoretische Planktonstudien, *Zool. Jahrb.*, **18**: 1–62, September, 1903.

———: Zur Theorie der Schwebevorgänge sowie der specifischen Gewichtsbestimmungen schwebender Organismen, *Arch. Ges. Physiol.*, **94**: 251–272, 1903.

PASCHER, A.: Versuche zur Methode des Zentrifugierens bei der Gewinnung des Planktons, *Internat. Rev. Gesamm. Hydrobiol. u. Hydrog.*, **5**: 93–120, 1912.

PAVILLARD, J.: L'évolution périodique du plankton végétal dans la Méditerranée Occidentale, *Assoc. for Adv. of Sci.*, **41**: 315–317, 1913; rev. *Jour. Ecology*, VI: 125, 1914.

PEARSE, A. S.: Distribution and Food of the Fishes of Green Lake, Wis., in Summer, *U. S. Bur. Fisheries Bull.*, XXXVII, 1921.

PURDY, W. C.: Investigation of Pollution and Sanitary Conditions of the Potomac Watershed. Plankton Studies, *U. S. Pub. Health Serv.*, *Hyg. Lab. Bull.* 104, pp. 130–204, 1916.

PÜTTER, A.: Der Umfang der Kohlensaeurereduktion durch die Planktonalgen, *Pflüger's Arch. Physiol.*, **205**: 293–312, 1924.

REIGHARD, JACOB: Some Plankton Studies in the Great Lakes, World's Fisheries Congress, Chicago, *U. S. Fish. Comm. Bull.*, pp. 127–142, pl. 9 and 10, 1893.

————: A Biological Examination of Lake St. Clair, *Mich. Fish. Comm. Bull.* 4, 1894. 60 pp.

————: Methods of Plankton Investigation in Their Relation to Practical Problems, *U. S. Bur. Fisheries Bull.*, **17**: pp. 169–195, 1897; Doc. 365, Aug. 8, 1898.

————: Methods of Collecting and Photographing, in Ward and Whipple's "Fresh Water Biology," pp. 61–90, 1918.

REICHELT, H.: Zur Diatomeenflora Pommerscher Seen, *Forschungsberichte aus der biologischen Station zu Plön*, **9**: 98–107, 1902.

————: Mikrophotographische Diatomeenaufnahmen (mit Tafel), *Arch. Hydrobiol. u. Planktonkunde*, **4**: 379–382, 1909.

ROSENTHAL, M.: Das Kammerplankton der Spree unterhalb Berlin Biol., *Internat. Rev. Gesamm. Hydrobiol. u. Hydrog.*, Biol. Suppl. **6**: 1–22, 1914.

RÜTTNER, FRANZ: Über die Anwendung von Filtration und Zentrifugierung bei den planktologischen Arbeiten an den Lunzer Seen, *Internat. Rev. Gesamm. Hydrobiol. u. Hydrog.*, **2**: 174–181, 1909.

————: Übertägliche Tiefenwanderungen von Planktontieren unter dem Eise und ihre Abhängigkeit vom Lichte, *Internat. Rev. Gesamm. Hydrobiol. u. Hydrog.*, **2**: 397–423, 1909.

————: Bericht über die Planktonuntersuchungen an den Lunzer Seen, *Internat. Rev. Gesamm. Hydrobiol. u. Hydrog.*, **6**: 318–527, 1914.

————: Bemerkung zur Frage der Vertikalen Plankton Wanderung, *Internat. Rev. Gesamm. Hydrobiol. u. Hydrog.*, **6**: 1–12, 1914.

————: Uferflucht des Planktons und ihr Einfluss auf die Ernährung von Salmonoiden Brut, *Internat. Rev. Gesamm. Hydrobiol. u. Hydrog.*, Biol. Suppl., **VI**: 1–8, 1914.

SAINT-HILAIRE, C.: Eine Dredge mit auswechselbaren Messern, *Internat. Rev. Gesamm. Hydrobiol. u. Hydrog.* **2**: 449–451, 1909.

SCHAEDEL, ALBERT: Production und Konsumenten im Teich Plankton, ihre Wechselierung und Beziehung zu den physikalischen und chemischen Milieu Einflüssen, *Arch. Hydrobiol. u. Planktonkunde*, **11**: 512–564, 1917.

SCHILLER, J.: Vorläufige Ergennisse der Phytoplankton-Untersuchungen auf den Fahrten S. M. S. *Najade* in der Adria, 1911–1912. i. Die Coccolithophoriden, *Sitzb. Kais. Akad. Wissensch.*, Wien, **122**: 597–617, 3 pl., 1913; rev. *Jour. Ecology*, 1914; vol. VI, p. 124; ii. Flagellaten and Chlorophyceen, *ibid.*, pp. 621–630; rev., *ibid.*, pp. 124–125.

SCHRÖDER, BRUNO: Das pflanzliche Plankton der Oder, *Forschungsberichte aus der biologischen Station zu Plön*, **7**: 15–24, 1899.

SCHURIG, W.: Hydrobiologisches und Plankton Practikum, eine erste Einführung in das Studium der Süsswasserorganismen, Quelle und Meyer, Leipzig, 1910. 160 pp., 6 pl., 215 text figs.

SCOTT, WILL: An Ecological Study of the Plankton of Shawnee Cave, *Biol. Bull.*, **XVII**: 386–406, 1909.

SHELFORD, V. E.: Ecological Succession. I. Stream Fishes and the Method of Physiographic Analysis, *Biol. Bull.*, **XXI**: 9–35, 1911.

SMITH, G. M.: Phytoplankton of the Inland Lakes of Wisconsin, *Wis. Geol. and Nat. Hist. Survey Bull.* 57, sci. ser. 12, 1920. 243 pp.

SNOW, JULIA W.: The Plankton Algae of Lake Erie, *U. S. Fish. Comm. Bull.* XXII, Doc. 371, 1902.

STEUER, A.: "Planktonkunde," Leipzig, 1910. 723 pp.

STEURER, ADOLPH: Horizontale und vertikale Verteilung der Copepoden nach den Ergebnissen der deutschen Tiefsee Expedition, *Internat. Rev. Gesamm. Hydrobiol. u. Hydrog.*, **7**: 205–213, 1914.

STOKES, ALFRED G.: "Aquatic Microscopy for Beginners," John Wiley & Sons, Inc., New York, 1918. 4th ed., 324 pp.

SUTHERLAND, G. G.: Some Methods of Plankton Investigation, *Jour. Ecology*, vol. I, **3**: 166–176, 1913.

TAYLOR, FRED B.: The Literature of Diatoms, *Trans. Amer. Micros. Soc.*, **40**: 187–194, 1919.

THIENEMANN, AUGUST: "Die Binnengewässer Mitteleuropas," Stuttgart, 1925. vol. I, 255 pp.

TSCHUGUNOFF, N. L.: Ueber das Plankton des nördlichen Teiles des Kaspischensees, *Arbeiten der biologischen Wolga Station*, vol. 6, **3**: 109–162, 1921.

VOIGT, MAX: Beiträge zur Methodik der Planktonfischerei, *Forschungsberichte aus der biologischen Station zu Plön*, **9**: 87–97, 1902.

WALTER, E.: Eine praktisch-verwerthbare Methode zur quantitativen Bestimmung des Teichplankton, *Forschungsberichte aus der biologischen Station zu Plön*, **3**: 145–179, 1895.

WARD, HENRY B.: A New Method for the Quantitative Determination of Plankton Hauls, *Trans. Amer. Micros. Soc.*, **17**: 255–259, 1895.

———: A Comparative Study in Methods of Plankton Measurement, *Studies from Zool. Lab.*, no. 37, Univ. of Neb., *Trans. Amer. Micros. Soc.*, pp. 227–247, pl. XV, XVI and XVII, 1899.

WARD, HENRY B., and G. C. WHIPPLE: "Fresh-water Biology," John Wiley & Sons, Inc., New York, 1918.

WESENBERG-LUND, C.: Plankton Investigations of the Danish Lakes, *Danish Fresh Water Biol. Lab.*, op. 5, pt. I, 389 pp.; pt. II, Copenhagen, 1908.

———: Grundzüge der Biologie und Geographie des Süsswasserplanktons nebst Bemerkungen über Hauptprobleme zukünftiger limnologischer Forschungen, *Internat. Rev. Gesamm. Hydrobiol. u. Hydrog.*, Biol. Suppl., **1**: 1–44, 1910.

WEST, W., and G. S. WEST: On the Periodicity of the Phytoplankton of some British Lakes, *Jour. Linn. Soc.* **40**: 395–432, 1912.

WHIPPLE, G. C.: "The Microscopy of Drinking Water," New York and London, 1914. 3d ed., 409 pp., 19 pl.

———: "The Microscopy of Drinking Water," John Wiley and Sons, Inc., New York, 1927. 586 pp.

WHIPPLE, G. C., and H. N. PARKER: On the Amount of Oxygen and Carbonic Acid in Natural Waters and the Effect of These Gases on the Action of Microscopic Organisms, *Trans. Amer. Micros. Soc.* **23**: 103–144, 1902.

WOLLE, FRANCIS: "Desmids of the United States," 1892. 182 pp. 64 pl.

———: "Diatomaceae of North America," 1894. 45 pp., 112 pl.

WRIGHT, A. H. (1895): A Graphic Method of Correlating Fish Environment and Distribution, *Amer. Naturalist*, **XLI**: 351–354, 1907.

YUNG, ÉMILE: Des variations quantitative du plankton dans le Lac Leman, *Arch. sci. phys. et nat.*, 1899; Quatrième Période, tome VIII, pp. 1–21, map, October, 1899.

ZACHARIAS, O.: "Das Süsswasserplankton," Leipzig, 1907.

————: Fortsetzung der Beobachtungen über die Periodizität der Plankton Wesen, *Forschungsberichte aus der Biologischen Station zu Plön*, **3**: 129–144, 1895.

————: Über die Wechselnde Quantität des Plankton im Grossen Plöner See, *Forschungsberichte aus der Biologischen Station zu Plön*, **3**: 97–117, 1895.

————: Quantitative Untersuchungen über das Limnoplankton, *Forschungsberichte aus der Biologischen Station zu Plön*, **4**: 1–64, 1896.

————: Vorwort, *Forschungsberichte aus der Biologischen Station zu Plön*, **6**: i–x, 1898.

————: Untersuchungen über das Plankton der Teichgewässer, *Forschungsberichte aus der Biologischen Station zu Plön*, **6**: 89–140, 1898.

————: Das Plankton des Arendsees, *Forschungsberichte aus der Biologischen Station zu Plön*, **7**: 50–58, 1899.

————: Über die Verschiedenheit der Zusammensetzung des Winter Planktons in grossen und kleinen Seen, *Forschungsberichte aus der Biologischen Station zu Plön*, **7**: 64–74, 1899.

————: Zur Kenntniss des Planktons sächsischer Fischteiche, *Forschungsberichte aus der Biologischen Station zu Plön*, **7**: 78–95, 1899.

————: Zur Kenntniss der Planktontoxverhältnisse des Schön- und Schliensees, *Forschungsberichte aus der Biologischen Station zu Plön*, **9**: 26–32, 1902.

————: Über Periodizität, Varieten und Verbreitung verschiedener Plankton-wesen in südlichen Meeren, *Arch. Hydrobiol. u. Planktonkunde*, **1**: 498–575, 1906.

————: Der Planktonseiher Ethmophor. *Arch. Hydrobiol. u. Planktonkunde*, **2**: 320–334, 1907.

————: Plankton Algen als Molluskennahrung, *Arch. Hydrobiol. u. Planktonkunde*, **2**: 358–361, 1907.

————: Zur Kenntniss des Planktons einiger Pommerschen Seen, *Forschungs-berichte aus der Biologischen Station zu Plön.*, **7**: 125–130, 1907.

————: "Das Plankton," 1909. 213 pp.

————: Ferienkurse in Hydrobiologie u. Planktonkunde an der Biologischen Station zu Plön, *Arch. Hydrobiol. u. Planktonkunde*, **4**: 267–272, 1909.

————: Der neue Zeichens-projektionsapparat von R. Winkel, *Arch. Hydrobiol. u. Planktonkunde*, **4**: 399–404, 1909.

————: Zur Frage der Einführung des Planktons als selbständigen Unterichts-gegenstandes an Höheren Schulen, *Arch. Hydrobiol. u. Planktonkunde*, **5**: 47–61, 1910.

ZÜSCHER, MATTHIAS: Das Plankton des Schlossgartens und des Schlossteiches zu Münster i. W. unter besonderer Berücksichtigung der Temporalvariation von *Anurea cochlearis, Ceratium hirudinella*, Inaug. Dissertation, Münster; Kl. 8°, 50 pp., 2 Tabellen; Book Review by Lemmerman in *Arch. Hydrobiol. u. Planktonkunde*, **9**: 176–177, 1914.

CHAPTER XV

LENITIC ENVIRONMENTS

Viewed in the perspective of geologic time, lakes and ponds are but transient environments. The physical agents through erosion tend to fill their basins, and the remains of the plants and animals accumulate and hasten their disappearance. The origin may determine much of the physical character (Needham and Lloyd, 1916).

CHARACTERISTICS OF LENITIC COMMUNITIES—PONDS

Ponds are distinguished from lakes mainly by size. Vegetational growth is another distinguishing characteristic which is used by Needham and Lloyd (1916). The proportion of the bottom which is exposed to light is an important factor in determining how much of the bottom of a

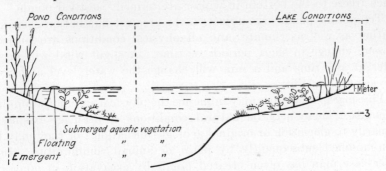

Fig. 90.—Diagram of spatial conditions in ponds and lakes.

lake or pond will be covered with plant growth. Rickett (1922) found vegetation scanty beyond three meters, though Hentschel (1923) shows potomogeton to a depth of six meters. The depth of a lake is added in the middle and the sides remain very much the same in the large and the small ponds. If we assume 50 feet to be a usual width for the plant zone and compare the bodies of water with a diameter of 500 feet, 1,000 feet, and 2,000 feet, we shall find that the plant zone in the first is 36 per cent of the total area, in the second it is 18.1 per cent of the total, and in the third it is only 8.8 per cent of the total. Consequently the larger the lake the less it is influenced by the plant zone (Fig. 90).

293

Temporary and Permanent Ponds. *Physical Characteristics in Space and Time.*—Ponds being characterized by shallowness have as a consequence a relatively large ratio of surface and bottom in proportion to the volume. Plants act to increase further the area of the substratum which is available as an animal habitat. Floating and submerged plants increase the area of the substratum by their leaf area plus their stem area which is exposed to the water. Potomogetons may be two meters tall with leaves 4 to 10 cm. long and 2 to 4 cm. broad, thus offering a large area of attachment for sessile animals and a resting place for aquatic insects.

Emergent aquatic plants increase the area of the substratum and also increase the area of the surface of the water when they are in a stand which is sufficiently dense to raise the water by capillarity. By thus increasing the substratum, plants in the pond society act to increase the volume of water to which an animal may be exposed for the gathering of food.

The relatively large ratio of surface to volume makes ponds more subject to climatic conditions than large bodies of water are. Our smaller ponds evaporate and cease to exist as aquatic environments each year. Those which survive for but a short time in the spring are termed "vernal." Those which are present in the spring and again in the fall are "vernal autumnal," and those which persist during the summer but which freeze to the bottom in winter are termed "aestival ponds."

Temporary ponds are subject to the greatest fluctuations because of weather as well as climate, and all physical conditions are subject to extreme change in short periods of time. A slight wind will mix the water at any time and a rain will change the water level and greatly increase the turbidity.

Physiographic factors may influence the physical and biotic conditions in ponds. These may be natural conditions of drainage basins, due primarily to glaciation or original geologic formations, or they may have been modified subsequently by plant or animal communities. In the latter case man has often created ponds by excavation in quarries or gravel pits. The materials in solution are often controlling factors in such cases.

Concentration of Materials in Solution.—Literature has little to offer on the subject of the content of pond waters. Transeau has unpublished data showing that the water of certain ponds retains the same relative concentration which characterized it at higher water, even when conditions become greatly crowded due to the evaporation of the water.

Shelford (1912) made comparisons of a series of ponds which had been cut off from Lake Michigan at different times by barrier reefs and which forms a series with regard to their age as separate ponds. The following table is a combination of two of Shelford's tables (1912) and represents ponds which are progressively "older" from 1 to 14b.

Concentration of Materials in Ponds of Different Ages

(In parts per million)

Materials	Pond 1	Pond 5	Pond 7	Pond 14
Magnesium carbonate..............	84.6	111.9	38.2	77.1
Calcium carbonate................	54.2	27.9	114.3	83.2
Calcium sulphate.................	149.6	146.6		18.5
Calcium chloride..................	......	......		11.4
Sodium sulphate..................	26.6	0.4	45.0	
Sodium chloride..................	30.3	81.9	16.4	11.3
Sodium carbonate................	......	......	7.7	
Iron oxide.......................	3.0	3.0	2.6	3.0
Silica...........................	6.6	3.4	2.0	3.0
Chlorine.........................	18.4	49.7	9.9	14.2
Free ammonia....................	0.100	0.170	0.040	Trace
Albuminoid ammonia.............	0.125	0.150	0.175	0.250
Nitrites.........................	0.160	0.030	0.030	0.040
Total........................	373.685	425.150	236.340	221.990

These data represent a single set of determinations on ponds which border on railroad tracks. Shelford does not give weight to these determinations but calls attention to the fact that the total solids tend to decrease in the older ponds.

Light.—The pond society is characterized by the presence of plants. These, in turn, are dependent upon certain physical factors, the most important of which is the penetration of light. This varies with the amount of material in suspension and also with the color of the water. In a small pond near McLean, N. Y., the author has seen Sechi's disc disappear in less than one meter, but readings attempted on a large series of ponds have given no measurement because the disc was visible at the bottom in all other cases. It is generally true of ponds, unlike lakes, that there is sufficient light for the growth of green plants all over the bottom.

Temperature.—Characterized by shallow depth, ponds are subject to complete circulation of the water by the agency of winds even though their surface is not great enough for extreme wave action. However, plants resist conduction currents and wind action to such an extent that certain Minnesota ponds may have a temperature difference of 5°C. between different parts during the warm days of early spring or late fall. Such differences are significant when their effect upon rates of metabolism is contemplated. It is not uncommon for these ponds to reach a temperature of 30°C. during the spring and summer.

Murray (1911) says, in connection with a discussion of the temperature of a pond near Glasgow: "Ponds in 77°30' south latitude, in a climate where the air just reaches above the freezing point for no more than a part of each day at midsummer, become almost as warm." The following graph from Murray (1911) gives the temperature of the air and of the water of a temporary pond in 55°50′ north latitude. The water follows very close to the temperature of the air (Fig. 91).

Pressure.—The increase of pressure due to depth in ponds is not great enough to have an appreciable effect on biological or physical processes. This is due to the fact that ponds are limited to a depth of approximately 3 m. or less, and 10.328 m. are required to increase pressure by the equivalent of 1 atmosphere.

Movements of Water.—Wave action is a physical factor modifying the shore line and is in proportion to the distance over which wind may act upon the water. The small size of ponds restricts this distance and the presence of plants offers resistance to rapid movements. The lack of thermal stratification of the water makes complete circulation possible whenever the wind blows, except as it may be impeded by the plants.

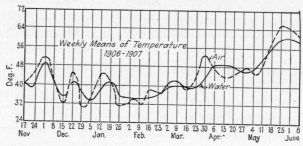

Fig. 91.—Graph showing the mean weekly temperature of the air and of the water of a temporary pond in 55°5′ north latitude. (*Murray*, 1911.)

The Gases in the Water.—Ponds are comparatively uniform in gaseous content and do not depart from the normal saturation point of gases to any great extent. The proportion of surface to volume and frequent mixing of the water tend to keep them in equilibrium with the atmosphere. Nevertheless, on warm days when the sun is shining brightly, the biotic processes may cause the supply and demand for oxygen and carbon dioxide to fluctuate greatly. At times, early in the summer, bubbles of oxygen may be seen rising to the surface from the luxuriant algal growths. At other times the ponds may be so crowded with animals that carbon dioxide may accumulate in excess during cloudy periods. Whipple (1927) calls attention to the effect of pollution upon the oxygen balance of ponds. He considers the "oxygen demand" or the amount of oxygen used up in a given period of time by a water sample as an important index of conditions.

Allee (1917) refers to a pond which he also calls a slough in which he says the oxygen content "was usually under 3 c.c. per liter and the free carbon dioxide usually over 10 c.c. per liter." In his table the maximum for oxygen is given as 5.1 and the minimum as 1.6 c.c. per liter.

Carbon dioxide is given in the same table as 11.7 and 8.6 c.c. per liter. Cowles and Schwitalla (1923) give the average carbon-dioxide content of a "Euglena pond" as 2.2 c.c. per liter.

Neutrality of the Medium.—Ponds are subject to fluctuations of hydrogen-ion concentration as is true with all other factors. Available data are too meager for any generalizations. Cowles and Schwitalla record a variation from 6.5 to 7.0. Peterson (*Ecology,* 1926) studied oxygen temperature, hydrogen-ion concentration, vegetation, animals, and depth of water in a Chara cattail pond, making quantitative readings each week for one year. He observed that the succession of animals seemed to follow the temperature and depth of water conditions more closely than other factors, and that the pH and oxygen frequently accompanied rather than caused the changes. Reed and Klugh (*Ecology,* 1924) found that the biota of two pools, differing widely in pH, were totally different. Although they found that the forms occurring in each, varied considerably in successive seasons, none of the species occurring in the acid pool were found in the alkaline pool and *vice versa.* The experience of Philip (1927) and the author at Crystal Lake leads one to suspect that there are much greater fluctuations than have been recorded.

Biotic Characteristics.—The animals of ponds are characterized by the fact that they may spend a part of their life cycles out of the water either in a resting stage or in an active stage on land or in the air. This is characteristic of all of the fauna of temporary ponds with more exceptions as the size of the environment approaches that of lakes.

The Taxonomic Groups Which Characterize the Community.— Protozoans, rotifers, crustaceans, insects, and amphibians are the important groups of animals found in ponds (Zacharias, 1903; Murray, 1911; Needham and Lloyd, 1916; and others). In Minnesota we find the presence of certain crustaceans of the family Gammearidae as indicative of permanent ponds and their absence a characteristic of temporary ponds. The fairy shrimp, *Branchipus,* is found almost entirely in temporary ponds.

Insects are characteristically abundant in ponds. Quantitative studies of their abundance have been more on the order of relative estimates than actual measurements. The Trichoptera, Ephemerida, Odonata, Hemiptera, Coleoptera, Diptera, and a few Lepidoptera are to be found. Damsel flies, Odonata Zygoptera, and May flies, Ephemerida, are usually very abundant as are certain Diptera. Among the Mollusca, the snails and a few Spheridae occur in large numbers.

The vertebrates are represented in relatively small numbers as compared with the population of lakes. A few Amphibia, frogs, toads, and salamanders are present, but with the exception of a few large permanent ponds which are more or less intermediate between ponds and lakes, the fish are absent.

Biotic Potential of the Fauna.—The high biotic potential of the pond fauna is probably more marked than any other single characteristic of this community of organisms belonging to such widely different taxonomic groups. In this brief outline, it will not be possible to describe the numerous individual mechanisms which are involved in each life history which contribute to this high biotic potential. It is obvious that, in a temporary pond at least, no organism could complete its life cycle if the time required was a full continuous year in the water. It is also obvious that organisms which become enormously abundant in a short period of time must have a high reproductive potential. Woodruff (1912) cites an example of *Monad,* which is found in ponds, increasing in an aquarium to 5,200 per cubic centimeter in the surface water during a period of about eight days.

The physical constants of biotic potential for pond animals have never been assembled for comparison with those of other more permanent environments. One would be tempted to postulate high coefficients of development for temperature and other physical factors. Eddy (1928) concluded that temperature and other physical factors did not have a great influence on the rate of change of the population of aquaria containing infusions of pond materials. The works cited in the bibliography are filled with interesting details of life histories and habits but nowhere do we find these records assembled on the basis of biotic potential.

Needham and Lloyd (1916) call attention to the fact that *Callibaetis,* a common pond May fly, lays 1,000 eggs and goes through its life cycle in six weeks. They state that four generations are possible in a single summer, and that the progeny of a single pair would thus amount to 125,000,000,000 individuals. Certain pond infusoria are capable of reproducing oftener than once each 24 hours. Woodruff is credited with the calculation that 1,073,741,324 infusoria may arise from a single individual in 30 days. In two months the protoplasmic volume of the progeny of this single individual would be equal to a cubic meter when packed 1,000 to the cubic millimeter. This calculation goes on to the point where in seven years the volume of progeny would equal 10,000 times that of the earth itself. It is no wonder then that such forms may quickly populate temporary ponds.

Schaedel (1917) calls attention to the balance between food production and consumption among the plankton organisms of ponds. The ability to use nitrogen and other food material in a state of simple combination rather than as highly organized animal protein is an important characteristic of many pond organisms. However, it is necessary only to grant the presence of a quantity of such organisms to make possible the existence of those which feed upon them.

Rather than build up a highly theoretical consideration of this subject, it will be passed over by calling attention to the fact that literature abounds in descriptions of the many methods by which these organisms procure food, take advantage of transient environments, and protect themselves from enemies, the algebraic sum of which amounts to their biotic potential.

Environmental Resistance.—Small environments and particularly temporary ones offer great resistance to organisms. The action of temperature alone which eliminates even aquatic existence so far as the environment itself is concerned, in summer through evaporation, and in winter through the formation of ice, is an example of the most extreme of these. The spatial distribution of organisms is very largely imposed by physical resistance. The silt on the bottom interferes with the respiration of certain forms, and makes it necessary for them to resort to the rooted plants for support. The gaseous content of the water makes it necessary for many of the aquatic insects to remain at or near the surface in order to carry a store of air into the environment which does not offer enough oxygen to support their metabolism.

Competition for food and escape from enemies that are seeking food constitute some of the important factors of biotic resistance. Woodruff (1912) believes that the excretions of organisms may accumulate to the detriment of the species which produced them, in greatly crowded conditions. One who has followed the course of events in a pond during the progress of a season is impressed by the rapid increase of the prototropic (synthesizing by use of sun's energy) and saprozoic (using organic materials from solution) organisms early in the season. Later the slower increase of the holozoic (ingesting organized material, the bodies of other organisms) forms which are relatively large and tend to dominate the situation, brings about the keenest of competition. The quantitative relationships of these groups must form the basis for the study of the values of biotic potential. Without such quantitative data, a discussion of the subject is mere speculation.

The Quantity of Animals Present.—Our quantitative information is much more restricted with respect to ponds than it is with respect to lakes. Being subject to greater fluctuations of factors and consequently greater fluctuations of environmental resistance, we might expect a greater fluctuation in the quantity of life than is found in lakes. There is little evidence to prove whether or not this is true. Much of the quantitative data are in terms of numbers of individuals, which makes valid comparisons in quantity impossible.

Counts of chironomid larvae in Ekman's dredge samples, taken by the author in the same pond, have varied from several thousand to the square foot to one or two individuals.

The following table gives the results of certain ecology students at the University of Minnesota in the study of the bottom fauna of a temporary (aestival) pond. The results are from a composite of two Ekman dredge samples giving a total area of approximately 450 sq. cm.

QUANTITATIVE SAMPLE OF THE BENTHIC FAUNA OF AN AESTIVAL POND
(Two Ekman dredge samples)

Organisms	Number of individuals	Weight, (grams)
Oligochaet worms.............................	182	Not weighed alone
Flat worms, Planaria.........................	3	Not weighed alone
Hirudinea, leeches............................	3	Not weighed alone
Molluscs, snails..............................	221	1.880
Insects:		
Ephemerida.................................	29	0.049
Odonata, Zygoptera........................	69	0.398
Odonata, Anisoptera.......................	3	Not weighed alone
Coleoptera, Dytiscidae.....................	2	Not weighed alone
Coleoptera, Haliplidae.....................	5	Not weighed alone
Diptera, Tabanidae........................	2	Not weighed alone
Diptera, Chironomidae.....................	1	Not weighed alone
Diptera, Ceratapogon......................	19	Not weighed alone
Diptera, Corethra.........................	16	Not weighed alone
Two samples—total........................	613	2.977

A similar study was made of a small permanent pond in the same locality. The data given in this table are from a composite of four samples taken from a depth of about 60 cm. The samples in both the aestival and permanent ponds were taken in the fall just as the ice had formed for the winter. In comparing the results it is necessary to keep in mind the fact that the sample from the permanent pond is twice the size of that from the temporary pond. The total weights of organisms correspond as closely as could be expected, in view of the errors of sampling and weighing. There were fewer individuals in the permanent pond and they were correspondingly larger. This weight of benthic organisms corresponds roughly with 550 lb. per acre.

QUANTITATIVE SAMPLE OF THE BENTHIC FAUNA OF A PERMANENT POND
(Four Ekman dredge samples)

Organisms	Number of individuals	Weight, grams
Oligochaet worms.........................	64	0.231
Other worms..............................	30	0.048
Hirudinea, leeches........................	172	0.841
Mollusca, snails...........................	1	0.028
Insects:		
Ephemerida.............................	16	0.038
Diptera		
Chironomidae..........................	299	4.263
Ceratopogan...........................	163	1.060
Unclassed.............................	5	
Four samples—total....................	750	6.509

Here we shall stop short of the question of greatest ecological interest, namely the balance of production and consumption in pond societies. Quantitative data are urgently needed for an understanding of these communities. Naturalists have observed the habits of many of the pond animals and it now becomes necessary to understand the laws which maintain this society on a conservative basis.[1]

This single comparison does not establish anything definite with regard to the quantity of life, but is interesting as a suggestion both as to the total quantity, and as to the relative quantities of animals of different habitats.

BIBLIOGRAPHY

PONDS

ATKINS, W. R. G., and G. T. HARRIS: Seasonal Changes in the Water and Heloplankton of Fresh-water Ponds, *Proc. Roy., Dublin, Soc. Sci.* **18**: 121, 1924; abstr. *Jour. Mar. Biol. Assoc.*, 1925.

ALLEE, W. C.: Seasonal Succession in Old Forest Ponds, *Trans. Ill. State Acad. Sci.*, **IV**: 126–131, 1911.

————: The Salt Content of Natural Waters in Relation to Rheotaxis in *Asellus*, *Biol. Bull.*, **32**: 93–97, 1917.

BARNEY, R. L., and B. J. ANSON: Relation of Certain Aquatic Plants to Oxygen Supply and to Capacity of Small Ponds to Support the Top Minnow (*Gambusia affinis*), *Trans. Amer. Fish. Soc.*, pp. 268–278, 1920.

BROWN, H. B.: Algal Periodicity in Certain Ponds and Streams, *Torrey Bot. Club Bull.*, **35**: 223–248, 1908.

CONSER, H. W.: Cocaine in the Study of Pond Life, *Trans. Amer. Micros. Soc.*, no. 17, October, 1896.

COWLES, R. P., and A. M. SCHWITALLA: The Hydrogen-ion Concentration of a Creek, Its Waterfall Swamp and Ponds, *Ecology*, **IV**: 402–417, 1923.

DYCHE, L. L.: "Ponds, Pond Fish and Pond Fish Culture," 1910–1914, Kans. State Dept. Fish and Game, pt. 1, Ponds, 1910.

EDDY, SAMUEL: Succession of Protozoa in Cultures under Controlled Conditions, *Trans. Amer. Micros. Soc.*, **47**: 283–319, 1928.

FRITSCH, F. E., and FLORENCE RICH: "Studies on the Occurrence and Reproduction of British Fresh-water Algae," chap. III, A Four-years Observation of a Fresh-water Pond, *Ann. biol. lacustre*, **6**, 1913, 83 pp.; rev. in *Jour. Ecology*, **I**: 295–296, 1913.

GRIFFITHS, B. M.: The August Heloplankton of Some North Worcestershire Pools, (F. E. F.) *Jour. Linn. Soc. Bot.*, London, **43**: 423–432, 1916; abstr. in *Jour. Ecology*, **V**: 117, 1916.

HAEMPEL, O.: Die Bisamratte, ein neuer Schädling der Teichwirtschaft, *Internat. Rev. Gesamm. Hydrobiol. u. Hydrog.* **7**: 435–441, 1916.

HENTSCHEL, E.: "Grundzüge der Hydrobiologie," G. Fischer, Jena, 1923.

KENNEDY, C. H.: The Ecological Relationships of the Odonata of the Bass Islands of Lake Erie, *Ecology*, vol. **III**: 325–337, 1922.

LEACH, GLEN C.: Culture of Rainbow Trout and Brook Trout in Ponds, *U. S. Dept. Com., Bur. Fisheries Econ. Circ.* 41, Feb. 20, 1919.

LEMMERMANN, E.: Resultate einer biologischen Untersuchung der Forellenteiche von Sandfort, *Forschungsberichte aus der Biologischen Station zu Plön*, **5**: 67–112, 1897.

————: Das Phytoplankton Sächsischer Teiche, *Forschungsberichte aus der Biologischen Station zu Plön.*, **7**: 96–135, 1899.

---

[1] See Appendix by Volterra.

List, Theodor: Über die Temporal- und Lokalvariationen von *Ceratium hirudinella* O. F. M. aus dem Plankton einiger Teiche in der Umgegend von Darmstadt und einiger Kolke des Altrheins bei Erfelden, *Arch. Hydrobiol. u. Planktonkunde,* **9**: 81–126, 1914.

Moore, Emmeline: The Potomogetons in Relation to Pond Culture, *U. S. Bur. Fisheries Bull.* **33**: 251–291, 17 pl., 1915.

Murray, James: The Annual History of a Periodic Pond, *Internat. Rev. Gesamm. Hydrobiol. u. Hydrog.,* **4**: 300–310, 1911.

Naumann, Einar: Über die Ursachen einer braunen Färbung des Wassers in einem Teiche der Fischereiversuchsstation Aneboda in Südschweden, *Internat. Rev. Gesamm. Hydrobiol. u. Hydrog.,* **6**: 8–11, 1913.

Needham, J. G., and J. T. Lloyd: "Life of Inland Waters," Pond Societies, pp. 334–341, Comstock Publ. Co., Ithaca, N. Y., 1916.

Peterson, Walburga: Seasonal succession of Animals in a Chara-cattail Pond, *Ecology,* **7**: 371–377, 1926.

Philip, C. B. (1927): Diurnal Fluctuations in the Hydrogen-ion Activity of a Minnesota Lake, *Ecology,* **8**: 73–89, 1927.

Reed, Guilford, and A. B. Klugh: Correlation between Hydrogen-ion Concentration and Biota of Granite and Limestone Pools, *Ecology,* **5**: 272–275, 1924.

Rickett, H. W.: A Quantitative Study of the Larger Aquatic Plants of Lake Mendota, *Trans. Wis. Acad. Sci., Arts and Letters,* **20**: 501–527, 1921.

Schaedel, Albert: Produzenten und Konsumenten im Teichplankton, ihre Wechselwirkung und Beziehung zu den physikalischen und chemischen Milieu Einflüssen, *Arch. Hydrobiol. u. Planktonkunde,* **11**: 404–477, 1917.

Schneider, George: Das Plankton der westfälischen Talsperren des Sauerlandes, *Arch. Hydrobiol. u. Planktonkunde,* **8**: 1–42, 207–263, 1913.

Schröder, B.: Die Algen der Versuchsteiche, *Forschungsberichte aus der biologischen Station zu Plön,* **5**: 29–66, 1897.

Scott, W.: The Fauna of a Solution Pond, *Proc. Ind. Acad. Sci.,* pp. 395–442, 1910.

Shelford, V. E.: "Animal Communities in Temperate America," chap. VIII, pp. 136–169; chap. X, Temporary Ponds, pp. 173–180, Geogr. Soc., Chicago; The University of Chicago Press *Bull.* 5, 1913.

————: Ecological Succession. III. A Reconnaissance of Its Causes in Ponds with Particular Reference to Fish, *Biol. Bull.,* **XXII**: 1–38, 1912.

Titcomb, John W.: Aquatic Plants in Pond Culture, U. S. Bur. Fish. Doc. 948, 1923. 2d ed., 24 pp.

Walter, E.: Eine praktisch-verwerthbare Methode zur quantitativen Bestimmung des Teichplankton, *Forschungsberichte aus der biologischen Station zu Plön,* **3**: 180–187, 1895.

Whipple, G. C.: "The Microscopy of Drinking Water," chap. XIX, p. 585, pl. XIX; revised by G. M. Fair and M. C. Whipple, John Wiley & Sons, Inc., New York, 1927.

Wilson, C. B.: Water Beetles in Relation to Pondfish Culture, with Life Histories of Those Found in Fishponds at Fairport, Iowa, *U. S. Bur. Fisheries Bull.* XXXIX, Doc. 953, pp. 231–345, text 1–48, 1923.

Woodruff, Lorande Loss: Observations on the Origin and Sequence of the Protozoan Fauna of Hay Infusions, *Jour. Exptl. Zool.,* **12**: 205–264, 1912.

Zacharias, Otto: Untersuchungen über das Plankton der Teichgewässer, *Forschungsberichte aus der Biologischen Station zu Plön,* **6**: 89–140, 1898.

————: Zur Kenntniss des Planktons sächsischer Fischteiche, *Forschungsberichte aus der Biologischen Station zu Plön,* **7**: 78–95, 1899.

————: Das Vorkommen von *Astasia haematodes* Ehrb. in deutschen Fischteichen, *Forschungsberichte aus der Biologischen Station zu Plön,* **7**: 44–49, 1899.

————: Biologische Charakteristik des Klinkerteichs zu Plön, *Forschungsberichte aus der Biologischen Station zu Plön,* **10**: 201–215, 1903.

ZUSCHER, MATTHIAS: Das Plankton des Schlossgartens und des Schlossteiches zu Münster i. w. unter besonderer Berücksichtigung der Temporal-Variation von *Anurea cochlearis, Ceratium hirudinella, Arch. Hydrobiol. u. Planktonkunde,* **9**: 176–177, 1914.

CHAPTER XVI

LAKES

A lake is to a naturalist, a chapter out of the history of a primeval time, for the conditions of life are primitive, the forms of life are, as a whole, relatively low and ancient, and the system of organic interactions by which they influence and control each other has remained substantially unchanged from a remote geological period . . . It is an islet of older, lower life in the midst of the higher, more recent life of the surrounding region. It forms a little world within itself—a microcosm within which all the elemental forces are at work and the play of life goes on in full, but on so small a scale as to bring it easily within the mental grasp.—FORBES.

The Classes of Lakes.—Lakes may be classified on the basis of depth heat budgets, oxygen content, "hardness" of the water, or, in fact, according to any of their physical or biotic characteristics. A classification which is based upon temperature, depth, and oxygen content is of great significance ecologically, and will therefore be adopted for the present purpose (Fig. 92).

Lakes may be grouped in three orders on the basis of depth. The lakes of the first order are those having a definite thermal stratification, or thermocline, as shown in the accompanying diagram, with the temperature of the water below the thermocline constant or very nearly constant throughout the year at or near the maximum density. The lakes of the second order are those which have a thermocline; but the temperature of the water at the bottom undergoes an annual fluctuation and is at a temperature slightly higher than 4°C. The lakes of the third order are those without thermal stratification, with little difference between the surface and bottom temperatures and in which there may be complete circulation of the water at any time.

Another classification of lakes, which is of ecological importance, is based on the physical characteristics, particularly the oxygen content of the water. This applies to the lakes with thermal stratification, for those with uniform temperature may have a complete circulation of the water at any time with the consequent aeration, see diagram (Fig. 92).

The oligotrophic type of lake is rich in oxygen even to the bottom. It owes its characteristic partly to a geologic formation which permits relatively little inwash of organic material to remain in solution, or to form an organic ooze on the bottom; and partly to biotic conditions which do not favor rapid decomposition with the consequent oxygen consumption. The lakes of this type are usually alpine with rocky shores. Thienemann (1925) designates these as *Tanytarsus* lakes because the benthic fauna is characterized by the predominance of fly larvae belonging to the genus *Tanytarsus*, of the family *Chironomidae*.

The eutrophic type of lake is characterized by the paucity or absence of oxygen in the bottom waters. This is due primarily to physical conditions which have given rise to a large supply of available nitrogen in the water and bottom ooze and, secondarily, to biotic conditions which favor rapid decomposition and the consequent consumption of oxygen. Thienemann (1925) calls lakes of this type *Chironomus* lakes, because fly larvae of the genus, *Chironomus* are predominant in the benthic fauna, along with *Corethra* larvae and *Tubifex* worms. The majority of the lakes of the first and second order in the temperate region are

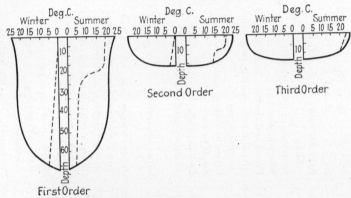

Fig. 92.—Diagram illustrating the characteristics of lakes of the first, second, and third orders. The right half of each diagram illustrates the temperature in summer; and the left half illustrates the conditions in winter. Temperature is indicated across the top for both summer and winter, and is plotted against depth as a dotted line. Depth is indicated in meters. First order lake Cayuga Lake, N. Y.; second order, Crystal Lake, Minn.; third order, Red Cedar Lake, Wis.

eutrophic. Green Lake, Wis., is probably in the early transition stage between the oligotrophic and eutrophic stages, but may be classed as oligotrophic.

The dystrophic lake, or brown-water lake, is found among peat bogs. These have not been studied extensively in America, and it is questionable whether generalizing with regard to them is justifiable on the basis of our present knowledge.

The lakes of each order may be designated as polar, temperate, and tropical, on the basis of their geographic distribution with respect to latitude. The temperature of polar lakes is like that of temperate lakes during the winter, and the temperature of the tropical lakes is like that of the temperate lakes in summer. It is obvious that the temperature of the water itself cannot be lower in the polar lakes than in the temperate lakes in winter. However, the water of tropical lakes may become warmer than that of the temperate lakes in summer.

TABLE XVI.—PHYSICAL CHARACTERISTICS OF LAKES OF DIFFERENT TYPES
(Modified from Thienemann)

Characteristics	Oligotrophic	Eutrophic	Dystrophic
Examples	Lake Tahoe, Crater Lake, Green Lake (Wis.)	Lake Mendota, Crystal Lake (Minn.)	Turtle Lake (Wis.)
Geographic distribution	Alpine, or rock formation	Morainic, or level country	
Type of basin	Rocky shores and bottom	Much humus	Peet
Morphometry	Deep and narrow; water mass of hypolimnion large in proportion to epilimnion	Broad and shallow, water mass of hypolimnion small in proportion to epilimnion	Deep or shallow
Color of water	Blue to green	Green to yellow, and yellowish	Yellow to brown
Transparency	Great	Small to very little	Like eutrophic
Materials in solution	Usually poor in available nitrogen; little humus; calcium variable	Rich in available nitrogen; rich in calcium, rarely lacking	Variable in nitrogen; rich in humus; little calcium
Materials in suspension	Minimum amounts	Large amounts	
Oxygen:			
Summer	Relatively uniform, near saturation from top to bottom; deep water usually at least 60 to 70 per cent of saturation	Oxygen varies from top to bottom; surface near saturation, sudden increase at thermocline, bottom usually lacking, seldom as much as 40 per cent of saturation	Same as eutrophic
Winter, under ice	As in summer	Deep lakes retain oxygen; shallow lakes, oxygen may be absent at bottom	Same as eutrophic
Cause of oxygen content	Diffusion	Production by phytoplankton consumption by zooplankton and organic decomposition in mud	

TABLE XVII.—BIOTIC CHARACTERISTICS OF LAKES OF DIFFERENT TYPES
(Modified from Thienemann)

Characteristics	Oligotrophic	Eutrophic	Dystrophic
Plankton:			
Quantitative	Poor, stratification not marked, some diurnal migration	Rich, stratified in epilimnion, little diurnal migration; water bloom abundant, zooplankton abundant	Poor; water bloom rare or lacking
Qualitative	Seldom water bloom; Chlorophyceae abundant		
Nekton	Few species; deep-water fish, trout, etc.	Rich in species; few deep-water fish; bass, perch, etc., predominant	
Littoral plants	Insignificant	Abundant	Insignificant
Differentiation between littoral and abyssal	Weakly marked, formed by margin of vegetation; sublittoral zone lacking	Clearly differentiated; oxygen content of water chief cause; sublittoral zone present	Clearly differentiated; sublittoral zone lacking
Benthos:			
Qualitative	Rich in species; Tanytarsus predominant, Corethra absent	Poor in species; Chironomus predominant, Corethra practically always present; rich—2,000 to 10,000 animals per m²; reduced in sublittoral	Very poor in species; Chironomus present, Corethra usually present; poor—10 to 20 animals per m²
Quantitative	Relatively rich, between 300 and 1,000 animals per m²		
Distribution in depth of zones	Uniform		
Quantitative relation between plankton and fauna	Existing	Non-existing	Phytoplankton poor; zooplankton often rich
Successional change due to sedimentation	To become eutrophic lake	To become pond, swamp, marsh, meadow	To become peat bog

The further discussion of stratification and circulation will be postponed until we consider the thermocline.

Physical Characteristics.   *Light.*—Solar radiation brings to the lake the energy to support photosynthesis in the actinic portion of its spectrum and is the chief source of heat in the red and infra-red portion of its spectrum.   Being familiar with the nature of the sun's spectrum, we cannot expect to find it easy to determine its penetration into a lake. In general, our information will give us the depth to which the actinic rays penetrate, either directly by photometer measurements or indirectly by transparency measurements; or it will give us the depth to which the heat rays penetrate as measured by the pyrlimnometer.

We have more data available from readings with Secchi's disc than from any other source.   Consequently, comparisons of lakes can better be made on the basis of such transparency readings than on any other, even though they are only the roughest estimate of light penetration. The following table gives data to show the great variation in the depth at which Secchi's disc may disappear in different lakes.

Lake	Year	Transparency, meters	Determined by
Mendota	1908	1.75	Birge and Juday
Canandaigua	1910	3.70	Birge and Juday
Otisco	1910	3.00	Birge and Juday
Conesus	1910	6.30	Birge and Juday
Cayuga	1910	5.10	Birge and Juday
Seneca	1910	8.30	Birge and Juday
Skaneatales	1910	10.30	Birge and Juday
Nipigon	1921	3.6 to 5.20	Clemens
Geneva	?	21.00	Forel
Crater	1913	25.00	Kemmerer *et al*
Tahoe	?	28.00	Kemmerer *et al*
Lucal	?	60.00	Whipple

Figure 93 shows the variations in transparency during the annual cycle of Montiggler Seen as given by Huber (1906) during the years 1901 and 1902.

It is seen that the transparency was greatest during the period of summer stagnation.   It must be borne in mind that all measures either of transparency or light penetration are measures of the physical plus the biotic environment and not of the water alone.   Referring to Knight's Lake (see Fig. 86), it will be seen that there were 100,000 algae to the liter of water at a depth of 3 m. on Aug. 25, 1909.   This quantity of algae would interfere with the penetration of light, even though the water was stagnant at that time.   The great excess of oxygen between 4 and 5 m.

(see Fig. 85) clearly indicates that photosynthesis was going on rapidly. In this case, the presence of sunlight at this depth has made it possible for algae to become so numerous that their own chlorophyll acts as a screen interfering with the further penetration of the sun's rays.

Birge and Juday (1921) say of the transmission of the sun's energy:

Lake water differs widely from pure water in the quantity of energy transmitted. If we assume a solar-energy curve corresponding to a path of the rays in the air of 1.5 atmospheres, with about 0.5 cm. condensable water in the atmosphere, about 47 per cent of the solar energy will be left after passing through one meter of pure water. The water of Seneca Lake, therefore, cuts off 25 per cent more than does pure water.

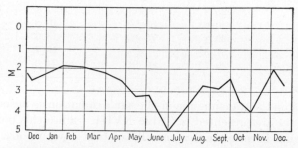

Fig. 93.—Transparency of Montiggler Seen as measured by Secchi's disc. The points on the graph indicate the maximum depth in meters at which the disc was visible. (*Adapted from Huber*, 1906.)

In a more recent paper, Birge and Juday (1929) say:

Transmission is determined by three main factors: (1) the selective action of water which is transparent to short-wave radiation and opaque to long waves; (2) the selective effect of stain which acts more strongly on the short-wave radiation and is effective in proportion to the amount and kind present; (3) the action of suspended matter—organic and inorganic—which offers more obstruction to short-wave radiation, but is not definitely selective.

Thus the selective action of water is a constant factor in all lakes; that of stain is very variable as between different lakes, and somewhat variable in the same lake at different times. It is usually, but not always, the same in the same lake at different depths of the same series. The influence of suspended matter may differ widely in different lakes, in the same lake at different times, and at different depths in the same lake at the same time. In eutrophic lakes its influence is very great and often dominant; in lakes with little plankton it is less; and stain or water itself may be more important factors in reducing radiation.

There is but a rough correlation between transparency and the transmission of solar radiation as measured by the pyrlimnometer. Deep lakes and especially eutrophic lakes are usually both highly transparent and transmit radiation to a great depth.

TABLE XVIII.—TRANSMISSION OF RADIATION MEASURED BY PYRLIMNOMETER

(Birge and Juday, 1929)

Lake	Per cent at 1 meter	Average transmission	One per cent at meters	Stratum transmitting 10 per cent. meters
Mary	4.7	24	2.0	1.4
Turtle..............	10.0	28	2.8	1.8
Mendota mean......	20.7	50	5.2	3.3
Mendota maximum...	30.3	66	8.9	5.6
Mendota minimum...	13.8	38	3.6	2.3
Beasley.............	25.8	60	7.1	4.6
Green..............	30.6	65–70	10.8	6.9
Blue...............	29.8	75–80	13.3	8.7
Crystal mean........	37.5	81	19.7	12.5
Crystal maximum....	39.7	80–91	ca. 34.0	ca. 20.0

The data on the transmission of the sun's radiation as measured by the pyrlimnometer are presented in Table XVIII. Since this portion of the sun's spectrum is composed essentially of heat rays, we are now led to the discussion of temperature.

Temperature.—The temperature of lakes passes through an annual cycle, as might be inferred from the diagram illustrating the summer and winter conditions in lakes of the three orders. The regularity of this change, year after year, and its similarity in different lakes under comparable conditions are of greatest importance in illustrating the principles which govern environmental changes. Its study instils the hope that the day may yet come when the majority of animal environments may be as accurately measured and their changes predicted with the same certainty.

The writings of Birge may be referred to for the discussion of the temperature phenomena, including the work of the wind and the biological significance of the thermocline.

The Thermocline—Its Significance.—Simony in Germany observed the peculiar stratification of water over 65 years ago (Buchanan, 1886). Richter investigated it in 1891 and termed it "Sprungschicht." Birge termed it the "thermocline" in 1897.

The change of density due to temperature and the absorption of the sun's heat by the surface water (compare the graphs Figs. 95 and 96) make it inevitable that the surface of lakes will be warmed rapidly by the sun and that the warmer they become the less tendency they will have to mix with the cooler waters which lie below. The wind is the chief agent of mixing and its action becomes more restricted as the season progresses until the difference of density between adjacent strata becomes so great that it cannot be materially disturbed even in violent storms.

The two figures representing the temperatures of the major Finger Lakes of New York for the years 1910 and 1911 illustrate how similar the temperatures of the lakes are. Although these lakes vary in length from 11 to 38 miles, they lie parallel to each other and are about equally exposed to the sun and wind (Figs. 94 and 95).

These curves are typical of the summer conditions of lakes of the first order in temperate North America. They illustrate the upper wind-

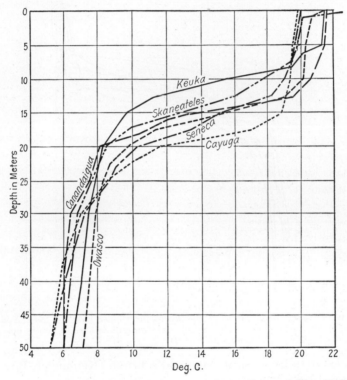

Fig. 94.—Temperature curves of the six major Finger Lakes of New York in 1910 shown to the depth of 50 m. One vertical space represents 5 m. of depth; one horizontal space represents 2°C.

disturbed layer or epilimnion (Birge, 1910). Below this is the layer of sudden decline of temperature, the thermocline, with its thin thermal strata constituting the record of the shifting balance between the opposing forces of the sun and the wind during the progress of the summer. Below the thermocline we have the hypolimnion, stagnant and uniform in temperature, for it is beyond the influence of either the sun or the wind.

Twice a year, in the spring when the surface waters are being warmed and in the fall when they are being cooled, the waters of first- and second-order lakes are of about uniform density. At these times the wind causes complete circulation of all of the waters. During these vernal and autumnal overturns the animals and other substances in suspension and in solution are redistributed.

The significance of the division of lakes into the epilimnion and hypolimnion, and the restriction of complete circulation of the water to two periods a year, can hardly be overemphasized. Practically all of the physical and biotic characteristics are affected by this stratification. This is less true of oligotrophic lakes with rocky shores than of lakes

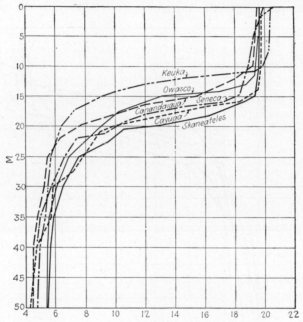

Fig. 95.—Temperature curves of the six major Finger Lakes of New York in 1911 shown to the depth of 50 m. One vertical space represents 5 m. of depth; one horizontal space represents 2°C. Compare with Fig. 94.

with much material in suspension and solution (Kemmerer, Bovard, and Boorman, 1923).

The Heat Budgets of Lakes.—From the foregoing considerations we find that there is a more or less fixed condition under which a lake may acquire temperature, and the amount of heat which a given lake can acquire will depend upon how near it comes to satisfying the optimum conditions for acquiring heat.

Birge (1915) discusses a number of conceptions of heat budgets. The amount of heat necessary to raise the temperature of the lake from 0° to the summer maximum is the *gross heat budget*. This is misleading, for the lakes do not use up all of the heat budget during the year. The amount of heat required to raise the water temperature from the winter minimum to the summer maximum is the *annual heat budget*. Halbfass used this in the comparison of European lakes.   It is of great importance. The amount of heat required to raise the temperature from 4° to the summer maximum is the *summer heat income,* or *the wind-disturbed heat.*

The annual heat budget may be computed from data as follows:

$$Dm \;=\; \text{mean depth in centimeters.}$$
$$Tm^s \;=\; \text{mean summer temperature.}$$
$$Tm^w \;=\; \text{mean winter temperature.}$$
$$Dm(Tm^s - Tm^w) \;=\; \text{annual heat budget in gram-calories.}$$

The mean winter temperature, Tm^w, can be taken at almost any time under ice, and there will be very little variation found.

The mean summer temperature, Tm^s, has been taken at Green Lake at times varying from Aug. 14 to Sept. 8 for nine seasons, and the total range of variation was less than 1°.   Wedderburn gives the example of the temperature of Loch Ness which was derived from a series of readings taken in the middle of the lake and compared with the mean temperature computed from three series from different parts of the lake.   The difference in the two values was less than 0.1°C.

The following table is of interest in comparing certain lakes as to the amount of heat required to raise them to the summer temperature and the heat budgets in gram calories per square centimeter of surface (Birge & Juday, 1912).

Lake	Dm, meters	$0°$ to Tm^s		Annual budget	
		1910	1911	1910	1911
Cayuga............................	54.5	50,000	49,000	38,200	36,500
Owasco............................	29.3	40,000	38,000	38,900	36,600
Seneca............................	88.6	68,000	65,000	38,300	35,100
Skaneateles.......................	43.5	44,000	47,000	39,200	42,400
Green (Wis.)......................	33.1	39,000	38,000	32,000	30,600

The budget is apparently independent of surface dimensions between the limits of 16 and 60 km. of length, and it is independent of depth between the limits of 30 and 90 m.   A depth of less than 30 m. would have a smaller budget, but a depth of more than 90 m. would make very little difference.

Birge's principle is stated by him (Birge and Juday, 1912) as follows:

Inland lakes of the first class include those whose area and depth are such as to permit the maximum annual heat budget possible under the weather conditions of the season.   Such a budget for lakes in the climatic and topographical conditions of the eastern United States ordinarily equals or exceeds 30,000 g. cal. per square centimeter of the lake's surface, and ordinarily lies between 30,000 and 40,000 g. cal.   Such lakes, under the conditions stated, will be 10 km. or more in length and will have a mean depth of 30 m. or more.

This statement applies to lakes with a simple outline whose length is five or more times the mean breadth.

When the outline of a lake is very irregular, it cannot be compared with others of different outline. The European lakes are not uniform among themselves, and so vary from the uniformity found in American lakes. However, these variations are said to be due to elevation and to the temperature of the air in the location where they are found.

Birge and Juday (1912) say of the Finger Lakes of New York:

The larger lakes of the Seneca basin take in and give out during the year an amount of heat whose aggregate is enormous. It has been computed that this is equal to the heat generated by the combustion of nearly 150,000 tons of coal for each square mile of surface of the lake. The total amount of heat from Seneca Lake would equal that from nearly 10,000,000 tons of coal. This heat is absorbed by the water in the spring and liberated in autumn and produces a considerable effect on the climate. The effect is intensified by the narrow valleys with their steep slopes which concentrate and localize the influence of the water. Frosts are delayed in the autumn, and in spring the cold water chills the air of the valleys so that vegetation does not start until the danger of killing frosts has passed. The slopes of the lake basins are, therefore, peculiarly well adapted for raising fruits, and many orchards and vineyards are found there. The steep shores of Keuka Lake, especially, are covered with vineyards, as thick set as those of the Rhine.

Schmidt (1915) calls attention to the fact that a lake in a homothermous condition is in a state of indifferent equilibrium. When the upper strata are warmed, it becomes proportionately stable. This stability may be measured by the amount of work necessary to complete the distribution of the heat in the lake and again bring it to the condition of indifferent equilibrium. He does this in respect to the amount of displacement of the center of gravity of the lake. His result is not very different from that of Birge (1916), in the work of the wind in distributing the heat throughout the lake.

The Work of the Wind.—It is evident from the discussion above that the amount of work which must be done in warming any stratum below the surface of a lake from one temperature to another will be equal to the amount of work which will be necessary to lower a stratum of water of this size from the surface to the position of the stratum in question. This amount of work is necessary to overcome the difference in density encountered.

There are two opposing forces at work in the process of the warming of a lake, the sun and the wind. As a result the lake does not receive all of the energy of the sun nor all of that of the wind.

The computation of the direct work of the wind in distributing the temperature may be made by the use of the following formula from Birge (1916):

A = the area of the lake; A_0 or A (no sign) = area at surface; A_5 = area at the depth of 5 m.

V = total volume of the lake; V_{5-10} = volume between 5 and 10 m.

RT = reduced thickness; the thickness of any given stratum when its volume is divided by the surface area of the lake.

$\dfrac{V^{n-m}}{A_0}$ = RT; n and m are the levels of the strata considered. RT is stated in centimeters.

T = temperature; T_m = mean temperature of whole lake.

T_{5-10} = mean temperature between 5 and 10 m.

D = density; D_n = density at any given temperature.

At 4° $D = 1$. At any other temperature it is less than 1.

Z = distance from the surface of the lake in centimeters.

W = work done in warming the lake as a whole; it is stated in gram-centimeters for the surface of the lake.

$W = (RT)(Z)(1 - D_n)$.

RT is taken as the weight in grams of a column of water whose base is 1 sq. cm. and whose height is equal to the thickness of the layer when its area has been extended to that of the surface of the lake. The product of $(RT)Z$ would then give the amount of work necessary to warm the stratum if D were reduced to zero, so that $1 - D$ equals 1. $(1 - D)$ states the loss of density in a fraction of 1, so that the final product is a measure of the work done in gram-centimeters per square centimeter of the surface of the lake.

In the expression $(1 - D_n)$, 1 is the density of the water at 4° and, therefore, is equal to D_4. If the lower limit of temperature considered is any other than 4°, its density, say D_m, must be substituted for 1.

Example (Birge, 1916).—The stratum between 20 and 21 m. in a given lake is warmed from 4 to 8°. How much work is involved in the rise in temperature?

Let $RT = 56$ cm. or 56 g. for a column, 1 sq. cm. in area.

$Z = 2,050$ cm.; D at 8° − 0.999876; ∴ $1 - D8 = 0.000124$.

∴ $W = 56 \times 2,050 \times 0.000124 = 14.235$ g.cm.

∴ in warming this stratum of the lake, 224g. cal. have been delivered at the cost of 14.235 g.cm. of work, or about 16 g.cal. per 1 g.cm. of work.

In a similar way the work required to warm each stratum of the lake may be computed and the sum of the products will give the total work expended in warming the whole lake.

It should be noted that it is not possible to let RT = the mean depth of the lake and D = the mean density. This will be evident from Birge (1916).

In Seneca Lake 42 cal.cm.[2] are transported to a mean depth of 55 m. for each 1 g.cm. of work. The length of this lake is 56.6 km. and its mean depth is 88.6 m. In Canandaigua Lake 18 cal.cm.[2] are transported to a mean depth of 55 m. for each 1 g.cm. of work. The length of this lake is 24.9 m. and its mean depth is 38.8 m. Geneva Lake in 1913 = 2,336.6 g.cm.; Green Lake = 2,022.6 g.cm. For Lake Mendota in 1910 it required 1,209.18 g.cm.[2] to distribute the heat in excess of 4°C.

The average annual heat budget for Lake Mendota has been determined as 23,000 to 24,000 cal. A study of the temperature of the bottom deposits has shown that they have a heat budget equal to an additional 2,000 cal. This would have to be added to that of the water to give the total heat budget of 25,000 to 26,000 cal. for each square centimeter of the surface (Birge, Juday and March, 1928).

Work of the Sun.—In this method of calculating the work done in distributing the heat, it is assumed that all of the heat has been placed

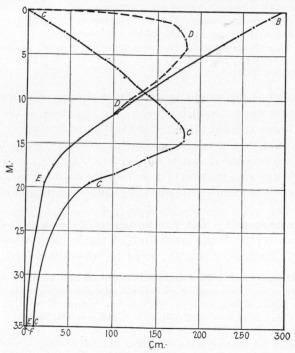

Fig. 96.—Work curves for Seneca Lake. The vertical axis shows depth; the horizontal axis shows gram centimeters of work per meter of depth and square centimeters of surface of lake. *OCC*, curve of direct work. About 145 g. cm. of work, for instance, are necessary to carry the heat of the 9- to 10-m. stratum from the surface and put it in place. *BDE*, curve of distributed work, derived from *OCC*, showing the amount of work done in each 1-m. stratum. The area *OBEFO* (distributed work) is equal to the area *OCCFO* (direct work). *ODD* shows the contribution of the sun in distributing the sun's energy. The area *ODDBO* gives the contribution of the sun, and that of the wind is represented by the area *ODEFO*. (*From Birge and Juday, 1921.*)

in the lake by the wind. The diagram (Fig. 96) indicates that this is not true; for a small percentage of the sun's energy may go unaided to a depth of 10 m. Birge and Juday (1920) have constructed a diagram showing the "direct work" involved in carrying the heat to the various parts of Seneca Lake by the wind and also the contribution made by the sun.

Movements of the Water.—Movements of the water are caused or originated by the wind. Differences of density and pressure are never of such magnitudes as to cause appreciable movements of the water in lakes.

The topography of the surrounding country and the direction of the prevailing winds determine very largely the location of open beaches due to wave action. On the great lakes, only the sheltered bays are exempt from wave action and many of the animals which comprise the fauna of these rocky shores may be typically lotic. During the spring when the ice is melting, blocks of it may be driven against the shore, breaking off much of the vegetation and aiding in the erosion of the shore line.

A tilting of the thermocline may be caused by a prevailing wind blowing much of the water of the epilimnion to the leeward end of the lake. When the velocity of the wind is reduced, this water will flow back and produce an oscillation or possibly a so-called "seich" (Birge, 1910).

Concentration.—Under this subject we might consider the concentration of all materials in solution including salinity. Since salinity has formed the basis of our major division of aquatic environments, we shall first consider it briefly.

There are many inland lakes, without outlets, into which water flows, laden with salts and other substances. In the course of time the water evaporates and the salts remain, thus increasing the concentration in the remaining water. Brannon (1911) says that Devil's Lake, N. D., had 8,471 parts of solid residue in 1899; 8,857 in 1905; and 10,514 in 1909. In this case the inflowing water has evaporated and left its load of material to accumulate year after year, until there has been a marked increase in 10 years' time.

Coker (1911) cites the example of Lake Poopo in the Inter-Andean region of South America, which receives the overflow from Lake Titicaca. The author says that Poopo contains 23 parts of salts per thousand, while Titicaca is clear and fresh, though he gives no data on its salt content.

The Great Salt Lake of Utah has a high salt content which reaches even the point of supersaturation in shallow water about its margin. Yet even here the larvae of certain flies are to be found.

Transeau has investigated the water of temporary ponds which dry up in summer. It might be expected that the water in these ponds would become greatly concentrated in the last stages of evaporation. The case was quite the reverse, however. The greatest concentration was found at the time of high water and the least at the time of low water, at least in certain ponds. Transeau thinks that this may be due to the materials in solution being adsorbed on the surface of particles in suspension. Late in the summer when these particles have had time to

adsorb the salts and to settle to the bottom, the water is left with a
reduced concentration.

The soluble nitrogen which is found in solution may serve to make
lake water a "culture medium" capable of supporting organisms much
as Pütter (1909 and 1922) believed that the sea would do.

Birge and Juday (1927) have studied the organic content of several
lakes and have classified them as to the source of their organic matter.
Some lakes are dependent wholly on internal sources and these are
called *autotrophic*. They receive almost no surface drainage and are
dependent upon the plankton, and other plants and animals, for their
source of dissolved organic matter. Other lakes receive surface drainage

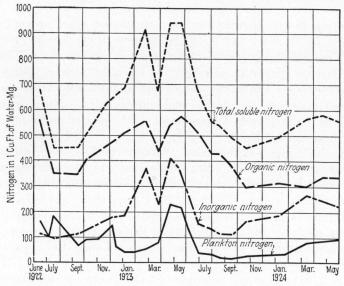

Fig. 97.—Forms of nitrogen found in 1 cu. m. of surface water of Lake Mendota. (*Domogalla et al.*, 1925.)

which brings with it much organic matter to add to that which is produced internally; these are called *allotrophic* lakes. As yet we do not
have enough information with regard to the quantities of organic matter
and the organisms to draw any very general conclusions. The organic
matter represented in the plankton is, on the average, only about 14 per
cent of the total organic matter in the water. Bog lakes which have a
high content of plant extracts may be very poor in plankton. It seems,
however, that the organic material in solution is fairly constant throughout any given lake, and that it does not vary greatly in time. Table
XIX gives a comparison of several lakes based upon a study made by
centrifuging the water to remove the plankton.

Domogalla, Juday, and Peterson (1925) centrifuged the water of
Lake Mendota and determined the nitrogen content of the water from

which the plankton had been removed. They found that at all times there was an excess of the soluble nitrogen over the insoluble nitrogen contained within the plankton organisms. This excess ranged from three to 20 times the amount of the plankton nitrogen. The following graphs compare the amounts of nitrogen found throughout the year in the surface and bottom waters of the Mendota (Figs. 97 and 98).

TABLE XIX.—FORMS OF NITROGEN IN WATERS OTHER THAN LAKE MENDOTA[1]

Sample	Date	Plankton N.	Soluble N.	N precipitated by phosphotungstic acid	Ammonia N.	Nitrite N.	Nitrate N.	Free amino N.	Peptide N	Non-amino N.
Devil's Lake	1922 Oct. 27	38.3	337.7	136.1	15.1[2]	0.0	20.8	21.8	103.6	343.6
Wingra Lake	1923 June 6	882.0	896.0	298.0	104.0	0.0	40.0	78.9	229.5	343.6
Monona Lake	June 28	388.8	885.8	326.6	119.2	3.6	50.9	49.0	315.8	347.3
Rock Lake	July 6	73.1	683.0	143.0	100.0	1.8	31.3	120.5	176.7	252.7
Devil's Lake	July 11	15.2	281.4	132.4	68.0	0.0	0.0	74.9	72.4	71.3
Geneva Lake	July 16	50.9	457.7	135.3	92.0	1.0	27.5	74.5	135.9	126.8
Green Lake	July 18	42.3	424.0	130.3	84.0	1.7	28.8	93.3	96.0	120.5
Kegonsa Lake	July 20	696.6	839.4	379.0	88.0	0.0	21.1	99.7	299.3	331.3
Waubesa Lake	July 20	229.0	842.6	367.2	76.0	0.0	22.7	115.5	294.0	334.4
Wisconsin River	July 30	161.4	655.8	352.0	148.0	0.0	21.2	83.5	302.8	100.3
Devil's Lake	Oct. 5	14.3	314.3	110.4	124.0	21.1	11.7	69.5	67.6	39.3
Wisconsin River	Oct. 12	90.3	506.4	143.8	116.0	0.0	19.3	54.1	143.5	173.5
Green Lake	Oct. 17	48.7	460.8	136.8	132.0	2.0	30.4	70.9	122.7	102.8
Wisconsin River	Nov. 21	53.4	521.2	209.2	100.0	1.6	26.1	64.5	277.1	51.9
Madeline Lake	Dec. 12	95.6	616.5	150.5	144.0	2.5	15.4	82.2	151.1	221.3
Bass Lake	Dec. 20	33.6	600.6	176.6	164.0	2.0	8.3	63.3	177.7	185.3
Turtle Lake	Jan. 18	30.5	650.6	196.6	132.0	4.2	27.8	82.5	192.5	211.6
Lake Michigan	Feb. 28	20.5	383.4	58.2	126.4	9.6	104.1	40.5	56.9	45.9
Yahara River	1922									
Before rain	July 6	609.3	596.2	301.2	14.7[2]	0.0	189.1	144.0	141.9	86.5
After rain	July 10	485.0	513.8	258.0	10.7[2]	0.0	78.7	107.1	100.1	137.2
Warner's Spring	Aug. 2	0.0	2,081.0	43.0	5.0[2]	0.0	2,058.0	0.0	0.0	18.0
	1923 Mar. 5	0.0	4,892.0	26.0	0.0	0.0	4,888.0	0.0	0.0	4.0
Yahara River	Mar. 14	186.1	1,967.1	107.1	260.0	4.6	1,076.7	74.7	186.7	364.4
Wingra Spring	July 12	.....	......	.....	40.0	1.8	2,702.0			

[1] DOMOGALLA *et al.*, 1925.
[2] Does not include free ammonia.

It seems from the types of nitrogen compounds and their seasonal distribution that they may play an important part in the nutrition of the organisms in the water.

Proteins and amino acids are present in the lake waters and are produced principally at the bottom where bacteria are active and few higher plants are present to make use of them. In the surface we have a reverse of these conditions. When the lake is stratified, there is no mixing of the top and bottom waters; consequently, a great difference exists, as for example, in the case of the free ammonia nitrogen and nitrate nitrogen in the following table.

TABLE XX.—THE DISTRIBUTION OF AMMONIA AND NITRATE NITROGEN IN LAKE
MENDOTA WATER

(In milligrams per cubic meter of water)

Station	Surface			10 meters			18–20 meters		
	Dates			Dates			Dates		
	2/1/24	3/3/24	3/11/25	2/1/24	3/3/24	3/11/25	2/1/24	3/3/24	3/11/25
Ammonia nitrogen									
I	104.0	180.0	152.0	120.0	204.0	196.0	176.0	392.0	472.0
II	120.0	196.0	164.0	128.0	216.0	280.0	200.0	640.0	544.0
III	120.0	193.0	180.0	144.0	236.0	236.0	208.0	528.0	528.0
IV	104.0	176.0	160.0	112.0	200.0	212.0	168.0	384.0	500.0
Nitrate nitrogen									
I	27.8	62.5	55.5	55.5	76.9	65.7	68.9	119.0	96.2
II	31.2	87.9	55.8	61.7	90.9	73.5	78.4	178.5	125.0
III	34.8	78.1	67.0	63.3	87.7	70.4	87.0	166.6	111.1
IV	29.7	66.6	61.6	58.8	96.1	68.5	80.0	125.0	104.2

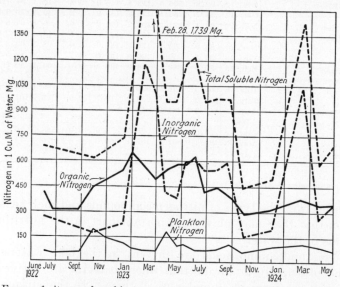

FIG. 98.—Forms of nitrogen found in 1 cu. m. of bottom water of Lake Mendota. (*Domogalla et al.*, 1925.)

Neutrality.—The general statement with regard to neutrality given
on pages 146 and 274 indicates that detailed studies of the hydrogen-ion

concentration of lakes are lacking and that until these have been made we cannot compare or classify lakes on this basis.

Birge and Juday's classification of "hard," "medium," and "soft-water" lakes includes the statement that "soft-water" lakes were acid, "hard-water" lakes were alkaline, and "medium" lakes were about neutral, at least at the surface. This classification is based on carbon-dioxide content and not hydrogen-ion measurement.

The pH of Lake Mendota has been studied by Juday (1924) over a period of years (Fig. 99). During the vernal and autumnal overturns

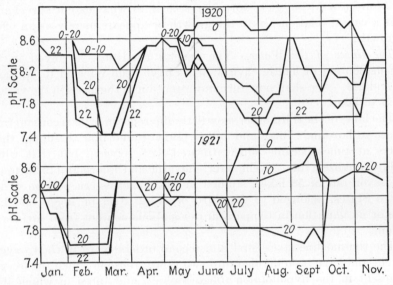

Fig. 99.—Diagram showing the distribution of hydrogen-ion concentration in Lake Mendota during the years 1920 and 1921. Vertical spaces represent the scales pH 7.4 to 9.0 for each year. Depth in meters is indicated on the curves. (*Adapted from Juday,* 1924.)

the water was mixed and the entire lake was about uniform. Conditions remained uniform and constant during the last half of November and all of December, 1920. There was an increase of pH in the epilimnion during the summer because of photosynthesis, and a decrease in the hypolimnion during the summer and winter periods of stagnation when decay was taking place.

Jewell and Brown (1924) have described a lake with a boggy margin which was found to have a pH value of 4.4. Phillip (1927) found pH values as high as 9.8 in mats of algae, while water, a meter away, showed pH values of 8.0 or less. Furthermore, it was found that these great differences in spatial distribution tend to be eliminated in the absence of photosynthesis during the night and are built up again in the presence of sunlight, reaching a maximum toward the end of the day. Such information leads one to believe that we must have more determinations on the subject of the distribution of hydrogen-ion concentration in time and space in individual lakes before we can compare one lake with another.

The true significance of hydrogen-ion concentration may be uncertain, as previously referred to. However, Brown and Jewell (1926) transferred great northern pike, the speckled bullhead, and yellow perch from a lake with a pH of 4.4 to 6.4, to water with a pH of 8.2 to 8.7, and the fish withstood this abrupt change. Whipple (1927) says: "It is well known that hydrogen-ion concentration will change with fluctuating plankton growth, but it is not always clear to what extent the change bears a causal relationship to the growth or appears merely as an effect of growth."

The Gases of the Water.—The general conditions involved in the gaseous content of lenitic environments have been referred to on pages 141 and 271. We shall now turn our attention to the gases in the various orders of lakes.

The lakes of the third order show little difference in oxygen content from surface to bottom. Birge and Juday (1911) found that the upper three meters at times became supersaturated with oxygen, but that winds readily equalized this. Kemmerer, Bovard, and Boorman (1923) found that seven out of 58 lakes, studied in the northwestern portion of the United States, belonged to the third order (2 to 11 m. deep) and had little or no variation in temperature or gaseous content from surface to bottom.

The thermocline lakes (first and second orders) vary in their oxygen content and have been divided into two types: those in which the oxygen is present in the hypolimnion (oligotrophic), and those in which it is entirely exhausted (eutrophic). This grouping does not correspond closely with the orders based upon temperature, but seems to be dependent upon the amount of dissolved organic matter, as previously stated.

The hypolimnion of Beasley and Garvin Lakes in Wisconsin may be devoid of oxygen for as long as five months, and half of the volume of Lake Mendota may be without oxygen in August. Most of the thermocline lakes of the northwestern United States, investigated by Kemmerer, Bovard, and Boorman (1923), had oxygen present in the hypolimnion throughout the year. Twenty-six of these were lakes of the first order, and seven were of the second order. Ten of these contained more oxygen in the hypolimnion than in the epilimnion.

Pressure.—Since a depth of 10.328 m. will increase pressure by one atmosphere, it follows that even third-order lakes may have the pressure nearly doubled at the bottom. Crater Lake, with a depth of 602 m., has a pressure of over 58 atmospheres or over 750 lb. per square inch at the bottom. This must be a considerable factor in the ecology of the benthic fauna.

The Taxonomic Groups of Animals.—A review of all the taxonomic groups of the typical lake fauna would be too extended for the present purpose. In general, the lake fauna is equivalent to the fresh-water fauna minus the lotic organisms. It differs from that of ponds in the greater number of vertebrates present and in a relatively small benthic and relatively large planktonic fauna when measured in per cent of the total fauna.

For the purpose of determinations Ward and Whipple (1918), Brauer (1909 to 1912) and other papers listed in the bibliography are referred to.

The Ecological Groups of Animals.—Our interest in the ecological groups is concerned with their ecological significance in the environment. Particular emphasis will be given to quantitative consideration not because qualitative studies are less deserving of attention, but because the quantitative data lend themselves to comparison and analysis.

Limnopelagic Animals—Plankton.—In spite of the voluminous literature of plankton, there is still a lack of qualitative and, particularly, quantitative data of such an order that direct comparisons can be made between one set of conditions and another. It is particularly difficult to calculate correlations between the various environmental factors and the quality and quantity of plankton.

The seasonal variations in plankton are more or less uniform throughout the temperate regions. In general, there are two maxima, one in the spring and the other in the fall, with periods of minimum amounts occurring shortly before each maximum. The spring maximum is largely due to an increase in diatoms. In some cases this may be due to several species increasing simultaneously, while in others it may be due almost entirely to a single species. This has been true in Crystal Lake, and Birge and Juday (1922) have found the same to be true of the Wisconsin lakes. In the diagram of the nannoplankton of Lake Mendota it is interesting to note the appearance of *Stephanodiscus astraea* in April, and May of each year, when it outnumbers all other planktonts for a short period of time.

During the summer period of minimum for the total plankton, the green and blue-green algae are present in large numbers and may, in the case of Crystal Lake, cause a summer increase in the total quantity of planktont. *Ceratium*, a flagellate, is consistently a summer planktont appearing in numbers shortly after the vernal overturn, and disappearing at or shortly after the time of the autumnal overturn. The following diagram from Birge and Juday (1922) is a graphic presentation of the numerical distribution of certain planktonts during 1916 and 1917 in Lake Mendota (Fig. 100). The work of Birge and Juday (1922) may be referred to for a comparison of a series of years which will show how typically this diagram represents the distribution of the plankton in time (Fig. 101).

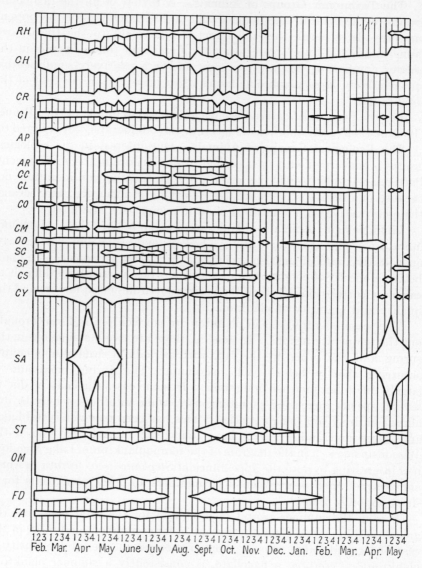

Fig. 100.—Diagram showing the numerical results obtained for the various organisms in the nannoplankton of Lake Mendota in 1916 and 1917. Number of individuals or colonies in 10 liters of water. The width of the area which represents the numbers of organisms is the radius of a circle with an area equal to the number of organisms. The following abbreviations have been used for the different organisms: *RH, Rhizopoda; CH, Chlorochromonas; CR, Cryptomonas; CI, Ciliates: AP, Aphanocapsa; AR, Arthrospira; CC, Chroococcus; CL, Closterium; CO, Coelospherium; CM, Cosmarium; OO, Oocystis; SC, Scenedesmus; SP, Sphaerocystis; CS, Cocconeis; CY, Cyclotella; SA, Stephanodiscus astraea; ST, Stephanodiscus; OM, organic matter; FD, fragments of diatoms; FA, fragments of Aphanizomenon.* (*From Birge and Juday, 1922.*)

The following diagram indicates the quantity of dry organic matter in the net plankton (nannoplankton), and total plankton for the same period as that covered by the diagrams of the numerical results. The dry organic matter has been selected as the measure because it eliminates a large amount of detritus ("Tripton" of Wilhelmi, 1917). The relative importance of the nannoplankton in the total plankton is well shown in this case (Fig. 102).

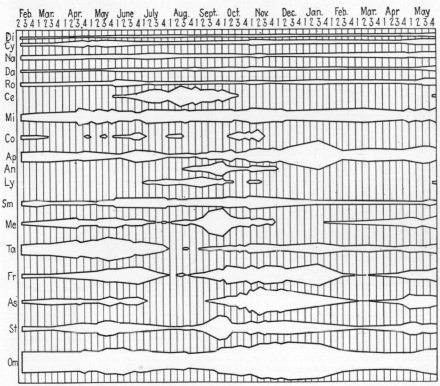

Fig. 101.—Diagram showing the numerical results for the net plankton of Lake Mendota in 1916 and 1917. Numbers of individuals or colonies per cubic meter of water. The width of the area which represents the number of organisms is the radius of a circle with an area equal to the number of organisms. The following abbreviations have been used for the different forms: *DI, Dioptomus; CY, Cyclops; NA,* Nauplii; *DA, Daphnia; RO, Rotifera; CE, Ceratium; MI, Microcystis; CO, Coelosphaerium; AP, Aphanizomenon; AN, Anabaena; SM, Staurastrum; ME, Melosira; TA, Tabellaria; FR, Fragilaria; OM,* organic matter. (*From Birge and Juday,* 1922.)

It seems evident from these data that the vernal and autumnal overturns have a profound influence on both the quantity and quality of the plankton. Thus the diatoms with their siliceous shells are brought into circulation during the period of complete circulation, and become the dominant plankton forms, only to decline in numbers after the waters become stratified and the hypolimnion stagnates, and they gradually settle to the bottom.

The vertical distribution of the plankton illustrates the importance of various physical factors in determining where organisms may live. Attention has already been called to the importance of viscosity and relative density as factors in determining the strata in which planktonts will float in a thermally stratified body of water. Perhaps there is no better way of emphasizing this than by studying Fig. 103. It is interesting to correlate the structure and habits of the various organisms with the physical conditions of the environment as evaluated by Stokes's formula (page 282). It will be noted that the vertical distribution of the plankton is profoundly influenced by the thermal stratification of the water.

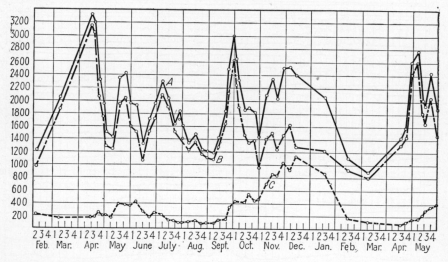

Fig. 102.—The amount of dry organic matter in the net plankton, the nannoplankton, and the total plankton of Lake Mendota in 1916 and 1917. Curve A represents the total plankton, curve B the nannoplankton, and curve C the net plankton. The curves show the number of milligrams per cubic meter of water. (*From Birge and Juday, 1922.*)

The vertical distribution of the plankton crustaceans has been a subject of considerable investigation and discussion. There is evidence to show that they are negative to strong light and consequently migrate upward at night and downward by day. Undoubtedly, other factors than light have an influence, for it has been shown that, in certain cases at least, the maximum numbers at the surface were reached during the night, and that the migration downward began sometime before daybreak (Juday, 1904). The general literature on this subject has been well summarized by Russell (1927).

Again, attention may be called to the inter-relations of the organisms and their environment which are so well illustrated by the plankton. The environment consists of water, the physical properties of which fix certain unalterable limitations of the aquatic environment. Super-imposed upon these limitations we have properties which are peculiar to bodies of water, which fix the amount of heat which the energy of insolation may impart to them and determine the degree of stratification and circulation which may result from the work of the wind. In this relatively fixed and stable physical system we have, in solution and suspension, various gases, chemical compounds, and organisms. The quantitative relationships of these are all intricately interdependent, yet not without the reasonable hope of ultimate analysis.

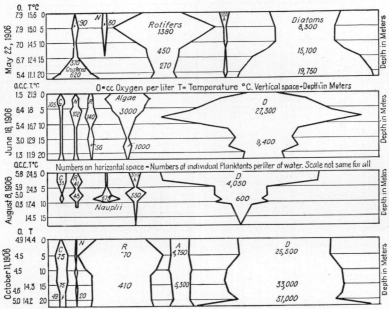

Fig. 103.—Graph showing depth, temperature, oxygen, and vertical distribution of net plankton in Lake Mendota.

The Biotic Potential of Plankton.—Lohmann (1911) stated that the quantities of bacteria, protozoa, and metazoa present in the water, should be weighted to correspond with their powers of reproduction. He suggested that one volume of bacteria equaled six volumes of Protista and 300 volumes of metazoa. Birge and Juday (1922) likened the quantity of plankton present at any given time, to the quantity of water present in a pool or a stream with water constantly flowing in on the one side and out on the other side. A measurement of the amount of water, present in the pool at any one time, would give no idea of the amount of water present in the pool throughout a year. In a similar way the quantity of plankton, present in an environment at any one time, gives no idea of the annual production. These authors estimate that bacteria may pass through several generations in one day; algae and protozoa may pass through one or two generations in a day; while certain crustacea may require two weeks or more for a generation. Taking all things into consideration, they estimate that there is a turnover in plankton production about once a week throughout the year. This implies a production of the average standing crop of plankton about 50 times each year and a consumption of a like amount by the environment, either by other organisms or a passing of it into solution or suspension in the water or its accumulation as a part of the bottom of the lake.

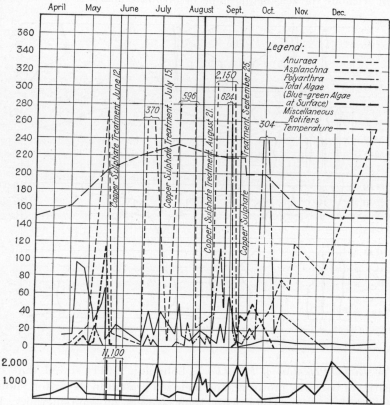

Fig. 104.—Graph showing the numbers of planktonts in a lake which was treated with copper sulphate at various times. (*Huff*, 1923.)

An examination of Huff's figure (Fig. 104) will emphasize the fact that certain planktonts do increase in numbers very rapidly. The same is true of *Stephanodiscus astraea* (Fig 100). This indicates an enormous potential which is more or less constantly held in check by the resistance of the environment. Possibly the consideration of the problem from the viewpoint of biotic potential and environmental resistance may make it possible to assign truer values to environmental factors.

The Total Quantity of Plankton.—It is not easy to make a comparison of the quantity of plankton in all three classes of lakes because of the lack of comparable data. The following table adapted from Birge and Juday (1922) will, however, give a comparison of lakes of the second and third order.

Lake	Mean depth, meters	Volume, cu.m.	Area, sq. km.	Average dry organic matter mg. per cu.m.	Yield, kg. per hectare	Yield, lb. per acre of surface
Mendota.........	25.6	478,370,000	39.40	1,974	240	214
Monona..........	22.5	118,887,000	14.10	3,163	267	238
Waubesa.........	11.1	59,060,000	8.24	4,398	241	215

It will be seen that the smallest lake produced the most plankton per unit volume of water, but that the depth was so much greater in the larger lakes that the quantity per unit area of surface was about the same in all cases.

The distribution of the total plankton in the various parts of Lake Mendota is shown in the following table from Birge and Juday:

THE QUANTITY OF ORGANIC MATTER IN THE TOTAL PLANKTON OF THE DIFFERENT STRATA OF LAKE MENDOTA ON AUG. 7, 1915.[1]

Stratum, meters	Kilograms per hectare	Pounds per acre	Percentage of total amount
0– 5	117.1	104.5	36.7
0–10	214.6	191.4	67.3
0–13	253.0	226.2	79.5
14–23	65.0	58.3	20.5
0–23	318.0	284.5	100.0

[1] From BIRGE and JUDAY, 1922.

When the rate of reproduction is taken into consideration, it was estimated that the annual production for Lake Mendota would amount to 12,000 kg. of dry organic matter per hectare of surface, or 10,700 lb. per acre. Estimating that the living organisms would weigh 10 times this amount, we may arrive at a yield of 107,000 lb. of plankton per acre of surface in a year's time.

Nekton.—Under the heading of Nekton we have the fishes as the predominating group. Certain phases of the activities of some of the aquatic insects may fall under this category, but in general they must be considered as benthic.

The majority of the studies of fish are qualitative rather than quantitative. The best quantitative comparison seems to be that based on Pearse's determinations (1921) on five Wisconsin lakes.

A COMPARISON OF FIVE WISCONSIN LAKES AND OF THE TOTAL AVERAGE CATCH OF FISH PER HOUR IN GILL NETS SET IN THESE LAKES[1]

Lake	Volume, cu.m.	Depth, meters	Surface, sq. km.	Temperature, summer, °C.	Total catch per hour
Wingra...............	2,761,000	4.3	2.2	26.8 to 26.8	7.703
Mendota..............	478,370,000	25.6	39.4	9.7 to 23.3	5.050
Geneva...............	434,773,000	43.3	22.1	7.3 to 23.6	3.285
Green................	984,825,000	72.2	29.7	4.9 to 21.6	3.677
Pepin................	594,350,000	17.1	65.0	23.7 to 26.4	2.553

[1] Adapted from PEARSE, 1920.

Lake Pepin has been included in the above comparison as a matter of interest. However, it is a part of the Mississippi River and is not directly comparable with the other lakes as may be seen from its temperatures. Omitting Lake Pepin and comparing the four other lakes on the basis of their temperatures, it will be evident that Wingra is a third-order lake and that Mendota is of the second order. (Compare Pearse's temperature data with those of Birge and Juday, page 313.) Geneva might be considered more or less intermediate between the first and second order on the basis of its temperature, while Green Lake is typically of the first order.

The total catch per hour is greatest in the shallow third-order lake, and least in the first-order lake with the lowest temperature of the bottom water. It happens that Green Lake, while a first-order lake, is of the oligotrophic type, and does not have its oxygen supply exhausted from its bottom water during the summer. Mendota, with a higher temperature in the hypolimnion, is eutrophic, and has no oxygen present for a considerable part of each summer.

Many factors are concerned with the abundance of fish, and it must not be assumed that any one factor can be relied upon to predict their abundance. Since we are not primarily concerned with the ecology of fishes, we shall not proceed with the analysis of the factors affecting their abundance in different lakes. Such quantitative studies as those of Pearse (1920, 1921), Smith (1925), and others may be referred to as significant in such work.

The distribution of fish in depth may be illustrated with the following diagrams which have been adapted from Pearse (1920). This comparison of a eutrophic lake, such as Mendota with its hypolimnion without oxygen, with the oligotrophic Green Lake, with oxygen in the hypolimnion, suggests that the ciscos, for instance, are predominantly bottom feeders, but that they are not permitted to get to the deep waters of the bottom in eutrophic lakes such as Mendota because of the absence of oxygen.

TABLE XXI.—SUMMARY OF GILL-NET CATCHES IN GREEN LAKE, 1919, GIVING DEPTH AND CATCH PER HOUR[1]

Depth, inches	Temp. range, °C	Size mesh, inches	Time set, hours	Blue-gill	Rock bass	Perch	Pick-erel	Carp	Sucker	Small-mouth black bass	Cisco
1 to 5	19.7	¾	117.5	....	0.01	0.11	0.01				
	1	117.5	....	0.01	....	0.04					
	to	1½	117.5	0.03	0.02	0.01	0.06	0.01			
		2	117.5	0.05	0.01	....	0.01	....	0.01		
	22.2	3	117.5								
			Total	0.08	0.05	0.12	0.012	0.01	0.01		
5 to 10	16.4	¾	97.2	....	....	0.01					
	1	97.2	....	0.02	....	....	....	....		0.01	
	to	1½	97.2	....	0.03	....	0.02				
		2	69.0	0.014	....	....	0.044				
	20.6	3	69.0								
			Total	0.014	0.05	0.01	0.064	....	....		0.01
10 to 20	8	¾	22.7								
	1	22.7									
	to	1½	22.7								
		2	46.2	....	....	....	0.043				
	16.6	3	46.2	....	....	....	....	.. ..	0.43	0.02	
20 to 40	5.8	¾	46.6								
	1	46.6									
	to	1½	46.6								
		2	46.6								
	7(?)	3	46.6								
40 to 72	4.8	¾	93.8	....	....	....	....	....	....	....	0.053
	1	93.8	....	....	....	....	....	....	....	0.980
	to	1½	93.8	....	....	....	....	....	....	....	0.350
		2	93.8	....	....	....	....	....	....	....	0.0320
	5.8	3	93.8	....	....	....	....	....	....	....	0.0320
										Total	1.4470

[1] Adapted from PEARSE, 1920.

Pearse (1918) found that perch make excursions to the oxygen free hypolimnion. His experiments showed that they might endure confinement in the hypolimnion for a period of two hours, during which time they used a part of the oxygen from the swim bladder.

Smith (1925) found that fish died when confined in cages below the thermocline. A difference of two and one-half feet in depth was sufficient to make the difference between death and survival.

Benthos.—Benthic animals have already been defined as those which live on or in the bottom of the aquatic environment and are primarily dependent upon the latter for support. It has been pointed out that many animals may be predominantly benthic and yet make rather extended excursions up into the open water, being limited, however, by the necessity of returning to the bottom when they cease active swimming because of their great specific gravity. This is true of most insects. The adult insects, in general, are heavier than water in the absence of

TABLE XXII.—SUMMARY OF GILL-NET CATCHES IN LAKE MENDOTA, 1919, GIVING DEPTH AND CATCH PER HOUR[1]

Depth, meters	Temp. range, °C	Size mesh, inches	Time set, hours	Perch	Crappie	Rock bass	Blue-gill	Sucker	Wall-eyed pike	White bass	Carp	Large-mouth black bass	Cisco	Pickerel	Cray-fish
0 to 5	20.3	3/4	70.0	0.07	0.01	0.01									
	to	1	70.0	0.34	....	....	0.01	0.01							
		1½	95.5	....		....	....	....							
	24.1	2	118.0	....					0.01	0.01	0.01				
		3	142.5	....						....	0.03				
		Total	Total	0.41	0.01	0.01	0.01	0.01	0.01	0.01	0.04				
5 to 10	14	3/4	47.5	0.03											
	to	1	71.0	2.52								0.01			
		1½	69.0	....		....		....		0.04	....	....	0.01	0.01	0.01
	24	2	23.5	....							0.04				
		3	47.5	....							0.04	0.02			
		Total	Total	2.55						0.04	0.08	0.03	0.01	0.01	0.01
10 to 15	10.4	3/4	48.0	0.38											
	to	1	48.0	1.36							0.01		0.01		
		1½	95.5	....							0.01		0.02		
	15.4	2	116.5	....											
		3	94.5	....											
		Total	Total	1.74							0.02		0.03	0.01	0.01
15 to 23	9.4	3/4	116.0	0.01									0.03		
	to	1	119.5												
		1½	71.5												
	10.4	2	71.5												
		3	71.5												
		Total	Total	0.01									0.03		

[1] Adapted from PEARSE, 1920.

their air store and lighter than water when in possession of it. Consequently, it is ordinarily necessary for them to attach themselves in order to remain on the bottom, and to swim actively to maintain themselves in the water.

We may subdivide the benthos into littoral, sublittoral, and abyssal on the basis of depth, or we may divide it into "phytobenthos" and "geobenthos" to distinguish between that portion of the bottom which is covered with plants and that which is not. In general, the latter distinction coincides with the former in that the phytobenthos is along the shore or in the littoral region. Indeed, the limit of the plant zone is a function of depth and may, therefore, constitute a biotic measure of depth. When used in this general way, it is not possible to distinguish between the bare shores because of wave action and the unvegetated bottom areas beyond the depth of the plant zone. A more specific use of the terms, phytobenthos and geobenthos, serves to distinguish between specific habitats; as on plants, or on the bottom soil or rocks, regardless of whether the soil be among plants or far beyond their depth zone.

The littoral benthos of lakes may be defined, arbitrarily, as extending to a depth equivalent to the outer limit of the phytobenthos. The abyssal benthos will then lie in the water deeper than the littoral benthos. For Crystal Lake, Minn., the limit of the littoral benthos is ordinarily between 3 and 4 m. Baker (1918) gives this as less than 3 m. for Oneida Lake, N. Y., and Rickett (1922) found the plant zones of Lake Mendota, Wisc., to extend as far as 7 m.

Rickett (1922) divided the plant zone into three zones as follows: zone 1:0 to 1 m.; zone 2:1 to 3 m.; zone 3:3 to 7m. *Potomogeton pectinatus*, *P. Richardsonii*, and *Vallisneria* dominated zone 1. *Potomogeton amplifolius* dominated zone 2, together with masses of *Cerotophyllum* and *Myriophyllum*. Zone 3 had only scanty vegetation and has probably been neglected in general observations by other investigators. The quantity of plants in these zones may be tabulated as follows (Rickett, 1922):

Quantity of plants	Zone 1	Zone 2	Zone 3
Kg. per hectare, wet..........................	16,000	24,000	13,000
Kg. per hectare, dry...........................	1,800	2,700	1,500
Lbs. per acre, wet.............................	14,000	21,000	11,000
Lbs. per acre, dry.............................	1,600	2,400	1,300

Attention has previously been called to the fact that the rooted plants greatly increase the subtratum to which organisms may be attached. .

The leaves of the submerged plants are characteristically covered with the immature forms of insects. Chironomid larvae form their tubes on the leaves, trichoperous larvae attach their cases, and ephemerid larvae feed about over the surface of the leaves. Near the sublittoral zone there may be large numbers of *Hydra* (Welch and Loomis, 1924). In Crystal Lake, Minn., as many as 90 *hydra* have been found on a square inch of leaf surface.

The sublittoral region is usually considered to lie just beyond the outer limit of plant growth. Lundbeck (1926) divides the sublittoral zone into the upper and lower sublittoral. This is usually near the lower limit of circulation of water and is consequently often characterized by a steep slope and an accumulation of molluscan shells. Temperature seichs may cause the level of the thermocline to fluctuate and expose the inhabitants to sudden changes of temperature and oxygen content.

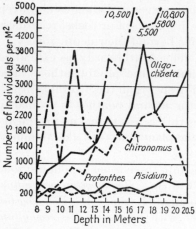

FIG. 105.—Graph showing the number of individual organisms per square meter of the bottom of Lake Mendota at the depths indicated. The numbers are the averages for the summer.

The consideration of the benthic animals will be confined to data with regard to the quantitative relationships. The biotic potential will be briefly considered, but space will not permit a detailed account of the natural history of the organisms. Needham and Lloyd (1916), Mial (1895), and others, cited in the bibliographies under the various groups of organisms, may be referred to for the details of the life histories.

The animals of the abyssal benthos are interesting in that they are adjusted to living in an environment which is among the most uniform in the constancy of its low temperature, continual darkness, and high pressure. In certain of the thermocline lakes—the eutrophic type—the oxygen varies from saturation to entire absence for a considerable period in the benthos of the hypolimnion. The substratum is an ooze which may be a suspension of particles almost colloidal in dimensions. Here, under these exceptional physical conditions, we have a considerable fauna.

The graph of the numbers of benthic organisms in Lake Mendota cannot express the fluctuations in the course of a year (Fig. 105). The following graphs of the abundance of *Chironomus* (Fig. 106) and *Corethra* (Fig. 107) indicate that *Chironomus* lives very well in the hypolimnion in the absence of oxygen, while *Corethra* shows a minimum in its numbers during the period of stagnation for each of the three years. This period represents the adult stage.

Johnson and Munger (1930) found as many as 7,000 *Chironomus plumosus* per square yard in Lake Pepin, which is a part of the Mississippi River. They estimated the average for the entire lake in July as 3,000 per square yard.

It is interesting to note that Needham and Lloyd (1916) consider *Corethra* as a plankton insect, while Juday (1922) says that it becomes benthic after a short period of larval life. The adult insects appear in great numbers during midsummer. Consequently, it is to be expected that the numbers of larvae would be greatly reduced at that time.

The littoral benthos of the phytal region (according to Mutt-kowski, 1918) is represented on the basis of the results of Muttkowski (1918), Fig. 108, and Adamstone (1924), and Adamstone and Hark-ness (1923), Figs. 109 and 110. Muttkowski's (1918) data should be comparable with those of Juday,

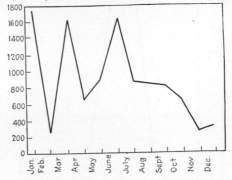

Fig. 106.—The numbers of *Chironomus* larvae per square meter of bottom below the 20-m. level in Lake Mendota. The numbers are the average of one to 23 samples for each month during 1917. (*Adapted from Juday, 1922.*)

as they give the data on the littoral benthos in the same way that Juday gives them for the abyssal benthos for Lake Mendota.

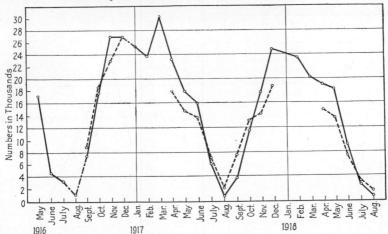

Fig. 107.—The average number of larvae of *Corethra punctipennis* in thousands per square meter of bottom for the different months during the period of the observations. The vertical spaces show the numbers of individuals from zero to 30,000. The solid line represents the average numbers for one station and the broken line represents the combined averages of five deep-water stations.

Many factors are concerned in determining the spatial distribution of organisms in lakes. The evidence presented does little more than

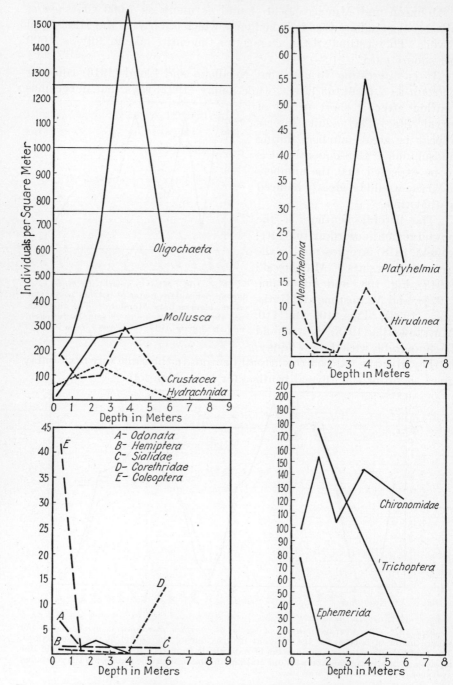

Fig. 108.—Graphs showing the numbers of benthic organisms per square meter at various depths in the littoral zone of Lake Mendota. (*Adapted from Muttkowski, 1918.*)

suggest the importance of depth and the distinction between the physical conditions of the littoral zone and the deep or abyssal zone. Adamstone and Harkness (1923) show the influence of the type of bottom on the numbers of *Chironomus* found (Fig. 111). Muttkowski (1918) has qualitative data on the effect of the type of bottom on the fauna. General conclusions must, however, wait until we have amassed sufficient data to make statistical correlations.

The aquatic insects in general are littoral with the exception of *Corethra* and certain *Chironomidae*, which reach their greatest abundance in the abyssal geobenthos. The insects which must have free air for

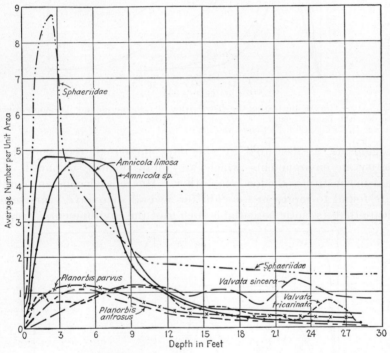

FIG. 109.—Curves illustrating the distribution of Mollusca according to depth in Lake Nipigon. (*Adapted from Adamstone, 1923.*)

respiration, the *Coleoptera* for instance, are quite limited to the littoral phytobenthos. Here, with the increased area of substratum and the quiet surface film, they are present in greatest numbers. The *Ephemerida*, May flies, and *Trichoptera*, caddis flies, are confined to the littoral region although some species are to be found as far out as the sublittoral region.

Nearly all of the data tend to show a reduction in the numbers of organisms between the littoral and abyssal areas. This is very nearly the area representing the thermocline and may possibly be due to its influence. Beyond the phytobenthos, the bottom ooze is largely inhabited by tube dwellers.

Biotic Potential and Environmental Resistance.—The biotic potential of the fauna is difficult to estimate because of the small amount of data at hand and the lack of organization of what is available.   The quantities

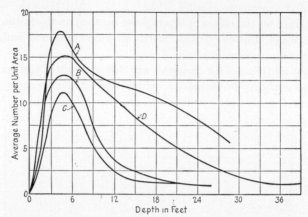

Fig. 110.—Curves illustrating the distribution of Ephemerida and Trichoptera according to depth in Lake Nipigon.   *A, Hexagenia bilineata; B, Ephemera simulaus; C, Caenus diminuta; D,* Trichoptera.   (*Adamstone,* 1924.)

of organisms, as measured by the data presented, represent the net quantity in environments which are more or less balanced.   Each organism constitutes the food of another.   Hence, such constant numbers as are found to represent *Corethra* for several successive years seem to indicate that its biotic potential is such that the environmental resistance

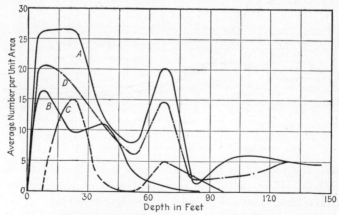

Fig. 111.—Curves illustrating the distribution of Chironomidae according to depth in Lake Nipigon.   *A,* on mud bottom; *B,* on sand bottom; *C,* on clay bottom; *D,* on all bottoms.   (*Adamstone and Harkness,* 1923.)

always reduces the numbers to about the same point.   This, in turn, must mean that the environmental resistance itself is relatively constant, which seems reasonable so far as physical conditions on the benthic regions are known.

TABLE XXIII.—MUTTKOWSKI'S (1918) SUMMARY OF ZONATION FOR LAKE MENDOTA

Area	Depth, meters	Physical	Physiological	Biota
I. *Littoral*-Phytal.				
A. Eulittoral-Euphytal.				
1. Shore line.	0–1	Varied.	Strong molar agents, extremes of temperature, intermittent feeding	Forms with shelters, clingers, burrowers, visitors-swimmers.
a. Rock.	0–1	Rock, boulders, rough aspect.	Strong surf, food-*Cladophora*.	*Cladophora*—pliant and clinging. Animals either flattened or with flat shelter, or with appressed methods; clingers.
b. Cobbles (stony).	0–1	Stones, pebbles and smooth aspect.	Fluctuating rubble, food scant-less *Cladophora*, fewer clinging surfaces.	Fewer clingers, no crawlers; visitors and burrowers.
c. Sand.		Sand with pebbles.	Shifting bottom, no clinging surfaces.	No vegetation, no clingers; visitors and burrowers.
2. Rachion (breaker line).	1–1½	Stones with pebbles.	Greatest wave action and under-tow; little plant food.	Burrowers, strongest clingers, sheltered species, swimmers.
3. Plant zone.	1–6	Upright plants. Potomogeton.	Exposed to molar agents, clinging surfaces, abundant food, shelter.	Clingers, crawlers, swimmers, no specially adapted species. *Phytophaga* and *carnivora*.
a. Upright plants.	1–5	Najas, Vallisn. Bottom sand.	Less exposure to molar agents, greatest photosynthesis.	Clingers, more crawlers, swimmers.
b. Recumbent plants.	4–6	Plants, bent and trailing	No exposure, food waste and plants.	Crawlers, sprawlers, swimmers, chiefly phytophags and carnivores, some necrophags.
c. Bottoms.	Various	Sand, plant marl, rarely mud.		
B. *Sublittoral*-Dysphytal.				
4. Shell Zone.	6–8	Shell, with sand and mud.	Lower limit of wave action, food-waste, dying plants.	Crawlers, burrowers, tube dwellers, scavengers, carnivores.
II. *Aphytal*-Plantless.				
C. Aphytal Zone.	7–25	Mud, with deflux.	No molar action, slight activities anaërobic for several months, stenothermal.	Anaërobes, tube builders, burrowers, swimmers, aestivators.

The high biotic potential of the May flies has been referred to in connection with the ponds. Their actual numbers as shown by the data presented are not great, which should indicate a great environmental resistance.

The energy relationships of lakes and their faunas are so circumscribed and measurable that quantitative studies should lead to the possibility of considering the relative numbers of the various organisms required to maintain the society in the state of a conservative biotic association.

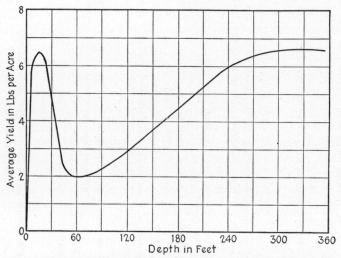

Fig. 112.—The average yield of fish food organisms, in pounds of dry weight per acre, at various depths throughout Lake Nipigon. (*Adamstone*, 1924.)

The Quantity of Life Present.—It has been shown (Rickett, 1924) that the rooted plants may produce from 1,300 to 2,400 lb. of dry matter to the acre in the littoral zone of Lake Mendota. This is quite comparable to the production of 2.5 tons of dry matter from alfalfa, 1.3 tons from oats, or 2.5 tons of corn on cultivated soil, which are good average yields for conditions of cultivation. Aquiculture might increase the yields just as agriculture has done in the past.

Adamstone's curve of the average yield of fish-food organisms for Lake Nipigon does not give an adequate idea of the total weight of these organisms because they were counted as individuals and the total weight computed (Fig. 112). Furthermore, the data on the rooted plants represent an annual crop, while Adamstone's data represent the standing crop at the time of the determination.

Juday (1922) determined the weights of the benthic animals of the intermediate and deep-water zones of Lake Mendota as follows:

Depth, meters	Live weight, kg. per H.	Lb. per acre	Dry weight, kg. per H.	Lb. per acre
8–20	359.6	320.7	48.2	42.9
20.5–23.5	696.8	620.7	76.6	68.1

This gives us a live weight of from 300 to 600 lb. per acre of *Oligochaeta*, *Pisidium*, *Chironomus*, *Corethra*, and *Protenthes*. Furthermore, this represents only the average standing crop which is not comparable with the annual production.

Our data on the production of fish are also rather limited, but Barney and Canfield (1922) report that the U. S. Biological Station at Fairport, Iowa, has produced a net weight of Bluegill sunfish which amounted to 286 lb. per acre in 1918; 203 lb. in 1919; 333 lb. in 1920; and 374 lb. in 1921. This was a net production which left the pond in the same relative condition at the start of each season and no food was introduced at the beginning of the year.

Summarizing our data, we have 284 lb. plankton per acre live weight; 300 to 600 lb. benthic organisms per acre live weight, and a net production of 300 lb. fish per acre live weight. The weight of the fish is a net weight, while the others are standing crops. Nevertheless, the example serves to illustrate the value of quantitative data in making comparisons and drawing conclusions.

BIBLIOGRAPHY

LAKES

ADAMS, CHARLES C.: The Ecology and Economics of Oneida Lake Fish, *Roosevelt Wild Life Ann.*, vol. 1, nos. 3 and 4, November, 1928; *Bull. of N. Y. State Coll. of Forestry*, Syracuse, N. Y.

ADAMSTONE, F. B.: The Distribution and Economic Importance of the Bottom Fauna of Lake Nipigon with an Appendix on the Bottom Fauna of Lake Ontario, *Univ. Toronto Studies* 25, *Bur. Fish. Lab. Pub.* 24, pp. 35–100, 1924.

ADAMSTONE, F. B., and W. J. K. HARKNESS: The Bottom Organisms of Lake Nipigon, *Univ. Toronto Studies*, *Ont. Fish. Res. Lab. Pub.*, series XX, no. 15, pp. 123–170, 1923.

ALLEN, W. E.: The Problem of Significant Variables in Natural Environments, *Ecology*, **10**: 223–237, 1929.

BAIL, OSKAR: Ergebnisse einer vorläufigen bakteriologischen Untersuchung der Nordosthälfte des Grossen Plöner Sees, *Forschungsberichte der biologischen Station zu Plön*, **X**: 50–59, 1903.

BAKER, F. C.: The Productivity of Invertebrate Fish Food on the Bottom of Oneida Lake, with Special Reference to Mollusks, *Tech. Bull. N. Y. State Coll. of Forestry*, vol. XVIII, no. 2, 1918. 246 pp.

BARNEY, R. L., and H. L. CANFIELD: The Farm Pond and Its Productivity, *Fins, Feathers, and Fur*, **30**: 3–7, 1922.

BIGELOW, N. K.: The Plankton of Lake Nipigon and Environs, *Univ. Toronto Studies, Ont. Fish. Res. Lab. Pub.*, **13**: 41–66, 1923.

BIRGE, E. A.: Plankton Studies of Lake Mendota. II. The Crustacea of the Plankton from July, 1894–December, 1896, *Trans. Wis. Acad. Sci., Arts and Letters,* 1897; vol. XI, pp. 274–448, 28 pl., Madison, 1896–1897.

————: The Heat Budgets of American and European Lakes, *Trans. Wis. Acad. Sci., Arts and Letters,* vol. XVIII, 1915–1916.

————: The Thermocline and Its Biological Significance, *Trans. Amer. Micros. Soc.,* **XXV**: 5–53, 2 pl., Menasha, Wis., 1903.

————: An Unregarded Factor in Lake Temperatures, *Trans. Wis. Acad. Sci.,* **XVI**: 989–1004, 1910.

————: On the Evidence for Temperature Seiches, *Trans. Wis. Acad. Sci., Arts and Letters,* vol. XVI, pt. II, pp. 1005–1016, 1910.

————: Absorption of the Sun's Energy by Lakes, *Science,* **38**: 702, 1913.

————: The Work of the Wind in Warming a Lake, *Trans. Wis. Acad. Sci., Arts and Letters,* pt. II, **XVIII**: 341–391, 1915.

BIRGE, E. A. (chairman), C. H. EIGENMANN, C. A. KOFOID, G. C. WHIPPLE, H. B. WARD: *Report of the Limnological Commission,* **XXII**: 193–196, 1903.

BIRGE, E. A., and CHANCEY JUDAY: Plankton Studies of Lake Mendota, *Trans. Wis. Acad. Sci., Arts and Letters,* **X**: 421–484, 1895; **XI**: 274–448, 1896.

————: The Inland Lakes of Wisconsin. The Dissolved Gases of the Water and Their Biological Significance, *Wis. Biol. & Nat. Hist. Survey Bull.,* vol. XXII, sci. ser. 7, 1911. Madison. 259 pp.

————: A Limnological Study of the Finger Lakes of New York, *U. S. Bur. Fisheries, Bull.,* **XXXII**: 525–609, 1912.

————: The Inland Lakes of Wisconsin. The Hydrography and Morphometry of the Lakes, *Wis. Geol. and Nat. Hist. Survey Bull.,* vol. XXVII, sci. ser. 9, Madison, 1914. 137 pp.

————: Further Limnological Observations on the Finger Lakes of New York, *U. S. Bur. Fisheries Bull.,* 1919–1920; vol. XXXVII; Doc. 905, pp. 211–252, October, 1921.

————: The Inland Lakes of Wisconsin. I. The Plankton, Its Quantity and Chemical Composition, *Wis. Geol. and Nat. Hist. Survey Bull.* 64, sci. ser. 13, pp. 192–219, 1922.

————: The Organic Content of the Water of Small Lakes, *Proc. Amer. Phil. Soc.,* **66**: 357–372, 1927.

————: Transmission of Solar Radiation by the Waters of Inland Lakes, *Trans. Wis. Acad. Sci., Arts and Letters,* **24**: 509–580, 1929.

BIRGE, E. A., CHANCEY JUDAY, and H. W. MARCH: The Temperature of the Bottom Deposits of Lake Mendota, *Trans. Wis. Acad. Sci., Arts and Letters,* **23**: 187–231, 1928.

BISHOP, SHERMAN C., and JOHN M. CLARKE: A Scientific Survey of Turners Lake, Ile-au Haut, Maine, N. Y. State Museum, Printed Privately, 1923. 29 pp., 2 maps, 20 pl.

BLACK, C. S.: Chemical Analysis of Lake Deposits, *Trans. Wis. Acad. Sci., Arts and Letters,* **24**: 127–133, 1929.

BORNER, LOUIS: Die Bodenfauna des St. Moritzer Sees. Eine monographische Studie, *Arch. Hydrobiol.,* **13**: 1–91, 209–281, 1921–22.

BRANNON, M. A.: Factors Influencing the flora of Devil's Lake, North Dakota, *Internat. Rev. Gesamm. Hydrobiol. u. Hydrog.,* **4**: 291–299, 1911.

BRAUER, A.: "Die Süsswasserfauna Deutschlands," Hrsg. von Prof. Dr. A. Brauer, 1909–1912.

BREHM, V.: Zur zoographischen Analyse der Fauna der Alpenseen, *Internat. Rev. Gesamm. Hydrobiol. u. Hydrog.,* **4**: 136–139, 1911.

————: Die Fauna der Lunzer Seen verglichen mit der der anderen Alpenseen, *Internat. Rev. Gesamm. Hydrobiol. u. Hydrog.*, **6**: 528–537, 1914.

BUCHANAN, J. Y.: On the Distribution of Temperature in Loch Lomond during the Autumn of 1885, *Proc. Roy. Soc.*, Edinburgh, vol. XIII, pp. 403–428, 1886.

CLEMENS, WILBERT A.: Limnology of Lake Nipigon in 1923, *Univ. Toronto Studies*, 1924; biol. ser. 25, *Pub. of the Research Lab.* **22**: 3–14, 1924.

————: The Limnology of Lake Nipigon in 1923, *Univ. Toronto Studies*, 1923; no. 25, *Bur. Fisheries Lab. Pub.* **22–26**: 1–14, 1924.

————: The Limnology of Lake Nipigon in 1922, *Univ. Toronto Studies*, biol. ser., *Bur. Fisheries Lab. Pub.* 17, 1924.

COKER, R. E.: Lake Titicaca: The Most Remarkable Lake of the World, *Internat. Rev. Gesamm. Hydrobiol. u. Hydrog.*, **4**: 174–182, 1911.

COLEMAN, A. P.: Glacial and Post-glacial Lakes in Ontario, *Univ. Toronto Studies*, *Ont. Fisheries Lab. Pub.*, ser. No. 21, No. X, 1923.

CUNNINGHAM, WILLIAM A.: The Fauna of African Lakes: A Study in Comparative Limnology with Special Reference to Tanganyika, *Proc. Zool. Soc.*, London, Pt. 4, pp. 507–622, 2 figs., 1920.

DILLER, J. S.: Geological History of Crater Lake, U. S. Dept. Int., "Crater Lake National Park," Washington, 1912. 31 pp., 27 figs.

DOMOGALLA, B. P., and E. B. FRED: Ammonia and Nitrate Studies of Lakes near Madison, Wis., *Jour. Amer. Soc. Agron*, **18**: 897–911, 1926.

DOMOGALLA, B. P., E. B. FRED and W. H. PETERSON: Seasonal Variations in the Ammonia Content of Lake Waters, *Jour. Amer. Waterworks Assoc.*, **15**: 369–385, 1926.

DOMOGALLA, B. P., CHANCEY JUDAY, and W. H. PETERSON: The Forms of Nitrogen Found in Certain Lake Waters, *Jour. Biol. Chem.*, **63**: 269–285, 1925.

EVERMANN, B. W., and H. W. CLARK: "Lake Maxinkuckee, a Physical and Biological Survey," Indianapolis, 1920. 2 vols.

FORBES, S. A.: The Lake as a Microcosm, *Peoria Sci. Assoc. Bull.*, pp. 77–87, 1887; Rept. with Revisions as from *Peoria Sci. Assoc. Bull.*, pp. 1–15, 1887.

FOREL, F. A.: Le Leman, monographie limnologique, Lausanne, 1892–1904. 3 vols.

GÖTZINGER, GUSTAV: Bericht über die physikalisch-geographischen Untersuchungen an dem Lunzer Seen, *Internat. Rev. Gesamm. Hydrobiol. u. Hydrog.*, **6**: 538–547, 1914.

HALBFASS, W.: Ergebnisse neuerer simultaner Temperaturmessungen in einigen tiefen Seen Europas, Petermann's Mitteil., vol. 56, II, p. 59, Gotha, 1910.

HANKINSON, T. L.: Biological Survey of Walnut Lake, *Rept. Geol. Survey*, Lansing, Mich., pp. 157–271, 1908.

HOFSTEN, N. VON: Zur Kenntniss der Tiefenfauna des Brienzer und des Thuner Sees, *Arch. Hydrobiol. u. Planktonkunde*, **7**: 1–62, 1912.

HUBER, GOTTFRIED: Monographische Studien im Gebiete der Montiggler Seen, *Arch. Hydrobiol. u. Planktonkunde*, **1**: 1–81, 123–210, 1906.

HUFF, N. L.: Observations on the Relation of Algae to Certain Aquatic Animals of Vadnais Lake, *Minn. Univ., Studies Biol. Sci.*, **4**: 185–198, 1923.

JEWELL, MINNA E., and HAROLD BROWN: The Fishes of an Acid Lake, *Trans. Amer. Micros. Soc.*, **43**: 77–84, 1924.

JOHNSON, M. S., and FRANCIS MUNGER: Observations on Excessive Abundance of the Midge *Chironomus plumosus* at Lake Pepin, *Ecology*, **11**: 110–126, 1930.

JUDAY, CHANCEY: Summary of Quantitative Investigations on Green Lake, Wisconsin, *Internat. Rev. Gesamm. Hydrobiol. u. Hydrog.*, pp. 2–12, 1924.

————: The Diurnal Movement of Plankton Crustacea, *Trans. Wis. Acad. Sci., Arts and Letters*, **XIV**: 534–568, 1903.

———: A Study of Twin Lakes, Colo., with Especial Consideration of the Food of Trout, *U. S. Bur. Fisheries Bull.*, **XXVI**: 147–178, 1907.

———: Studies on Some Lakes in the Rocky and Sierra Nevada Mountains, *Trans. Wis. Acad. Sci., Arts and Letters*, **15**: 781–794, 2 pl., 1 map, 1907.

———: Limnological Studies on Some Lakes in Central America, *Trans. Wis. Acad. Sci., Arts and Letters*, **XVIII**: 214–250, 1915.

———: A Second Report on Limnological Apparatus, *Trans. Wis. Acad. Sci., Arts and Letters*, **XX**: 533–553, 1921.

———: Quantitative Studies of the Bottom Fauna in the Deeper Waters of Lake Mendota, *Trans. Wis. Acad. Sci., Arts and Letters*, **XX**: 461–493, 1921.

JUDAY, CHANCEY, E. B. FRED, and FRANK C. WILSON: The Hydrogen-ion Concentration of Certain Wisconsin Lake Waters, *Trans. Amer. Micros. Soc.*, vol. **XLIII, 4**: 177–190, 1924.

KEMMERER, GEORGE, J. F. BOVARD, W. R. BOORMAN: Northwestern Lakes of the United States. Biological and Chemical Studies with Reference to Possibilities in Production of Fish, *U. S. Bur. Fisheries Bull.*, vol. XXXIX, Doc. 944, pp. 51–140, 1923.

KLUGH, A. BROOKER: The Productivity of Lakes, *Quart. Rev. Biol.*, **1**: 572–577, 1926.

———: Light Penetration into the Bay of Fundy and into Chamcook Lake, New Brunswick, *Ecology*, **7**: 90–93, 1927.

KNIPOWITSCH, N.: Hydrobiologische Untersuchungen im Kaspischen Meer in den Jahren 1914–15, *Internat. Rev. Gesamm. Hydrobiol. u. Hydrog.*, **10**: 394–440, 561–602, 1922.

LECONTE, JOHN: Physical Studies of Lake Tahoe, pt. I, *Overland Monthly*, **II**: 506–516, 1883; *ibid.*, pt. II, **II**: 595–612, 1883; *ibid.*, pt. III, *Overland Monthly*, pp. 41–46, 1893.

LOHMANN, H.: Über das Nannoplankton und die Zentrifugierung kleinster Wasserproben zur Gewinnung desselben in lebendem Zustande, *Internat. Rev. Gesamm. Hydrobiol. u. Hydrog.*, **4**: 1–38, 1911.

LUNDBECK, J.: Die Bodentierwelt Norddeutscher Seen, *Arch. Hydrobiol.*, 1926.

MARSH, C. D.: The Plankton of Fresh-water Lakes, *Trans. Wis. Acad. Sci., Arts and Letters*, **XIII**: 163–187, 1901.

———: The Plankton of Lake Winnebago and Green Lake, *Wis. Geol. and Nat. Hist. Survey Bull.*, 12, sci. ser. 3, 1903.

MATHESON, ROBERT, and E. H. HINMAN: *Chara fragilis* and Mosquito Development, *Amer. Jour. Hyg.*, vol. VIII, **2**: 279–292, 1928.

MIAL, L. C.: "The Natural History of Aquatic Insects," The Macmillan Company, New York, 1895. 395 pp.

MINDER, LEO: Zur Hydrophysik des Züricher und Walensees, nebst Beitrag zur Hydrochemie und Hydrobakteriologie des Zürichersees, *Arch. Hydrobiol. u. Planktonkunde*, **12**: 122–194, 1918.

MOBERG, ERIK G.: Variation in the Horizontal Distribution of Plankton in Devil's Lake, N. D., *Trans. Amer. Micros. Soc.*, **37**: 239–268, 1918.

MUTTKOWSKI, R. A.: The Fauna of Lake Mendota—a Qualitative and Quantitative Survey with Special Reference to the Insects, *Trans. Wis. Acad. Sci., Arts and Letters*, **19**: 374–482, 1918.

NEEDHAM, J. G.: Notes on the Aquatic Insects of Walnut Lake, *Mich. State Bd. Geol. Survey Rept.*, pp. 252–271, 1907.

NEEDHAM, J. G., CHANCEY JUDAY, EMMELINE MOORE, CHARLES K. SIBLEY, J. W. TITCOMB: "A Biological Survey of Lake George," N. Y. State Conserv. Comm., 1922.

NEEDHAM, J. G., and J. T. LLOYD: "Life in Inland Waters, Lakes," pp. 59–77, 1916.

Pearse, A. S.: The Food of the Shore Fishes of Certain Wisconsin Lakes, *U. S. Bur. Fisheries Bull.*, 1915–16; vol. XXXV, pp. 247–292, Washington, 1918.

————: The Fishes of Lake Valencia, Venezuela, *Wis. Univ. Studies*, sci. ser., vol. I, pp. 1–51, 1920.

————: The Distribution and Food of the Fishes of Three Wisconsin Lakes in Summer, *Wis. Univ. Studies*, sci. ser., No. 3, 1921. 61 pp.

————: The Distribution and Food of the Fishes of Green Lake, Wisconsin, in Summer, *U. S. Bur. Fisheries Bull.*, 1919–20; vol. XXXVII, Doc. 1906, pp. 254–272, 1921.

————: The Parasites of Lake Fishes, *Trans. Wis. Acad. Sci., Arts and Letters*, vol. XXI, pp. 161–195, July, 1924.

Pearse, A. S., and H. Achtenberg: Habits of Yellow Perch in Wisconsin Lakes, *U. S. Bur. Fisheries Bull.*, 1917–18; vol. XXXVI, pp. 293–366, Washington, 1920.

Peterson, W. H., E. B. Fred, and B. P. Domogalla: The Occurrence of Amino Acids and Other Organic Nitrogen Compounds in Lake Water, *Jour. Biol. Chem.*, **63**: 287–295, 1925.

Philip, Cornelius B.: Diurnal Fluctuations in the Hydrogen-ion Activity of a Minnesota Lake, *Ecology*, **8**: 73–89, 1927.

Pietenpol, W. B.: Selective Absorption in the Visible Spectrum of Wisconsin Lake Waters, *Trans. Wis. Acad. Sci., Arts and Letters*, vol. XIX, pt. I, 562–594, 1918.

Pütter, A.: "Die Frage der Parenteralen Ernährung der Wassertiere," G. Fischer, Jena, 1909.

————: Die Ernährung der Wassertiere, *Jena. Biol. Zentralbl.*, **XLII**: 72–86, 1922.

Reighard, Jacob: A Biological Examination of Lake St. Clair, *Bull. Mich. Fish. Comm.*, pp. 4–60, 1894.

Richardson, R. E.: The Small Bottom and Shore Fauna of the Middle and Lower Illinois River and Its Connecting Lakes, Chillicothe to Grafton, *Ill. Nat. Hist. Survey Bull.*, **113**: 363–524, 1921.

Rickett, H. W.: Quantitative Study of the Larger Aquatic Plants of Lake Mendota, *Trans. Wis. Acad. Sci., Arts and Letters*, **XX**: 501–527, 1921.

————: *Ibid.*, *Trans. Wis. Acad. Sci., Arts and Letters*, **XXI**: 381–414, 1924.

Russell, F. S.: The Vertical Distribution of Plankton in the Sea, *Biol. Rev.*, **2**: 215–262, 1927.

Schmidt, W.: Über den Energiegehalt der Seen, *Internat. Rev. Gesamm. Hydrobiol. u. Hydrog.*, Hydrog. Suppl. zu Band VI, 1915.

Schuette, H. A.: A Biochemical Study of the Plankton of Lake Mendota, pp. 594–614.

Scott, Will: Report on the Lakes of the Tippecanoe Basin (Indiana), *Ind. Univ. Studies*, vol. III, *Study* 31, 1916. 39 pp., 11 maps.

Sellards, G. E. H.: Some Florida Lakes and Lake Basins, *Fla. Geol. Survey Ann. Rep.*, **6**: 115–160, 1914.

Shantz, H. L.: A Biological Study of the Lakes of the Pikes Peak region, *Trans. Amer. Micros. Soc.*, pp. 75–98, 2 pl., 1907.

Shelford, V. E.: Animal Communities of Large Lakes, pp. 73–85 in "Animal Communities of Temperate America," chap. VII: Animal Communities of Small Lakes, p. 124.

Smith, Frank: Variation in the Maximum Depth at Which Fish Can Live during Summer in a Moderately Deep Lake with a Thermocline, *U. S. Bur. Fisheries Bull.*, vol. XLI, Doc. 970, pp. 1–7, 1925.

Smith, G. M.: Phytoplankton of the Inland Lakes of Wisconsin, *Wis. Geol. and Nat. Hist. Survey Bull.* 57, sci. ser. 12, 1920. 243 pp.

Thienemann, August: "Die Binnengewässer Mitteleuropas," vol. I, Stuttgart, 1925. 255 pp.

WARD, HENRY B.: Biol. Examinations of Lake Michigan in the Traverse Bay Region, *Mich. Fish. Comm. Bull.* 6, 1897. (Appendix by Jennings, Walker, Woodworth and Kofoid.)

WARD, H. B., and G. C. WHIPPLE: "Fresh Water Biology," 1918.

WEDDERBURN, E. M.: The Temperature of the fresh-water Lochs of Scotland, with Special Reference to Loch Ness. With Appendix Containing Observations Made in Loch Ness by Members of the Scottish Lake Survey, *Trans. Roy. Soc. Edinburgh*, **XLV**: 407–489, 1907.

———: Notes on the Temperature of the Water in Loch Ness, *Geogr. Jour.*, **XXXI**: 41, 52–56, 1908.

———: Some Analogies between Lakes and Oceans, *Internat. Rev. Gesamm. Hydrobiol. u. Hydrog.*, **4**: 55–64, 1911.

WELCH, PAUL S., and HELEN A. LOOMIS: A Limnological Study of *Hydra oligactis* in Douglas Lake, Mich., *Trans. Amer. Micros. Soc.*, **43**: 203–235, 1924.

WESENBERG-LUND C.: "Plankton Investigations of the Danish Lakes," Danish Fresh-water Biol. Lab., op. 5, pt. I, 389 pp., 1908; pt. II, Copenhagen.

———: Über eigentümliche Temperaturverhältnisse in dern Littoral Region der Baltischen Seen und deren Bedeutung nebst einem Anhang über die geographische Verbreitung der zwei Geschlechter von *Stratiotes aloides*, *Internat. Rev. Gesamm. Hydrobiol. u. Hydrog.*, **5**: 287–316, 1913.

WEST, W., and G. S. WEST: On the Periodicity of the Phytoplankton of Some British Lakes, *Jour. Linn. Soc.*, **40**: 395–432, 1912.

WHIPPLE, GEORGE CHANDLER: "The Microscopy of Drinking Water," 4th ed.; revised by Gordon M. Fair and Melville S. Whipple, John Wiley & Sons, Inc., New York, 1927. 585 pp.

WILHELMI JULIUS: Plankton u. Tripton, *Arch. Hydrobiol. u. Planktonkund.*, **11**: 113–150, 1916–17.

ZACHARIAS, OTTO: Fauna des Grossen Plöner See, *Forschungsberichte aus der biologischen Station zu Plön.*, **1**: 1–13, 1893.

———: Über die wechselnde Quantität des Plankton im Grossen Plöner See, *Forschungsberichte aus der biologischen Station zu Plön*, **3**: 97–117, 1895.

———: Über die Verschiedenheit der Zusammensetzung des Winterplanktons in grossen und kleinen Seen, *Forschungsberichte aus der biologischen Station zu Plön*, **7**: 64–74, 1899.

———: Über Algenanhaüfungen in Seen und Flüssen, *Arch. Hydrobiol. u. Planktonkunde*, **4**: 375–378, 1909.

CHAPTER XVII

LOTIC ENVIRONMENTS

General Characteristics.—Lotic environments have received much less attention than the lenitic. Forbes (1928) says:

The attention of biologists especially interested in the aquatic biota was naturally drawn first, to the wonderful assemblage of animals and plants and the system of life in the great seas; and, next, to those of the fresh-water lakes, concerning both of which there are ample stores of knowledge from various sources to draw upon; but the rivers of the country have received so little comprehensive attention from our biologists that I do not know of a single attempt anywhere in America to develop and disclose the complete biology of a river system, except that which has been made by us in Illinois.

The environments which are characterized by the motion of the water and termed "lotic" are the streams. Along the shores of the Great Lakes there are lotic communities where the wave action is incessant, thus producing the fundamental conditions of a lotic environment and presenting an exception to the general statement that all lotic environments are streams.

In general, the lotic environments differ from the lenitic ones in their narrower breadth and their shallower depth and all of the accompanying physical characteristics which are influenced by these dimensions. It is true, however, that some of the larger and slower flowing streams approach the conditions of lenitic environments. Lake Pepin is a portion of the Mississippi River in which the breadth and depth are greater than is general for the rest of its course. All of the water of the Mississippi River flows through Lake Pepin but it is so wide and deep that the conditions are more lenitic than lotic. There are also many oxbow lakes and sloughs which are connected with the main stream at high water but which become disconnected at low water. These are sometimes called "furiotile lakes." Their fauna is derived from the river, but as the season progresses the environmental conditions become lenitic.

Physical Characteristics. *Morphometry.*—The topography and geography of a region determine the general type of streams which may be present. In regions of rock outcrops the streams reduce their beds to a base level very slowly, with the result that there are rapid streams with waterfalls and gorges. In alluvial regions, the streams, particularly the larger ones, soon reduce their beds to a base level and thus produce a relatively uniform slow rate of flow.

The type of bottom is determined by the rate of flow; and this, as has just been stated, is determined by the nature of the region. The size of the material of which the stream bottom is composed varies directly as the rate of flow. The various sizes are described as rock, rubble, gravel, sand, and silt. The rolling coefficient is an expression of the ratio of weight to surface.

The types of bottom vary with their distribution in space and time. In general, streams are swifter near the source and slower as they approach the base level of the mouth. At the bend of a stream the coarser material is deposited on the outside of the bend where the flow is the swiftest.

The seasonal changes in streams are much greater than those in lenitic environments. During the periods of flood when the snow is melting and the ice is breaking up the bottoms of streams are remade by the changed rates of flow. This creates extreme conditions for the organisms.

Hydrometry. The Rate of Flow.—Since lotic environments are characterized by the rate of flow of the water and the type of bottom, and as a result the type of fauna is determined by it, the movement of the water must be given first consideration. The velocity of the flowing water depends principally upon the slope of the stream bed, the roughness of the bottom, and the hydraulic radius. The hydraulic radius is the area of the cross-section divided by the wetted perimeter. The relationships of these factors are expressed by Chezy's formula (Galtsoff, 1924) as follows: $V = c\sqrt{Rs}$, where V is the velocity, c is a coefficient which takes into consideration the effects of the type of bottom, s is the slope, and R the hydraulic radius.

The determination of the velocity of the water is most conveniently accomplished by means of a pitot tube (Rowse, 1913). This instrument consists of a glass U-tube connected with two metal tubes, one of which is opened at the end and directed against the current; and the other is opened either down stream or at the side to avoid the pressure of the water. The reading is made by observing the difference in level of water which has been placed in the U-tube. A graph may be prepared for each instrument from which the difference of level of water, as indicated by the U-tube, can be translated into rate of flow in feet per second or any other convenient terms.

The vertical velocity curves are rather uniform, so that the velocity of a film of water at a point between 0.5 and 0.7 of the depth, measured from the surface, is as great as the mean of the velocities in that line. This is a result of the friction of the bottom and the surface of the film.

Ecologically it is important to know the rates of flow in certain parts of the stream where the organisms are living. Clemens (1917) made a study of the rate of flow of water in a creek and found the following measurements for a period of high water:

Inches below surface	Flow, feet per second	Flow, feet per second	Flow, feet per second
2	4.5	4.5	3.9
3	4.2	4.4	3.7
4	4.0	4.3	3.7
5	3.8	4.1	3.3
6	3.7	3.8	3.0
7	3.7	3.3	2.9
8	3.7	3.1	2.8
9		2.9	
10	3.4	2.9	2.7
11			
12	3.2	2.7	2.6
14	3.0	2.4	2.5
15	2.9		2.2
16	2.2	2.2	1.7 bottom
17	1.7 bottom	1.7 bottom	

This agrees very well with the generalization above, and shows the influence of the bottom in controlling the rate of flow, regardless, in this case, of the rate above it.

In a swift stream with the characteristic community of *Simulium* and *Hydropsyche*, the rate of flow was shown by Clemens (1917) to vary from three to five feet per second, or more, at the surface, and to be two to four per second at the bottom. However, a great variation was found about the stones on and under which the fauna was found. When a stone 12 by 10 by 2.5 inches was placed in the creek, the rate of flow of the water was found to be 1.9 feet per second half-way between the stone and the surface, and 1.5 feet per second at the surface of the stone. Three-quarters of an inch behind the stone there was no current and on the bottom of the stream behind the stone, the rate was only 0.5 feet per second.

It is evident that, while there may be general changes in the rates of streams as shown by Galtsoff (1924) for the Mississippi River, there are also many local differences in the rates of flow which may be very significant ecologically.

Light.—The fact that lotic environments are capable of holding a large amount of material in suspension means that the transparency of the water may be lower than that of lenitic environments; and consequently the depth to which light may penetrate will be correspondingly less. In the absence of data on light, the following graph is presented to illustrate the change of transparency in the water of the Mississippi River as it enters Lake Keokuk at Burlington, Iowa (Fig. 113). During the summer, the sediment settles out and greatly increases the trans-

parency of the water.   During September, the transparency is uniformly
low as a result of the fall rains.

It is true that the waters of spring brooks with rock bottom are very
transparent and so shallow that the light penetrates to the bottom with
very little reduction.   The large muddy streams would present the other
extreme of the series.

Temperature.—Lotic environments are characterized by temperatures
which are very uniform as to spatial distribution, but which exhibit great
change with distribution in time.   The greatest difference of temperature

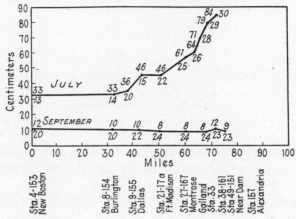

Fig. 113.—Transparency of water in the Mississippi River and Lake Keokuk, between
New Boston, Ill., and Alexandria, Mo.   The figures on the line represent the transparency
in centimeters; the figures under the lines represent the day of observation.   (*Galtsoff*,
1924.)

observed by Galtsoff (1924) in a study of the vertical distribution of
temperature in the Mississippi River was 3.5°C. at a depth of 13.4 m.
He states that for the river as a whole, the difference between the surface
and bottom temperatures was usually less than 1°.   This is in striking
contrast to the conditions found in lenitic environments.

The motion of the water and the relatively large surface exposed
cause it to conform much more closely to the temperature of the air
than lenitic environments do.   The following graph from Clemens (1917)
illustrates the correlation between the temperature of the water and air
during summer and winter.   It is obvious that the water temperature
will be more independent of the air in the winter than in the summer.
Here we see the effect of the latent heat of water.

The materials in suspension usually increase as the water passes from
the source to the mouth.   This is regardless of the fact that the rate of
flow is usually decreased, which results in a settling out of the larger
particles.   In the case of the Mississippi River, the material in suspension
amounts to only 7.9 parts per million at Minneapolis (Townsend, 1915),

and may reach the ratio of 280 parts per million in the lower part of the river.

The materials in solution vary greatly with the type of soil to be found in the drainage basin of the stream. The following table indicates that the total materials in solution at the upper part of the Mississippi River are about the same as in the lower portion.

	CO_2	SO_4	Cl	NO_3	Ca	Mg	Na, K	SiO_2	Fe_2O_3	Salinity, parts per mill.
Minneapolis .	47.04	9.61	0.85	0.85	20.59	7.67	5.33	8.01	0.05	200
Memphis.....	32.02	11.31	5.72	0.10	17.45	6.98	6.19	19.45	0.78	197

It is interesting to note the slight decrease in salinity which is the reverse of what might be expected from evaporation as the water proceeds to the mouth of the river. Some of the changes are undoubtedly influenced by the large amount of water which flows into the Mississippi from the Missouri River.

Clemens (1917) examined the water of a relatively short swift stream which flows through a limestone gorge near its mouth. His data are as follows:

PARTS PER MILLION, JUNE 18

O_2............................	8.0	Nitrates......................	0.025
CO_2...........................	1.5	Cl............................	2.0
Free bicarbonates..............	52.9	Sulphates....................	33.3
Free NH_3.....................	0.058	Fe_2O_3........................	0.42
Alb. NH_3.....................	0.101		

When compared with the conditions found in the lenitic waters, it seems that lotic environments have more salts and may have less soluble nitrogen than the waters of lakes.

The Gases of the Water.—The relatively great surface area of the lotic environments which is exposed to the air and the continual mixing of the water results in maintaining the gases in equilibrium with the air. In this respect the lotic environments differ markedly from the lenitic ones. The oxygen concentration found by Clemens has been shown in connection with the temperature conditions (Fig. 114). The oxygen concentration so closely approaches that of saturation that it may almost be considered as saturation for general purposes. The fauna is typically adapted to a high oxygen concentration; and it is not possible to rear the lotic organisms under artificial conditions unless the oxygen content of the water is maintained at about the point of saturation.

The Neutrality of the Medium.—The general conditions described in connection with the lenitic environments will apply to the lotic environ-

ments with two differences.   In the first place, the continual mixing of
the water tends to prevent the accumulative effect of photosynthesis
and the accompanying diurnal cycle of pH values.   In the second place,
the long course of the stream makes it possible to have changes from one
end to the other, due to tributaries and differences in the general
watershed.

The limits of acidity are apparently about the same as for lenitic
environments.   The fauna of an acid stream and the conditions found in
such an environment are described by Jewell (1922).   Creaser and Brown
(1927) studied a series of 31 streams of northern Lower Michigan which
varied in pH from 7.1 to 8.2.   They concluded that the brook trout,
Salvelinus fontinalis Mitchell, thrived and completed its life cycle in
streams with this range of alkalinity, even though Coker (1925) had
suggested that neutral or slightly acid streams were most favorable for
them.   Spring brooks are influenced by the type of soil from which the
water flows, and the surface drainage streams may receive bog waters

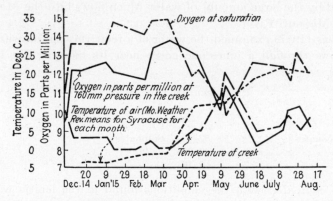

Fig. 114.—Physical conditions in Cascadilla Creek, N. Y.   (*Clemens,* 1917.)

which are strongly acid.   Thus lotic environments may differ among
themselves as much as or more than lenitic environments in this respect,
but they are subject to less diurnal fluctuation.

Biotic Characteristics of Lotic Environments.—Attention has been
called to the fact that the typical rapidly flowing water of the lotic environment presents a very characteristic environment, but that in the slower
streams conditions may approach those of the lenitic environment.
What has been said of the environmental conditions may also be said
of the fauna.   The swift water has a very characteristic fauna.   In fact,
there are a number of groups which are characteristically lotic.

The order Plecoptera, stone flies, is characteristically lotic.   The
family Hydropsychidae, net-spinning caddis flies, is characteristically
lotic as is the family Simulidae, black flies, of the Diptera.   There are

many groups of species and genera of Trichoptera, caddis flies, and Ephemerida, May flies, which are also characteristically lotic.

The plankton is characterized by the presence of many diatoms which are better supported in running water than in quiet water, where their relatively heavy siliceous shells cause them to settle out.

For general considerations of the faunas of streams Needham and Lloyd (1916), Shelford (1913), Hart (1892), and others cited in the bibliography may be consulted. It is the intention here to consider the principles involved in the ecology and certain quantitative data with regard to the fauna of the lotic environments.

In general, the number of species is not great, but the number of individuals may be very great. The mode of life is, of necessity, specialized. In the swifter water the organisms as a group are relatively sessile. In a lenitic environment it is necessary for most of the animals to move about to come in contact with enough water to obtain the necessary amount of food. In the lotic environment a large amount of water is continually passing; and sessile animals which are provided with a means of obtaining food from the water as it passes have little need of locomotion.

The Hydropsychidae spin nets which strain the plankton from the water as it flows through. The Simulidae have appendages modified for the purpose of straining the microorganisms from the water. Even the May flies have hairs projecting from their appendages to form "plankton baskets." Clemens (1917) made a study of the plankton baskets of the May fly, *Chirotonetes*, and found that the area through which the water flowed was 8 sq.mm. His experiments with plankton nets in water with a velocity of four feet per second showed that such a net would collect about 0.05 c.c. of plankton in a period of 12 hours in the stream which he was studying. He also found that the alimentary canal of the May fly had a capacity of 0.0065 c.c. It would therefore be possible for the digestive tract of *Chirotonetes* to be filled eight times in 12 hours under the conditions given.

A further study of the amount of plankton to be collected by nets in a stream inhabited by *Chirotonetes* gave the following results:

Date	Edible plankton per 8 sq.mm. in 12 hr. at 1.5 ft. per second	Times the capacity of the digestive tract of *Chirotonetes*
June 25...............	0.050	8.0
June 29...............	0.097	15.0
July 6...............	0.041	6.0
July 13...............	0.048	7.5
Aug. 12...............	0.066	10.2

This seems to indicate that the lotic organisms are able to obtain sufficient food by maintaining fixed position in the stream and straining out the plankton as the water flows past them.

The Biotic Potential of Lotic Organisms.—Many of the physical conditions of a lotic environment are extreme, making it necessary for a species to have a high biotic potential to maintain its numbers in the environment. It is no easier to assemble data on the biotic potential of lotic organisms than on any other group.

Claassen (Walker and others, 1923), in making a study of certain Chironomidae found in a stream, made the statement that the possible increase from a single pair of midges in a season amounts to 7,800,000 con-

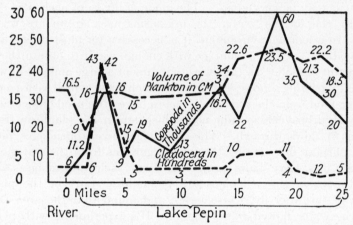

Fig. 115.—Distribution of Crustacea in Lake Pepin. The mean content and the mean numbers of Copepoda and Cladocera in cross-sections of Lake Pepin, August to September, 1921, from head of lake down to the foot. Stations 96 to 98 are located at the inflow of the Mississippi River; Stations 101 to 103 at the outflow of the lake. Heavy line represents the mean volume of plankton per cubic meter of water; plain line, the number of Copepoda per cubic meter of water; dotted line, the number of Cladocera per cubic meter of water. The figures on the lines are the averages computed from the data of three stations in the given cross-section of the lake. The serial numbers of stations are given under the abscissae. Scale: One division of the abscissae, 1 mile; one division of the ordinate, 5cm. of plankton for heavy line, 10,000 individuals of Copepoda for plain line, and 1,000 individuals of Cladocera for dotted line. (*Galtsoff*, 1924.)

sidering four cycles to a season. The general ability of the lotic insects to distribute themselves and deposit their eggs is illustrated by certain small streams located in central Minnesota, which are separated from other similar environments by several miles; and yet they contain the typical *Simulium-Hydropsychae* community with large numbers of individuals.

The environmental resistance is great in a lotic environment, due to the fact that if an organism is displaced it will be carried down stream and will not be deposited until the water has slowed down, which means that the conditions will not be favorable for lotic organisms to live in. The great fluctuation in the spring and fall, and the action of the ice at the time that it breaks up in the spring, both tend to reduce the number of individuals.

The resistance of the environment begins to have its effect in the egg stage when the female introduces her eggs into the swift water, and continues until the adult insect emerges from the pupal case and escapes into the air above the water.

The Quantity of Organisms Present.—Quantitative methods for lotic environments are not as well developed as for other aquatic conditions. The plankton have been most studied by quantitative methods by Kofoid (1903), Allen (1920), and others. Galtsoff (1924) found the quantity of plankton to be rather uniform in vertical distribution on the Mississippi River, but to vary from place to place. He found a slight increase in the plankton as the water flowed through Lake Pepin, as is shown in the following graph (Fig. 115).

Claassen (Walker and others, 1923) found as many as 20,000 *Chironomus* larvae to the square foot on the bottom of a stream in New York. An examination of a stream flowing through a canal near St. Paul revealed the following quantitative data with regard to the population.

QUANTITATIVE SAMPLES FROM THE ST. PAUL WATER CANAL
(One Ekman dredge or an equal volume, about 216 cu. in., in each)

Species	Sample from bank	Sample from tuft in stream
Hydropsychidae	6,193	1,689
Leptoceridae	12	
Chironomidae	396	48
Ceratopogan	95	46
Simulidae	136	14
Gammaridae	21	257
Snails	3	5
Other Trichoptera	3	
Planaria	.....	2
Belostomadae	.....	1
Damsel flies, larvae	11	
Ephemeridae	1	34
Hydrachnidae	1	1
Coleoptera	25	
Molluscs	3	5
Worms	2	
Total number	6,902	2,102
Total weight	95.7 grams	14 grams

This stream represents artificial conditions in that it connects certain reservoir lakes and has a controlled flow through alluvial deposits. In contrast to natural lotic environments, the bottom and sides of the stream are soft with overhanging herbaceous vegetation. There are many tussocks along the shore, and the stream bed is kept open by occasional cleaning.　This lake water flows rapidly through the canal, laden with plankton and dissolved organic substances, which serve as food for the multitude of lotic organisms which live on the vegetation in the stream.

This seems to indicate that the conditions of a lotic environment are not strictly comparable to those of a lenitic environment in that a lenitic environment has a fixed amount of water in which the food cycle repeats itself over and over.　In the lotic environment the water is forever moving past the organisms, and the amount of food available at any one point is dependent upon the amount of water that passes in a unit of time, and upon what has taken place in the water before it reaches that point.

Conditions in Various Types of Lotic Environments.—The discussion which has preceded has been with regard to typical lotic environments.

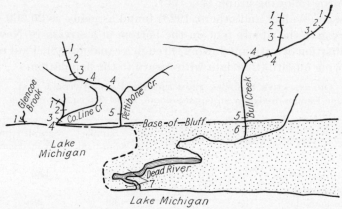

Fig. 116.—Diagrammatic arrangement of the North Shore streams.　The streams are mapped to a scale of 1 mile to the inch, and the maps are placed as closely together as possible in the diagram.　The intermediate shore-lines are shown in broken lines which bear no relation to the shore lines which exist in nature.　Toward the top of the diagram is west. Each number on the diagram refers to the pool nearest the source of the stream which contains fish, as follows: 1, the horned dace; 2, the red-bellied dace; 3, the black-nosed dace; 4, the suckers and minnows; 5, the pickerel and blunt-nosed minnow; 6, the sunfish and bass; 7, the pike, chub-sucker, etc.　The bluff referred to is about 60 ft. high.　The stippled area is a plain just above the level of the lake.　(*Shelford*, 1913.)

It was previously stated that streams vary from the typical swift, truly lotic conditions to those of lenitic environments.　The typically lotic conditions are those just described and the lenitic conditions were described previously.　It may be said in general that the physical and biotic conditions are intermediate between the two, or resemble the one or the other, depending upon the rate of flow of the water.

Shelford (1913), Klugh (1923), and others have proposed classifications of lotic environments.　Temporary or intermittent streams are characterized by the fact that their flow is discontinuous as to both space and time.　They often consist of a series of pools connected by streams during a part of the year when there is a series of pond and stream communities. Later the streams may dry up leaving only the ponds, and later even these may disappear.

Of the permanent streams we have the swift-source streams such as the spring brooks which are the most typical of lotic conditions. Proceeding along the series of streams we come to the swollen base-level streams in which the conditions are much like those of lenitic environments except that they are subject to greater fluctuations of level with the resulting increase of rate of flow and change of bottom, due to washing at high water and silting down at low water.

Shelford (1911) has called attention to the succession of communities as one proceeds from the mouth of a stream to the source. He has given the diagram (Fig. 116) and explanation of the conditions:

It is conceivable that Glencoe Brook might, in time, and with sufficient drainage, extend its course back from the lake until it reaches the size of Pettibone Creek, and would acquire the additional fauna found in the larger streams. In the same way it may be supposed that the larger streams were once as small as Glencoe Brook with only the horned-class community. As they cut their beds back from the lake the new conditions arose accompanied by the new communities.

BIBLIOGRAPHY

LOTIC ENVIRONMENTS

ALLEN, W. E.: A Quantitative and Statistical Study of the Plankton of the San Joaquin River and Its Tributaries in and near Stockton, California, *Calif. Univ. Pubs.*, Zool., **22**: 1–292, 1920.

BAKER, F. C.: The Molluscan Fauna of the Big Vermillion River, Illinois, *Ill. Biol. Monog.*, vol. 7, **2**: 105–224, 1922.

————: The Fauna of the Lake Winnebago Region, *Trans. Wis. Acad. Sci., Arts and Letters*, **21**: 109–146, 1924.

BROWN, H. B.: Algal Periodicity in Certain Ponds and Streams, *Bull. Torrey Bot. Club*, **35**: 223–248, 1908.

CLAASSEN (See Walker and others, 1923).

CLEMENS, W. A.: An Ecological Study of the Mayfly, *Chirotonetes*, *Univ. Toronto Studies*, biol. ser. 17, 1917.

COKER, R. E.: Waterpower Development in Relation to Fishes and Mussels of the Mississippi. Appendix VIII to the Report of the U. S. Commissioner of Fisheries for 1913 (1914), *U. S. Bur. Fisheries Bull.*, Doc. 805, 1914.

————: Observations on Hydrogen-ion Concentration and of Fshes in Waters Tributary to the Catawba River, North Carolina (with Supplemental Observations in Some Waters of Cape Cod, Massachusetts), *Ecology*, **6**: 52–65, 1925.

COWLES, R. P., and A. M. SCHWITALLA: The Hydrogen-ion Concentration of a Creek, Its Waterfall, Swamp and Ponds, *Ecology*, **4**: 402–416, 1922.

CREASER, CHARLES W., and HAROLD W. BROWN: The Hydrogen-ion Concentration of Brook Trout Waters of Northern Lower Michigan, *Ecology*, **8**: 98–105, 1927.

DODDS, G. S., and F. L. HISAW: Ecological Studies of Aquatic Insects. I. Adaptation of Mayfly Nymphs to Swift Streams, *Ecology*, **5**: 137–149, 1924.

————: Ecological Studies of Aquatic Insects. III. Adaptation of Caddis Fly Larvae to Swift Streams, *Ecology*, **6**: 123–138, 1925.

FORBES, STEPHEN A.: The Biological Survey of a River System, Its Objects, Methods, and Results, *Ill. State Lab. Nat. Hist. Bull.* 17, pp. 277–284, 1928.

FORBES, S. A., and R. E. RICHARDSON: Recent Changes in Illinois River Biology, *Ill. Nat. Hist. Survey Bull.* 13, p. 6, 1919.

GALTSOFF, P. S.: Limnological Observations in the Upper Mississippi 1921, *U. S. Bur. Fisheries Bull.* 39, pp. 347–438, Doc. 958, 1924.

GRIER, N. M.: Final Report on the Study and Appraisal of Mussel Resources in Selected Areas of the Upper Mississippi River, *Amer. Midland Nat.*, pp. 1–33, Jan., 1922.

HART, C. A.: Entomology of the Illinois River, *Ill. State Lab. Nat. Hist. Bull.* 4, pp. 149–273, 1892.

HERRON, W. H.: Profile Surveys of Rivers in Wisconsin, *U. S. Geol. Survey Water-Supply Paper*, 417, 1917. 16 pp.

HOOKER, E. H.: The Suspension of Solids in Flowing Water, *Trans. Amer. Soc. Civ. Engin.*, **36**: 239–324, 1897.

HORA, S. L.: Observations on the Fauna of Certain Torrential Streams in the Kashi Hills, *Rec. Indian Mus.*, **25**: 579–600, 1923.

HOYT, J. C., and N. C. GROVER: "River Discharge Prepared for the Use of Engineers and Students," 4th ed., John Wiley & Sons, Inc., New York, 1916. 210 pp.

HUMPHREY, A. A., and H. L. ABBOTT: Report upon the Physics and Hydraulics of the Mississippi River; upon the Protection of the Alluvial Region against Overflow; and upon the Deepening of the Mouths; Based upon Surveys and Investigations, Govt. Printing Office, Washington, 1876. 691 pp.

JEWELL, MINNA E.: The Fauna of an Acid Stream, *Ecology*, **3**: 22–28, 1922.

KLUGH, A. B.: A Common System of Classification in Plant and Animal Ecology, *Ecology*, **4**: 366–377, 1923.

KOFOID, CHAS. A.: Plankton Studies. I. Methods and Apparatus in Use in Plankton Investigations at the Biological Experiment Station of the University of Illinois, *Ill. State Lab. Nat. Hist. Bull.*, art. 1, pp. 1–25, 1897.

―――: The Plankton of the Illinois River and Its Basin, *Ill. State Lab. Nat. Hist. Bull.* 6, pp. 95–629, 1903.

―――: Plankton Studies. V. The Plankton of the Illinois River, 1894–1899; Constituent Organisms and Their Seasonal Distribution, *Ill. State Lab. Nat. Hist. Bull.* 8, pp. 1–361, 1908.

LINTNER, J. A.: Report on the Insects and Other Animal Forms of Caledonia Creek, N. Y., N. Y. Fish Comn., 1877; *Tenth Ann. rept.*, pp. 12–36, 1878.

MEYER, ADOLPH: Power Development at the High Dam between Minneapolis and St. Paul, *Jour. Amer. Soc. Mech. Engin.*, **36**: 305–315, 1914.

MISSISSIPPI RIVER COMMISSION: "Survey of the Mississippi River, Lake Itasca Basin, Minnesota within Itasca State Park. Projected from a Trigonometrical Survey Made in 1900," scale 1:15000, Mississippi River Commission, St. Louis, 1900.

―――: "Detail Map of the Upper Mississippi River from the Mouth of the Ohio River to Minneapolis, Minnesota," scale 1:20,000, Mississippi River Commission, St. Louis, 1903.

―――: "Stages of the Mississippi River and of Its Principal Tributaries for 1911-21," Mississippi River Commission, St. Louis, 1922.

MISSISSIPPI RIVER POWER CO.: Electric Power from the Mississippi River, *Bull.* 10, Kansas City, July, 1913.

―――: Electric Power from the Mississippi River. A Description of the Water Power Development at Keokuk, Iowa, 1913.

NEEDHAM, J. G.: Burrowing Mayflies of our Larger Lakes and Streams, *U. S. Bur. Fisheries, Bull.* 36, pp. 269–292, 1917–1918.

NEEDHAM, J. G., and J. T. LLOYD: "The Life of Inland Waters," Comstock Publ. Co., Ithaca, N. Y., 1916. 438 pp.

NEERACHER, F.: Die Insektenfauna des Rheins und seiner Zuflüsse bei Basel, *Arch. Hydrobiol. u. Planktonkunde*, **7**: 140–162, 1912.

RICHARDSON, R. E.: Changes in the Bottom and Shore Fauna of the Middle Illinois River and Its Connecting Lakes Since 1913–15 as a Result of the Increase Southward of Sewage Pollution, *Ill. Nat. Hist. Survey Bull.* 14, pp. 33–75, 1921.

RIVERS AND HARBORS COMMITTEE: "Mississippi River, Impounding of Water above Keokuk Dam. Hearing on Subject of *House Resolution* 468, Direction Investigation of Alleged Impounding of Water above Dam in Mississippi River at Keokuk and Its Effect upon Navigation of the River," Washington, Feb. 14–15, 1917. 121 pp.

ROWSE, W. C.: Pitot Tubes for Gas Measurement, *Jour. Amer. Soc. Mech. Engin.*, **35**: 1321–1381, 1913.

RUSSELL, I. C.: "Rivers of North America," New York, 1898. 327 pp.

SCHORLER, B.: Mitteilung über das Plankton der Elbe bei Dresden in Sommer 1904, *Arch. Hydrobiol. u. Planktonkunde*, **2**: 355–358, 1907.

SHELFORD, V. E.: Ecological Succession. I. Stream Fishes and the Method of Physiographic Analysis, *Biol. Bull.*, **21**: 9–35, 1911.

————: "Animal Communities in Temperate America," The University of Chicago Press, 1913. 362 pp.

TOWNSEND, C. M.: The Flow of Sediment in the Mississippi River and Its Influence on the Slope and Discharge. With Especial Reference to the Effects of Spillways in the Vicinity of New Orleans, La., *Professional Memoirs*, Corps of Engineers, U. S. Army and Engineer Dept. at large, N. C. 33, pp. 357–377, May–June 1915.

VOLK, R.: Über die Elbuntersuchungen des Herrn R. Volk, *Arch. Hydrobiol. u. Planktonkunde*, **4**: 49–58, 1909.

WALKER, C. W., and others: Studies on the Treatment and Disposal of Dairy Wastes, *Cornell Univ. Bull.*, p. 425, 1923.

WEDDERBURN, E. N.: Some Analogies between Lakes and Oceans, *Internat. Rev. Gesamm. Hydrobiol. u. Hydrog.*, **4**: 55–64, 1911.

ZIMMER, CARL: Das tierische Plankton der Oder, *Forschungsberichte der biologischen Station zu Plön*, **7**: 1–14, 1899.

CHAPTER XVIII

TERRESTRIAL SYNECOLOGY—COMMUNITIES OF THE SOIL

The progress which has been made in the quantitative study of terrestrial synecology is hardly comparable to that which has been made in aquatic studies. The reason is that the terrestrial environment is much more complicated and is less susceptible to measurement than the aquatic environments.

It is not a difficult matter to investigate the physical properties of water, but the terrestrial environment consists of the soil, the vegetation, and the atmosphere. The atmosphere is most closely comparable with the water. The soil is infinitely more complicated than water, being more like protoplasm itself, as it is composed partly of organisms and their products. The vegetation consists of communities of organisms.

It is true that conditions similar to those found on land are to be encountered in the marginal areas of aquatic environments among the rooted vegetation. But it is also true that in these localities the quantitative study of aquatic environments has made the least progress.

It is a peculiarly inconsistent state of affairs that has resulted in aquiculture lagging far behind agriculture when aquatic environments have been demonstrated to be more susceptible to quantitative investigation than terrestrial environments are. Terrestrial zooculture has progressed because of the economic pressure, until many of the superficial phases of it have come to a fairly high state of quantitative development, making it possible to determine the number of pounds of beef or pork that can be supported by a given area of ground. But aside from certain of the larger animals we have little information with regard to the quantities of animals present in terrestrial environments and, what is more serious, we are lacking in methods for making such determinations.

For the purpose of description the terrestrial environments may be placed in the following classification without entering into a discussion of the relative merits of the different categories of classification which have been proposed (Shelford, 1913; Klugh, 1913; Pearse, 1926, and others).

Exposed surfaces:
  Bare rock associations
  Sand associations
    Beaches
    Sand dunes

Grassland associations
  Marshes
  Meadows
  Low prairies
  High prairies
Shrub associations
Forest associations
  Poplar association
  Coniferous associations
  Oak association
  Elm-maple association
  Basswood-maple association

This order is in general agreement with the order of plant succession and also places the various strata in their proper relationships. It is, however, not adequate for the purpose of the classification of all environments. The authors of papers on systems of classification have been cited, although there may be some doubt as to whether any system will appear adequate to all.

Without regard to any system of plant succession or classification of communities, it is logical to consider, first, the environments which consist essentially of only the soil stratum; next, those which consist essentially of an herb or gas stratum; then, the shrub stratum; and, finally, the tree or forest stratum. The environments increase in complexity in this order as each category adds another stratum to the preceding one. The action of physical factors, such as solar radiation, wind, and the consequent effect upon temperature and moisture, all are correlated with the order of these strata in natural environments.

The general characteristics of different strata will first be considered, following which certain characteristic data will be presented with regard to typical associations of different types.

The Soil Stratum as an Environment.—The greatest interest in soil is to be found in the study of it, not as a substance, but as a biotic reaction. It is of interest primarily as an environment of microscopic and macroscopic organisms. Its inorganic constituents are relatively inert. The dynamic constituents are organisms. It may be considered a part of the earth's biosphere. In humus soils as much as 80 per cent of the dry weight may be organic matter; and in mineral soils only 4 per cent may be organic matter (Lyon and Backman, 1929).

It is possible to present only the briefest summary of the conditions in the soil and the communities which are found there. The study of soils has developed to the point where it is not possible to summarize adequately the information in a limited chapter such as this. The student is referred to the recent texts on the subject of soils and the biology of soils for an adequate treatment of the subject (Waksman, 1927; Russell, 1923; Emerson, 1930; and Ramann, 1928, translated by Whittles).

Soils, like faunas and floras, may be classified on the basis of the climatic conditions to which they are exposed. The physical conditions, such as moisture and temperature, are influenced directly by the climate, and the biotic reactions are influenced indirectly. Ramann (1928) considers the climatic categories of primary importance. Emerson (1930) gives an interesting discussion of the problems of soil classification which involve physical and biotic characteristics as well as the genesis of soils.

The Physical Properties of Soil.—Three layers may be recognized in a general way: the débris (humus) layer, the surface soil, and the sub-soil. In general, the depth of the débris layer increases from a condition in which it is absent on the sand dunes, to a condition of a considerable depth in the climax forest.

The Texture of the Soil.—In the order of the size of particles we may arrange the soils as: clay (the finest particles), silt, sand, and gravel. The size of the particles is important as a factor in determining the moisture and gaseous conditions which may obtain in the soil.

The structure of the soil is of much the same importance biologically as the texture. The particles may be arranged either singly or in groups. Clay soils which "puddle" may have their particles adhering to each other singly and thus present a solid, more or less homogeneous mass. When the particles form groups, the structure is open, as each group of particles acts more or less as a single large particle, and thus a porous soil is produced. The particles, however, are not all of the same size and the smaller ones tend to pack in between the larger ones.

Lyon and Backman (1929) state that the volume composition of a silty-loam soil in good condition for plant growth would be represented by about 50 per cent of solid space and 50 per cent pore space. The pore space is occupied by air and water in about equal volume, so that 25 per cent of the total volume of such a soil would be water and 25 per cent would be air. About 5 per cent of the total would be organic material and 45 per cent would be mineral.

The Temperature of the Soil.—The temperature of the soil varies most at the surface and least at depths of several feet where conditions approach a constant temperature. The temperature at the surface of soils varies much more than that of the air in summer, as it is more dependent upon the radiations from the sun than upon the temperature of the air. In winter a covering of plant material and snow protects the soil from heat conduction.

The annual and diurnal fluctuations of the soil surface on the desert present probably the greatest temperature fluctuations of any natural environment. Certain Egyptian soils are essentially sterilized each year at the time of the greatest angle of incidence of the sun's rays. Taylor and Burns (1924) published the following graph of the diurnal fluctuations of

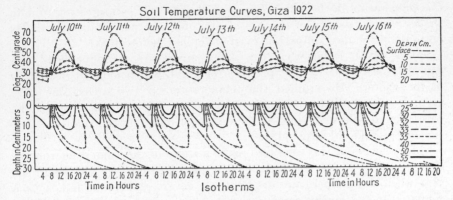

Fig. 117.—Soil temperatures and isotherms at various depths to show the diurnal fluctuations. (*Taylor and Burns*, 1924.)

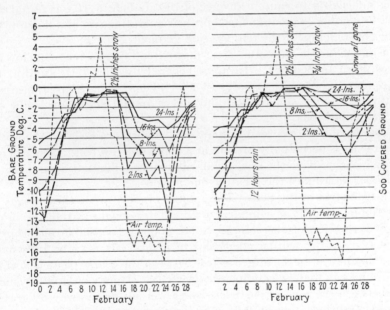

Fig. 118.—A comparison of soil temperatures at various depths for bare ground and sod-covered ground during February at St. Paul, Minn. (*Mail*, 1930.)

PROTOZOA, FLAGELLATES, PER GRAM OF SOIL[1]

Soil	Depth, 1 in.	Depth, 4 in.	Depth, 8 in.	Depth, 12 in.	Depth, 20 in.	Depth, 30 in.
Garden........	2,000–5,000	2,000–5,000	2,000–5,000	10–100	0	0
Meadow	5,000–10,000	1,000–2,000	100–1,000	10–100	0	0
Orchard.......	1,000–2,000	100–1,000	100–1,000	10–100	0	0
Woods........	10–100	10–100	1–10	0	0	0

[1] WAKSMAN, 1916.

the temperature in the soil in Egypt (Fig. 117). It is interesting to note that a vertical section of the soil at any one time may show the effects not only of the day before but even of the day before that.

Mail (1930) found that the soil temperature is influenced to a considerable extent by the presence of grass, which acts as insulation in the winter. He studied the temperature on two areas: one bare ground, and the other sod-covered ground. The temperature of the bare ground followed that of the air much more closely than the sod-covered ground did (Fig. 118).

McColloch and Hayes (1923) made a study of the annual fluctuation of temperature in the soil and called attention to the two periods in the year when the temperature gradient was reversed. In the fall, a time comes when the surface temperature becomes colder than the soil below and this condition obtains until the sun has warmed the surface in the spring sufficiently to cause a reverse of the gradient. It was found that the "white grubs" were influenced in their migrations up and down in the soil by the direction of the temperature gradient.

In the Arctic the perpetual frost may extend several meters below the surface, even to bedrock. In areas covered by the arctic tundra, the surface may thaw to a depth of only 30 or 40 cm. This limits the organisms to a relatively shallow soil and makes annual migration below the frost line impossible.

Cases have been recorded in many of the northern bogs of Minnesota where the ice is perpetually present at a depth of a few feet. The soil of a forest appears to have the least annual and diurnal fluctuation and that of the deserts and dunes the greatest fluctuations.

The Moisture of the Soil.—The amount of moisture in the soil may be expressed in per cent as compared with the dry weight of the soil, in per cent of saturation of the soil, or in terms of the available moisture as determined by the wilting coefficient of plants. It may be present as *gravitational* water in the larger spaces between the coarse particles, which may drain away under the influence of gravity. It may be *capillary* moisture, between the smaller particles, which will not drain away by gravity because of surface tension but may be evaporated. Or it may be a film adsorbed on the surface of the particles and equivalent to the water content of air-dry soil. The moisture thus adsorbed is the *hygroscopic* moisture. The amount of moisture present when the soil contains all the hygroscopic moisture possible may be expressed in per cent of the dry weight of the soil, as the hydroscopic coefficient. The finer the particles the more surface there is available to be covered by the film of moisture. Silt and clay soils retain both gravitational and capillary moisture and present a large amount of surface on the particles. The methods of determining soil moisture may be found in the various textbooks. Bouyoucos (1927) gives a convenient and rapid method of determining soil moisture which can be used in the field.

The Atmosphere of the Soil.—The atmosphere of the soil is said to be dependent upon the structure and texture of the soil (Russell and Appleyard, 1915–1916). There seem to be two atmospheres of the soil. One is to be found in the spaces between the soil particles. It is largely in the upper six inches of the soil and is much like that of the atmospheric air. The composition of this air fluctuates seasonally and daily. Its approach to the conditions of the atmospheric air depends upon the freedom with which the gases can diffuse to the outer atmosphere. It is usually lower in oxygen content than the atmospheric air.

Deeper in the soil the gases are dissolved in the surface film of the

TABLE XXIV.—RELATION BETWEEN MOISTURE CONTENT AND RELATIVE HUMIDITY OF THE SOIL AIR IN CHERNOZEM (BLACK SOIL OF RUSSIA), PODSOL (LIGHT SOIL WITH HUMUS COVERING), AND SAND[1]

Chernozem		Podsol		Sand	
Max. hygroscopicity, 7.35 per cent		Max. hygroscopicity, 3.18 per cent		Max. hygroscopicity, 0.41 per cent	
Moisture content, per cent	Relative humidity of the soil air, per cent	Moisture content, per cent	Relative humidity of the soil air, per cent	Moisture content, per cent	Relative humidity of the soil air, per cent
15.27	100	12.51	100	8.15	100
11.44	100	8.45	100	5.79	100
8.07	100	5.13	100	2.21	100
7.10	94	3.32	100	1.34	100
5.62	68	3.07	95	0.62	100
4.43	49	2.16	73	0.32	69

[1] LEBEDEFF, 1927.

TABLE XXV.—MOISTURE, RELATIVE HUMIDITY OF THE SOIL AIR AND TEMPERATURE OF AN ODESSA CHERNOZEM (BLACK SOIL) WITH A MAXIMUM HYGROSCOPICITY OF 5.62 PER CENT[1]

Soil moisture, 5.34 per cent		Soil moisture, 3.99 per cent		Soil moisture, 2.43 per cent	
Temperature, °C.	Relative humidity, per cent	Temperature, °C.	Relative humidity, per cent	Temperature, °C.	Relative humidity, per cent
10	94	17	81	10	39
17	95	35	86	21	41
45	99	50	92	45	51
70	99	60	98	60	57

[1] LEBEDEFF, 1927.

water and the colloids on the soil particles.   This is essentially an anaërobic condition with very little oxygen present.

Lebedeff (1928) concluded that the relative humidity of soil air is
always at saturation (100 per cent), if the soil contains moisture in an
amount greater than the maximum hygroscopicity.   If the moisture
content is below the maximum, then the drier the soil is, the less is the
relative humidity of its air.   When the moisture content of the soil
remains constant, the relative humidity of the air increases with an
increase in the temperature of the soil and *vice versa*.   He substantiates
these conclusions with Tables XXIV and XXV on page 365.

It is easy to understand that when the moisture has passed the point
of maximum hygroscopicity, it is available for evaporation; and therefore
the air should saturate itself.   When there is less than this amount of
water present, evaporation of hygroscopic water becomes a factor, and
this takes place most rapidly at high temperatures.

The Neutrality of the Soil.—The condition of our knowledge of the
importance of the pH values in soil in the ecology of animals is much like
that for the aquatic habitats.   Judgment will have to be reserved until
further investigations have been made.   Arrhenius (1921) stated that
earthworms were found only in soil in which the pH values ranged
between 6 and 7, but Phillips (1923) found certain of them at pH5, and
Wherry (1924) found *Helodrilus lonnebergi* living in peat at pH 4.7 to 5.1.
It seems, therefore, that it is too soon to draw conclusions as to the
restriction of the distribution of animals by a factor which may be the
result of so many conditions in the soil.

The Chemical Constituents of the Soil.—It has already been stated
that the soil is about as complicated as protoplasm itself; consequently
to pretense will be made at describing its constitution.   Emerson (1930)
states that only eight elements are ordinarily present in an amount
exceeding one per cent of the earth's crust, and these eight constitute
98.63 per cent of the entire crust.   They are oxygen 46.43 per cent, silicon
27.77, aluminum 8.14, iron 5.12, calcium 3.63, sodium 2.85, potassium
2.60, and magnesium 2.09.   Soils are so varied that it will be sufficient
to call attention to them as the greatest culture media in nature, media in
which the food cycles are forever revolving, and from which nearly all of
the essential elements of nutrition ultimately come, and to which they
ultimately return.

The Biotic Characteristics of the Soil.—The soil is a general environment in that a great majority of any fauna spends a portion, at least, of
the life cycle in the soil.   During the period of hibernation it is undoubtedly the most heavily populated stratum of all environments.

The microorganisms of the soil are of fundamental importance in
connection with the cycles of food materials in the environment.   Soil
microbiology has developed to such an extent that a recent treatise on

the subject by Waksman (1927) comprises 897 pages. This is an excellent source book of information on the bacteria, algae, protozoa, flatworms, nematodes, rotifers, annelids, crustacea, arachnids, myriopods, and insects. Indeed, much of soil science or pedology is concerned with the organisms of the soil. Waksman (1916) has investigated both the bacteria and the protozoans and obtained quantitative results. The following graph of the abundance of the bacteria and the table representing the abundance of the protozoans give some idea of the enormous numbers of individuals to be found (Fig. 119).

The forest is the only one of the environments included in this investigation which may be considered to be a natural environment; for all of the others have been subject to cultivation, although the meadow had not been plowed for a period of six years. The distribution of the micro-

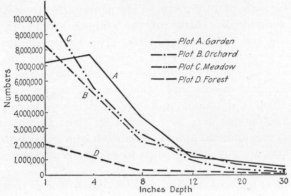

Fig. 119.—Numbers of bacteria in different depths of soil, average for whole year. (*Waksman*, 1916.)

organisms in the garden, in the first eight inches, is undoubtedly influenced by the fact that it has been cultivated and fertilized. It is possible that the condition in the forest suffers by the comparison with artificial habitats.

Waksman (1927) makes the following ecological grouping of the invertebrate soil fauna other than the protozoa:

1. Those that spend all their life in the soil, coming to the surface only occasionally or not at all. These include various worms and rotifers.

2. Those that spend only a part of their life cycle in the soil or on its surface, as in the case of various insects.

3. Those that find only their habitat in the soil, while they may spend a large part of their time on the surface of the soil. These include ants, termites, and many insects.

This author, Waksman (1927), then presents a tabulation of the direct and indirect effect which these organisms have on various soil processes and on plant growth, as follows:

1. They cause a change in the physical condition of the soil, by modifying the mechanical structure of the soil, through their continued motion or by passing the soil through their bodies as in the case of earthworms.

2. They cause various chemical changes in soil, either directly, in their digestive processes, or indirectly, by influencing the activities of the soil fungi and bacteria.

3. They bring about a more uniform distribution of various soil bacteria and other organisms.

4. They may devour other members of the soil flora and fauna, like algae, fungi, and protozoa. In this way, the higher fauna also contributes to the complex system of numerous activities going on in the soil.

5. Damage may be done to crops by certain representatives of these groups, particularly by some of the nematodes, earthworms, insects, etc.

Certain of these animals are often present in such numbers as to be a predominant factor in plant growth. The nematodes are among the most abundant as individuals. Most of the animals are found within the upper 10 cm. of soil. Waksman (1927) gives the minimum number of nematodes per acre in the upper six inches of soil in certain sections of the United States as from approximately 100,000,000 to over 600,000,000.

Many generalized insects and apodiform larvae are to be found in the soil where food is abundant, moisture relatively constant, and where temperature fluctuations may be avoided by short vertical migrations. Some of the species undergo annual migration to a point below the frost line, while others go only low enough to avoid the greatest extremes of temperature.

In the tropical regions, the soil may become so hot as to kill all forms which do not migrate to a considerable distance below the surface. On the sand dunes the surface itself may become unendurable for even the characteristic fauna during the hottest part of the day, as will be shown in connection with the data on the sand dunes.

The results of McAtee (1907), in a study of the insect fauna on the surface, seemed to indicate that there were fewer in the forest than on the prairie. Cameron (1913) published a rather extended table of species of soil insects, indicating the type of soil and the depth at which each was found. Of the 156 species found, 53 are listed as having been found in decaying animal or vegetable refuse.

There is an urgent need for convenient and accurate methods for quantitative population studies of soil populations. Waksman (1927) gives a general account of the common methods used in the study of microorganisms. Morris (1922a and b) describes methods used in the Rothamsted experiments, which are now being used, with certain modifications, by Kenneth King at Saskatoon, Canada; and are also in use at the University of Minnesota. Morris took his sample with the aid of four iron plates which were driven into the ground to enclose a square area of soil nine inches on a side. One of the plates was but four inches long, while the others were 12 inches long. After the plates were driven into the ground, the earth was removed along the outside of the four-inch plate. The plate could then be taken out and the soil from the enclosure removed by layers down to the four-inch level. The small plate could then be put back in place and the process repeated for the lower levels.

King (unpublished) and others have placed a closed killing chamber over the area, before taking the sample, in order to kill all active organisms to prevent them from escaping or migrating about in the sample. A section of sharpened pipe may be driven into the soil to remove a

Fig. 120.—Soil-washing apparatus.

cylinder of soil. The sample may then be forced out of the pipe and separated as to the different levels.

A convenient sample washer and separator was devised by Morris (1922b) which greatly reduces the routine work of evaluating a sample. It consists of a frame holding three sieves of graded openings, the top sieve having the largest openings, and the bottom one, the smallest. The size of the openings depends upon the type of soil and fauna. Morris used 3.5 mm. openings in the top sieve, 1.5 mm. for the second, and a screen of 50 meshes to the inch for the bottom sieve. Sufficient water pressure can be used through a nozzle which sprays on the sample in the top sieve to accomplish the separation with relatively little additional agitation (Fig. 120).

The number and size of sample must be adjusted to suit the number and size of the organisms to be studied. A large number of small samples permits of a better random sample and a fuller appreciation of the uniformity of distribution of the fauna.

Cameron (1913), McColloch (1923), and others have found that the majority of the soil insects are normally to be found within the first

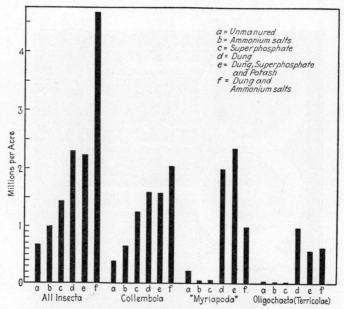

Fig. 121.—Number of individuals in the more important arthropod groups in the various plots at Rothamsted. (*Morris*, 1927.)

four inches below the surface during the period of activity. This corresponds very well with the distribution of the microorganisms.

It is too soon to draw generalizations with regard to the quantities of insect life in the various soils and during the various times of the year. It is interesting to note that Morris (1927) found an average of 673,000 insects per acre in the unmanured control plot which he studied. Among the more important groups were: Collembola, 379,000; and Coleoptera, 163,000. Thompson (1924) gives data which represent the equivalent of 4,500,000 insects per acre of which 94 per cent were Collembola. Data from field studies in Minnesota indicate about two million insects per acre. The study made by Morris (1927) was primarily for the purpose of determining the effect of various fertilization practices upon the insect fauna. His data are presented diagrammatically in Fig. 121. In a previous paper, Morris (1922) states that although 198,653 and 164,983

Elateridae larvae per acre occurred in two plots, they did not produce any appreciable effect on the crop.

The data on depth distribution are all more or less consistent. It is well established that certain insect larvae migrate downwards in the fall,

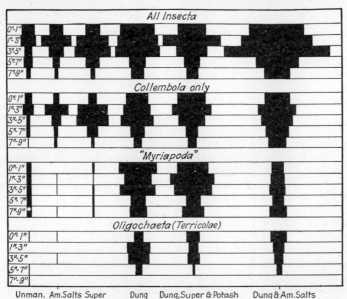

Fig. 122.—Distribution in depth of the more important arthropod groups in the various plots. (*Morris*, 1927.)

but during the active season all are confined near the surface of the soil. The accompanying figure from Morris (1927) is one of the best illustrations of the distributions of insects and other invertebrates in depth (Fig. 122).

A further consideration of the soil organisms will be taken up under each of the various associations.

BIBLIOGRAPHY

SOIL

Buckle, P.: A Preliminary Survey of the Soil Fauna of Agricultural Land, *Ann. Appl. Biol.*, **8**: 135–145, 1921.

Cameron, A. E.: General Survey of the Insect Fauna of the Soil within a Limited Area near Manchester; a Consideration of the Relationships between Soil Insects and the Physical Conditions of Their Habitat, *Jour. Econ. Biol.*, **8**: 159–204, 1913.

————: Soil Insects, *Sci. Prog.*, London, **77**: 92–108, 1925.

Cobb, N. A.: Nematodes and Their Relationships, U. S. Dept. Agr. "Yearbook," pp. 457–490, 1914.

Diem, K.: Untersuchungen über die Bodenfauna in den Alpen, "Jahrb. St. Gall. naturw. Gesell.," Vereinsjahr 1901–1902.

Emerson, Paul: "Principles of Soil Technology," p. 402, The Macmillan Company, New York, 1930.

KING: Unpublished.

KLUGH, A. B.: A Common System of Classification in Plant and Animal Ecology, *Ecology*, **4**: 366–378, 1923.

LEBEDEFF, A. F.: The Movement of Ground and Soil Waters, First Internat. Cong. *Soil Sci. Proc. and Papers*, pp. 459–494, Washington, 1928.

LYON, T. L., and HARRY O. Buckman: "The Nature and Properties of Soils," p. 428, The Macmillan Company, New York, 1929.

McATEE, W. L.: Census of Four Square Feet, *Science*, n.s., **526**: 447–449, 1907.

McCOLLOCH, J. W.: The Rôle of Insects in Soil Deterioration, *Jour. Amer. Soc. Agron.*, **18**: 143–159, 1926.

McCOLLOCH, J. W., and W. P. HAYES: Soil Temperature and Its Influence on White Grub Activities, *Ecology*, **4**: 29–36, 1923.

MAIL, G. ALLEN: Winter Soil Temperatures and Their Relation to Subterranean Insect Survival; Univ. of Minn., thesis for Master's degree, 1929; to be published.

MORRIS, H. M.: Observations on the Insect fauna on Permanent Pasture in Cheshire, *Ann. Appl. Biol.*, **VII**: 141–155, 1920.

————: The Insect and Other Invertebrate Fauna of Arable Land at Rothamsted, *Ann. Appl. Biol.*, **IX**: 282–305, nos. 3 and 4, November, 1922.

————: On a Method of Separating Insects and Other Arthropods from Soil, *Bull. Ent. Research*, **13**: 197–200, 1922.

————: The Insect and Other Invertebrate Fauna of Arable Land at Rothamsted, *Ann. Appl. Biol.*, **XIV**: 442–464, no. 4, November, 1927.

PEARSE, A. S.: "Animal Ecology," McGraw-Hill Book Company, Inc., New York, 1926.

RAMANN, E.: "The Evolution and Classification of Soils," p. 127, transl. by C. L. Whittles, Hoffer and Sons, Cambridge, Eng., 1928.

RUSSELL, SIR E. JOHN: "The Micro-organisms of the Soil," p. 188, Longmans, Green and Co., London, 1923.

RUSSELL, E. J., and APPLEYARD: The Atmosphere of the Soil, *Jour. Agr. Sci.*, England, **7**: 1, 1915.

SANDOW, H.: "The Composition and Distribution of the Protozoan Fauna of the Soil," p. 237, Oliver and Boyd, London, 1927.

SHELFORD, V. E.: "Animal Communities of Temperate America," The University of Chicago Press, 1913.

TAYLOR, E. McKENZIE, and A. CHAMLEY BURNS: Preliminary Note on the Soil Temperature in Sharâqi Land, *Egypt. Min. Agr., Tech. and Sci. Serv. Bull.* 34, 1924. 12 pp. and 20 pl.

THOMPSON, M.: The Soil Population. An Investigation of the Biology of the Soil in Certain Districts of Aberystwyth, *Ann. Appl. Biol.*, vol. XI, nos. 3 and 4, pp. 349–394, 1924.

WAKSMAN, SELMAN A.: Studies on Soil Protozoa, *Soil Sci.*, **1**: 135–152, 1916.

————: Principles of Soil Microbiology, chap. XXVIII, p. 897, Williams & Wilkins Co., Baltimore, 1927.

WHERRY, E. T.: Soil Acidity Preferences of Earth Worms, *Ecology*, **5**: 309, 1924.

CHAPTER XIX

COMMUNITIES OF THE SAND DUNE

The sand dune represents an early stage in plant succession and a simple environment in that there is little added to the soil stratum. It is, however, a severe environment and the organisms living in it are highly specialized. As an environment, the sand dune has been studied much more by botanists than by zoologists. The various insects which comprise the fauna have been studied individually, but the community has

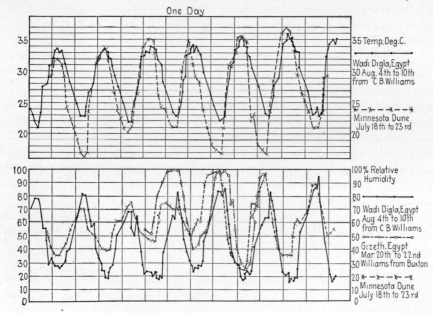

Fig. 123.—A comparison of the temperature and relative humidity at Wadi Digla, Egypt, and on a Minnesota sand dune.

been neglected. Buxton's "Animal Life in Deserts" (1923) is probably the best general description. From the viewpoint of animal ecology, Kashkarov and Kurbatov (1930) give a good description of the Central Kara-Kum Desert in West Turkestan. It is, however, primarily a study of the vertebrate fauna.

The discussion of the ecology of the sand-dune environment is based on a study of a Minnesota dune, as it furnishes concrete illustrations of the actual conditions. The area is relatively restricted, being surrounded by cultivated fields. It is situated just north of Minneapolis, and is characterized by blowouts and partially vegetated areas (Chapman, Mickel, Parker *et al*, 1926).

The daily fluctuations of temperature and humidity during the summer are comparable to those described by Buxton (1923) and Williams (1923) for the Egyptian deserts. The graph below (Fig. 123) shows a comparison of the temperature and humidity records from the Minnesota sand dune for July 18–23; and Gizeth, Egypt, for March 20 to 22, and August 4 to 10. The severity of the diurnal fluctuations, which Buxton stresses as characteristic of deserts, is shown to be as marked in Minnesota as in Egypt, at least on certain days. · It will be noticed that the relative humidity rose 75 per cent in seven hours in Minnesota, and that the temperature dropped 19°C. the same evening. The relative humidity was more consistently low in Egypt than in Minnesota. This is not surprising when it is realized that the station in Egypt was six miles from the nearest cultivated land, while the dune in Minnesota is surrounded by cultivated fields and a lake.

The conditions on the surface of the sand were much more extreme than those in the instrument shelter. A change of 23°C. in three hours was recorded on the surface of the sand, July 24. A difference of 14°C. was found between the temperature in the shade and in the sun at a distance of four feet on July 12. Buxton (1923) states that Prezharalsky has said that the surface of the sand may become as cold as −26.5°C. during the winter in the Gobi Desert. He also says that the highest readings taken so far are 84°C. on the Loango coast and 78°C. on the sand dunes of the Sahara. Sinclair (1922) recorded 71.5°C. as the highest soil surface temperature observed by him in Arizona.

Kashkarov and Kurbatov (1930) state that the members of their expedition observed frost in the Kara-Kum Desert on May 2. They also give a record of the temperature of the soil surface at 3:30 p.m. on May 1 of 45°C. They do not state whether the frost occurred in the same area as the high temperature of the preceding day; but it illustrates the generalization that desert environments are characterized by extreme changes of temperature.

The annual fluctuation of the sand temperature for Minnesota can only be estimated, as no winter-temperature records have been made. The lowest winter temperature recorded by the U. S. Weather Bureau station in St. Paul, just south of the dune, is −41°F. or −5°C. The highest record obtained on the surface of the sand was 56°C. There were, however, other days when the thermograph indicated a temperature much higher than on the day of this record, but unfortunately no surface temperatures were taken on these days. Assuming that the ratio of the thermograph record to the soil temperature is the same at high temperatures as at the lower ones, we would find that the soil temperature on July 23 would have been 74°C. when the thermograph recorded 101°F. This possible annual range of temperature from −40°C. to 74°C. seems to be comparable with some of the greatest extremes which have ever been recorded for similar environments.

The evaporation averaged 394 c.c. per week during the summer, but on July 7 and on several other occasions it was as great as 5 c.c. per hour during the middle of the day.

The following table shows representative readings and illustrates the temperature gradient above and below the surface of the sand. It will be noticed that there may be a drop of 10°C. within an inch above or below the sand surface when the temperature is high.   Also, there may be a drop as great as 20°C. within six inches above the surface.

Distance, inches	Temperatures, °C.			
	Raining	Clear	Clear	Clear
24 above surface..........................	16	25	31	31
12 above surface..........................	18	27	31	31
6 above surface...........................	18	31		
3 above surface...........................	19	32	34	33
1 above surface...........................	19	43	41	40
Sand surface..............................	22	51	47	50
1 below surface...........................	23	42	40	45
2 below surface...........................	23	40	38	43
6 below surface...........................	23	38	38	40
12 below surface..........................	22	39	38	40

The table below illustrates the changes of temperature on the morning of July 24.   In this case the sand warmed perceptibly even to a depth of 12 inches from the time that the sun first shone on it.

Distance, inches	Morning temperatures soil and air						
	5:50 a.m.	6:15 a.m.	6:45 a.m.	7:30 a.m.	8:15 a.m.	8:45 a.m.	9:15 a.m.
24 above surface..............	23	23	24	24	23	23	23
12 above surface..............	24	24	24	24	24	24	24
6 above surface...............	24	24	24	24	24	24	24
3 above surface...............	23	24	24	24	24	24	24
1 above surface...............	18	19	20	23	25	25	27
Sand surface..................	16	18	22	25	30	25	37
1 below surface...............	16	18	22	25	28	28	31
2 below surface...............	16	18	23	24	27	28	30
6 below surface...............	16	17	23	24	26	26	28
12 below surface..............	16	18	23	24	27	26	27

The wind velocity, like all other physical factors on the sand dune, is subject to great variation. Not only does the velocity become very high at times, but the sand which it drives for hundreds of feet produces a severe cutting action. No other environment is subject to such changes in such short periods of time.

The Effect of the Physical Conditions of the Environment on the Insect Fauna.—In observing the diurnal activity of the insects, it was noticed that the population on the sand at night was entirely different from that of the daytime and that the shift from night to day seemed to be correlated with the change of temperature in the morning. Consequently observations were carried on beginning before daybreak and continuing until after the conditions of the day were established. The table gives a record of the time, temperature, and activities of the various more common insects for the mornings of July 24 and Aug. 2. The night of July 23 was much warmer than that of Aug. 1; consequently all of the events took place earlier on the first day.

ACTIVITIES OF INSECTS—MORNING OF JULY 24, 1923

Time, a.m.	Air temperature, °C.	Sand temperature, °C.	Insect	Activity
5:15	. .	17	*Geopinus*	Many digging in.
5:15	. .	17	*Psammachares*	Crawling, unable to fly.
5:45	23	17	*Dasymutilla*	One male seen on sand.
6:00	24	17	*Cicindela*	One seen on sand.
6:15	24	18	*Geopinus*	Last one seen.
6:15	24	18	*Microbembex*	First one seen.
6:30	24	19	*Bembix*	First one seen.

ACTIVITIES OF INSECTS—MORNING OF AUG. 2, 1923

Time, a.m.	Air temperature, °C.	Sand temperature, °C.	Insects	Activity
5:20	10.0	11	*Geopinus*	Geopinus finished digging in, only one seen on sand.
5:55	10.6	. .	*Psammachares*	Crawling about on sand.
6:00	11.1	. .	*Pompilid*	Crawling about on sand.
6:15	12.0	14	*M. femur-rubrum*	On grass active, inactive on sand.
6:35	13.3	. .	*Pompilid*	Flying.
6:40	13.5	. .	*Spharagemon*	Spharagemon start moving about.
6:55	15.0	. .	*Dasymutilla*	Come out of a hole.
7:12	16.0	19	*Spharagemon*	Flying.
7:20	16.5	. .	*Dasymutilla*	Flying about (mole).
7:45	18.5	23	*Microbembex*	One seen.
9:00	23.0	31	Usual day fauna	Normal activities.

On July 24, all of the temperature readings were made at one station; while the observations on the activity of the insects were made at various places on the dune.   As a result the temperatures to which the insects were exposed, may have been quite different from those recorded by the thermocouples.   On Aug. 2 temperatures were read from mercurial thermometers at points as near the insects as possible.   The long shadows cast by the horizontal rays of the rising sun create great differences of temperature and make it difficult to know just what temperature a given insect has been subjected to.

Before the break of day the dune was dominated by *Geopinus* which was as noticeable everywhere as the bembicids are during the day.   At about the time that the sun came up, the beetles all ceased other activities and began to dig down into the sand.   This happened everywhere on the dune at the same time.   It suggests that the changes in temperature, relative humidity, and light, which are marked at this time of day, may be important in bringing about this change in activity.

On cool days the fauna of the night tended to remain on the sand throughout the day.   July 26 was a cool day with a drizzling rain at times.   At 3:10 p.m. the air temperature was 18° and the sand surface 22°. *Geopinus* was found on the sand at this time feeding in places where it was sheltered from the rain.   The bembicids were not out; and *Sphex* was clinging to the bunch grass with its mandibles as it does during the night.   August 7 the temperature was about 15.5° at 11:30 a.m. with a light rain falling.   No *Geopinus* was seen, but *Sphex* was clinging to the grass and a few *Spharagemon* were moving slowly about the sand. No bembicids or mutillids were observed.

In the normal course of the day the insects leave the surface of the sand when its temperature nears 50°C.   Some climb grasses and some enter their burrows while others fly about some distance above the sand, making hurried landings to enter their burrows.   The female mutillids were consistently the last to retreat when the temperature rose, and the first to return to the open sand when the temperatures again lowered. These observations tend to show that temperature may play an important part in controlling the diurnal activities of the sand-dune fauna.   There is, however, no evidence with regard to the importance of light other than the observation that on certain cloudy days the insects were behaving much as they would at night.

The reactions of the insects to changes of temperature on the sand were studied by confining them within a moat which surrounded a square meter of sand.   The moat was a galvanized iron trough which was kept filled with water.   All insects which did not fly were simply released within this area.   The temperature of the sand was read at intervals, and the reactions of the insects were observed.   This type of experiment was not the most successful because the temperature fluctuations were often unexpected and always uncontrollable, especially when there were clouds in the sky.

TEMPERATURE EXPERIMENTS ON SAND

Insect	Start		Finish		Observations
	Time	Tempera-ture, °C.	Time	Tempera-ture, °C.	
Gryllus.............	1:15	56	1:16	56	All dead (13 specimens)
Gryllus.............	3:30	49	3:31	49	All dead (10 spec.)
Bembix.............	11:40	49	12:10	..	All dead (3 spec.)
Dasymutilla........	11:40	49	12:10	..	Living (2 spec.)
Microbembex larva..	10:45	48	11:45	50	Dead (1 spec.)
Tetraopes..........	11:50	50	11:55	..	All dead (3 spec.)
Oecanthus..........	2:45	50	3:50	..	All dead (2 spec.)
Anosia larva.......	10:45	47	11:25	48	Dead (1 spec.)

The table above indicates the results of these observations. The female mutillids were the only insects which withstood the highest temperature. Since these insects cannot fly, their only escape is to climb a plant, seek shade, or enter a burrow, and this they do when the sand temperatures approach 50°C. Great difficulty was experienced in keeping them exposed to the sun, for they began to dig into the sand whenever the temperature neared 50°C. This tendency to dig or crawl under the edge of the moat, together with their great resistance to temperature, made it impossible to kill them by exposure on the surface of the sand.

On the other hand, insects which do not normally live on the dune were found to be unable to withstand the high temperatures. The crickets, *Gryllus assimilis* Fab., for instance, died very quickly. The dune grasshopper, *Spharagemon aequale* Say, would rise up on its feet, thus lifting its body off the hot sand when the temperature reached 50°C., but the crickets made no attempt to protect themselves in this way. They remained in contact with the hot sand and died.

It was necessary to clip the wings of the bembicids in order to confine them on the sand, for they attempted to fly when the temperature rose. Although typical of the sand dune, the bembicids could not survive even the moderately high temperatures when thus confined on the surface of the sand. Control experiments were carried on with insects, with their wings clipped, and confined in the shade. These insects always survived the experiments. This result with regard to the inability of the bembicid wasps to withstand the temperatures of the sand was rather surprising, and will be returned to later in the discussion.

Insects which do not normally live on the dunes seem to lack the proper endurance and reactions to avoid the high temperatures. They may engage in frantic random movements as the crickets do, but these efforts do not aid them in escaping the extreme temperature on the open sand. The success of the insects which normally inhabit the dune seems to lie in their ability either to endure or escape the extremely high temperatures.

Neither the observations on the diurnal activities of the insects, nor the experiments with the moat on the open sand yielded results which were satisfactory for comparing the various insects and measuring the differences in their temperature responses.

In order to have uniform conditions with a gradual rise of temperature and constant light, a comparative test of the temperature reactions of about a dozen species of the sand-dune insects was made in a carrier cabinet in the laboratory. For this purpose from three to a dozen individuals of each species were obtained and confined in glass tubes one and one-half inches in diameter, eight inches in length, and covered with cheesecloth at each end. The tubes were placed on racks so situated that the air could circulate through them. The authors stationed themselves where each could observe a certain number of species. The reactions of all species could thus be recorded as the temperature changed.

The temperature was first lowered to 0°C., at which point all of the insects were inactive. The temperature was then slowly raised so that the curve, measured by temperature and time, was a straight line over 56°C. and 160 minutes of time. The following figure shows this curve, repeated in a parallel series to facilitate a comparison of all of the more common species (Fig. 124).

As the temperature rose, records were made to indicate various activities. Point 1 indicates the first movement which was noticed. This was usually a slight movement of a leg or an antenna. Point 2 represents the point at which the first individual of a species stood up on its feet. Point 3 is the point at which the first crawling was observed. Point 4 is very definite, as it represents the point at which all of the individuals were crawling. At point 5 activities were normal, as nearly as could be judged. When point 6 was reached, there was the first evidence of paralysis in some part of an individual. At 7, one of the individuals of each species fell over and was unable to stand. At 8, all of the individuals of each species were unable to stand.

For the purpose of comparison, the cricket, *Gryllus assimilis* Fab., was included, though it does not belong to the sand-dune association. In the preceding figure the insects are arranged in an order determined by the temperature, at which point 4 is located. This point was chosen as a basis for the comparison because it represents activity on the part of all the individuals of a species and also because it was determinable with more precision than that of normal activity. *Geopinus incrassatus* Dejean, with the lowest point 4, is at the left in the upper row, and *Microbembex monodonta* Say, with the highest point 4, is at the right in the lower row.

The most significant fact brought out by this comparison is that the sand-dune insects are not all alike in their temperature adjustments. In general the insects which live on the dunes during the heat of the day have their minimum and maximum effective temperatures located at higher points on the scale than the others do. *Geopinus*, which is active on the dune at night, has the lowest minimum effective temperature of all. On the other hand, both *Bembix* and *Microbembex*, which are characteristic of the day fauna, have high minimum effective temperatures and

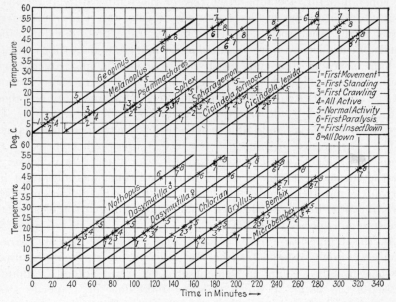

Fig. 124.—Graph showing the results of exposing certain insects from the sand dune and other environments to a rising temperature. All insects were inactive at the start. Temperature in degrees Centigrade at the left, time in minutes at the bottom. In reading the time for any activity, deduct the number of minutes at the lower end of the line for a given insect, *e.g.*, first movement (1) for *Grylus* is 160 − 120 = 40 min. (*Chapman, Mickel et al.,* 1926.)

low maximum effective temperatures, leaving but a narrow range of activity.

Another rather noticeable characteristic of some of the sand-dune insects is the small difference between the effective temperatures and those of normal activity. In the case of *Chlorion*, for example, a change of 2°C. brought it from dormancy to normal activity. Similarly, at the upper limit of the scale it passed from normal activity to heat rigor very quickly.

The difference between the location of the points on the curves does not give a true idea of the comparative differences between the various insects, although the curves do represent the actual course of events during the experiments. This is because changes of both time and temperature are involved. In comparing *Geopinus* with *Melanoplus*, which is a grasshopper found at the edge of the dune, point 4 is but 3° higher in the case of *Melanoplus* than for *Geopinus*, but there is also 10 minutes' difference in the time.

The maximum temperature, as represented by point 8 is also included in the following table, together with the range of effective temperature. There seems to be no correlation between point 4 and point 8. The bembicids have the lowest point 8 and may be compared with *Nothopus*, a carabid beetle, found principally at night and on cloudy days, and with *Cicindela lepida*, a small pale tiger beetle, which is active on hot days. This comparison emphasizes the narrowness of the temperature zone within which the activities of the bembicids are confined while living in an environment which is characterized by its extremes of temperature.

	Point 4 °C.	Point 8 °C.	Zone of effective temp., °C., 8–4
Geopinus incrassatus Dejean...................	7.0	46.0	39.0
Melanoplus femur-rubrum DeG................	10.0	53.0	43.0
Psammacheres sp...........................	13.5	50.0	36.5
Sphex argentatus Hart.......................	15.5	51.5	36.0
Spharagemon aequale Say....................	16.0	55.0	39.0
Cicindela formosa generosa Degean...........	18.0	54.0	36.0
Cicindela lepida Degean.....................	18.0	48.0	30.0
Nothopus grossus Say........................	18.0	49.0	31.0
Dasymutilla bioculota Cresson ♂..............	18.0	53.0	35.0
Dasymutilla bioculota Cresson ♀..............	20.0	55.0	35.0
Chlorion cyaneus aerarius Patten.............	21.0	51.5	30.5
Gryllus assimilis Fab........................	21.0	49.0	28.0
Bembix pruinosa Fab.........................	25.0	44.0	19.0
Microbembex monodonta Say..................	30.0	49.0	19.0

By subtracting the value for point 4 from that for point 8 we got a measure for the zone of activity. For *Bembix* this value of the zone of activity is 19, and for *Microbembex* it is also 19, as compared with 39 for *Geopinus*, 39 for *Spharagemon*, 36 for *Cicindela formosa*, and 35 for *Dasymutilla*. Thus the bembicids' zone of activity as measured by these values is little over half that of the other insects.

Williams (1923) has called attention to the fact that great variations of temperature are to be found in time and space in Egypt. Extremes of temperature may be found in a given location during a period of time, and, at any given time a variety of temperatures may be found in closely adjacent places. Possibly no other environment offers such extremes. The same conditions have been found to obtain on the little sand dunes in Minnesota. The variation of temperature with time is illustrated by the graph (Fig. 133), which gives the temperature extremes during the day. Possible annual extremes have been shown to be −40.56° and 74°C. The variations of temperature with vertical space are illustrated in the tables on that factor, showing that there may be a difference of 20° from the surface of the soil to six inches above it. The variation of temperature in shaded and exposed places in close horizontal proximity has been referred to and data given to show that this difference has been found to be as great as 14°C. High temperature and low humidity are often considered as the outstanding characteristics of dunes and deserts, but it is more likely that extreme variation of these factors is the more important characteristic.

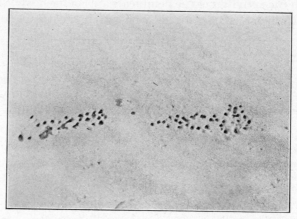

Fig. 125.—Holes in the sand leading to the nests of *Bembix*.

The data on the temperature zones of activity of the insect fauna of the dunes show that these insects are not similar in their adjustment to temperature. Since there are such variations of temperature in the dune environment, the insects adjust themselves to time and place. *Geopinus*, for instance, is active on the sand surface by night and retires to a depth of a foot or more below the sand surface by day.

The bembicids are limited to narrow temperature zones of activity. On the sand dune, with the great variations of temperature to be found in time and space, they have the opportunity to suit themselves, by exercising a choice better, perhaps, than in a more constant environment, unless that environment was constant within their narrow zone of activity. Constancy either above or below this narrow zone would be prohibitive.

The larvae of the bembicids are reared in burrows below the surface of the sand where temperature conditions are relatively constant. The adults fly about in the air searching for insects with which to provision their nests; and while so doing, they may select widely different temperatures by changing their altitude but a few inches (Fig. 125).

In the digging of their burrows their narrow temperature zones limit their activities. So long as they live on the dune their choice of the place for starting their burrows is limited to the surface of the sand, and this is the hottest place. In a medium which shifts with the wind, as the sand does, these burrows must be dug and re-dug many times with the result that digging constitutes no small part of their activity. Returning to the first table on temperature it will be recalled that the extremely high point is just at the surface of the sand and that at short distance either above or below, the temperature may vary as much as 20°C.

Observations have been shown that the penetration of this hot-surface layer is accomplished by a juggling of time and space during which the wasps alternately dig furiously at the surface for a short period of time and fly about six to 12 inches above the surface of the sand. As the burrow deepens, these flights become less frequent until the wasps are well within the uniformly lower temperature of the deeper sand.

At a time when wasps with their wings clipped were dying on the sand surface within the area where experiments were being carried on, others were alternately digging and flying even within the same area. At times the bembicids swooped down on our experiment and stole the insects which had just died at temperatures considerably above those which the bembicids themselves could endure if confined on the surface of the sand.

This habit of leaving the surface of the sand at frequent intervals was interpreted by the Peckhams to be for the purpose of watching for enemies. However, the present explanation seems to have more basis, for when the wasps were experimentally confined to the hot surface of the sand they died, while others which were confined to the sand surface in a shaded place survived.

Thus, while the bembicids with their narrow temperature zones of activity may not seem to be well adapted to the sand dunes, the dunes seem to be a suitable place for them to live in. The dunes furnish a substratum in which burrows may be dug easily, and they present a range of temperature from which they can choose their optimum.

The mutillids which parasitize the larvae of the bembicids are limited in their choice of space by the lack of wings in the females. Being unable to leave the surface of the sand except by entering burrows or climbing the sparse vegetation, their success on the dune seems to be due to the high temperature which they can endure. Thus their limitation in space seems to be compensated by their increased endurance of high temperature.

It is interesting to consider the fact that, while the bembicids must juggle time and space in order to accommodate their narrow temperature zones of activity to the conditions on the sand dunes, they are the key to certain consocies which involve a considerable part of the fauna including some of the mutillids. *Microbembex* provisions its nest with the bodies of dead insects which it finds upon the sand, while *Bembix* provisions its nest with blowflies. The second member of the consocies dependent on the bembicids is *Dasymutilla bioculata* Cresson. The third member is a species of bombyliid fly. The evidence seems to indicate that this species is parasitic upon *Dasymutilla bioculata*, although this is not certain. The fourth member of the consocies is a species of *Conopidae*. Little is known regarding this fly other than that it is evidently a parasite of *Bembix pruinosa*.

Many other consocies exist in the sand-dune association, but their elements are not nearly so well known as those of the bembicids. *Sphex argentata* is undoubtedly a key species to one of these consocies, of which one of the elements is very likely another species of mutillid. The basis of a third consocies is the various species of spiders, and one of the important elements is the psammocharid wasps which use the spiders in provisioning their nests. It is very likely that the various species of cicindelids (Shelford, 1908), *Geopinus* and certain species of Hymenoptera are the basic or key species to several other consocies.

BIBLIOGRAPHY

SAND DUNE COMMUNITIES

BUXTON, A.: "Animal Life in Deserts. A Study of the Fauna in Relation to the Environment," London, 1923.

CHAPMAN, R. N., C. E. MICKEL, J. R. PARKER and others: Studies in the Ecology of Sand Dune Insects, *Ecology*, **7**: 416–426, no. 4, 1926.

HAYES, WM. P.: Prairie Insects, *Ecology*, **8**: 238–250, 1927.

JEWELL, MINNA E.: Aquatic Biology of the Prairie, *Ecology*, **8**: 289–298, 1927.

KASHKAROV, DANIEL, and VICTOR KURBATOV: Preliminary Ecological Survey of the Vertebrate Fauna of the Central Kara-Kum Desert in West Turkestan, *Ecology*, vol. XI, no. 1, January, 1930.

KROGERUS, R.: Anpassningsföreteelser hos dyninsekter, *Ent. Meddel.*, Copenhagen, **16**: 133–135, 1928.

SHACKLEFORD, M. W.: Animal Communities of an Illinois Prairie, *Ecology*, **10**: 126–154, 1929.

SHELFORD, V. E.: Life-histories and Larval Habits of the Tiger Beetles (Cicindelidae), *Jour. Linn. Soc.*, London, Zool., **30**: 157–184, 1908.

SINCLAIR, J. J.: Temperature of Soil and Air in a Desert, *U. S. Monthly Weather Rev.*, **50**: 142–144, 1922.

WILLIAMS, C. B.: A Short Bioclimatic Study in the Egyptian Desert, *Egypt. Min. Agr., Tech. and Sci. Serv. Bull.* 29, 1923.

CHAPTER XX

COMMUNITIES OF THE GRASS OR HERB STRATUM

The structure of the herb stratum itself is biotic and consequently it offers great possibilities for specialized biotic relationships with the fauna. The food relationships extend from the generalized habits of certain Orthoptera which may feed on nearly all species to the specific feeders which are restricted to a single species of host plant. Among the monophytophagous forms there are leaf miners, stem borers, gall-forming insects and many others.

The majority of the studies which have been made have been of the nature of observation with regard to their natural history. For this reason they will not be considered at this time.

Grassland Associations.—Shelford (1913) presented a good description of the grassland associations of various types for the region of Chicago. Vestal (1913) made a more detailed study of some of the Illinois prairies. His paper (1913) may be referred to for lists of species and groups which he considers ecological units. His ecological groups are largely based upon the food habits of the organisms.

Morse (1904) classified the grasshopper associations on much the same basis as had been used by botanists for the plant communities. Shull (1911) concluded that such a scheme was not applicable to the conditions which he studied. He found that the distribution of species was not as limited as Morse had indicated. Local conditions were found to be of great importance in many cases. This was also found by Parker (1930).

It would seem that definite progress might be made in this field by using definite experimental methods to analyze the physical conditions as illustrated for the sand dunes. For the study of the associations of organisms under the general conditions of grassland associations a statistical method similar to that proposed by Arrhenius (1922) for the study of prairie or grassland communities might be used.

The addition of a stratum of low vegetation above the soil stratum introduces a biotic factor which alters the physical environment. Solar radiation is interfered with by the vegetation, the action of the wind is impeded, evaporation is consequently reduced, and the roots tend to alter the soil.

No attempt will be made to give a general description of the prairie regions of the world or to classify them on the basis of topography or plant and animal communities. Such regions are usually semi-arid and have had their successional development arrested so that the grassland represents a sort of climatic climax or sub-climax association. On the map illustrating the biotic areas of North America (page 225) these areas are included in the savanna and steppe areas.

Detailed studies of the "micro-climate" of the grasslands are lacking. Vestal (1913) says that the physical factors of the environment are of the greatest importance, but he gives only a few data showing that the rate of evaporation among the bunch grass may be as great as or greater than on the open sand. Unpublished data of students at the University of Minnesota show that the temperature of the soil surface in exposed areas may be as high as or even higher than on the exposed sand. This is no doubt partly due to the reduced wind and consequent reduced heat radiation from the soil. There may be a difference of 40°C. within a few centimeters on the soil surface between exposed and shaded areas. The wind may be reduced from 850 feet per minute at five feet above the ground to 150 feet per minute four inches from the ground, due to resistance offered by the vegetation.

Shackleford (1929) studied the animal communities of the "high prairie" and "low prairie" of Illinois. This was a quantitative study of areas along a railroad right-of-way which may not have been typical of a primitive prairie environment. General data were obtained with reference to the seasonal climate, but little attention was given to the details of local environment.

Shackleford (1929) states that the high and low prairies are distinctly different as to physical and biotic conditions. This difference is based mainly on ground water, and during dry periods he found certain of the organisms from the high prairie migrating into the low prairie.

Quantitative data were obtained by taking 50 sweeps with an insect net. The population was classified on the basis of activity, seasonal abundance, and probable influence. The species which were abundant and active throughout the growing period were called predominant, and those which were abundant and active for a lesser period were called seasonals. On the basis of seasonal abundance "biotic seasons" were recognized which were said to be characterized by the activity of biotic groups which were called "prevernal," "vernal," "aestival" and "hiemal." The designation of "influent" and "subinfluent" was an attempt to evaluate the influence which the different species might have on the community as a whole. It combines size and numbers in the criteria of influence. For example, more individuals were found of the hemipteron, *Triphleps insidiosus* Say, than of the grasshopper, *Melanoplus femur-rubrum* DeG, but the large size of the grasshopper caused it to be placed above the hemipteron in the list of influent species.

It is Shackleford's conclusion that there are two distinct communities, one on the high prairie, and one on the low prairie. These are designated as *Cambarus-Eucrangonyx* on the low prairie, and *Lygus-Formica-Microtus* on the high prairie. The high-prairie community is more homogeneous than that of the low prairie. Animals must be capable of remaining alive under a wider range of conditions to be predominant in the

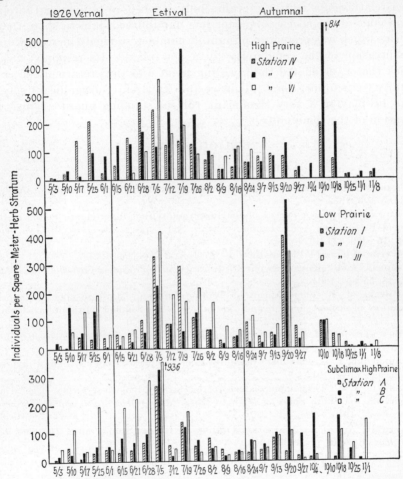

FIG. 126.—Graph showing the total number of individuals per square meter, herb stratum, for each of the nine prairie stations during the seasons when an herb stratum was present, 1926. (*Shackleford*, 1929.)

low prairie as compared with the high prairie. Figure 126 gives a general idea of the numbers and seasonal distribution of the prairie fauna per square meter. The general seasonal fluctuations are quite similar in all three prairie types.

It is difficult to present data as to species in a fauna. Shackleford gives a tabulation of the high-prairie fauna. Long lists of species are difficult to evaluate even when we resort to the statistical methods of

Arrhenius (1922).   The statistical methods are designed to show when the occurrence of species together is constant enough to indicate an association between them.

The judgment as to the significance of numbers of species and the inter-relationships can be of value only when it rests upon a thorough knowledge of the species.   Carter has unpublished data to show that a species which was present in minimum numbers suddenly increased upon the invasion of the community by a new plant.   Its response was so quick that it defoliated the invading plant and thus returned the community to its former flora.   Thus certain apparently insignificant species may be playing a very significant rôle in standing guard against the invasion of the community.

BIBLIOGRAPHY

GRASS OR HERB STRATUM

ARRHENIUS, O.: A New Method for Analysis of Plant Communities, *Jour. Ecology*, **10**: 185–199, 1922.

EDWARDS, E. E.: A Survey of the Insect and Other Invertebrate Fauna of Permanent Pasture and Arable Land of Certain Soil Types at Aberystwyth, *Ann. Appl. Biol.*, **16**: 299–323, 1929.

HAYES, WILLIAM P.: Prairie Insects, *Ecology*, **8**: 238–250, 1927.

MORSE, A. P.: Researches on North American *Acridiidae*, *Carnegie Inst. Wash. Pub.* 18, 55 pp., 1904.

PARKER, J. R.: Some Effects of Temperature and Moisture upon *Melanoplus mexicanus mexicanus*, Saussure and *Camnula pellucida* Scudder (Orthoptera), *Univ. of Mont. Agr. Expt. Sta., Bull.* 223, Bozeman, Montana, 1930.

SHACKLEFORD, M. W.: Animal Communities of an Illinois Prairie, *Ecology*, vol. X, **1**: 126–154, January, 1929.

SHELFORD, V. E.: "Animal Communities of Temperate America," The University of Chicago Press, 1913.

SHULL, A. F.: Thysanoptera and Orthoptera, in a Biological Survey of the Dune Region on the South Shore of Saginaw Bay, Mich., *Mich. Geol. and Biol. Survey, Ann. Rept.*, 1910.

VESTAL, A. G.: An Associational Study of Illinois Sand Prairie, *Ill. State Lab. Nat. Hist. Bull.* 10, pp. 1–96, 1913.

CHAPTER XXI

COMMUNITIES OF THE SHRUB AND TREE STRATA

The superimposing of strata of shrubs and trees upon the herb and soil strata increases the complexity of both the physical and biotic conditions of the environment. Infinitely more possibilities of specialization are presented. It is impossible to go into all of the details of the study of forest insects (see Graham, 1929) or even to give an adequate summary of the more important generalizations in the limited space available.

The Physical Conditions of Shrub and Tree Strata.—Light, temperature, relative humidity, and air movements are all modified by the presence of trees. The various types of forests, dominated by different species of trees, represent environments which are physically and biotically different. We shall first review briefly some of the physical characteristics.

The radiations from the sun are intercepted to a much greater extent in the forest than on the prairie. The following graphs from Zon and Graves (1911) show the comparative light intensities in the crowns of trees and in the open. It is interesting to note how the light is reduced at noon as compared with the forenoon and afternoon in the case of the tree of heaven, *Ailanthus glandulosa*. This is undoubtedly due to the large compound leaves which intercept the vertical rays but permit the more horizontal ones to penetrate (Fig. 127).

In the following table compiled from various sources, the intensity of the light in forests of various types of trees is compared with a standard.

Tree	Light, per cent of standard	Tree	Light, per cent of standard
Hazel	33	Poplar	15.6
Plum	33	Pine	9.9
Elm-ash	25	Black Oak	4(?)
Larch	25	Basswood maple	2(?)

In the last two cases there may be some question as to whether the data are strictly comparable to the others. However it is interesting to note how the light decreases, beginning with the two shrubs and proceeding to the climax forest, in essentially the same order as is presented in the course of plant succession.

Shirley (1929) says:

Measurements of the light intensity under forest canopies show it to be from 0.1 to 20 per cent of full daylight. Under ordinary continuous canopies the light is usually reduced below 10 per cent of full light. Even in "sun flecks" the intensity is seldom more than 20 per cent. The green leaves change the quality of the light filtering through them to some extent by absorbing more energy in the red and blue than in the green spectral regions. Since the canopy also cuts out a higher percentage of yellow sunlight than the blue skylight, only the red region is likely to be deficient.

The temperature of forests is modified by the interruption of the sun's rays and the reduction of air currents. This results in less extreme conditions than are found in open environments. Pearson (1914) published results from the study of forests and "parks," which are given in the following table:

Temperature	5 feet above ground	8 feet above ground
Mean minimum in forest.............	6.4°F. higher than park	2° higher than park
Mean maximum in forest.............	1.0°F. lower than park	About the same

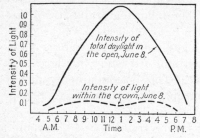 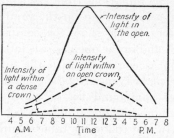

Fig. 127.—Hourly light intensities within the crown of Ailanthus (horizontal arrangement of leaves) and black locust *Rovinia* (vertical arrangement of leaves). (*Adapted from Zon and Graves*, 1911.)

The heat of evaporation of all of the water which is evaporated from a forest is also an important factor in reducing the temperature on hot days.

Larsen (1922) studied the physical conditions in an area from which the forest had been cut as compared with the uncut forest and found that the air in the forest was about 10°F. warmer than in the open at night and about 10° cooler during the heat of the day.

Larsen (1922) also found that the soil temperature at the depth of his readings varied 4 or 5°F. between the daily maxima and minima while the soil of the forest showed less than 1° variation.

A study of a series of environments in the region of Minneapolis and St. Paul showed that the basswood-maple climax forest represents a considerable modification of temperature as compared with the sand dune. The climax forest was on the average 6.5° cooler during the middle of the day and 1.5° warmer during the night than the sand dune. The forest canopy intercepts the sun's rays during the day and prevents the escape of the warm air during the night. When compared with the tamarack bog and the oak forest, Fig. 128, it can be seen that the temperature conditions are less modified in the other types of forest.

All of the forest environments are very much alike in their air and soil temperatures, and differ consistently from the sand-dune tempera-

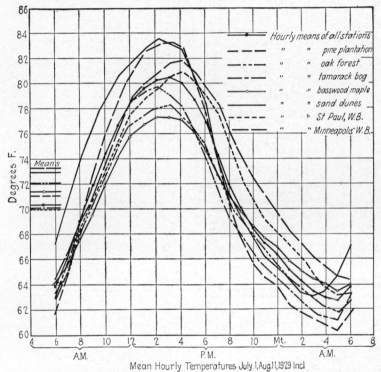

Fɪɢ. 128.—Mean hourly temperatures of five environments, July 1 to August 11, 1929.

tures which are considerably higher in all cases. There are certain limited areas between the trees of the young pine forest upon which the sun shines for a long period each day and in which the soil temperature rises even higher at times than that on the sand dunes. This is due to the shelter from the wind offered by the young trees and applied only to relatively limited areas. In general, the temperature conditions in the various types of forests were very closely similar and very much like those reported at the Weather Bureau stations. Measurements in one day showed a variation of hardly more than 1°C. from the ground surface to 25 feet in various parts of the interior of the tamarack bog. The greatest difference between the sand-dune and the forest environments is at the surface of the soil which happens to be a very important stratum in the sand-dune environment. The temperatures at various depths down to 18 inches show a very consistent difference between the sand dune and the other environments. The soil surface temperatures may often be from 15 to 25°C. higher than the soil surface in the forests (Fig. 129). Even at 5 a.m. when the temperatures in general are at

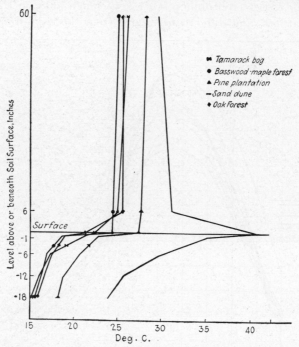

FIG. 129.—Comparison of afternoon temperatures recorded simultaneously in five different environments.

their minima the soil in the sand dunes is about 5°C. above the other environments. A study of the table will show that there are not sufficient data available to make distinctions between the soil temperatures of the various types of forest. It seems at present that their soil surface temperatures are about the same with the possible exception explained for the young pine forest.

Evaporation is influenced by the reduced wind velocity, the reduced light, and the reduced temperature. The following data seem to be comparable and give a good idea of the relative rates of evaporation in different forest communities.

Cottonwood = 35 c.c.;
Pine = 17 c.c.;

Oak = 16 c.c.;
Beech-maple = 13 c.c.

These are maximum rates of evaporation in a unit of time. Again the order of decrease is essentially the order of development of the association in plant succession.

The relative humidity cannot be treated in the same way because of the lack of comparable data. Readings have been made on the prairie and in the forest on the same day and at the same time, in which the results at times have shown a lower relative humidity in the forest than on the prairie. Such data, however, lack substantiation by a large enough series to make them significant.

There are many local conditions in so complicated an environment which deserve consideration. The trunks of trees, the logs of fallen

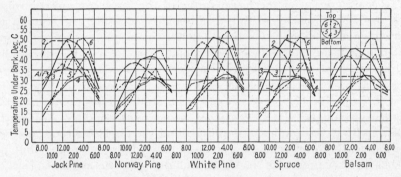

Fig. 130.—Graph showing the temperature under the bark of logs from various species of trees when lying north and south. Temperatures were recorded throughout the day for six places in each log. (*Graham*, 1920.)

trees, the foliage, and the plants of the under-strata all present specific problems with regard to both the physical and biotic factors.

Graham (1920 and 1925) has made studies of the conditions in logs which have shown that the variations of temperature, even within the same log, may be greater than the differences found between widely different types of environment. The following graph shows how, within the same white pine log, the temperature on the top of the log may exceed the maximum effective temperature of ordinary insects while that on the lower side may be only moderate.

It was also found as shown that the temperature did not reach such a high point in logs of other species which were lighter in color. The temperatures could be changed by changing the position of the log with respect to the angle of incidence of the sun's rays or by placing it in various degrees of shade. In full sunlight the temperature of the sub-cortical layer of a log might be as much as 29°C. above that of the air (Fig. 130).

As might be expected, the fauna of the log was influenced by the temperature conditions. The buprestid beetles were found most abundantly on the side which was exposed to the sun and the high temperature. Certain insects required a longer period for the completion of their life cycles on the lower portion of the log than on the upper portion.

The Biotic Conditions of the Shrub and Forest Environments.—The fauna of the forest is more varied than that of the prairie because the environment offers a wider range of conditions. There is a portion of the fauna in the soil, and a portion on the vegetation. The fauna of the vegetation may be divided between the foliage and the tree trunks. The insects on the foliage may be surface feeders, leaf rollers, leaf miners, or gall formers. The insects of the tree trunk may be cambium dwellers, cambium-wood dwellers, or heart-wood dwellers and bark dwellers.

In consideration of the insect fauna of the forest we are confronted with the subject matter of forest entomology to which the student will find volumes devoted. Graham (1929) treats the subject of forest entomology from the ecological viewpoint. In this volume the student will find references to manuals of the various taxonomic groups of forest insects, as well as studies of the habits and life histories of the insects.

The fauna of the forest soil has been studied by Trägårdh (1928), who has given particular attention to the microarthropods. This author took quantitative samples of material from the forest floor and placed it in a funnel with different sizes of mesh. He did not use heat but permitted the slow process of drying to stimulate the organisms to crawl out of the material and fall into containers below the funnel.

From a comparative study of the microarthropods of the forest soil in the Sorek mountains of Sweden, Trägårdh concludes that the number of species and of individuals is correlated with the amount of litter which covers the ground. He says:

Above the tree region there are in the Lapland mountains three zones, one above the other, called respectively birch zone, willow zone, and lichen zone. In these zones the number of species of *Orbotidae* decreased from 19 to 15 and 8, that of the *Prostigmata* from 15 to 7 and 8, but that of the *Mesostigmata* from 15 to 11 and 3. The herbaceous species, subsisting as they do on moss and lichen, occur up to the greatest altitudes, whereas the carnivorous *Mesostigmata* decrease very rapidly in numbers of species and specimens, the obvious reason for this being that there is not food enough for them in the lichen region.

The fauna of microarthropods is also influenced by the soil and litter. Trägårdh states that the fauna becomes 70 times as rich when the ground is covered with leaves as compared with that covered with moss. The quantitative data are presented in the accompanying table.

NUMBER OF MICROARTHROPODS PER KILOGRAM DRY SUBSTANCE (Trägårdh, 1928)

1. Dry more or less decayed birch leaves in the south of Sweden......... 5,000
2. Dry more or less decayed willow leaves in the north of Sweden........ 950
3. Dry spruce needles at the base of a spruce........................... 13

4. Dry pine needles and a little moss............................... 80
5. Moss *Hylocomium proliferum* and *H. parietinum* under spruce boughs on
   cutting.. 830
6. *Hyloconium parietinum*... 17

The fauna of the tree trunk is discussed by Graham (1925 and 1929). He concludes that a log is an ecological unit with a distinctly characteristic and well-adapted fauna.   The distribution of the insects in logs is said to be regulated by many factors of which food, moisture, and temperature appear on the average most important.   The temperature of the log, which is more or less independent of the air temperature, and varies directly with the intensity of solar radiation, is a very important limiting factor in logs.   Logs lying in full shade have a low temperature and high moisture content but most species prefer to oviposit in the sun.   Other species which occur only on the lower side of logs in the sun occur on all sides of logs in the shade.

The foliage-feeding insects which live between the upper and lower epidermal layers of the leaves as leaf miners have been studied by Needham, Frost, and Tothill (1928) in America, and by Hering (1926) in Europe.   In general, the leaf miners have shorter life cycles than the surface feeders.   They are highly specialized and are usually restricted as to food plants.

The gall-forming species represent an interesting inter-relationship between insects and plants.   They are highly specialized both as to the insect species and as to the gall formed.   The latter, called *zoocedidea* are so characteristic that they may be classified more or less independently by the insect and the plant from which they arise.   An impression of the subject of insect galls may be gained from a consideration of a recent monograph by Kinsey (1929), which contains 577 pages devoted to the single genus, *Cynips*, of gall wasps.   Felt (1918), Beutenmiller (1901), and others also have published general information with regard to galls and gall insects.   The subject offers interesting possibilities in the analysis of the ecological and physiological problems involved in the formation of galls.

The foliage feeders consist of various groups of insects which differ widely in habits.   Some of them possess mandibulate mouth parts with which they chew the entire leaf, while others have piercing mouth parts which make it possible for them to suck the plant sap.   Graham (1929) gives general references to the literature on these insects.

FOREST ASSOCIATIONS

More will be gained for the present purpose from a consideration of published work of a quantitative type than from a general discussion of miscellaneous papers of a more general nature.   Such papers present the results of determinations from which one may draw his own conclusions with regard to the conditions which exist in a forest.

There is a correlation between the fauna and the stages of plant succession as has been pointed out in the chapter on Succession. The relative abundance of the various species of insects in environments representing various stages of plant succession is shown in Fig. 131 from Smith (1928). This gives a general impression of faunal change with plant succession. The grasshopper and the red and tarnish-plant bug seem to belong to the early stages of succession rather than to the forest. While other species, such as the mirid bug, *Dicyphus*, the springtail, and the spider, *Mangora*, are characteristically more abundant in the forest.

The Pine-dune Association.—This association is chosen to represent

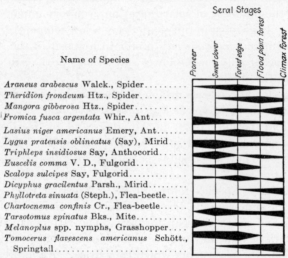

FIG. 131.—A graphic representation of the ranges of abundant influent predominants and seasonals through the seral stages leading to a red oak-maple climax. The width of the line shows the relative numbers in each station on the basis of the total number secured at the station during the whole year. Different scales are used for the various species. (*Smith*, 1928.)

a forest association partly because it is an early stage in plant succession and partly because there is available a paper based on quantitative work (Sanders and Shelford, 1922). One would expect that this early stage in the development of a forest would represent conditions more or less intermediate between grassland and forest, or at least that the conditions would be less characteristically those of the forest than those of the sub-climax or climax stages. The chief tree studied at the stations was the jack pine, *Pinus banksianna*.

The Physical Conditions in a Pine-dune Association.—Temperature fluctuation increased from the ground to the tree strata as shown in the following graph from Sanders and Shelford (1922). The ground temperature was considerably higher than the herb level and showed by far the greatest fluctuation during the day (Fig. 132).

Evaporation, however, was 14 c.c. at the ground, 12 c.c. in the herb stratum, 15 c.c. in the shrub stratum, and 22 c.c. in the tree stratum as represented by the mean rate for July and August. This indicates that wind is more important than temperature in determining the rate of evaporation.

The Biotic Conditions in a Pine-dune Association. Methods of Sampling.—Quantitative samples in the ground stratum were taken by forcing an inverted bucket, 25 cm. in diameter, into the ground and introducing an anesthetic to kill the organisms, after which the bucket was removed and the organisms counted. The other samples were taken by means of three sweeps of an air net mounted on a ring 30 cm. in diameter and on a

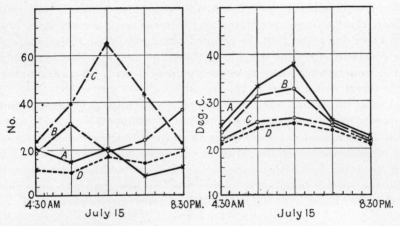

FIG. 132.—Temperatures in a pine dune environment July 15, 1914. *A*, at ground; *B*, at herb level (16 in.); *C*, at shrub level (5 ft.); *D*, at tree level (16 ft.). (*Sanders and Shelford*, 1922.)

handle 70 cm. long. It is stated that repeated trials showed that the samples taken by these two methods had the same value. The use of such small samples necessarily increases the probable error. These quantitative collections by Sanders and Shelford (1922) would indicate that the number of organisms increases from the herb stratum to the shrub stratum as follows:

	Herb	Shrub	Tree
Total collected	256	473	96
Average per hectare	28,595,000	49,142,000	93,675,000

In comparing the numbers of species from the different strata with the temperature conditions in the strata, the authors have made the following summary:

Ground.............. 10 species, av. temperature = 25.4°, range 25°
Herbs.............. 34 species, av. temperature = 21.2°, range 16°
Shrubs.............. 38 species, av. temperature = 21.0°, range 8°
Trees.............. 11 species, av. temperature = 21.2°, range 11°

The authors concluded from these results that the greater number of species was to be found at the level where changes of temperature are least, and also where the temperature itself is medium as compared with other levels. It hardly seems possible to draw such conclusions from such meager data.

Garthside (unpublished thesis) made a study of the insect populations of 15 different jack-pine plots in northern Minnesota. He used traps covered with adhesive and "quantitative net sweepings." His results indicate that the insect population of the tree is much greater in the crown than lower down and that the greatest population is on the ground. He also concluded that the density of the stand and the resultant density of the undergrowth, was a more inportant factor than the character of the forest with respect to the tree species.

A most important result of the work of Garthside is the large number of species found and the small number of individuals of each species. Table 24 (Garthside's thesis), gives an analysis of the numbers of individuals of each species of the different orders of insects which were taken with the traps and with the net. It will be noted that more than half of all the species taken were represented by less than five individuals. On the other hand, over 500 individuals of some species were taken.

TABLE XXVII.—ABUNDANCE OF INDIVIDUALS IN SPECIES—TRAPS[1]

Class	Diptera		Hymen.		Homop.		Hemip.		Coleop.		Corrod.		Lepid.	
	No. of spec.	Per cent	No. of spec.	Per cent	No. of spec.	Per cent	No. of spec.	Per cent	No. of spec.	Per cent	No. of spec.	Per cent	No. of spec.	Per cent
1 individual.........	53	32	67	48	16	59	3	23	25	69	5	38	2	40
2–5 (incl.) ind.......	48	28	48	35	5	19	6	46	8	22	...	..	3	60
6–10...............	19	11	11	8	4	15	2	15	2	6	1	8		
11–20..............	15	9	10	7	2	7	1	8	1	3	4	31		
21–50..............	12	7	1	1	..	..	1	8	..	..	2	15		
Over 50 ind.........	19	11	2	1	..	..	..	..	..	..	1	8		
Totals............	166	..	140	..	27	..	13	..	36	..	13	..	5	
1–5 (incl.) indiv.....	101	61	116	83	21	78	9	69	33	91	5	38	5	100
Highest number of individuals........	576	..	297	..	16	..	29	..	18	..	124	..	3	

[1] The species of the orders are grouped according to the abundance of the individuals in them for the traps and nets.

TABLE XXVIII.—ABUNDANCE OF INDIVIDUALS IN SPECIES—NETS[1]

Class	Diptera		Hymen.		Homop.		Hemip.		Coleop.		Corrod.		Lepid.	
	No. of spec.	Per cent	No. of spec.	Per cent	No. of spec.	Per cent	No. of spec.	Per cent	No. of spec.	Per cent	No. of spec.	Per cent	No. of spec.	Per cent
1 individual.........	39	28	74	45	14	25	9	25	13	43	3	38	7	54
2–5 (incl) ind........	46	33	69	42	13	23	12	33	10	33	5	62	4	31
6–10..............	21	15	9	5	5	9	4	11	3	10	..	...	1	7
11–20.............	11	8	8	5	11	20	3	8	1	3				
21–50.............	9	1	2	1	6	11	5	14	2	6				
Over 50 ind.........	14	10	3	2	7	13	3	8	1	3	..	...	1	7
Totals............	140	..	165	..	56	..	36	..	30	..	8	...	13	
1–5 (incl.) indiv.....	85	61	143	87	27	48	21	58	23	76	8	100	11	85
Highest number of individuals........	241	..	171	..	272	..	162	..	80	..	4	...	181	

[1] The species of the orders are grouped according to the abundance of the individuals in them for the traps and nets.

This raised two important questions. How is such quantitative work to be done so as to assure one that the important species are studied and to minimize the routine work connected with the handling and determining of hundreds of species which may not be of significance? Certainly we are not in a position to say that the number of individuals is a valid measure of significance.

The second question has to do with the balance between biotic potential and environmental resistance. How do these species which are represented by so few individuals maintain their relative numbers at such a low level? Some of them would seem to be on the verge of extinction, yet there is every evidence that they are able to maintain their equilibrium.

The Elm-maple Forest Association.—The more mesophytic forests may be expected to have more moderate physical conditions and to be more stable in composition of flora and fauna.

The Physical Conditions in an Elm-maple Forest Association.—The light, in the work of Weese (1925), was found to be but 0.35 per cent of full sunlight under the cover of the herbage in the elm-maple forest. In the shrub stratum it reached an intensity equal to 1.25 per cent of full intensity but once during the day.

The temperature in the forest in general is shown by the following graph from Weese. Weese (1925) states that the mean weekly temperatures at 10 m. above the ground were higher than those recorded near the ground, averaging 0.35°C. for the summer months. After the leaves had fallen during October and November this condition was reversed. For the week ending Sept. 13, 1921, the temperature at the 10-m. level was about 1°C. higher than at 0.6-m. level (Fig. 133).

The moisture conditions were recorded by Weese (1925) in both relative humidity and rates of evaporation. The relative humidity was recorded at a height 0.6 m. above the ground and 10 m. above the ground. The station in the herb and shrub stratum averaged 3.55 higher relative humidity than the one in the tree stratum. During the hottest part of each day the relative humidity dropped considerably, and at this time the relative humidity was at times as much as 10 to 12 per cent lower in the tree zone than in the shrub zone (Fig. 133).

The evaporation was measured by Weese at a series of stations which represent a vertical section of the forest and the bordering grassland.

Station	Elevation	Weekly evaporation, c.c.	Remarks
1	1 m.	9.16	Under shrub.
2	10 cm.	5.96	South side of tree trunk.
3	1.5 m.	9.90	North side of tree trunk.
4	1.5 m.	9.63	Under bough of maple.
5	2.5 m.	10.4	In hollow stump.
6	(?)	4.4	In grass near roadside.
7	10 cm.(?)	14.03	In elm tree.
8	6 m.	12.30	In maple tree.
9	10 m.	12.31	At top of elm tree.
10	12 m.	15.71	In grass sub for No. 7, above
11	10 cm.(?)	11.91	

This gives a graded series of evaporation rates from the ground to the tree tops. There is a uniformity in the thick portion of the tree crowns which seems to represent a region in which conditions are more or less uniform because of the dense foliage.

The Biotic Conditions in an Elm-maple Forest Association.—The quantitative data obtained by Weese (1924) are of particular interest because few such studies have been made. The methods used were somewhat like those of Sanders and Shelford (1922). Random samples were taken in this case by taking the leaves from one square foot and the soil from the same area to a depth of 10 cm. The samples from the other zones were taken by 10 sweeps of an air net, the circular opening of which was 30 cm. in diameter.

While there may be some question as to the ultimate accuracy of the results, they form a basis for a discussion of the quantitative relationships of the insects which is to be obtained nowhere else. It is to be noticed that there are two peaks in the population curves, particularly in the cases of the herb and shrub strata. Weese believes that the increase in the population in the fall was due to a migration of the insects from the surrounding habitats to the forest when the temperature began to decline. Later the organisms went into hibernation and were not obtained in the samples and hence the decline in numbers. In the spring as the organisms came out of hibernation, Weese believes they were obtained in greater numbers until they had left the forest for the fields.

The population of the leaf stratum seemed to be more uniformly high than that of any other stratum. It did not increase at the time that the great population left the upper stratum and went into hibernation, as one might have supposed. This may mean that the hibernating forms

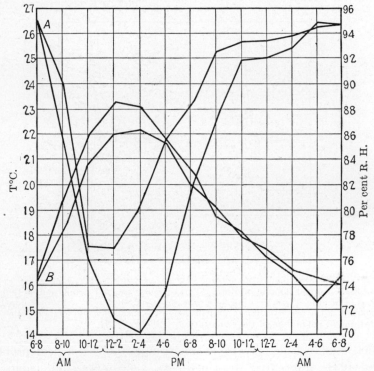

FIG. 133.—Temperature and humidity data. Mean temperature and mean humidity of an ideal day (computed from the 2-hour means for week ending September 13, 1921) at the 0.6-m. and 10-m. levels in the forest. *A*, humidity; *B*, temperature. The upper curve of *A* and the lower curve of *B* represent conditions at the 0.6-m. level. (*Weese*, 1924.)

went deeper into the ground than the samples took account of, or that the eggs and other stages of hibernation were difficult to obtain and count (Fig. 134).

The series of graphs illustrating the seasonal occurrence of the various species are of particular interest in bearing out the statement of Weese with regard to the insects which move into the forest for the purpose of hibernation. From the fact that so many of the prairie forms do so migrate, Weese concludes that the life cycles of the fauna are adjusted to the annual rhythm of physical conditions which are to be found in the savana and temperate forest (Figs. 135, 136, and 137).

Experiments performed with regard to the behavior of spiders and other forms seemed to indicate that the reactions to gradients of evaporating power of the air might be of importance in the case of some of the species, but that there were other more important factors in many cases. The condition is no doubt comparable to that of the sand-dune insects in which a careful study is necessary to determine the controlling factors. The mere factor of chance distribution is a confusing one, when no method is employed to determine the rôle which it may be playing.

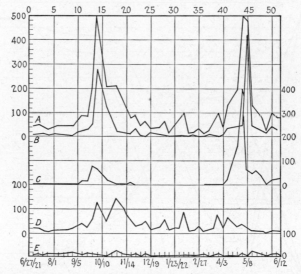

Fig. 134.—Animal population data. Total population, and population of the shrub, herb, leaf, and ground strata of an area of 4 sq. ft. in the forest. *A*, total population; *B*, population of the herb stratum; *C*, population of the shrub stratum; *D*, population of the leaf stratum; *E*, population of the soil stratum. (*Weese*, 1924.)

Such studies lead one to the more important ecological problems. Weese (1924) states that the Hemiptera, Coleoptera, and spiders were chosen for particular study because of their abundance and more conspicuous character. Smith (1928) proposes a classification based upon length and period of activity with a secondary or qualifying classification based upon the effect on the biotic community. Organisms which are active throughout the year are called predominant, and those active during a part of the year are called seasonals. Those which are judged to affect noticeably the community are called subinfluent and those which are judged to be important because of abundance, bulk or range, and tensity of activity are called influent.

A knowledge of the dynamic relationships will have to follow upon the descriptive and quantitative studies. It is to be regretted that we have so little information on the importance of the various members of the fauna on the ecological structure of a community. It would seem that the greatest progress might be made in gaining an understanding of the dynamic structure of a community when field and laboratory work would be combined in a critical study.

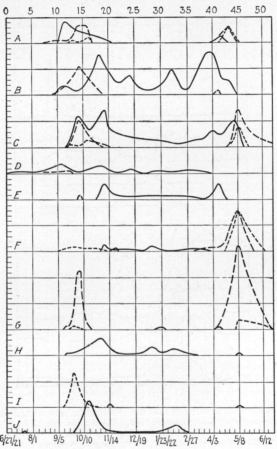

Fig. 135.—Seasonal occurrence of insects (Coleoptera). Time is represented below. The vertical scale is relative, only, and is not the same for all species. The solid line represents the relative numbers found in the leaf-soil strata, the broken line the herb stratum, and the dotted line the shrub stratum. *A, Diabrotica vittata* Herbst; *B, Notoxus monodon* Fab.; *C, Phalacrus politus* Melsh.; *D, Phytonomus nigrirastris* Fab.; *E, Telephanus velox* Hald.; *F, Glyptina spuria* Lec.; *G, Epitrix brevis* Schw.; *H, Epitrix fuscula* Crot.; *I, Chaetocnema conifinis* Crot.; *J, Phyllotreta sinuata* Sleph.

The most influential organisms are the species which exert the greatest influence upon the numbers of organisms which serve as their food, and also upon the organism for which these species serve as food. Elton (1927) has stressed the importance of these food chains. Still other organisms must be important because they can fit into niches in a community without seriously affecting the rest of the relationships.   A third group, which is difficult to evaluate, consists of the great number of species which are present in very small numbers of individuals and which exert an important influence in keeping other species in a minority position.

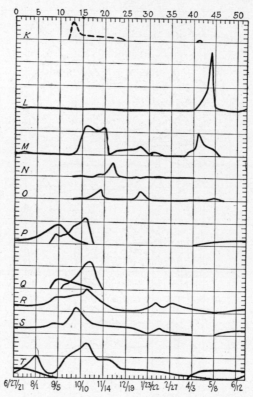

Fig. 136.—Seasonal occurrence of insects (Coleoptera and Hemiptera) and spiders. In graph *K* the different strata are indicated as in Fig. 4.   In graphs *P*, *A*, and *T* the heavy lines represent adult spiders and the light lines young spiders.   In graphs *L*, *M*, *N*, *O*, *R*, and *S* the total population only is shown.   *K*, *Longitarus melanurus* Melsh.; *L*, *Corythvcha aesculi* O and D.; *M*, *Corimelaena pulicaria* (Germ); *N*, *Lygus pratensis* (L); *O*, *Blissus leucopteris* (Say); *P*, *Dendryphantes aestivalis* Emer.; *Q*, *Ulolorus americanus* Walck; *R*, *Anyphaena rulera* Emer.; *S*, *Dictyna* Sp?; *T*, *Xysticus elegans* Keys.   (*Weese*, 1924.)

APPLIED ECOLOGY

The application of the principles of animal ecology extends to two great fields of human interest.

One is the field of economic entomology to which man must look for his protection in the struggle against his most serious natural enemy, the insect.   Here, when entomologists have come to the limits of the possibilities of poisons and the mechanical means of destroying the insects, attention must be turned, in the last resort, to the possibilities of so modifying the environmental conditions that the pest can no longer play a dominant rôle in agriculture.

Wardle and Buckle (1923), Wardle (1929), and Friederichs (1930) have emphasized the importance of the principles of ecology in the field of entomology.   It is not the purpose of this treatise to cover the field of economic entomology.   It is sufficient to call attention to some of the recent volumes on the subject and to express the hope that there may be at least a few centers of research devoted to some of the fundamental phases of ecology.   They need not be devoted to the study of species which are of economic importance or are ordinarily considered important in nature.   It is far more important that they be species which lend themselves to the study of fundamental phenomena concerned with the equilibrium of nature and an evaluation of the forces which bring about changes in the equilibrium of populations.

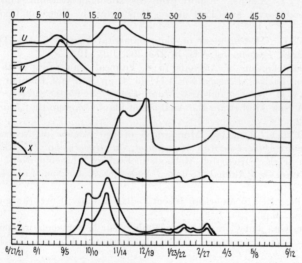

Fig. 137.—Seasonal occurrence of spiders and insects (Cicadellidae).   U, *Linyphia phrygiana* Koch; V, *Acrosonia rugosa* Hentz; W, *Epeira gibberasa* Henta; X, *Tetragnatha* Sp?; Y, *Empoasca viridescens* Walsh; Z, Total Cicadellidae and *Erythroneura oblequa* Say. (*Weese*, 1924.)

Such applications of the principles of animal ecology require qualitative and quantitative investigations of the highest order.   As entomological problems become more complex, due to the increased facilities for transportation, the requirements of such investigations will become more exacting.   It is difficult to imagine a field of science which is fuller of possibilities for mathematical, physical, and biological investigations than this field of applied animal ecology.

The second great field of application is in the study of human sociology.   Fundamentally, man is endowed with a certain biotic potential which is pitted against the resistance of his environment.   The great problems of human population are undoubtedly better understood by knowing the conditions under which all natural populations fluctuate and attain conditions of relative stability. In the investigation of the ecology of insects, a single year may represent 15 centuries of human history; and a population equal to the present numbers of man may be produced and observed in a modern laboratory.

It would seem that the future of these branches of applied animal ecology holds possibilities that should challenge the best intellects of the generation of students which is now entering the field of science.

BIBLIOGRAPHY

SHRUB AND TREE STRATA

ADAMS, C. C.: "An Ecological Survey of Isle Royale, Lake Superior, under the Direction of C. C. Adams," Report from the Michigan Museum, Published by the State Biological Survey as a Part of the Report for the Board of Geol. Survey for 1908.

ALLEE, W. C.: Measurement of Environmental Factors in the Tropical Rain-forest of Panama, *Ecology*, vol. VII, 3, 273–302, July, 1926.

————: Distribution of Animals in a Tropical Rain-forest with Relation to Environmental Factors, *Ecology*, vol. VII, no. 4, pp. 445–469, October, 1926.

ARRHENIUS, O.: Species and Area, *Jour. Ecology*, **9**: 95–99, 1921.

————: A New Method for the Analysis of Plant Communities, *Jour. Ecology*, **10**: 185–199, 1922.

BEUTENMÜLLER, WILLIAM: Monograph of the *Sesiidæ* of America, North of Mexico, *Memoirs of the American Museum of Nat. History*, pp. 217–352, 8 pl., 1901.

CLEMENTS, F. E.: "Research Methods in Ecology," Lincoln, Neb., 1905.

ELTON, CHARLES: "Animal Ecology," Sidgwick & Jackson, Ltd., London, 1927. 207 pp.

FELT, E. P.: "Key to American Insect Galls," Albany, Univ. State of New York, 1918. 310 pp., 16 pl.

FLAHAULT, CH., and C. SCHRÖTER: Rapport sur la nomenclature phytogéographique, *Reports and Propositions*, Third International Congress of Botany, vols. 1–2, 1910.

FRIEDERICHS, KARL: "Die Grundfragen und Gesetzmässigkeiten der land- und forstwirtschaftlichen Zoologie besonders der Entomologie," Parey, Berlin, 1930.

GARTHSIDE, STANLEY: Quantitative Studies upon the Insect Fauna of Jack-pine Environments, Univ. of Minn., unpublished thesis for the degree of Master of Science, 1928. 110 pp.

GRAHAM, S. A.: Factors Influencing the Subcortical Temperatures of Logs, *Eighteenth Report*, State Entomologist of Minnesota, 1920, pp. 26–42.

————: The Felled Tree Trunk as an Ecological Unit, *Ecology*, **7**: 397–411, 1925.

————: The Need for Standardized Quantitative Methods in Forest Biology, *Ecology*, **10**: 245–250, 1929.

HERING, MARTIN: "Die Oekologie der blattminierenden Insectenlarvan," Berlin, 1926. 254 pp.

HUMBOLDT, A. VON (1807): "Essai sur la géographie des plants."

KINSEY, A. C.: The Gall Wasp Genus *Cynips*, a Study in the Origin of Species, *Ind. Univ. Studies*, **16**: 1–577, 1929.

KLUGH, A. BROOKER (1923): A Common System of Classification in Plant and Animal Ecology, *Ecology*, **4**: 366–377, 1923.

LARSEN, J. A.: Effect of Removal of the Virgin White Pine Stand upon the Physical Factors of Site, *Ecology*, **3**: 302–306, 1922.

MÖBIUS, (1877): "Die Auster und die Austernwirthschaft."

NEEDHAM, J. G., S. W. FROST and B. H. TOTHILL: "Leaf-mining Insects," Baltimore, 1928. 351 pp.

NICHOLS, G. E.: The Interpretation and Application of Certain Terms and Concepts in the Ecological Classification of Plant Communities, *Plant World*, p. 20, 1917.

————: A Working Basis for Ecological Classification of Plant Communities, *Ecology*, **4**: 11–23, 155–179, 1923.

PEARSE, A. S.: "Animal Ecology," McGraw-Hill Book Company, Inc., New York, 1926.

SANDERS, NELL JACKSON, and VICTOR SHELFORD: A Quantitative and Seasonal Study of a Pine-dune Animal Community, *Ecology*, **3**: 306–321, 1922.

SHELFORD, V. E.: Physiological Animal Geography, *Jour. Morph.*, **22**: 551–618, 1911.

————: Ecological Succession. V. Aspects of Physiological Classification, *Biol. Bull.*, **23**: 331–370, 1912.

————: "Animal Communities in Temperate America," The University of Chicago Press, 1913.

SHIRLEY, HARDY L.: Light Requirements and Silvicultural Practice, *Jour. Forestry*, **27**: 535–538, 1928.

————: The Influence of Light Intensity and Light Quality upon the Growth of Plants, *Amer. Jour. Bot.*, **16**: 354–390, 1929.

SHULL, A. F.: Thysanoptera and Orthoptera, in a Biological Survey of the Sand Dune Region on the South Shore of Saginaw Bay, Mich., *Mich. Geol. Biol. Survey Pub.* 4, Biol. ser. 2, pp. 177–231.

SINCLAIR, JOHN G.: Temperature of the Soil and Air in a Desert, *U. S. Monthly Weather Rev.*, **50**: 142–144, 1922.

SMITH, V. G.: Animal Communities of a Deciduous Forest Succession, *Ecology*, **9**: 479–500, 1928.

TRÄGÅRDH, IVAR: Studies in the Fauna of the Soil in Swedish Forests, *Trans. of IV. Intern. Congress of Entomology*, pp. 780–792, 1928.

VESTAL, A. G.: Local Distribution of Grasshoppers in Relation to Plant Associations, *Biol. Bull.*, **25**: 141–180, 1913.

———— : An Associational Study of Illinois Sand Prairie, *Ill. State Lab. Nat. Hist. Bull.* 10, pp. 1–96, 1913.

WAKSMAN, SELMAN A.: Studies on Soil Protozoa, *Soil Sci.*, **1**: 135–152, 1916.

————: Bacterial Numbers in Soils, at Different Depths, and in Different Seasons of the Year, *Soil Sci.*, **1**: 363–380, 1916.

WARDLE, R. A.: "The Problems of Applied Entomology," Manchester University Press, 1929.

WARDLE, R. A., and PHILIP BUCKLE: "The Principles of Insect Control," Manchester University Press, 1923.

WARMING, E. (1909): "Oecology of Plants."

WEESE, A. O.: Animal Ecology of an Illinois Elm-maple Forest, *Ill. Biol. Monog.*, **9**: 351–437, 1924.

WHERRY,: Soil Acidity Preferences of Earth Worms, *Ecology*, **5**: 309, 1924.

WILLIAMS, C. B.: A Short Bio-climatic Study in the Egyptian Desert, *Egypt. Min. Agr., Tech. and Sci. Serv. Bull.* 29, 1923.

ZON, R., and H. S. GRAVES: Light in Relation to Tree Growth, *U. S. Dept. Agr. Forest Serv. Bull.* 92, 1911.

APPENDIX

VARIATIONS AND FLUCTUATIONS OF THE NUMBER OF INDIVIDUALS IN ANIMAL SPECIES LIVING TOGETHER[1]

PROFESSOR VITO VOLTERRA

§1. PRELIMINARY CONSIDERATIONS

1. Many applications of mathematics have been made to biology. In the first place come the researches on physiological questions relative to the senses, to the circulation of the blood, to the movement of animals, which can be viewed as subjects of optics, of acoustics, of hydrodynamics or of the mechanics of solid bodies, and hence have not called for new methods outside the scope of the classical mathematical physics. Biometry, on the other hand, with its own modes of procedure, has recourse to the use of calculus of probability and has created a mass of new and original studies.[2] And, too, the recent geometrical researches on the form and growth of organized existence have a particular character. In them geometry has been used to describe the forms themselves and their development just as for a long time it has been employed in astronomy to describe the orbits and the motions of the celestial bodies.[3] Moreover it is to be hoped that the methods allied to the analysis used for heredity may be advantageously employed in questions concerning biology.[4]

Putting aside other applications of mathematics, these points, of which I shall speak in this article, I consider worthy of study and research, as being able to clarify various points actually interesting to biologists.[5]

---

[1] Reprinted by permission of the author, Professor VITO VOLTERRA, Rome, from *Journal du Conseil international pour l'exploration de la mer*, III, vol. 1, 1928; transl. by Mary Evelyn Wells, Doctor of Mathematics.

[2] *Cf.* VOLTERRA, "Saggi Scientifici," I. Sui tentativi di applicazione delle matematiche alle Scienze biologiche e sociali, Zanichelli, Bologna, 1920.—For Biometry see the periodical *Biometrika* founded by Karl Pearson in 1901.

[3] WENTWORTH, D'ARCY THOMPSON, "On Growth and Form," Cambridge, 1917.

[4] VOLTERRA, *ibid.*, VII. L'evoluzione delle idee fondamentali del calcolo infinitesimale; VIII. L'applicazione del calcolo ai fenomeni d'eredità.

[5] The complete work has been published by me in *Memoria della R. Accademia Nazionale dei Lincei*, division on mathematical, physical and natural sciences, ser. VI, vol. II, and in *Memoria CXXXI, of R. Comitato Talassografico Italiano*, with the title: "Variazioni e fluttuazioni del numero d'individui in specie animali conviventi." After the publication of this note I received word that in the study of parasites relative to malaria there existed the equations of Ross, and I learned that in the volume:

2. Biological associations (biocoenosis) are established by many species which live in the same environment. Ordinarily the various individuals of such an association contest for the same food, or else some species live at the expense of others on which they feed. But nothing prevents them from being able to take advantage of each other. All this comes back again to the general phenomenon called "the struggle for life."

The quantitative character of this phenomenon is manifested in the variations of the number of individuals which constitute the various species. In certain conditions such variations consist in fluctuations about a mean value, in others they show a continuous decrease or increase of the species.

The study of these variations and of these different tendencies is important theoretically, but often has also a practical importance worthy of notice, as in the case of the species of fish which live in the same seas and whose variations interest the fisheries.[1] And also agriculture is interested in the fluctuations of parasites of plants when these parasites are attacked by parasites of these parasites. Also infective diseases (malaria, etc.) show fluctuations which are probably of an analogous nature.

The question presents itself in a very complex way. Certainly there exist periodic circumstances relating to environment, as would be those, for example, which depend upon the changing of the seasons, which produce forced oscillations of an external character in the number of individuals of the various species.

"Elements of Physical Biology," New York, 1925, Doctor Lotka had considered the case of two species developed by me in §3 of part 1, arriving by other methods at the integral, to his diagram, and to the period of small oscillations. However the general laws obtained by me in this same section, the various cases developed in the other sections of the first part, as likewise all the other three parts of my memoir, in which I consider the applications of the aforesaid laws and the cohabitation of n species in the hypothesis of conservative and dissipative associations, are new and treated for the first time.

[1] Doctor Umberto D'Ancona has many times spoken to me about the statistics which he was making in fishery in the period during the war and in periods before and after, asking me if it were possible to give a mathematical explanation of the results which he was getting in the percentages of the various species in these different periods. This request has spurred me to formulate the problem and solve it, establishing the laws which are set forth in §7. Both D'Ancona and I working independently were equally satisfied in comparing results which were revealed to us separately by calculus and by observation, as these results were in accord; showing for instance that man in fisheries, by disturbing the natural condition of proportion of two species, one of which feeds upon the other, causes diminution in the quantity of the species that eats the other, and an increase in the species fed upon. (See D'Ancona, Dell' influenza della stasi peschereccia del periodo 1914—18 sul patrimonio ittico dell' Alto Adriatico, *Memoria CXXVI R. Comitato Talassografico Italiano.*)

These actions of external periodic nature were those which were specially studied from the statistical point of view, but are there others of internal character, having periods of their own which add their action to these external causes and would exist even if these were withdrawn?

Observation inclines to an affirmative reply and mathematical calculation confirms it, as we shall see in this article. But on first appearance it would seem as though on account of its extreme complexity the question might not lend itself to a mathematical treatment, and that on the contrary mathematical methods, being too delicate, might emphasize some peculiarities and obscure some essentials of the question. To guard against this danger we must start from hypotheses, even though they be rough and simple, and give some scheme for the phenomenon.

For that we shall begin by studying that which could be called the "purely internal phenomenon," due only to the reproductive power and to the voracity of the species as if they were alone. Later we shall study the addition of foreign or forced periodic actions which are the result of environment.

3. And what mathematical methods will it be convenient to use? Perhaps the methods founded on the calculus of probability which might suggest themselves first? Let me say at once it is not these which lead us to the goal.

Permit me to indicate how the question can be considered: Let us seek to express in words the way the phenomenon proceeds roughly: afterwards let us translate these words into mathematical language. This leads to the formulation of differential equations. If then we allow ourselves to be guided by the methods of analysis we are led much farther than the language and ordinary reasoning would be able to carry us and can formulate precise mathematical laws. These do not contradict the results of observation. Rather the most important of these seems in perfect accord with the statistical results.[1] The road followed is thus clearly indicated with these few words. We shall see after a little how the difficulties met were overcome.

4. On the basis of the ideas expressed above, in order to simplify the treatment, we shall assume that the species increase or decrease in a continuous way, that is to say we shall assume that the number which measures the quantity of individuals of a species is not an integer, but any real positive number whatever which varies continuously. In general the hatchings take place in definite periods separated from each other by an interval of time; we shall neglect these particulars assuming that

[1] D'Ancona establishes from the examination of the statistics of the markets of Trieste, Venice, and Fiume that during the war there took place in the Upper Adriatic a change of the proportions of the individuals of the various species of fish to the advantage of the selacians which must be considered among the most voracious. This result agrees with the law of the disturbances of the average which we express farther along.

births may take place with continuity every moment and that, on a parity with all the other conditions, they may be verified proportionally to the number of living individuals of the species. Let the same assumption be made on death and, according as births may prevail over deaths, or *vice versa*, an increase of diminution of individuals will occur. Thus we shall assume the homogeneity of the individuals of each species neglecting the variations of age and size.

If there is only one species or if the others have no influence on it, so that the circumstances of birth and death do not vary, we shall have, if N denotes the number of individuals,

$$\frac{dN}{dt} = nN - mN = (n - m)N,$$

where t denotes time and n and m are constants, respectively the coefficients of birth and mortality. Letting $n - m = \epsilon$ we shall have

$$\text{(I)} \quad \frac{dN}{dt} = \epsilon N, \qquad\qquad \text{(II)} \quad N = N_0 e^{\epsilon t},$$

where N_0 denotes the number of individuals at the time zero; ϵ will be called the coefficient of increase of the species and if it is positive there will be a true increase, otherwise a decrease. If the circumstances of birth and death change, ϵ will vary with time or with N or with other elements. In such a case (I) will always exist, but evidently we shall no longer have (II).

§2. BIOLOGICAL ASSOCIATION OF TWO SPECIES WHICH CONTEND FOR THE SAME FOOD

1. Let us suppose we have two species living in the same environment: let the numbers of the individuals be respectively N_1 and N_2 and let ϵ_1 and ϵ_2 be the values which their coefficients of increase would have if the quantity of the common food were always such as to amply satisfy their voracity. We shall have

$$\frac{dN_1}{dt} = \epsilon_1 N_1, \quad \frac{dN_2}{dt} = \epsilon_2 N_2 \qquad (\epsilon_1 > o, \quad \epsilon_2 > o).$$

Let it be admitted now that the individuals of the two species, continually increasing in number, diminish the quantity of food of which each individual can dispose. Let us suppose that the presence of the N_1 individuals of the first species diminishes this quantity by an amount $h_1 N_1$ and the presence of the N_2 individuals of the second species diminishes it by the amount $h_2 N_2$ and that therefore by the combination of the two, the diminution amounts to $h_1 N_1 + h_2 N_2$ and that by virtue of the unequal need of food of the two species, the two coefficients of increase are reduced to

$$\epsilon_1 - \gamma_1(h_1N_1 + h_2N_2), \qquad \epsilon_2 - \gamma_2(h_1N_1 + h_2N_2) \tag{1}$$

We shall then have the differential equations

$$\frac{dN_1}{dt} = [\epsilon_1 - \gamma_1(h_1N_1 + h_2N_2)]N_1, \tag{2_1}$$

$$\frac{dN_2}{dt} = [\epsilon_2 - \gamma_2(h_1N_1 + h_2N_2)]N_2, \tag{2_2}$$

in which we must suppose ϵ_1, ϵ_2, h_1, h_2, γ_1, γ_2 to be positive constants.

2. From the preceding equations it follows that

$$\frac{d \log N_1}{dt} = \epsilon_1 - \gamma_1(h_1N_1 + h_2N_2), \tag{3_1}$$

$$\frac{d \log N_2}{dt} = \epsilon_2 - \gamma_2(h_1N_1 + h_2N_2), \tag{3_2}$$

and hence

$$\gamma_2\frac{d \log N_1}{dt} - \gamma_1\frac{d \log N_2}{dt} = \epsilon_1\gamma_2 - \epsilon_2\gamma_1, \tag{4}$$

that is to say

$$\frac{d \log \dfrac{N_1^{\gamma_2}}{N_2^{\gamma_1}}}{dt} = \epsilon_1\gamma_2 - \epsilon_2\gamma_1 \tag{5}$$

and integrating and passing from logarithms to numbers,

$$\frac{N_1^{\gamma_2}}{N_2^{\gamma_1}} = Ce^{(\epsilon_1\gamma_2-\epsilon_2\gamma_1)t}, \tag{6}$$

where C is a constant quantity

3. If the binomial $\epsilon_1\gamma_2 - \epsilon_2\gamma_1$ is not zero we can suppose it positive, for if it were not positive it would suffice to exchange species 1 with species 2 to make it positive.

In this case

$$\lim_{t = \infty} \frac{N_1^{\gamma_2}}{N_2^{\gamma_1}} = \infty.$$

For N_1 equal to or greater than ϵ_1/γ_1h_1, by virtue of (2_1), the differential coefficient dN_1/dt is negative, hence N_1 cannot exceed a certain limit.

N_2 then must approach zero.

It is easy to compute the expression asymptotic to N_1.

In fact when N_2 becomes small enough to remain negligible, equation (2_1) will become

$$\frac{dN_1}{dt} = (\epsilon_1 - \gamma_1 h_1 N_1)N_1$$

or, separating the variables

$$dt = \frac{dN_1}{N_1(\epsilon_1 - \gamma_1 h_1 N_1)}$$

and integrating and passing from logarithms to numbers,

$$\frac{N_1}{\epsilon_1 - \gamma_1 h_1 N_1} = C_o\, e^{\epsilon_1 t}$$

C_o being a constant.   Hence

$$N_1 = \frac{C_o \epsilon_1 e^{\epsilon_1 t}}{1 + \gamma_1 h_1 C_o e^{\epsilon_1 t}} = \frac{C_o \epsilon_1}{e^{-\epsilon_1 t} + \gamma_1 h_1 C_o}.$$

Therefore N_1 approaches asymptotically the value $\epsilon_1/\gamma_1 h_1$ for increasing or decreasing values according as C_o is positive or negative.

We can sum up the results we have obtained, in the following proposition: If $\epsilon_1/\gamma_1 > \epsilon_2/\gamma_2$ *the second species continually decreases and the number of individuals of the first species approaches* $\epsilon_1/\gamma_1 h_1$.

§3. ASSOCIATION OF TWO SPECIES ONE OF WHICH FEEDS UPON THE OTHER

1. Let N_1 and N_2 be the numbers of individuals of the two species. Let $\epsilon_1 > 0$ represent the coefficient of increase which the first would have if the other did not exist.   Let us suppose that the second would die out because of lack of food if it were alone; therefore let its coefficient of increase be negative and equal to $-\epsilon_2$ (ϵ_2 can be considered as a coefficient of decrease).   If each of the two species were alone we should have

$$\frac{dN_1}{dt} = \epsilon_1 N_1, \tag{7_1}$$

$$\frac{dN_2}{dt} = -\epsilon_2 N_2. \tag{7_2}$$

But if they are together and the second species feeds upon the first ϵ_1 will diminish and $-\epsilon_2$ will increase, and evidently the more numerous the individuals of the second species become the more ϵ_1 will diminish, and the more the individuals of the first species increase, the more will $-\epsilon_2$ increase.   To represent this fact in the simplest manner let us suppose that ϵ_1 diminishes proportionally to N_2, that is by the amount $\gamma_1 N_2$, and that $-\epsilon_2$ increases proportionally to N_1, that is by the amount $\gamma_2 N_1$.

We shall have then the differential equations

$$(\text{A}_1)\ \frac{dN_1}{dt} = (\epsilon_1 - \gamma_1 N_2)N_1, \quad (\text{A}_2)\ \frac{dN_2}{dt} = (-\epsilon_2 + \gamma_2 N_1)N_2.$$

The assumption that the coefficients of increase and of decrease be respectively linear in relation to N_2 and N_1 may seem very loose, but it is justified as we shall see in §5, if we compute these coefficients by means of the probable number of encounters of the individuals of the two species. And even if we take for the coefficients any functions whatever of N_2 and N_1 respectively, the mode of integration used in this section, in which they are supposed linear, works out just the same.

2. While the constants ϵ_1 and ϵ_2 sum up the conditions of birth and death of the two species, the coefficients γ_1 and γ_2 measure in a numerical way the aptitude of the first species to defend itself and the means of offense of the second species. In fact if we increase these means of offense then γ_1 and γ_2 must increase, and if we increase the means of protection of the first species then a diminution of these coefficients must follow.

In order to have a method of measuring ϵ_1 and ϵ_2 it will be sufficient to integrate (7_1) and (7_2); we should have if each of these two species were alone

$$N_1 = C_1 e^{\epsilon_1 t}, \qquad\qquad N_2 = C_2 e^{-\epsilon_2 t},$$

where C_1 and C_2 are respectively the values of N_1 and N_2 for $t = 0$. Let us place $N_1 = 2C_1$, $N_2 = \frac{1}{2}C_2$ and denote by t_1 and t_2 the times necessary respectively for the first species to double itself and the second to be reduced by half. We shall have

$$\epsilon_1 = \frac{\log_e 2}{t_1} = \frac{0.693}{t_1}, \qquad \epsilon_2 = \frac{\log_e 2}{t_2} = \frac{0.693}{t_2}.$$

From this it follows that ϵ_1 and ϵ_2 have the dimensions -1 with respect to time. It would always be possible to take the units of time in such a way that $\epsilon_1 = 1$. In fact if we take as the unit of time necessary for the first species to increase in the ratio $e = 2.728$, we shall have $e = e^{\epsilon_1}$ and hence $\epsilon_1 = 1$. ϵ_2 could be treated similarly.

Letting

$$\frac{\epsilon_2}{\gamma_2} = K_1, \qquad\qquad \frac{\epsilon_1}{\gamma_1} = K_2, \qquad\qquad (8)$$

the equations (A_1) and (A_2) show us that if

$$N_1 = K_1 \qquad N_2 = K_2$$

then

$$\frac{dN_1}{dt} = \frac{dN_2}{dt} = 0,$$

that is to say, the two species are in a stationary state.

We shall have then

$$\gamma_1 = \frac{\epsilon_1}{K_2}, \qquad \gamma_2 = \frac{\epsilon_2}{K_1}.$$

Now let us pass to the integration of equations (A_1) and (A_2).

From (A_1) and (A_2) it follows that

$$\frac{d\frac{N_1}{K_1}}{dt} = \epsilon_1\left(1 - \frac{N_2}{K_2}\right)\frac{N_1}{K_1}, \qquad \frac{d\frac{N_2}{K_2}}{dt} = -\epsilon_2\left(1 - \frac{N_1}{K_1}\right)\frac{N_2}{K_2}, \qquad (9)$$

whence, by placing

$$N_1 = K_1 n_1, \qquad N_2 = K_2 n_2, \qquad (10)$$

the preceding equations may be written

$$(A_1') \quad \frac{dn_1}{dt} = \epsilon_1(1 - n_2)n_1, \qquad (A_2') \quad \frac{dn_2}{dt} = -\epsilon_2(1 - n_1)n_2.$$

Multiplying these equations respectively by ϵ_2 and ϵ_1 and adding we have

$$\frac{d}{dt}(\epsilon_2 n_1 + \epsilon_1 n_2) = \epsilon_1\epsilon_2(n_1 - n_2). \qquad (11)$$

Multiplying them respectively by ϵ_2/n_1 and ϵ_1/n_2, and adding, we find

$$\frac{\epsilon_2}{n_1}\frac{dn_1}{dt} + \frac{\epsilon_1}{n_2}\frac{dn_2}{dt} = \epsilon_1\epsilon_2(n_1 - n_2),$$

that is to say

$$\frac{d}{dt}(\log n_1^{\epsilon_2} + \log n_2^{\epsilon_1}) = \epsilon_1\epsilon_2(n_1 - n_2). \qquad (12)$$

Equating the first members of (11) and (12) there follows

$$\frac{d}{dt}(\epsilon_2 n_1 + \epsilon_1 n_2) = \frac{d}{dt}(\log n_1^{\epsilon_2} + \log n_2^{\epsilon_1}),$$

and integrating and passing from logarithms to numbers

$$n_1^{\epsilon_2} n_2^{\epsilon_1} = C e^{\epsilon_2 n_1 + \epsilon_1 n_2}$$

where C is a positive constant. Whence

$$\left(\frac{n_1}{e^{n_1}}\right)^{\epsilon_2} = C\left(\frac{n_2}{e^{n_2}}\right)^{-\epsilon_1}. \qquad (13)$$

From (A'_1) and (A'_2) it follows that

$$dt = \frac{dn_1}{\epsilon_1(1 - n_2)n_1} = \frac{dn_2}{-\epsilon_2(1 - n_1)n_2}.$$

If by means of the integral (13) we express n_2 in terms of n_1 or n_1 in terms of n_2 and substitute respectively these values in the preceding equations the variables remain separate, and the integration is reduced to a quadrature.

3. But we wish to examine directly the solution, and especially the integral (13).

Therefore let us place

$$x = \left(\frac{n_1}{e^{n_1}}\right)^{\epsilon_2} = C\left(\frac{n_2}{e^{n_2}}\right)^{-\epsilon_1} \tag{14}$$

and let us consider the curve Γ_1, which has n_1 and x for abscissa and ordinate, and the curve Γ_2, which has n_2 and x for abscissa and ordinate (Fig. 1).

We shall have

$$\frac{d}{dn_1}\left(\frac{n_1}{e^{n_1}}\right) = e^{-n_1}(1 - n_1), \tag{15}$$

which is positive for $n_1 < 1$ and negative for $n_1 < 1$. Then while n_1 varies between 0 and ∞, x increases from 0 to its maximum value $\left(\frac{1}{e}\right)^{\epsilon_2}$ for $n_1 = 1$, and then approaches 0 as n_1 increases indefinitely. Whereas while n_2 varies between 0 and ∞, x decreases from ∞ to its minimum value Ce^{ϵ_1} for $n_2 = 1$, then increases without limit becoming ∞ for $n_2 = \infty$. The nature of the curves Γ_1 and Γ_2 appears then as shown in Fig. 1.

The constant C is determined from (13) whenever the initial values of n_1 and n_2 are known, and it is

$$C \leqq e^{-(\epsilon_1 + \epsilon_2)}.$$

If $C < e^{-(\epsilon_1 + \epsilon_2)}$, that is if $e^{-\epsilon_2} > C e^{\epsilon_1}$, for every value of x between Ce^{ϵ_1} and $e^{-\epsilon_2}$ there correspond two values of n_1 and two of n_2, excluding the two values corresponding to the points C_1 and C_2 of maximum and minimum ordinates of the two curves Γ_1 and Γ_2. Having arranged the two curves as in Fig. 1, with one axis of abscissas the continuation of the other, let us draw the normals to x from the vertices C_1 and C_2 and consider the sections $A_1C_1B_1$, $A_2C_2B_2$ of the two curves lying between these two parallels. Let $a_1 < 1$ and $b_1 > 1$ be the abscissas of A_1 and B_1, $a_2 < 1$, $b_2 > 1$ the abscissas of A_2 and B_2.

Then let us try to construct the curve λ having n_1 for abscissa and n_2 for ordinate. First let us make the point A_2 correspond to the point C_1 and trace the arc C_1B_1 with the point G_1. Then in the curve Γ_2 let us trace the arc A_2C_2, and, corresponding to G_1 on Γ_1 we shall have G_2 on Γ_2, on the same perpendicular to x. Then the value $n_2 = g_2$ will correspond to $n_1 = g_1$, g_1 and g_2 being respectively the abscissas of G_1 and G_2. Then while n_1 increases from 1 to b_1, n_2 will increase from a_2 to 1, that is the curve of Fig. 2 will be traced from the point R_2 of coordinates $(1, a_2)$ to the point S_1 of coordinates $(b_1, 1)$. Continuing, while n_1 decreases from b_1 to 1, n_2 will increase from 1 to b_2, that is we shall move in Fig. 2 from the point S_1 of coordinates $(b_1, 1)$ to the point S_2 of coordinates $(1, b_2)$; and as n_1 decreases from 1 to a_1, n_2 decreases from b_2 to 1, that is in Fig. 2 we move from point S_2 or coordinates $(1, b_2)$ to the point R_1 of coordinates $(a_1, 1)$. Finally when n_1 increases from a_1 to 1, n_2 will decrease from 1 to a_2 and in Fig. 2 we go from the point R_1 of coordinates $(a_1, 1)$ to the point R_2 of coordinates $(1, a_2)$.

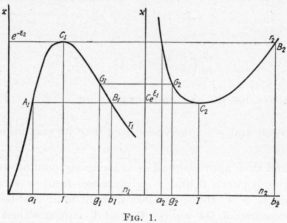

Fig. 1.

On our return to the point of departure there begins again the periodic tracing of the closed cycle of Fig. 2, and by virtue of (14), (as follows also from Fig. 1), when n_1 and n_2 take again the same values x also takes the same value.

4. From (14) it follows that $\log x = \epsilon_2(\log n_1 - n_1)$, and then, taking the derivative with respect to t and using (A_1'),

$$\frac{1}{x}\frac{dx}{dt} = \epsilon_2\left(\frac{1}{n_1} - 1\right)\frac{dn_1}{dt} = \epsilon_1\epsilon_2(1 - n_1)(1 - n_2)$$

that is

$$dt = \frac{dx}{\epsilon_1\epsilon_2 x(1 - n_1)(1 - n_2)}.$$

From which it follows that each time we trace with n_1 and n_2 the closed cycle of Fig. 2, t will increase by a constant quantity T. From this it follows that n_1 and n_2, and by virtue of (10) also N_1 and N_2 will be periodic functions of the time, with the period T. The curve Λ of Fig. 3 obtained from Fig. 2 by multiplying the abscissas by K_1, and the ordinates by K_2, namely the curve which gives us the diagram of the cycle which relates N_1 to N_2 may be called "the cycle of fluctuation" and $K_1(b_1 - a_1)$, $K_2(b_2 - a_2)$ the amplitudes of the fluc-

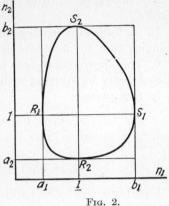

tuations of the two species. In general the cycle of fluctuation will not have a center of symmetry, yet the point Ω whose coordinates are K_1 and K_2 stands inside all the possible cycles of fluctuation Φ, Λ, Ψ, X, . . . dependent upon all the possible initial conditions of the two species as is indicated in Fig. 3. The name "center of fluctuation" may be given then to the point Ω. All the curves of diagram 3 will be obtained by keeping ϵ_1, ϵ_2, γ_1, γ_2 constant and letting constant C take different values. These curves do

FIG. 2.

not meet each other, but lie one within the other.

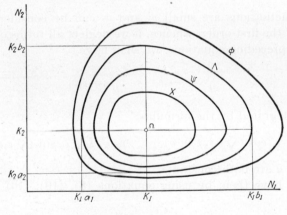

FIG. 3.

We have then in this case a *periodic fluctuation of the number of individuals of the two species, with period T*, or the phenomenon will have a *cyclically periodic* character.

Let us represent the fluctuation of n_1 and n_2 as functions of the time and we shall have Fig. 4.

5. To determine the period T we shall need to calculate the integral

$$\int \frac{dx}{\epsilon_1\epsilon_2 x(1 - n_1)(1 - n_2)}$$

extending it in succession over the four arcs R_2S_1, S_1S_2, S_2R_1, R_1R_2.

The sum of the four integrals will give us the period T.

The function under the integral sign becomes infinite at the four vertices R_1, R_2, S_1, S_2, but as is easily recognized, the order of infinitude is such that the integrals are convergent.

The preceding integral proves that the period T depends only on ϵ_1, ϵ_2 and C.

In the following section we shall calculate approximately this period, assuming that the fluctuations are small.[1]

6. The approximate case in which the fluctuations are small can be treated easily by starting with equations (A_1) and (A_2).

In fact placing

$$n_1 = 1 + v_1, \qquad n_2 = 1 + v_2 \tag{16}$$

we shall have

$$N_1 = K_1(1 + v_1), \qquad N_2 = K_2(1 + v_2). \tag{17}$$

Equations (A_1'), (A_2') will become

$$(A_1'') \quad \frac{dv_1}{dt} = -\epsilon_1 v_2 - \epsilon_1 v_1 v_2, \qquad (A_2'') \quad \frac{dv_2}{dt} = \epsilon_2 v_1 + \epsilon_2 v_1 v_2.$$

If the fluctuations are small v_1 and v_2 can be considered as small quantities of the first order, whence, if we neglect all terms of the second order in the preceding equations, we shall have

$$\frac{dv_1}{dt} = -\epsilon_1 v_2, \qquad \frac{dv_2}{dt} = \epsilon_2 v_1$$

which are integrated by the formulas

$$v_1 = L\sqrt{\epsilon_1} \cos(\sqrt{\epsilon_1 \epsilon_2}\, t + a), \qquad v_2 = L\sqrt{\epsilon_2} \sin(\sqrt{\epsilon_1 \epsilon_2}\, t + a)$$

where L and a are both constants.

We shall have then, by using equations (8), (10), (16) and placing

$$L\frac{\epsilon_1 \epsilon_2}{\gamma_1 \gamma_2} = E,$$

$$N_1 = \frac{\epsilon_2}{\gamma_2} + \frac{\gamma_1}{\sqrt{\epsilon_1}} E \cos(\sqrt{\epsilon_1 \epsilon_2}\, t + a)$$

$$N_2 = \frac{\epsilon_1}{\gamma_1} + \frac{\gamma_2}{\sqrt{\epsilon_2}} E \sin(\sqrt{\epsilon_1 \epsilon_2}\, t + a) \tag{18}$$

whence N_1 and N_2 appear periodic with the period $2\pi/\sqrt{\epsilon_1 \epsilon_2}$.

We should have arrived at this same value by calculating directly the integral T of the preceding section and neglecting terms of infinitesimal order.

[1] For the exact calculation of the period T, I refer to the article already cited, *Memoria della R. Accademia dei Lincei*, pt. 1, §3, No. 5.

We can assume then that the period of the cycle of fluctuations of the two species is given approximately by

$$T = \frac{2\pi}{\sqrt{\epsilon_1 \epsilon_2}}.$$

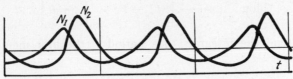

FIG. 4.

If, as in article 2, we call t_1 and t_2 the two times in which respectively the first species doubles itself and the other is reduced by half, we shall have

$$T = \frac{2\pi\sqrt{t_1 t_2}}{0.693} = 9.06\sqrt{t_1 t_2}.$$

The cycle of fluctuation will become an ellipse having its center at the center of fluctuation and having for semi-axes

$$E\frac{\gamma_1}{\sqrt{\epsilon_1}}, \qquad E\frac{\gamma_2}{\sqrt{\epsilon_2}}$$

whence the amplitudes of the fluctuations will be

$$f_1 = 2E\frac{\gamma_1}{\sqrt{\epsilon_1}}, \qquad f_2 = 2E\frac{\gamma_2}{\sqrt{\epsilon_2}}.$$

The ratio of the amplitudes of the two fluctuations will be

$$\frac{f_1}{f_2} = \frac{\gamma_1}{\gamma_2}\sqrt{\frac{\epsilon_2}{\epsilon_1}}.$$

The family of cycles of fluctuation will in this case consist of a group of homothetical ellipses having for common center the center of fluctuation (see Fig. 5).

7. Now let us consider the average number of individuals of the two species during a cycle.

For that let us take equations (A_1'), (A_2'). Dividing both members respectively by n_1 and n_2 we shall have

$$\frac{d \log n_1}{dt} = \epsilon_1(1 - n_2), \qquad \frac{d \log n_2}{dt} = -\epsilon_2(1 - n_1),$$

and integrating between the times t' and t'' at which times n_1 and n_2 assume respectively the values n_1', n_1''; n_2', n_2'', the following equations will be obtained:

$$\log \frac{n_1''}{n_1'} = \epsilon_1 \left[(t'' - t') - \int_{t'}^{t''} n_2 dt \right],$$

$$\log \frac{n_2''}{n_2'} = -\epsilon_2 \left[(t'' - t') - \int_{t'}^{t''} n_1 dt \right].$$

If we extend the integrals to a period T the first members vanish and we have

$$T = \int_0^T n_1 dt = \int_0^T n_2 dt$$

which is equivalent to saying

$$\frac{1}{T} \int_0^T n_1 dt = \frac{1}{T} \int_0^T n_2 dt = 1.$$

Then the averages of the values of n_1 and n_2 in a period are equal to 1 and by (10)

$$\frac{1}{T} \int_0^T N_1 dt = K_1 = \frac{\epsilon_2}{\gamma_2}, \qquad \frac{1}{T} \int_0^T N_2 dt = K_2 = \frac{\epsilon_1}{\gamma_1},$$

i.e., the coordinates of the center of fluctuation are the average values of the numbers of individuals of the species during a cycle. From this it

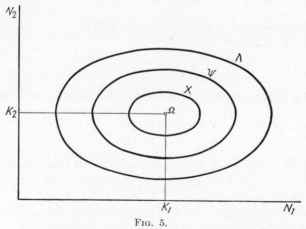

Fig. 5.

follows that if ϵ_1, ϵ_2, γ_1, γ_2 stay constant, the averages of the individuals of the two species during a cycle of fluctuation will always be the same whatever may be the initial numbers of individuals of the two species.

Let us see how these averages change with variation of ϵ_1 and ϵ_2, supposing γ_1 and γ_2 constants. It is seen at once that the average of the first species increases in proportion with ϵ_2, and that of the second species decreases in proportion with ϵ_1 so long as this quantity remains positive. Now to make ϵ_2 increase means destroying uniformly individuals of the second species in a quantity proportional to their number, and to make ϵ_1 decrease means destroying uniformly individuals of the first species in a quantity proportional to their number; from which it follows that if we try to contemporaneously destroy individuals of both species in the aforesaid manner but always keeping ϵ_1 positive, there will be an increase in the average of the individuals of the first species (those fed upon) while there will be a decrease in the average of the individuals of the second species (those feeding upon others). In Fig. 6 we have repre-

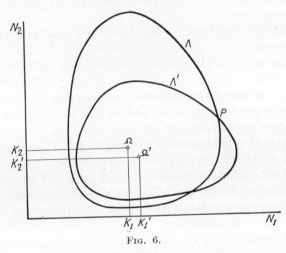

Fig. 6.

sented the transition from a cycle Λ corresponding to the parameters ϵ_1 and ϵ_2 to a cycle Λ' corresponding to parameters $\epsilon_1' < \epsilon_1$, $\epsilon_2' > \epsilon_2$ (the parameters γ_1 and γ_2 are supposed invariable and $\epsilon_1' > 0$). We may conceive of this transition as occurring in an instant corresponding to the point P of intersection of the two cycles, that is to say, without having any sensible change at that instant in the number of the individuals of the two species, although a change is disclosed with the passage of time by virtue of the constant action due to the variation of the parameters ϵ_1 and ϵ_2. The center Ω' of Λ' is moved to the right of and below Ω which indicates a diminution in the average value of N_2 and an increase in the average value of N_1.

To increase the protection of the species that is eaten from the voracity of the other means to diminish γ_1 and γ_2 and this corresponds to an increase in the average quantity of the two species.

8. We can sum up the various results obtained in the following laws which we shall call the "fundamental laws of the fluctuations" of the two species living together:

a. Law of the Periodic Cycle.—The fluctuations of the two species are periodic and the period depends only upon ϵ_1, ϵ_2 and C (namely upon the coefficients of increase and decrease and the initial conditions).

b. Law of the Conservation of the Averages.—The averages of the numbers of individuals of the two species are constant whatever may be the initial values of the numbers of individuals of the two species just so long as the coefficients of increase and decrease of the two species and those of protection and of offense (ϵ_1, ϵ_2, γ_1, γ_2) remain constant.

c. Law of the Disturbance of the Averages.—If an attempt is made to destroy the individuals of the two species uniformly and in proportion to their number, the average of the number of individuals of the species that is eaten increases and that of the individuals of the species feeding upon the other diminishes.[1]

Increasing the protection of the species fed upon increases, however, both the averages.

In the case in which the fluctuations are small, we have the following approximate laws:

(1) The small fluctuations are isochronous, that is to say their period is not affected perceptibly either by the initial number of individuals or by the conditions of protection and offense.

(2) The period of fluctuation is proportional to the geometric mean of the times in which the first species, alone, would double itself and the second, by itself, would be reduced by half. ($T = 9.06\sqrt{t_1 t_2}$.)

(3) The uniform destruction of individuals of the species feeding upon the other accelerates the fluctuations, and the destruction of individuals of the species eaten retards them.

If the individuals of the two species are destroyed, contemporaneously and uniformly, the ratio of the amplitude of the fluctuation of the species eaten to the amplitude of the fluctuation of the species feeding upon the other increases.

It seems that the animal species for which in their natural state the verifications of these laws can most easily be carried out are fish, of which there are in fact species which feed upon others. Continual fishing constitutes a uniform destruction of individuals of various species.

The cessation of fishing during the period of the recent war and its resumption after the war established transitions comparable to those considered above, from one cycle to another. Besides, the greater or less abundance of fish of various species determined by statistics gives a measure of the abundance of the individuals of the various species; hence the statistics of fishery furnish data on the fluctuations.

---

[1] It is understood that this law is valid within certain limits as is explicitly said in N. 7, that is as long as the coefficient of increase ϵ_1 remains positive. In §5 a special study will be made of the limit within which an element destructive of two species assists the species that is eaten.

The results of the statistics are seen to be in accord with the mathematical predictions.[1]

§4. EFFECTS OF THE VARIOUS ACTIONS WHICH TWO SPECIES LIVING TOGETHER CAN HAVE ON EACH OTHER

1. Let us suppose we have two species living together, and let N_1 and N_2 be respectively the numbers of individuals in each. The number of encounters of individuals of the first species with those of the second species, which occur in a unit of time, will be proportional to N_1N_2 and can therefore be assumed equal to αN_1N_2, α being a constant. Let λ_1 and λ_2 be the coefficients of increase, positive or negative, of the two species when each is alone. In the case which we have already treated λ_1 is positive and λ_2 is negative. Moreover these meetings are unfavorable to the first species (the species fed upon), while they are favorable to the second species (the species feeding upon the other). Let us indicate by β_1 the increase of individuals of the first species and by β_2 the increase of individuals of the second species due to a certain number of encounters, for example n. In the preceding case β_1 would have to be taken negative and β_2 positive. In the time dt the increases of the two species will be respectively

$$dN_1 = \lambda_1 N_1 dt + \frac{\beta_1}{n}\alpha N_2 N_1 dt,$$

$$dN_2 = \lambda_2 N_2 dt + \frac{\beta_2}{n}\alpha N_1 N_2 dt.$$

Using

$$\frac{\beta_1}{n}\alpha = \mu_1, \qquad \frac{\beta_2}{n}\alpha = \mu_2$$

the preceding equations will become

$$\begin{cases} \dfrac{dN_1}{dt} = N_1(\lambda_1 + \mu_1 N_2) \\ \dfrac{dN_2}{dt} = N_2(\lambda_2 + \mu_2 N_1) \end{cases} \tag{19}$$

[1] *Cf.* footnote 2, §1, No. 2, in which the statistics of Doctor D'Ancona are spoken of.

Charles Darwin had an intuition of the phenomena connected with the law of disturbance of averages, when, speaking of the struggle for life, he said:

"The amount of food for each species of course gives the extreme limit to which each can increase; but very frequently it is not the obtaining food, but the serving as prey to other animals which determines the average numbers of a species. Thus, there seems to be little doubt that the stock of partridges, grouse, and hares on any large estate depends chiefly on the destruction of vermin. If not one head of game were shot during the next 20 years in England, and, at the same time, if no vermin were destroyed, there would, in all probability, be less game than at present, although hundreds of thousands of game animals are now annually shot."

CHARLES DARWIN, "The Origin of Species by Means of Natural Selection, or the Preservation of Favoured Races in the Struggle for Life," 6th ed., pp. 53–54; with corrections to 1871, John Murray, London, 1882.

and if we make evident the signs which are given in the preceding case, writing

$$\lambda_1 = \epsilon_1 \qquad\qquad \lambda_2 = -\epsilon_2$$
$$\mu_1 = -\gamma_1 \qquad\qquad \mu_2 = \gamma_2$$

we arrive again at the equations (A_1) and (A_2) of §3, namely

$$\frac{dN_1}{dt} = N_1(\epsilon_1 - \gamma_1 N_2)$$

$$\frac{dN_2}{dt} = N_2(-\epsilon_2 + \gamma_2 N_1).$$

Thus appears a justification (as mentioned in (No. 1 of §3) of the assumption that the coefficients of increase are linear with respect to N_2 and N_1.

2. Let us now take equations (19) without concerning ourselves with the signs of the coefficients, that is admitting that they may be positive or negative; we may assume that they repre-

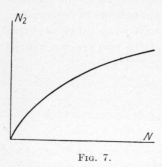

FIG. 7.

sent the laws of increase of two species living together for which λ_1 and λ_2 are the *coefficients of increase*, while μ_1 and μ_2 are the *coefficients of increase depending on encounters*. The signs of λ_1 and λ_2 tell us if the species are increasing or decreasing by themselves, while the signs of the coefficients μ_1 and μ_2 indicate whether the encounters are favorable or unfavorable to one species and to the other respectively. For example if λ_1 and λ_2 are positive and μ_1, μ_2 are negative this will show that the species are increasing by themselves, and that the encounters are unfavorable to both species. We shall consider all possible cases, making all possible combinations of these coefficients taking them positive or negative. According to the signs of λ_1, μ_1, λ_2, μ_2 the different cases relating to equations (19) are represented in Figs. 7, 8, 9, 10, 11, 12, and 13.

The following table indicates which cases correspond to the preceding figures.

$$\left.\begin{array}{l}\lambda_1 > 0,\ \mu_1 > 0,\ \lambda_2 > 0,\ \mu_2 > 0,\\ \lambda_1 < 0,\ \mu_1 < 0,\ \lambda_2 < 0,\ \mu_2 < 0,\end{array}\right\} \text{Fig. 7} \left\{\begin{array}{l}\text{l. r.}\\ \text{r. l.}\end{array}\right.$$

$$\left.\begin{array}{l}\lambda_1 < 0,\ \mu_1 < 0,\ \lambda_2 > 0,\ \mu_2 > 0,\\ \lambda_1 > 0,\ \mu_1 > 0,\ \lambda_2 < 0,\ \mu_2 < 0,\end{array}\right\} \text{Fig. 8} \left\{\begin{array}{l}\text{r. l.}\\ \text{l. r.}\end{array}\right.$$

$$\left.\begin{array}{l}\lambda_1 > 0,\ \mu_1 > 0,\ \lambda_2 > 0,\ \mu_2 < 0,\\ \lambda_1 < 0,\ \mu_1 < 0,\ \lambda_2 < 0,\ \mu_2 > 0,\end{array}\right\} \text{Fig. 9} \left\{\begin{array}{l}\text{l. r.}\\ \text{r. l.}\end{array}\right.$$

$$\left.\begin{array}{l}\lambda_1 < 0,\ \mu_1 < 0,\ \lambda_2 > 0,\ \mu_2 < 0,\\ \lambda_1 > 0,\ \mu_1 > 0,\ \lambda_2 < 0,\ \mu_2 > 0,\end{array}\right\} \text{Fig. 10} \left\{\begin{array}{l}\text{r. l.}\\ \text{l. r.}\end{array}\right.$$

$$\left.\begin{array}{l} \lambda_1 > 0,\ \mu_1 < 0,\ \lambda_2 > 0,\ \mu_2 < 0, \\[2ex] \lambda_1 < 0,\ \mu_1 > 0,\ \lambda_2 < 0,\ \mu_2 > 0, \end{array}\right\} \text{Fig. 11} \left\{\begin{array}{l} \text{l. r. 1st branch} \\ \text{r. l. 2nd branch} \\ \text{r. l. 1st branch} \\ \text{l. r. 2nd branch} \end{array}\right.$$

$$\left.\begin{array}{l} \lambda_1 > 0,\ \mu_1 < 0,\ \lambda_2 > 0,\ \mu_2 < 0, \\[2ex] \lambda_1 < 0,\ \mu_1 > 0,\ \lambda_2 < 0,\ \mu_2 > 0, \end{array}\right\} \text{Fig. 12} \left\{\begin{array}{l} \text{u. 1st branch} \\ \text{d. 2nd branch} \\ \text{d. 1st branch} \\ \text{u. 2nd branch} \end{array}\right.$$

$$\left.\begin{array}{l} \lambda_1 > 0,\ \mu_1 < 0,\ \lambda_2 > 0,\ \mu_2 < 0, \\[2ex] \lambda_1 < 0,\ \mu_1 > 0,\ \lambda_2 < 0,\ \mu_2 > 0, \end{array}\right\} \text{Fig. 13} \left\{\begin{array}{l} \text{l. r. 1st branch, 2nd branch} \\ \text{r. l. 3rd branch, 4th branch} \\ \text{r. l. 1st branch, 2nd branch} \\ \text{l. r. 3rd branch, 4th branch} \end{array}\right.$$

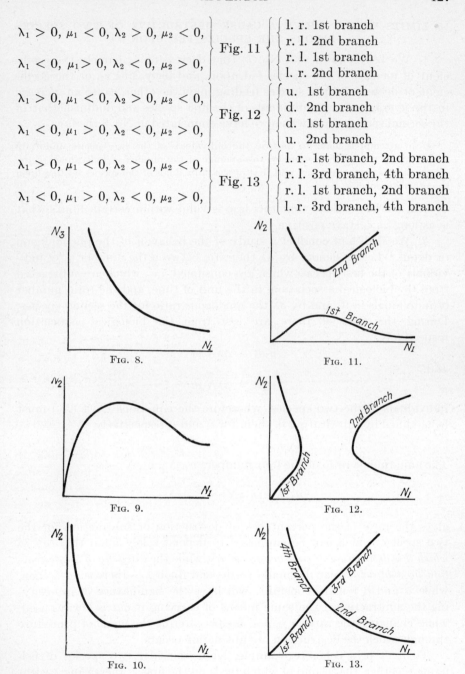

Fig. 8. Fig. 11. Fig. 9. Fig. 12. Fig. 10. Fig. 13.

In the preceding table l. r. signifies that with increase in time the curve is traced from left to right, r. l. from right to left, d. downward and u. upward.

§5. LIMITS WITHIN WHICH A CAUSE DESTRUCTIVE OF TWO SPECIES FAVORS THE SPECIES FED UPON

1. We have shown (§3, No. 7) that decreasing ϵ_1, namely the coefficient of increase of the species fed upon, and increasing ϵ_2, or the coefficient of decrease of the species feeding upon the other, cause an increase in the average of the individuals of the first species and diminish that of the second species, from which we have enunciated in No. 8 the law:

If an attempt is made to destroy the individuals of the two species uniformly and in proportion to their number, the average of the number of individuals of the species that is eaten increases, and that of the individuals of the species feeding upon the other diminishes.

But we have added that this law is valid within certain limits, that is as long as ϵ_1 stays positive.

2. We shall now conduct a study of the behavior of the phenomenon in detail. Let us denote by $\alpha\lambda$ the ratio between the number n_1 of individuals of the first species which are consumed, *i.e.*, which are subtracted from the biological association, in the unit of time, and the total number of individuals in it, and by $\beta\lambda$ the analogous ratio for the second species. During the time dt there are lost from the biological association respectively

$$n_1 dt = \alpha\lambda N_1 dt$$

and

$$n_2 dt = \beta\lambda N_2 dt$$

individuals of the two species, wherefore the equations (A_1), (A_2) must be modified by substituting in them for ϵ_1 and ϵ_2 respectively

$$\epsilon_1 - \alpha\lambda, \qquad\qquad \epsilon_2 + \beta\lambda.$$

The anharmonic ratio of the four numbers n_2, N_2, n_1, N_1, *i.e.*

$$n_2 : N_2 :: n_1 : N_1 = \frac{\beta}{\alpha} = \delta,$$

gives the ratio of the percentages of destruction or subtraction for the two species, which can be supposed to depend solely upon the *way in which this destruction or subtraction occurs*, while the *intensity of the destruction or subtraction* can be made to depend upon λ. Increasing λ then, while α and β remain constant, will have the significance of intensifying the subtraction if the same means of carrying it out is always used, while changing the ratio $\delta = \beta/\alpha$ means altering the mode of procedure through which the destruction or subtraction occurs.

To refer to a concrete example, let us consider two species of fish living together, the second of which feeds on the first. Increasing λ without varying either α or β means intensifying the fishing, always employing the same method of fishing, while changing $\delta = \beta/\alpha$ means changing the method of fishing.

3. The equations (A_1) and (A_2) will become then

$$\frac{dN_1}{dt} = (\epsilon_1 - \alpha\lambda - \gamma_1 N_2)N_1 \tag{20}$$

$$\frac{dN_2}{dt} = (-\epsilon_2 - \beta\lambda + \gamma_2 N_1)N_2. \tag{20'}$$

If $\epsilon_1' = \epsilon_1 - \alpha\lambda > 0$ the fluctuation will occur with a period T (§3, No. 4). The number of individuals of the first species subtracted in the time dt will be

$$\alpha\lambda N_1 dt,$$

and during the period T

$$\int_0^T \alpha\lambda N_1 dt,$$

whence the average of individuals subtracted in the unit of time will be

$$P = \frac{1}{T}\int_0^T \alpha\lambda N_1 dt = \frac{\alpha\lambda}{T}\int_0^T N_1 dt.$$

But since from §3, No. 7

$$\frac{1}{T}\int_0^T N_1 dt = \frac{\epsilon_2 + \beta\lambda}{\gamma_2} = \frac{\epsilon_2'}{\gamma_2},$$

we have

$$P = \frac{\alpha\lambda(\epsilon_2 + \beta\lambda)}{\gamma_2}.$$

As $\epsilon_1 - \alpha\lambda > 0$, the upper limit of λ will be ϵ_1/α and consequently the upper limit of P will be

$$P_m = \frac{\epsilon_1(\epsilon_2 + \delta\epsilon_1)}{\gamma_2}.$$

If we refer to the concrete example of fishing, we may conclude that, if the same method of fishing is maintained (that is if δ is constant), the average quantity of the first species, caught in the unit of time, during a cycle of fluctuation, can not exceed P_m, though it may approach this number as closely as we please.

Also we may say that P_m will be greater according as the harmonic ratio δ is greater.

4. If λ exceeds the value ϵ_1/α so that

$$\epsilon_1 - \alpha\lambda < 0,$$

then the fluctuation will cease to exist, both the species will tend to disappear (see §4) and we shall have the case denoted in §4 with the type represented in Fig. 9 in which the curve is to be read from right to left.

It is interesting to examine the boundary case in which λ attains the value ϵ_1/α. We arrive then at the point of transition from the type represented in Fig. 2 to the type represented in Fig. 9. As indicated in §4, we have not considered the several cases of transition among the various types; but we shall examine this now because the subject which we are now treating requires it. It can serve as an example of the treatment of the various cases of transition from one type to another.

If $\lambda = \alpha/\epsilon_1$ the equations (20), (20') become

$$\frac{dN_1}{dt} = -\gamma_1 N_1 N_2, \tag{21}$$

$$\frac{dN_2}{dt} = (-\epsilon_2'' + \gamma_2 N_1)N_2, \tag{21'}$$

where

$$\epsilon_2'' = \epsilon_2 + \epsilon_1 \delta.$$

These equations have the integral

$$N_1^{\epsilon_2''} e^{-\gamma_2 N_1} = C e^{\gamma_1 N_2}, \tag{22}$$

where C is a positive constant.

Letting

$$x = N_1^{\epsilon_2''} e^{-\gamma_2 N_1} = C e^{\gamma_1 N_2}$$

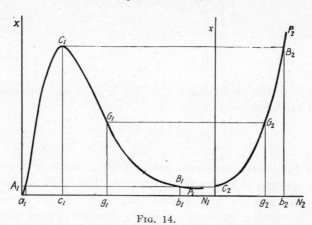

Fig. 14.

the two curves Γ_1 and Γ_2 which have (N_1, x) and (N_2, x) respectively for abscissa and ordinate are represented in Fig. 14, whence employing the same mode of procedure which was followed in §3, No. 3, (*cf.* Fig. 1 and Fig. 2) we can draw the curve which has (22) for its equation (see Fig. 15).

The minimum and maximum values a_1, b_1 of N_1 will give the two real roots of the equation

$$N_1^{\epsilon_2''} e^{-\gamma_2 N_1} = C. \tag{22'}$$

When $\epsilon_1' = \epsilon_1 - \alpha\lambda$ becomes 0, the cyclical curves of Fig. 3 assume, at the limit, the form of the curve of Fig. 15. The lower part of the former curves approaches the straight line segment a_1b_1 of Fig. 15. But while the curves of Fig. 3 are traced clear around periodically, which constitutes the phenomenon of fluctuation, the line segment a_1b_1 can never be traced because an infinite period of time is necessary for reaching the point a_1. Then any point whatever on the straight line a_1b_1 corresponds to N_1 constant and $N_2 = 0$.

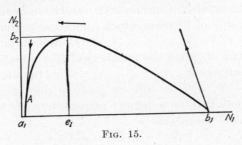

FIG. 15.

In Fig. 16 three curves are represented, I, II, III, which issue from the same point P. Their respective equations are

$$\text{I. } N_1{}^{\epsilon_2'}e^{-\gamma_2 N_1} = C'N_2{}^{-\epsilon_1'}e^{\gamma_1 N_2}$$
$$\text{II. } N_1{}^{\epsilon_2''}e^{-\gamma_2 N_1} = C''e^{\gamma_1 N_2}$$
$$\text{III. } N_1{}^{\epsilon_2'''}e^{-\gamma_2 N_1} = C'''N_2{}^h e^{\gamma_1 N_2}.$$

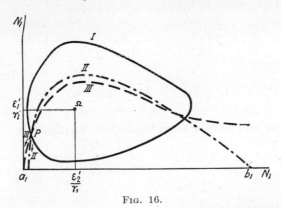

FIG. 16.

No. I is a curve of fluctuation which therefore corresponds to $\epsilon_1' > 0$ (for this reason it is of the type of those in Fig. 2), No. II is a curve of the type of those in Fig. 15 (curve of transition from the type in Fig. 2 to the type of Fig. 9), No. III is a curve of the type of those in Fig. 9 and corresponds to $\epsilon_1 - \alpha\lambda$ negative and equal to $-h$. We have besides

$$0 < \epsilon_2' < \epsilon_2'' < \epsilon_2'''.$$

The curves mentioned refer respectively to the three cases in which the intensity of destruction of the species does not attain the limit ϵ_1/α, or is equal to it, or exceeds it.

§6. THE CASE OF ANY NUMBER WHATEVER OF SPECIES WHICH CONTEND FOR THE SAME FOOD

1. It is easy to extend what has been done in the case of two species living together, which contend for the same food, to the case of any number of species.

Let us take the number of species to be n and let us assume $\epsilon_1, \epsilon_2, \ldots \epsilon_n,$ to be the coefficients of increase which each species would have if alone. Let us denote by $F(N_1, N_2, \ldots, N_n)dt$ the diminution in the quantity of food in the time dt, when the numbers of individuals of the different species are respectively $N_1, N_2, \ldots, N_n$. This function will be zero for $N_1 = N_2 = \cdots N_n = 0$; it will be positive and increasing and will increase indefinitely with an indefinite increase in each N_r. For simplicity we could take F linear, that is

$$F(N_1, N_2, \cdots, N_n) = \alpha_1 N_1 + \alpha_2 N_2 + \cdots + \alpha_n N_n$$

where the coefficients α_r are positive. But we shall leave F general.

The presence of N_1 individuals of the first species, of N_2 of the second, etc. will influence the coefficients of increase reducing ϵ_r to $\epsilon_r - \gamma_r F(N_1, \cdots, N_n)$ where the positive coefficient γ_r measures the influence which the diminution of the food has upon the increase of the species.

We shall have then the differential equations

$$\frac{dN_r}{dt} = N_r[\epsilon_r - \gamma_r F(N_1, \cdots, N_n)], \quad (r = 1, 2, \cdots, n) \quad (23)$$

from which follows

$$\frac{1}{\gamma_r N_r}\frac{dN_r}{dt} - \frac{1}{\gamma_s N_s}\frac{dN_s}{dt} = \frac{\epsilon_r}{\gamma_r} - \frac{\epsilon_s}{\gamma_s}$$

and integrating and passing from logarithms to numbers

$$\frac{N_r^{\frac{1}{\gamma_r}}}{N_s^{\frac{1}{\gamma_s}}} = Ce^{\left(\frac{\epsilon_r}{\gamma_r} - \frac{\epsilon_s}{\gamma_s}\right)t}$$

where C is a positive constant.

2. Let us arrange the ratios ϵ_r/γ_r in order of size, that is let us suppose[1]

$$\frac{\epsilon_1}{\gamma_1} > \frac{\epsilon_2}{\gamma_2} > \frac{\epsilon_3}{\gamma_3} > \cdots > \frac{\epsilon_n}{\gamma_n},$$

then we shall have, if $r < s$

---

[1] Let us exclude the cases of equality as of infinitesimally small probability.

$$\lim_{t = \infty} \frac{N_r^{\frac{1}{\gamma_r}}}{N_s^{\frac{1}{\gamma_s}}} = \infty.$$

As a consequence of this result either N_r, can, with increase of time, take values as large as we please, or

$$\lim_{t = \infty} N_s = 0.$$

But the first case is to be excluded, because F increases indefinitely with indefinite increase of N_r, therefore in (23) the second member becomes negative when N_r exceeds a certain limit; whence the upper limit of N_r is finite. Then the second case must hold. From this it follows that all the species tend to disappear except the first.

To have the asymptotic variation of N_1 it will suffice to repeat what has been done in the case of two species alone.

§7. CASE OF ANY NUMBER WHATEVER OF SPECIES SOME OF WHICH FEED UPON OTHERS

1. Let us consider the case of n species and let us suppose that the encounter of two individuals of different species always carries a result favorable to the species to which one belongs, and unfavorable to that to which the other belongs, or else a zero result for both. If N_r is the number of individuals of the species r and N_s the number of individuals of the species s the probability of an encounter of an individual of one with an individual of the other will be proportional to $N_r N_s$ whence we can assume that the number of encounters which take place in the unit of time is equal to $m_{rs} N_r N_s$. Let us suppose that at each encounter there are destroyed p_{rs} individuals (p_{rs} will evidently be a fraction) of one of the two species, for example of the species r, then in the unit of time $m_{rs} p_{rs} N_r N_s$ individuals of this species will be destroyed. Let us see how the influence that this has on the number of individuals of the other species can be calculated.

A rough calculation can be made in this way: Let us denote by $\beta_1, \beta_2, \ldots, \beta_n$ the average weights of all the individuals of the n species and by $P_1, P_2, \ldots, P_n$ the total weights of all the individuals belonging to each species. To get the number of individuals of each species it will suffice to take

$$N_1 = \frac{P_1}{\beta_1}, \ldots, N_r = \frac{P_r}{\beta_r}, \ldots, N_n = \frac{P_n}{\beta_n}.$$

Now if an individual of the species r is eaten by individuals of the species s the weight P_r will become $P_r - \beta_r$ while the weight P_s will become $P_s + \beta_r$ and for this reason the respective numbers of individuals of the two species will become roughly

$$\frac{P_r - \beta_r}{\beta_r} = N_r - 1, \qquad \frac{P_s + \beta_r}{\beta_s} = N_s + \frac{\beta_r}{\beta_s}.$$

Then in a very rough way we can say that in the unit of time, by virtue of the encounters of individuals of the species r with individuals of the species s, the diminution of individuals of species r will be given by

$$m_{rs} p_{rs} N_r N_s$$

and the increase of individuals of species s, also in the unit of time, will be given by

$$m_{rs} P_{rs} N_r N_s \frac{\beta_r}{\beta_s}.$$

Letting $m_{rs} p_{rs} \beta_r, = a_{rs}$ the diminution of individuals of the species r will be

$$\frac{1}{\beta_r} a_{rs} N_r N_s$$

and the increase of individuals of the species s will be

$$\frac{1}{\beta_s} a_{rs} N_r N_s$$

or also letting $a_{rs} = -a_{sr}$ (supposing a_{sr} to be negative) we can say that in the unit of time, by virtue of their encounters, the numbers of individuals of the species r and of the species s increase respectively by

$$\frac{1}{\beta_r} a_{sr} N_r N_s, \qquad \frac{1}{\beta_s} a_{rs} N_r N_s,$$

and hence in the time dt, through their encounters, they increase respectively by

$$\frac{1}{\beta_r} a_{sr} N_r N_s dt, \qquad \frac{1}{\beta_s} a_{rs} N_r N_s dt.$$

The same can be said of each other pair of species. In other words the numbers $1/\beta_1, 1/\beta_2, \ldots , 1/\beta_n$ have been assumed as the *equivalents* of the individuals of the various species. In fact to grant that $1/\beta_r$ individuals of the species r can be transformed into $1/\beta_s$ individuals of the species s means that $1/\beta_r$ individuals of the species r are *equivalent* to $1/\beta_s$ individuals of the species s. Thus, taken in a very rough first approximation, we have as *equivalent* the reciprocals of the average weights, but it will suffice for us to take as *hypothesis the existence of equivalent numbers*, even if these do not coincide with the reciprocals of the average weights, in order to obtain the same results which we have now secured.

2. Let us call ϵ_r the coefficient of increase of the species r while that is alone, then if all the n species live together we shall have for the increase of the individuals N_r in the time dt

$$dN_r = \epsilon_r N_r dt + \frac{1}{\beta_r} \sum_1^n{}_s a_{sr} N_r N_s dt,$$

whence we shall have the differential equations:

$$\frac{dN_r}{dt} = \left(\epsilon_r + \frac{1}{\beta_r} \sum_1^n a_{sr} N_s \right) N_r, \qquad (r = 1, 2, \cdots, n)$$

or likewise

(B) $$\beta_r \frac{dN_r}{dt} = \left(\epsilon_r \beta_r + \sum_1^n a_{sr} N_s \right) N_r, \qquad (r = 1, 2, \cdots, n)$$

in which

$$a_{rs} = -a_{sr}, \qquad a_{rr} = 0, \qquad \beta_1, \beta_2, \cdots, \beta_n > 0.$$

In the case of two species only, one of which feeds upon the other, we have considered the equations (§3, No. 1)

$$\frac{dN_1}{dt} = (\epsilon_1 - \gamma_1 N_2) N_1, \qquad \frac{dN_2}{dt} = (-\epsilon_2 + \gamma_2 N_1) N_2.$$

If we put

$$-\gamma_1 = \frac{a_{21}}{\beta_1} \qquad\qquad \gamma_2 = \frac{a_{12}}{\beta_2}$$

these equations assume the form (B), with the need only of writing ϵ_2 instead of $-\epsilon_2$ and understanding that ϵ_2 is negative. We see therefore that in this case there is no need of a special hypothesis.

For an association of n species we must distinguish the case in which the number of the species is *even* from that in which the number is *odd*.

In the first case the following statement can be proved: *If there exists a stationary state,*[1] *placing the species in any state whatever different from the stationary state, the number of individuals of each species will remain limited between two positive numbers.*

3. We must now establish some definitions in order to enunciate certain propositions without ambiguity.

If $N(t)$ indicates the number of individuals of a species and always remains included between two positive numbers, the species will be said to have *limited variation between positive numbers.*

If $N(t)$ approaches zero this signifies that the species is *exhausting* itself or also that the *variation* consists in a *depletion.*

If $N(t)$ is limited between two positive nunbers, $N(t)$ will be said to have *fluctuations* if for $t > t_o$ (for t_o however large) N has maximum and minimum values.

The fluctuations will be said to be damped if the oscillation (the difference between the upper and the lower limit) of $N(t)$ for $t > t_o$ can be made as small as we please by sufficiently increasing t_o. In this case and

---

[1] That is a system of positive values of $N_1, N_2, \ldots, N_n$ satisfying the equations

$$0 = \epsilon_r \beta_r + \sum_1^n a_{sr} N_s \qquad (r = 1, 2, \cdots, n).$$

in this case only the fluctuations permit that N approach a fixed and finite limit for $t = \infty$.

$N(t)$ will be said to *vary asymptotically* and to *approach asymptotically* the limit q, if $N(t)$ has no fluctuations and approaches the fixed and finite limit q for $t = \infty$.

The limits for $t = \infty$ of the averages of $N_1, N_2, \ldots, N_n$ in the time t_1t, will be called the asymptotic averages.

4. For an association of an even number of species we now express the following general propositions, omitting the demonstrations:

(I) *If there exists a stationary state for the biological association, the numbers of individuals of each species are limited between positive numbers, fluctuations always existing which are not damped, and the asymptotic averages of the numbers of individuals of all the separate species are the values corresponding to the stationary state.*

(II) *The deviations from the stationary state can be made as small as we please, provided the initial state is sufficiently near to the stationary state.*

In other words:

The stationary state is always a stable state.[1]

(III) *The small fluctuations of n species living together can be obtained by means of the superposition of $n/2$ fluctuations not damped and each having a period of its own.*

As in general the periods $T^{(h)}$ will be incommensurable with each other, so the resulting fluctuation will not be periodic. Let it be observed that the number of the periods $T^{(h)}$ is equal to half the number of the species living together, but let it be called to mind that the laws of fluctuation now obtained hold in the case in which the number of species living together is even.

To summarize, the three theorems which we have designated by I, II, III, can be considered as *three general laws of variation of an even number of species living together.*

We can also enunciate the proposition.

In order that there may exist a stationary state and ensuing fluctuations, some of the coefficients ϵ_r of increase must be positive and others negative, that is to say:

If by themselves all the species increase or all decrease, neither a stationary state nor ensuing fluctuations can exist.

If the number of species is odd it is not possible that the number of individuals of each species should stay limited between two positive numbers.

To thoroughly understand the significance of this theorem it is necessary to consider it as a purely theoretical result. Let us observe in the meantime that if one of the species should tend toward depletion, the number of the species will tend to become even and we shall return to the case considered previously.

---

[1] The stability here is thought of in the sense analogous to the stability of equilibrium in mechanics.

But if the number of individuals of one of the species should increase indefinitely, it can be recognized that equations (B) will no longer be valid. In fact we have supposed the ϵ_r constants, that is to say independent of the number of individuals present, which can be allowed if this number does not exceed a certain limit, but beyond this it cannot be true any longer, whence the equations will be modified, at least for the changed value which will have to be attributed to the constants ϵ_r, in order to arrest the increase of that species which would increase indefinitely.

§8. EXTENSION OF THE THREE FUNDAMENTAL LAWS ON FLUCTUATIONS TO THE CASE OF ASSOCIATIONS OF ANY NUMBER WHATEVER OF SPECIES

1. In §3 three fundamental laws on the fluctuations of two species living together have been stated. What is the extension of these to the general case of n species?

In §7 it has been stated that *in the case of an even number of species, if the fundamental determinant* (the determinant of the system of equations B) is *different from zero and if there exists a stationary state of the species without depletion, the variations of the numbers of individuals of the several species are limited between positive numbers and some fluctuations always exist which are not damped.* Thus is enunciated the extension of the *first law* relative to two species. Evidently with this extension the property of periodicity is lost while that of fluctuation remains.

2. Let us admit as verified the aforementioned hypotheses and let us begin with an observation with regard to the extension of the second law (that is to say that of the invariability of the averages of the number of individuals) which, lacking periodicity, can not specify the duration of the time in which the averages must be taken. But we know that, taking the averages for infinitely long durations of time, these approach the roots of the equations of equilibrium. Now these roots are independent of the initial conditions, whence the *second law remains unaltered if we take as averages (cf. §7) of the numbers of individuals of separate species, the limits of the same averages for infinitely long durations of time (asymptotic averages).*

3. The question now is to see what form the third law will assume in general, namely the law of disturbance of the averages, always granting as verified the aforesaid hypotheses. For the averages of the numbers of individuals of the several species we shall always assume the asymptotic averages.

In the third law (§3 No. 8) a distinction is made between the species that is eaten and the species feeding upon the other. When we pass to more than two species, it may be that the individuals of one species are eaten by those of another and themselves feed upon the individuals of a third species. Wishing to keep the distinction between species that are eaten and those feeding upon others it is necessary to admit that if a species A feeds upon another there is not any species that eats A and hence that if a species B is eaten by another, it does not feed upon any other species of the biological association.

4. Now we can state the theorem that if we keep the preceding hypotheses *the numbers of the species eating others must be equal to the number of the species fed upon.*

Whence we can suppose that $n = 2p$ and that the species $1, 2, \ldots, p$ are feeding upon others and the species $(p + 1), (p + 2), \cdots, 2p$ are fed upon. Then for the existence of a stationary state $\epsilon_1, \epsilon_2, \ldots, \epsilon_p$ must be negative and $\epsilon_{p+1}, \epsilon_{p+2}, \ldots, \epsilon_{2p}$ must be positive.

Now let us increase

$$|\epsilon_1|, \qquad |\epsilon_2|, \ldots, |\epsilon_p|$$

and let us diminish

$$|\epsilon_{p+1}|, \qquad |\epsilon_{p+2}|, \ldots, |\epsilon_{2p}|$$

namely, let us destroy one set of species as much as the other in proportion to the number of individuals which they have respectively. Some one of the

$$N_{p+1}, N_{p+2}, \ldots, N_{2p}$$

satisfying the equations of equilibrium will have to increase and some one of the

$$N_1, N_2, \ldots, N_p$$

satisfying the same equations must diminish. Reciprocally if none of the $N_{p+1}, \ldots, N_{2p}$ decreases, but all or some increase, if none of the $N_1, \ldots, N_p$ increases, but all or some diminish, then $|\epsilon_{p+1}|$, $|\epsilon_{p+2}|, \ldots, |\epsilon_{2p}|$ must diminish and $|\epsilon_1|, |\epsilon_2|, \ldots, |\epsilon_p|$ must increase, that is to say, individuals of the species feeding upon others must be destroyed, as well as of the species eaten, in proportion to their number.

It is in this that the extension of the third law consists, which (recalling the significance of the roots of the equations of equilibrium) can be enunciated as follows:

In a conservative association of even order, with determinant different from zero, for which a stationary state exists and the species feeding upon others can be distinguished from those eaten, if all the species are destroyed uniformly and in proportion to the number of their individuals, the asymptotic averages of the number of individuals of some of the species eaten (if not of all) will increase, and the asymptotic averages of the numbers of individuals of some of the species feeding upon others (if not of all) will diminish.

Naturally this proposition holds up to a certain limit of destruction (*cf.* §§4, 5), and if the roots of the equations of equilibrium are positive.

§9. CASE IN WHICH THE COEFFICIENT OF INCREASE OF EACH SEPARATE SPECIES DEPENDS ON THE NUMBER OF INDIVIDUALS OF THAT SAME SPECIES

1. Various times in preceding sections we have had occasion to consider cases in which the calculation would lead to an indefinite increase of the number of individuals of one or more species. Such a result must be considered theoretical and we have not failed to give explicit warning on this as in No. 1 of §4, observing that with the increase of the number of individuals the equations must become invalid, and in particular that the coefficients of increase must be modified because of the indefinite increase in the number of individuals.

This necessitates a consideration of the influence which the number of individuals of one species has upon its coefficient of increase. It is evident that this effect can be neglected as long as the number of individuals does not exceed certain limits, but it is necessary to take it into account when the calculation leads to an infinite increase of individuals. Let us see how this can be done.

In the case in which only one species exists, and if we admit the coefficient of increase as constant and equal to ϵ, we shall have

$$\frac{dN}{dt} = \epsilon N$$

where N denotes the number of individuals, whence

$$N = N_o e^{\epsilon t}$$

where N_o is the initial number of individuals. If ϵ is positive N will increase indefinitely.

Now let us suppose that the coefficient of increase is not constant, but is given by $\epsilon - \lambda N$ where ϵ and λ are positive constants. We shall have

$$N = \frac{C\epsilon e^{\epsilon t}}{1 + C\lambda e^{\epsilon t}}$$

and hence

$$\lim_{t = \infty} N = \frac{\epsilon}{\lambda}.$$

Corresponding changes can be made in equations (B), and from a study of them we may state the theorem:

If a stationary state exists and if the coefficients of increase of one or more species decrease linearly with the increase of the number of the respective individuals, while the coefficients of increase of the other species are constants, starting out from any initial state whatever different from the stationary state, we shall have for the first species either asymptotic variations or fluctuations which will be damped. If all the coefficients decrease in the aforesaid manner the system will tend toward the stationary state.[1]

[1] Also if some coefficients λ_r are zero, the state of the system can approach the stationary state. (*Cf.* §8, No. 4.)

It is easy to be convinced with particular examples that according to different cases there may be asymptotic variation and damped fluctuations.

In certain ways the actions which tend to damp the increase of each species with the increase of the number of individuals belonging to it produce an effect analogous to that of internal attritions in a material system, that is they damp the fluctuations.

§10. CONSERVATIVE AND DISSIPATIVE BIOLOGICAL ASSOCIATIONS

1. The considerations of the last section can be notably extended; we shall thus be led to a fundamental classification of biological associations.

To this end let us suppose that the coefficients of increase depend linearly in any way upon the number of individuals, not only of each species, but of the various species and let the effects of the encounters of individuals of different species be felt in any way whatever, but constant, by the species themselves, proportional to the number of encounters, without further concern over the satisfaction of the hypothesis of §7, No. 1.

Equations (B) then assume the general form

(C)
$$\frac{dN_r}{dt} = \left(\epsilon_r - \sum_{1}^{n}{}_s p_{rs} N_s \right) N_r$$

where the coefficients ϵ_r and p_{rs} are any constants whatever.

We can consider the ϵ_r as dependent on the constant causes of increase or decrease of the species, and the other terms as dependent upon the reciprocal actions of the individuals. Evidently with this there is shown an extension of the concept of reciprocal action among the various individuals much greater than has been done previously.

If each species were alone the ϵ_r would be their coefficients of increase, while

$$\epsilon_r - \sum_{1}^{n}{}_s p_{rs} N_s$$

are the coefficients of increase of the same species as a result of their living together. We shall call these last the *true coefficients of increase* and ϵ_r the *rough coefficients of increase* or also we shall call them simply *coefficients of increase* when confusion can not arise between the two sets.

2. First of all we can say that *it is sufficient that one of the coefficients be positive, in order that all the species should not be exhausted.*

Let the quantities $\alpha_1, \alpha_2, \ldots, \alpha_n$ be positive and let us place

$$F(N_1, N_2, \cdots, N_n) = \sum_{1}^{n}{}_r \sum_{1}^{n}{}_s \alpha_r p_{rs} N_s N_r.$$

We shall have the theorem:

If the form F is positive definite, there will exist a number N such that none of the numbers N_1, N_2, . . . , N_n can remain larger than N, starting from a certain instant.

In fact from (C) it follows that

$$\sum_{1}^{n} \alpha_r \frac{dN_r}{dt} = \sum_{1}^{n} \alpha_r \epsilon_r N_r - F(N_1, N_2, \cdots, N_n).$$

Letting $N_r = 1$, let us denote by m_r the lower limit of the values of F for all possible values of N_1, N_2, . . . , N_{r-1}, N_{r+1}, . . . , N_n. m_r will be > 0. Let m be the smallest of the numbers $m_1, m_2, \ldots, m_n$. Besides let

$$\sum_{1}^{n} |\alpha_r \epsilon_r| < E.$$

Let us suppose that N_r after a certain instant t_1 stays greater than

$$\frac{E+1}{m} = N.$$

Let us denote by $M(t_2)$ the greatest of the numbers $N_1(t_2)$, $N_2(t_2)$, . . . , $N_n(t_2)$ where $t_2 > t_1$.

Then we shall have

$$F(N_1, N_2, \cdots, N_n)_{t=t_2} > mM^2(t_2)$$

$$\sum_{1}^{n} \alpha_r \epsilon_r N_r(t_2) < EM(t_2)$$

whence it follows that

$$\left(\sum_{1}^{n} \alpha_r \frac{dN_r}{dt} \right)_{t=t_2} > [E - mM(t_2)]M(t_2).$$

Now

$$M(t_2) > \frac{E+1}{m}$$

hence

$$\left(\sum_{1}^{n} \alpha_r \frac{dN_r}{dt} \right)_{t=t_2} < -\frac{E+1}{m}, \qquad (t_2 > t_1),$$

a consequence of which would be that starting from a certain moment, some one of N_1, N_2, . . . , N_n would have to become negative which is absurd, since N_r can be only positive as follows also from (C). In fact from these equations is derived

$$N_r = N_r{}^o e^{\int_0^t (\epsilon_r - \Sigma_s p_{rs} N_s) dt}$$

where $N_r{}^o$ is the value of N_r for $t = 0$, whence as $N_r{}^o$ is positive so will N_r remain. Therefore there exists the number $N = \dfrac{E+1}{m}$ such that each N_r after a certain instant t_1 can not remain greater than that number.

Combining the last two theorems now we can state the proposition: *If at least one of the coefficients of increase is positive and if the form E is positive definite the biological association will be stable.*

The stability consists in the fact that the whole association does not tend toward depletion, and no one species can increase indefinitely.

As the N_i are all positive so the preceding theorem can be extended to the case in which the form F is not zero except when every $N_i = 0$ and is positive for all positive values of the N_i.

3. We can easily see that if the form F is positive definite the determinant formed with the p_{rs} can not be zero. Let us suppose that it is zero. Then there would exist some numbers $N_1, N_2, \ldots, N_n$ (positive, negative, or zero, but not all zero) which would satisfy the equation

$$\sum_{1}^{n}{}_s p_{rs} N_s = 0$$

and hence

$$0 = \sum_{r}^{n} \sum_{1}^{n}{}_s \alpha_r p_{rs} N_s N_r = F(N_1, N_2, \cdots, N_n)$$

which contradicts the hypothesis that the form F is positive definite.

Having made this premise, let us suppose that the equations

$$(C') \qquad\qquad \epsilon_r - \sum_{1}^{n}{}_s p_{rs} N_s = 0$$

when solved with respect to N_s give the solutions $q_s \neq 0$. We shall have then the identities

$$\epsilon_r = \sum_{1}^{n}{}_s p_{rs} q_s$$

whence equations (C) will become

$$\frac{dN_r}{dt} = -\sum_{1}^{n}{}_s p_{rs}(N_s - q_s) N_r$$

that is by letting

$$\frac{N_r}{q_r} = n_r$$

we shall have

$$\frac{dn_r}{dt} = -\sum_{1}^{n}{}_s p_{rs} q_s (n_s - 1) n_r. \qquad (24)$$

From these equations it follows that

$$\frac{1}{n_r} \frac{dn_r}{dt} = -\sum_{1}^{n}{}_s p_{rs} q_s (n_s - 1).$$

Let α_r represent positive constant quantities; then we shall have

$$\sum_r \alpha_r q_r \frac{n_r - 1}{n_r} \frac{dn_r}{dt} = -\sum_1^n{}_r \sum_1^n{}_s p_{rs}\alpha_r q_r q_s (n_s - 1)(n_r - 1).$$

Let us place

$$\tfrac{1}{2}(p_{rs}\alpha_r + p_{sr}\alpha_s) = m_{rs} = m_{sr}, \tag{25}$$

$$F(x_1, x_2, \cdots, x_n) = -\sum_r \sum_s m_{rs} x_r x_s, \tag{26}$$

then the preceding equation can be written

$$\frac{d}{dt}\sum_r \alpha_r q_r (n_r - \log n_r) = -F(x_1, x_2, \cdots, x_n)$$

where

$$x_r = (n_r - 1)q_r.$$

Integrating and passing from logarithms to numbers, we shall have

$$\left(\frac{e^{n_1}}{n_1}\right)^{\alpha_1 q_1}\left(\frac{e^{n_2}}{n_2}\right)^{\alpha_2 q_2} \cdots \left(\frac{e^{n_n}}{n_n}\right)^{\alpha_n q_n} = Ce^{-\int_0^t F dt}$$

where C is a positive constant.

If $q_1, q_2, \ldots, q_n$ are positive, namely, *if there exists a stationary state* and if $\alpha_1, \alpha_2, \ldots, \alpha_n$ can be so chosen that the quadratic form (26)[1] is identically zero, *the numbers of individuals of the separate species will be limited between positive numbers and fluctuations must exist which are not damped.* If a stationary state exists and if the positive constants α_1, $\alpha_2, \ldots, \alpha_n$ can take such values as to make the form (26) positive we can say that *the variation of the numbers of individuals of the separate species is confined between two positive numbers;*[2] but if the form is *positive definite* besides this it will follow that *all the variations of the separate species will be asymptotic or there will be damped fluctuations which make the biological association tend toward the stationary state.*

The proof of this proposition is analogous to the proof of the proposition of §9.

Besides we find that *every time the form* (26) *is positive the limits of the average of* $N_1, N_2, \ldots, N_n$ *in intervals of time increasing indefinitely will be* $q_1, q_2, \ldots, q_n$.

The expression F can be written

$$F = \sum_1^n{}_r \sum_1^n{}_s \alpha_r p_{rs}(N_r - q_r)(N_s - q_s). \tag{27}$$

In §9 the action damping the fluctuations has been compared to an internal attrition. The preceding form F can be taken as a measure of

---

[1] In this case, in order that the determinant of the p_{rs} be different from zero, n will have to be even.

[2] This property leads at once to the recognition that the limits of the averages of $N_1, N_2, \ldots, N_n$ in intervals of time increasing infinitely are $q_1, q_2. \ldots, q_n$.

this damping action, which characterizes the tendency toward the stationary state of the group of all the species, and in fact, if F is zero the biological association will not tend toward a limit state, while if it is positive definite the association will tend toward the stationary state.

We shall call the form $F(x_1, x_2, \ldots, x_n)$ the "fundamental form" and the equations (C') the "equations of equilibrium." We exclude the case in which these equations have zero roots, that is we exclude the possibility that the stationary state can coincide with the exhaustion of any one of the species.

4. Now we can review the hypothesis of §7, No. 1, and get a deeper insight into its significance.

Let us suppose we give to each individual of the species r a positive value α_r. The value of the whole biological association will be $V = \sum_{1}^{n} \alpha_r N_r$ whence, from the equations (C) will follow

$$dV = \sum_{1}^{n} \alpha_r \epsilon_r N_r dt - \sum_{1}^{n} \sum_{1}^{n} p_{rs} \alpha_r N_r N_s dt.$$

The increase of value of the biological association in the time dt consists then of two parts

$$dV_1 = \sum_{1}^{n} \alpha_r \epsilon_r N_r dt$$

$$dV_2 = \sum_{1}^{n} \sum_{1}^{n} p_{rs} \alpha_r N_r N_s dt.$$

The first is due to the constant causes of increase and decrease of each species (particularized by ϵ_r), and the second is due to the reciprocal actions of the various individuals in the general sense understood before.

If the α_r can be chosen in such a way that dV_2 be zero whatever may be $N_1, N_2, \ldots, N_n$, the value of the biological association will not change in consequence of the reciprocal actions of the individuals. A biological association of this nature, namely in which it is possible to assign to the separate individuals such values that their reciprocal actions keep the value of the entire association constant will be said to be *conservative*. Evidently for a conservative system the hypothesis of §7, No. 1 is satisfied. Reciprocally, if that hypothesis is holding and the reciprocal actions between individuals of the same species are negligible, the biological association will be conservative.

Absolutely conservative biological associations are probably ideals which can only approximate the conditions effective in nature. But a special example of conservative systems is considered in §7, No. 2.

When to separate individuals there can be assigned values (equal for those of the same species) such that *the fundamental form F be positive definite* the reciprocal actions between individuals will tend to diminish the value of the entire association which can therefore be called dissipative. It seems that in many real cases biological associations must approximate dissipative associations.

§11. GENERAL THEOREMS ON CONSERVATIVE AND DISSIPATIVE BIOLOGICAL ASSOCIATIONS

1. A proposition can be stated which says the value of a conservative biological association: (1) *approaches zero if all the coefficients of increase are negative and only when all are negative;* (2) *approaches infinity if all are positive.*[1]

The *first part* of this proposition can be extended to *dissipative systems*. In fact from (C) using (25), it follows that

$$\sum_{1}^{n} {}_{r} \alpha_r \frac{dN_r}{dt} = \sum_{1}^{n} {}_{r} \alpha_r \epsilon_r N_r - \sum_{1}^{n} {}_{r} \sum_{1}^{n} {}_{s} m_{rs} N_r N_s.$$

If the form

$$\sum_{1}^{n} {}_{r} \sum_{1}^{n} {}_{s} m_{rs} N_r N_s$$

is positive definite or semi-positive definite then

$$\sum_{1}^{n} {}_{r} \alpha_r \frac{dN}{dt} \leqq \sum_{1}^{n} {}_{r} \alpha_r \epsilon_r N_r$$

and if

$$\epsilon_r < - \epsilon, \qquad (r = 1, 2, \cdots, n)$$

ϵ being a positive quantity, we shall have

$$\sum_{1}^{n} {}_{r} \alpha_r N_r < \sum_{1}^{n} {}_{r} \alpha_r N_{r0} e^{0-\epsilon t}$$

which proves that the value of the biological association approaches zero if all the coefficients of increase are negative; then in order that the biological association should not exhaust itself it is sufficient that one only of these coefficients should be positive (*cf.* §10 No. 2).

As for the *second part* of the preceding proposition, by virtue of what is shown in §10, No. 2 it must be replaced by: *the value of a dissipative biological association stays limited.*

For a conservative association it is possible to prove the following theorem: *None of the several species can either exhaust itself or increase indefinitely in a finite time.*

2. Let us pass to the case of dissipative associations: For these we know that the number of individuals of each species is limited, but it can be proved that the number can not however become zero in a finite time.

[1] In this statement we have excluded the case of zero coefficients of increase as we shall also exclude it in the extension of the proposition.

The conclusion will be: *In a dissipative association no species can exhaust itself in a finite time, whereas the number of individuals of each species is limited.*

3. Then we can state the theorem: *In order that in a dissipative association or in a conservative association of even order (with determinant different from zero) the number of individuals of each species should remain between positive numbers, a necessary and sufficient condition is that the roots of the equations of equilibrium be positive.*

§12. FLUCTUATIONS PECULIAR TO THE SYSTEM, FORCED FLUCTUATIONS, AND THE PRINCIPLE OF THEIR SUPERPOSITION

1. In equations (C) of §10, which can be considered as the most general and as summing up all those preceding, we have supposed that the coefficients of increase ϵ_r be constants; but really these change and in general their changes are periodic or due to the addition of more periodic terms. Certainly in all practical cases we shall have to consider an annual period in connection with the changes of seasons and meteorological conditions. But nothing precludes the existence of other periods.

Let us try to take account of these periodic disturbances of the coefficients of increase, for which let us substitute

$$\epsilon_r + g_r' \cos kt + g_r'' \sin kt$$

for ϵ_r where g_r', g_r'' and k are constant quantities.

Equations (C) will become

(D) $$\frac{dn_r}{dt} = (\epsilon_r + g_r' \cos kt + g_r'' \sin kt - \sum_1^n {}_s p_{rs} N_s) N_r$$

and (24)

$$\frac{dn_r}{dt} = (g_r' \cos kt + g_r'' \sin kt - \sum_1^n {}_s p_{rs} q_s (n_s - 1)) n_r$$

in which we shall suppose each q_s positive.

Let us observe that ϵ_r are the average values of the coefficients of increase during the period $2r/k$; we can then state the theorem: *If the coefficients of increase are periodic and their average values differ little from the changeable values, and if taking these average values as the coefficients of increase, there result asymptotic variations or damped fluctuations or fluctuations not damped near to a stationary state (variations peculiar to the system), then for small fluctuations corresponding to periodic coefficients of increase the principle of superposing on the forced fluctuations the variations peculiar to the system will be applicable, that is to say small fluctuations will be obtained, superposing on the variations peculiar to the system those which are forced having the period of the coefficients of increase, when that period does not coincide with any of the periods of the casual fluctuations peculiar to the system.*

§13. DISTURBANCE PRODUCED IN A BIOLOGICAL ASSOCIATION HAVING A STATIONARY STATE BY THE ADDITION OF A NEW SPECIES

1. By using results of preceding sections we can state the following theorem: *If a stationary state exists for a certain biological association, but by adding a new species to it the possibility of the stationary state is lost because the equations of equilibrium have a negative root for the number of individuals of the species added, the small variations of the whole association (supposed dissipative) will consist of a variation of the original association near to its stationary state superimposed on a depletion of a new species.*[1]

For this reason the species added will tend to a depletion and the others will approach a variation near to the stationary state, whence the addition of the new species will produce a disturbance which will tend to disappear.

§14. STUDY OF A PARTICULAR BIOLOGICAL ASSOCIATION OF THREE SPECIES

1. As an example of the treatment developed previously let us examine a particular case which, because of the theory shown above, can be treated mathematically in full.

Let us suppose three species living together in a limited environment, for example on an island. Of these three species let the first eat the second and this the third and not *vice versa*. For example we can take a species of carnivorous animals that feed upon an herbivorous species and this in turn feeds upon a vegetable species, admitting that for this last the same treatment holds as that used for the animals. Another example is furnished by plants their parasites and parasites of these parasites.

2. Let us admit the biological association to be *conservative* (*cf.* §10).

If we indicate the number of individuals of the three species by N_1, N_2, N_3 we shall have equations (see (B), §7, No. 2).

$$\beta_1 \frac{dN_1}{dt} = (\beta_1 \epsilon_1 + a_{21}N_2 + a_{31}N_3)N_1$$

$$\beta_2 \frac{dN_2}{dt} = (\beta_2 \epsilon_2 + a_{12}N_1 + a_{32}N_3)N_2$$

$$\beta_3 \frac{dN_3}{dt} = (\beta_3 \epsilon_3 + a_{13}N_1 + a_{23}N_2)N_3$$

where $\beta_1, \beta_2, \beta_3$ are constant quantities.

In our case we must take

$\epsilon_1 = -l < 0,$	$a_{21} = a > 0,$	$a_{31} = 0,$
$\epsilon_2 = -m < 0,$	$a_{12} = -a < 0,$	$a_{32} = b > 0,$
$\epsilon_3 = k > 0,$	$a_{13} = 0,$	$a_{23} = -b < 0,$

where a, b, l, m, k are constant quantities.

According to values of these coefficients of increase and of voracity and values of $\beta_1, \beta_2, \beta_3$, the following cases and subcases can be presented:

[1] It is opportune to compare this theorem with that of §11.

Case 1: $\beta_3 ka - \beta_1 lb < 0$

The food furnished to the carnivori by the herbivori is not sufficient to maintain the carnivorous species and this is depleted, while the herbivori and the plants tend toward a periodic fluctuation not damped. (We can suppose the coefficient of increase of the plants, k, to be constant because in this case the vegetable species can not increase indefinitely.)

Case 2: $\beta_3 ka - \beta_1 lb > 0$

If the coefficient of increase of the vegetable species were constant, the number of individuals in it would grow indefinitely, hence it is proper to suppose that this coefficient decreases proportionally to the number of individuals.

Subcase a.—The food provided by the plants is not sufficient to maintain the herbivori, hence the herbivorous species and the carnivorous species die out, while the vegetable species tends toward a constant value.

Subcase b.—The plants are sufficient to maintain the herbivori, but there is not sufficient food for the carnivori through the herbivori, hence the carnivorous species is depleted, while the herbivori and plants tend toward a damped fluctuation, and finally to a stationary state.

Subcase c.—The food is sufficient so that all the species live, and through asymptotic and damped variations they all tend toward a stationary state.

INDEX

A

"*a*" point, 49
A vitamin, 158
Abbott, C. H., 27
Abyssal, 285
  plain, 253
Acidity, 148
Acquatic communities, biotic characteristics of, 280–285
  physical characteristics of, 261–275
Actinometer, 11
Adams, C. C., 2, 219
Adamstone, F. B., 247, 285, 335, 337, 340
Aestival, 386
Agassiz, Louis, 248
Agriculture, 340
Agrilus bilineatus, 242
Air, dehumidifying, 94
  humidifying, 94
Aktinophotometer, Heyde, 11
Alabama argillacea, 137
Albuminoids, 169
Aleurobius farinae, 97
Alkalinity, 148
Allee, W. C., 28, 139, 239, 296
Allen, W. E., 355
Alphitobius piceus, effect of vacuum on, 131
Altitudes, 137
Aluminum, 366
Amino acids, 319
Ammonia nitrogen, 320
Amoeba, protozoa, 240
Amphibia, 297
Amphibious organisms, 84
Andrews, E. A., 103
Anemometer, Buram's portable, 136
  Robinson's cup, use of, 135
Anemotropism, 139
Aneroid barometer, 128
Ångström, Anders, 11
  pyrheliometer, 11
  units, 9, 18
Animal ecology, subject matter of, 3–6

Animals, communities of, 42, 385
  ecological groups of, 323
  geographic distribution of, 105
  homoiothermic, 42
  limnopelogic, 323
  poikilothermic, 42
  population data, 402
  taxonomic groups of, 323
  xerophytic, 84
Anobium paniceum, 164
Anthrenus fasciatus, effect of vacuum on, 131
Anthrenus museorum, 170
Aphids, 163
Aphytal-plantless, 339
Aquatic synecology, 247–257
Arcella, 64
Arctics, 64
Areas, biotic, of North America, 225
Arktogaisches Reich, 225
Arrhenius, Svante, 45, 47, 151, 366, 385, 388
Arthropod groups, distribution in depth, 371
Association, biological, 412, 428
  conservative, of even order, 438
    and dissipative biological, 440
  elm-maple forest, 399
  grassland, 385
  of two species, one of which feeds upon other, 414
    periodic fluctuations, 419
  of two species which contend for same food, 412
Atmometer, 12, 89
  of Livingston, 90
  rate-recording, 92
  of Reinhard, 91
Atmosphere, currents of, 135
  effect of, on distribution of animals, 136–138
  measuring, methods of, 135
Attagenus piceus, effect of vacuum on, 131
Autecology, 5, 205
  biotic, 6, 181